INTRODUCTION TO
PARASITOLOGY

INTRODUCTION TO

PARASITOLOGY

WITH SPECIAL REFERENCE TO THE PARASITES OF MAN

Asa C. Chandler, M.S., Ph.D.

Professor of Biology, Rice Institute, Houston, Texas.
Former Officer-in-Charge, Hookworm Research Laboratory,
School of Tropical Medicine and Hygiene, Calcutta, India

EIGHTH EDITION

New York · John Wiley & Sons, Inc.
London · Chapman & Hall, Limited

PRINTED IN THE UNITED STATES OF AMERICA

PREFACE

In 1918 the writer prepared a book on *Animal Parasites and Human Disease* designed to set forth interesting and important facts of human parasitology in a readable form that would make them available to a wide range of intellectually curious readers. Scientific work flourishes best when intelligent public sentiment is behind it, and such sentiment is dependent upon utilization of discoveries already made and upon an understanding of future goals.

Although *Animal Parasites and Human Disease* was not so widely taken up by the general public as anticipated, it was at once accepted as an introductory textbook in parasitology, and year by year it has been adopted by more and more normal schools, universities, and medical schools throughout the country. With the fourth edition, in 1930, the book was entirely rewritten, rearranged to serve its function as a textbook more efficiently, and presented under a new title, *Introduction to Human Parasitology*. The book was, however, widely used as a *general* introductory textbook, so with succeeding editions its scope was broadened to include more and more references to, or discussion of, parasites of lower animals, particularly those of importance in veterinary medicine. To reflect this extension the title was again changed in the sixth (1940) edition to its present form. The parasites of man are still most fully considered and are used as examples of their respective systematic groups, but in the present edition all the parasites of veterinary importance are at least mentioned, and many of them discussed. It would obviously be impossible to make detailed reference to parasites of other animals in an introductory text, but general statements are made concerning the occurrence of representatives of groups of parasites in various types of hosts. For completeness, such groups as the monogenetic flukes, strigeids, etc., are discussed in this edition.

When *Animal Parasites and Human Disease* was first published, parasitology was taught in only a few universities, but there has been a steady increase in the attention given to this subject. This increase was gradual up to the time of World War II but has been very rapid since then. The writer hopes that this book may have played some part in the development of this popularity by stimulating the interest of students and by making easier the task of the teacher. The sharp upturn in interest in parasitology during and after World War II, however, was due to a belated realization of the importance of the sub-

ject. It was not until the outbreak of World War II that parasitology
took its rightful place of prominence in the community of sciences and
came of age in America. During the war parasitological problems all
over the world presented themselves for immediate solution, and the
neglect with which parasitology had been treated in the past became
painfully apparent, for there were distressingly few individuals who had
had experience with even such common parasitic diseases as malaria or
amebiasis, not to mention schistosomiasis, leishmaniasis, scrub typhus,
etc., which few had ever even heard of. Our military forces performed
a veritable miracle in correcting the situation. Not only were thousands of people trained for the efficient application of what was already
known, but research in parasitology flourished as never before.

The rapid advances in knowledge in the field of parasitology have
made it necessary to revise and rearrange this book every four or five
years. In the five years that have elapsed since the seventh edition
was written, more advances have been made than in any similar period
since the book was first published, so again it has been entirely rewritten,
with changes on every page. A few important alterations or additions
have been made. A new section has been added on arthropod-borne
bacteria, rickettsias, and filtrable viruses to give the student a more
comprehensive view of these disease agents and their relations to their
vectors than can be gathered from disjointed discussions of them under
their individual vectors. Another new section has been added to deal
with insecticides and repellents. The Acanthocephala have been segregated into a separate chapter. New keys to some of the arthropod
parasites have been added. References to and consideration of parasites
of domestic animals have been greatly extended. Most of the illustra-
tions have been improved or are entirely new.

As in previous editions, a chapter on spirochetes has been included.
These organisms are now quite generally regarded as related to bacteria
rather than Protozoa, and they might logically be omitted from a book
on parasites of animal nature. However, since the spirochetes are given
inadequate treatment in most bacteriology books and are repeatedly
referred to in this book in connection with their arthropod vectors, most
parasitology instructors prefer to have them included.

It is the writer's opinion that in an introductory book in parasitology
only enough classification and taxonomy should be incorporated to give
the student an understanding of the general relationships of the parasites
considered. Outlines of classification of major groups have been set in
small type, so that they do not interfere with the general readability of
the text and can be omitted in courses in which they are not considered
necessary. In the section on arthropods a number of simple keys to
important groups of genera and species have been included, but these,

too, have been set off in small type so that they can be omitted if not required. Most students, however, will benefit from a little experience in the use of keys for identification.

No attempt has been made to give complete descriptions of all the parasites dealt with, although where it is particularly important to distinguish between related or similar species, sufficiently detailed descriptions or figures have been given to make a correct identification possible. Discussions of correct scientific names and synonymy have been mostly omitted as inappropriate in an introductory text. An effort has been made to use scientific names which are most generally accepted as correct. Names that have long been in common use, although not now accepted as correct under rules of zoological nomenclature, are given in parentheses.

Throughout the book special emphasis has been laid on the biological aspects of the subject. Considerable space is devoted to life cycles, epidemiological factors, interrelations of parasite and host, and underlying principles of treatment and prevention, rather than on such phases as classification, nomenclature, and morphology, which occupy much of the space in some textbooks of parasitology. This book, as an introductory one, is more concerned with fundamental principles than with the details that would interest a specialist. Treatment and clinical aspects have not been dealt with in sufficient detail to satisfy a medical practitioner, but the extent to which various parasitic infections are amenable to treatment and the general principles of treatment properly fall within its scope. The specific effects of drugs on parasites and their hosts, the manner in which the drugs reach the parasites, the mechanism by which the effect is brought about, and factors that contribute to success or failure of treatment are true biological aspects and are included.

Parasitology has grown so rapidly in recent years and covers such a wide field that it is difficult to go very far into the subject within the limits of one book. Nevertheless it is the writer's belief that a comprehensive, integrated account of the entire field is much the most desirable method of approaching the subject at the start. Protozoology, helminthology, and medical entomology have many interrelations, and no one of them can be satisfactorily pursued very far without some knowledge of the others. For more advanced work a comprehensive text is too cumbersome; the subject naturally splits into its three component parts.

A brief list of references is provided at the end of each chapter for the student who wishes to pursue the subject farther. Included are books or papers which give extensive reviews or summarizations of the subjects with which they deal or which contain good bibliographies;

also included are a few of the more recent contributions of importance which would not be found in bibliographies of the other works cited, and which contain information beyond that cited in the present book. In the text, references that are included in the bibliographies have the date cited in parentheses; other references are made in the form "Smith in 1948 . . ." It should not be too difficult for a student to trace down most of these references, if he wishes, through such journals as *Biological Abstracts, Helminthological Abstracts, Tropical Diseases Bulletin, Review of Applied Entomology, Index Medicus, Veterinary Bulletin*, etc.

In "Sources of Information" at the end of the book is a list of the leading journals in which important articles on parasitology frequently appear. Particular attention is called to the periodicals mentioned in the preceding paragraph. The *Tropical Diseases Bulletin* reviews practically all current work in the field of human parasitology, especially protozoology and helminthology. The *Review of Applied Entomology, Series B*, contains abstracts of all important contributions in the field of medical and veterinary entomology. The *Veterinary Bulletin* reviews important work on diseases of domestic animals. *Helminthological Abstracts* covers all important findings in helminthology. *Biological Abstracts* contains abstracts of interest in parasitology in its sections on parasitology, sanitary entomology, and in appropriate subsections under systematic zoology. The *Index Medicus* lists references to nearly all writings of medical interest, and the *Journal of the American Medical Association* lists references in all the leading medical journals of the world, and reviews many of the more important articles. These valuable bibliographic and abstracting journals are necessary for anyone who attempts to keep pace with the progress of parasitology; without them this book could not have been kept up to date.

There are few if any of the journals listed under "Sources of Information" or of books or articles listed under chapter references that have not been drawn upon for help in the preparation of this book. All of them, collectively, have made the book possible, and to their authors or contributors are due, therefore, the thanks both of the writer and of everyone who may profit in any way from the present volume.

In conclusion, the writer wishes to express his appreciation of the kindness of many friends and colleagues who have helped in weeding out errors and in suggesting changes in the text. He hopes that those who make use of the book will continue to offer criticisms or suggestions; they will be given careful consideration in future editions.

ASA C. CHANDLER

RICE INSTITUTE, HOUSTON, TEXAS
July, 1949

CONTENTS

CONTENTS

PART III — ARTHROPODS

CHAPTER 1

Introduction

One of the most appalling realizations with which every student of nature is brought face to face is the universal and unceasing struggle for existence which goes on during the life of every living organism, from the time of its conception until death. We like to think of nature's beauties, to admire her outward appearance of peacefulness, to set her up as an example for human emulation. Yet under her seeming calm there is going on everywhere — in every pool, in every meadow, in every forest — murder, pillage, starvation, and suffering.

Man often considers himself exempt from this interminable struggle for existence. His superior intelligence has given him an insuperable advantage over the wild beasts which might otherwise prey upon him; his inventive genius defies the attacks of climate and the elements; his altruism, which is perhaps his greatest attribute, protects to a great extent the weak and poorly endowed individuals from the quick extinction which is the inevitable lot of the unfit in every other species of animal on the earth. Exempt as we are to a certain extent from these phases of the struggle for existence, we have not yet freed ourselves from two other phases of it, namely, competition among ourselves, resulting in war, and our fight with parasites which cause disease.

We seem to have made considerably more progress toward the latter than toward the former. Some optimists thought that, after World War I had burned itself out in 1918, there would never again be a similar spectacle on the earth, and a few even thought so after World War II, but it is evident that this phase of our struggle for existence constitutes a greater peril today than ever before. But, although science has been making our struggles with each other constantly more terrible and devastating, it has in the meantime largely freed us from the helpless bondage in which we were once held by the organisms of disease. Here progress has been almost entirely one-sided, for the slow process of evolution on which our parasitic enemies must depend is no match for the swift development of advantages afforded by human ingenuity; we purposely refrain from saying " intelligence," since the application of our ingenuity to destruction of each other can hardly be construed as intelligence.

One by one the diseases which formerly held the world in terror, or

1

made parts of it practically uninhabitable, have had their power broken by the onslaught of modern scientific research. With few exceptions, so far as man and his domestic animals are concerned, the enemy has been discovered; his resources and limitations are known, his tactics are understood, and weapons of offense and defense have been developed. What sensational advances have been made in the last few years — sulfonamides and antibiotics for treatment, new vaccines for protection, DDT and other insecticides in aerosols, residual sprays, and airplane dispersal for longer-range prevention on a scale undreamed of in World War I! In the United States malaria, lice, and houseflies may soon be as extinct as the passenger pigeon, a thing that a few years ago would have seemed a fantastic dream. We may be reasonably sure that at least in civilized communities such diseases as smallpox, plague, typhus, yellow fever, and typhoid will never again break loose in devastating epidemics, although they will continue to snipe at us from their ambushes in field and jungle, or to take advantage of weakened defenses in local areas or in times of stress.

Although some of the diseases that were most spectacular in the past — plague, cholera, and smallpox — are caused by bacteria or viruses not included within the scope of this book, the importance of animal parasites and of arthropod vectors of disease is enormous. Malaria is the most important of all human diseases, and no one questions the importance of trypanosomiasis, leishmaniasis, amebiasis, or piroplasmosis among protozoan diseases; or of hookworm disease, filariasis, schistosomiasis, or scabies among diseases caused by higher organisms.

Even many of the diseases that are caused by bacteria or viruses owe their importance and often their very existence to arthropod vectors which fall within our field of interest. Plague, tularemia, typhus, spotted fever, trench fever, relapsing fever, yaws, yellow fever, dengue, and sandfly fever are outstanding among these. The demonstration that helminths may play important roles in the transmission of viruses, and in at least one instance of a protozoan, opens up an entire new field in epidemiology.

Even many of the lesser lights among parasites, of rarer occurrence or of local distribution, are of importance to the human race far out of proportion to popular interest or knowledge of them. Many educated people have never heard of parasitic infections that affect the health of millions of people and sap the vitality of entire nations.

Recently our armed forces were scattered over the entire face of the earth, and the medical personnel of the Army and Navy were forced to cope with diseases that many of them never heard of before, because we had thought that such things as kala-azar and sandfly fever and trypanosomiasis were not of sufficient interest to warrant considering them in medical schools. In the postwar years many a hometown physician had to deal with diseases that previously had only been names to him. This situation is not a temporary one, for the human animal is endowed by nature with a wanderlust and an itchy foot. We think no more of a trip to China or Brazil than our fathers did of going from New York to Denver or Mexico City. Besides, whether we like it or not, air travel and transportation have killed isolationism forever; the world is fast becoming an economic unit, and a disease that affects the production of rice in China or of meat in Argentina will inevitably affect us economically.

Even when it took weeks or months to go from continent to continent, dispersal of parasites was common. Traders brought filariasis from the South Seas to Egypt, slaves brought hookworms and schistosomes from Africa to America, and trading vessels carried yellow fever from the American tropics to New York and Philadelphia. What can be expected when we can have breakfast in Colombia and supper in Florida?

With the progress of civilization, however, many human parasites have gradually been falling by the wayside. As M. C. Hall said, the louse had its welfare imperiled when the Saturday night bath supplanted occasional immersion from falling into water; it had a struggle for survival when modern plumbing and laundering facilities laid the foundation for a daily bath even in winter, and clean clothes once a week; but its actual extermination has become an easily realizable possibility with the advent of DDT. The housefly got a severe setback when the automobile replaced the horse. The housefly, too, is now a candidate for extinction because of DDT, as are many other arthropod pests; it is only a matter of how seriously we want extermination.

Among helminths, substitution of privies and toilets for the rush-covered floors of the Middle Ages and the shaded soil of unsanitated areas is spelling extinction for hookworms and Ascaris, and cooking and refrigeration are doing away with Trichinella and Taeniae. Among Protozoa, improved water supplies, good sewage disposal, and elimination of flies are making intestinal infections rarer, and we can confidently look forward to the complete elimination of malaria from continental United States in the not too distant future. New methods of chemotherapy, new insecticides, and new methods of insecticide application have made radical changes, even since the last edition of this book was published in 1944, in the outlook with respect to such diseases as yaws, syphilis, typhus, plague, malaria, yellow fever, and dengue.

For our domestic animals, domestication and increasing concentration have long meant increasing parasitization, for they soil their table with their feces, they eat uncooked food, they drink contaminated waters from ponds and streams, they bathe only by accident, and they have hairy bodies that provide ideal playgrounds for ectoparasites. The parasite egg that had to pursue a deer or antelope to a new bed-ground five miles away was out of luck, said Hall, whereas when millions of eggs are sowed on limited pastures, the parasites have all the advantage. For human parasites, increased concentration had an opposite effect owing to better opportunity for improved water, control of foods, and sanitary sewage disposal. But now the parasites of the roaming deer and antelope are actually in a less vulnerable position than those of cattle or sheep. Some years ago the U. S. Department of Agriculture exterminated Texas fever in the United States, and eliminated *Boöphilus annulatus* (except on wild animals), but it took years of hard and expensive work. Today warbles, hornflies, screwworms, sheep bots, and cattle lice could be exterminated in a fraction of the time and at relatively insignificant cost.

But let us not think that the battle is won. A few diseases, e.g., poliomyelitis, still baffle our efforts to cure or understand them. Worse still, many that we *do* understand and could control are by no means subdued, e.g., plague in India, malaria throughout the tropics, syphilis in the United States, and filariasis and schistosomiasis in many parts of the world. In 1947 Stoll made the startling statement that there are in the world today 2200 million helminthic infections — enough for one for every inhabitant if they were evenly distributed!

It is evident that there is need not only for additions to our knowledge of the causes and control of diseases, but also, and perhaps even more pressing, a need for the efficient application of what we already know. Apathy to parasitic diseases is largely the result of ignorance concerning them. Our minds are relatively impervious to new ideas; we prefer to cling to traditions. When we consider that practically all our knowledge concerning parasites has been obtained within the last hundred years, and an astonishing amount of it within the last twenty-five, it is not surprising that mistaken notions of our grandparents still compete successfully with modern scientific knowledge. It takes decades, if not centuries, to modify or correct popular notions. One need only mention the popular disbelief in evolution, the credulity with respect to the origin of " horsehair snakes " from horse hairs in water, and the existence of antivaccination societies which denounce vaccination as an impractical and illogical proceeding. Little wonder that popular skepticism still exists with respect to the transmission of malaria by mosquitoes, and that people still fear the miasmas of damp night air.

History

Early Views. Up to the middle of the seventeenth century knowledge of parasitology was limited to recognition of the existence of a few self-asserting external parasites such as lice and fleas, and a few kinds of internal parasites which were too obvious to be overlooked, such as tapeworms, Ascaris, pinworms, and guinea worms. These parasites were, however, thought to be natural products of human bodies, comparable to warts or boils. Even such immortal figures in parasitology as Rudolphi and Bremser at the beginning of the nineteenth century supported this idea. In Linnaeus' time this view gradually gave way to another, that internal parasites originated from accidentally swallowed free-living organisms. Flukes, for instance, were thought to be " landlocked " leeches or " fish "; in fact, the name fluke is said to come from the Anglo-Saxon *floc,* meaning flounder. Until the middle of the seventeenth century the necessity for parents was regarded as a handicap placed upon the higher vertebrates alone. Biology students struggling with required insect collections sometimes wonder how Noah ever succeeded in collecting all the species which must have been known even in his day for rescue in the Ark, but that was no worry of Noah's; he anticipated that insects, worms, snakes, and mice would be spontaneously generated after the flood as well as before.

Redi. The grandfather of parasitology was Francesco Redi, who was born in 1626. In the latter half of the seventeenth century he demonstrated to an unbelieving world that maggots developed from the eggs of flies, and that even Ascaris had males and females and produced eggs. He extended the idea of parenthood so far that it is really remarkable that its universal application, even to bacteria, had to wait for Pasteur's ingenious experiments two centuries later. Although Redi's recognition of obligatory parenthood in lower animals was his outstanding achievement, he was the first genuine parasite hunter; he searched for and found them not only in human bowels but in other human organs, in the intestines of lower animals, in the air sacs of birds, and in the swim bladders of fish.

Leeuwenhoek. This same half-century marked the origin of protozoology, for it was then that the Dutch lens grinder, Leeuwenhoek, perfected microscopes which enabled him to discover and describe various kinds of animalculae, many recognizable as Protozoa, in rain water, saliva, feces, etc.; among the organisms in feces he discovered what was probably a Giardia, although the first protozoan definitely recognized as a human parasite was *Balantidium coli*, discovered by Malmsten in Sweden in 1856, nearly two centuries later.

Rudolphi. In spite of the work of these pioneers, parasitology made little progress until about a century later, when Rudolphi came upon the scene. He was born in Stockholm in 1771, but did most of his work in Germany. He did for parasitology what Linnaeus did for zoologists in general; he collected and classified all the parasites known up to his time. Zeder, in 1800, recognized five classes of worms which Rudolphi named Nematoidea, Acanthocephala, Nematoda, Cestoda, and Cystica; the last had to be discarded about 50 years later when bladderworms were found to be the larval stages of the Cestoda.

Developments to 1850. During the first half of the nineteenth century numerous new species of parasites were discovered and described by Dujardin, Diesing, Cobbold, Leidy, and others. Meanwhile, observations on the life cycles of flukes and cestodes were being made. O. F. Muller discovered cercariae in 1773 but thought they were protozoa; Nitzsch, in 1817, recognized the resemblance of the cercarial body to a fluke and regarded the creature as a combination of a Fasciola and a vibrio; Bojanus, in 1818, saw the cercariae emerge from " royal yellow worms " in snails, and Oken, the editor of *Isis,* in which the work was published, felt willing to wager that these cercariae were the embryos of flukes; contributions by Creplin, von Baer, Mehlis, von Siebold, von Nordman, and Steenstrup finally added enough pieces to the puzzle so that by 1842 the general pattern of the picture could readily be seen.

Meanwhile, light was also shed on the true nature of bladderworms and hydatids. As the result of observations by Redi, Tyson, Goeze, Steenstrup, von Siebold, and van Beneden, their relationships with tapeworms gradually became apparent, but up to 1850 they were generally regarded as " hydropically degenerated " as the result of development in an abnormal host into which they had accidentally strayed. It was during this period also that Trichinella was discovered in human flesh by Peacock (1828), and in pigs by Leidy (1846); that Dubini discovered human hookworms (1842); that Hake discovered the oöcysts of Coccidia in rabbits; that Gluge and Gruby discovered trypanosomes in frog blood (1842); and that Gros found the first human ameba, *Endamoeba gingivalis* (1849).

Introduction of Experimental Methods. The next important milestone in parasitology was the introduction of experimental methods. Although Abildgaard had observed as far back as 1790 that sexless tapeworms (Ligula) from sticklebacks would become mature when fed to birds, experimental work in parasitology really began in the middle of the nineteenth century, when Herbst (1850) experimentally infected animals with Trichinella, and Kuchenmeister in 1851, having the right idea about the nature of cysticerci, proceeded to prove it by feeding Taeniae from rabbits to dogs and obtaining adult tapeworms. Two years later Kuchenmeister proved that bladderworms in pigs gave rise to tapeworms in man, as he had suspected because of the similarity of their heads.

These results gave a tremendous impetus to work in parasitology which has persisted to the present day, although it was temporarily eclipsed by the spectacular advances in bacteriology from about 1880 to the end of the century. The name of Leuckart stands out with especial brilliance in the early days of experimental parasitology; other shining lights in heminthology, who began their work before the beginning of the twentieth century, were Braun, Hamann, von Linstow, Looss, Lühe, and Schneider in Germany; Blanchard, Brumpt, Moniez, and Railliet in France; Cobbold and Nuttall in England; van Beneden in Belgium; Odhner in Sweden; Fuhrmann and Zschokke in Switzerland; Galli-Valerio, Grassi, and Stossich in Italy; and Cobb, Curtice, Leidy, Theobald Smith, Stiles, and Ward in America. In protozoology there were Bütschli, Doflein, Koch, von Prowazek, Schaudinn, and von Siebold in Germany; Davaine, Mégnin, Laveran, Leger, Nicolle, Sergent, and Aimé Schneider in France; Bruce, James, and Ross in England; and Calkins, Craig, and Leidy in America.

Insects as Intermediate Hosts and Vectors. Following work on life cycles of helminths came the demonstration of the role of insects as intermediate hosts and vectors of parasites. Leuckart was the pioneer here when in 1867 he observed the development of *Mastophorus* (*Protospirura*) *muris* of mice, a spiruroid, in mealworms. Two years later Leuckart's pupil, Melnikov, showed that Dipylidium developed in dog lice, and in the same year Fedschenko observed the development of the guinea worm in Cyclops. The pioneer work on the role of bloodsucking arthropods was by Manson in 1878, when he observed the development of *Filaria bancrofti* in mosquitoes. This suggested to him the probability of mosquitoes having a comparable role in connection with malaria, and it was his advice and encouragement that led to Ross's proof of it in 1898. Meanwhile, however, two American workers, Theobald Smith and Kilbourne (1893), ingeniously worked out the transmission of Texas fever by ticks; this was the first demonstration of an arthropod as an intermediate host and vector of a protozoan parasite. Two years later Bruce showed that *Trypanosoma brucei* was transmitted by tsetse flies, and this paved the way for proof of the role of tsetse flies in sleeping sickness, though the proof of a developmental cycle in the fly was not made until 1909 by Kleine. The year 1898 brought not only the epoch-making demonstration of the role of mosquitoes in the transmission of malaria made by Ross in India and by Grassi in Italy, but also the discovery of penetration of the skin by hookworm larvae, made by Looss in Egypt. In 1900 the important discovery of the transmission of yellow fever by mosquitoes was made by the American Yellow Fever Commission in Havana. From this time on, discoveries in the life cycles and modes of transmission of parasites came thick and fast.

Chemotherapy. Important progress has also been made in the chemotherapy of parasitic infections. One of the earliest specific remedies known was quinine for malaria, introduced into Europe in the seventeenth century; with the other alkaloids of cinchona it held the field until the synthetic drugs, plasmochin and atebrin, were introduced in 1926 and 1933, respectively. During World War II chloroquine and paludrine were discovered and found to be superior to atebrin or quinine for the blood forms of malaria parasites, and since the war pentaquine and isopentaquine have replaced the too-toxic plasmochin for killing gametocytes and the tissue-dwelling forms, thus preventing relapses.

The next epoch-making discovery was Ehrlich's Salvarsan in 1910 which, with its derivatives, held the field as a specific for syphilis and other spirochetal diseases until penicillin made its dramatic entry in 1943. Other outstanding therapeutic discoveries against Protozoa have been emetin for acute amebic dysentery, by Rogers in 1912; tartar emetic for leishmaniasis, by Vianna in 1914; tryparsamide for sleeping sickness, by Brown and Pearce in 1920–21; and certain of the sulfonamides, which had been so spectacularly successful for some bacterial diseases, for Coccidia about 1943.

In the field of anthelmintics a few remedies — male fern, cusso, and areca nut for tapeworms, and santonin for nematodes — have long been known. The first great advance was made when some Italian workers established the value of thymol for hookworms in 1880. This held the field for over 30 years but was succeeded by oil of chenopodium in 1913, carbon tetrachloride in 1921, and tetrachlorethylene in 1925. Chenopodium was also very useful for Ascaris but was supplanted by hexylresorcinol about 1930. Meanwhile the value of antimony compounds for schistosomiasis was discovered by McDonagh and Christopherson. Gentian violet was introduced as an anthelmintic for Clonorchis by Faust and Khaw in 1927, was used by deLangen for Strongyloides in 1928, and by Wright et al. for Enterobius in 1938. Also, in 1938, Harwood set a landmark when he showed the value of phenothiazine as a veterinary anthelmintic. Hexachlorethane for

Fasciola was introduced in Europe in 1926 but was not fully appreciated until 1941. During and after World War II the usefulness of antimony and arsenic compounds for filariasis was established by Brown, Culbertson, and others. After the war hetrazan was introduced for filariasis and onchocerciasis, and it has proved effective against Strongyloides and Trichinella. Other highly promising discoveries since the war are atebrin and acranil for tapeworms and Enterobius; hexylresorcinol by duodenal tube for tapeworms; and oral emetin for Trichuris.

In the field of insecticides, the outlook for control of nearly all arthropod parasites and arthropod-borne diseases was revolutionized by the advent of DDT and other new chemicals such as benzene hexachloride and chlordane, beginning about 1943. Development of aerosols and use of effective repellents, also during World War II, are playing a part in the downfall of insect parasites and vectors.

Immunity. Study of the nature and mechanism of immunity to parasitic infections is fairly recent, having been developed mainly by American workers. The work of W. H. and L. B. Taliaferro in 1925 on the mechanism of immunity in trypanosome and malaria infections was the beginning; W. H. Taliaferro, with Cannon, Huff, Sarles, and other collaborators, has been prominent in further work in connection with immunity both to malaria and to nematode infections. A pioneer piece of work in acquired metazoan immunity was done by Blacklock and Gordon on the skin maggot (Cordylobia) in 1927, and another by Miller (1931) on larval tapeworms in rats. Since then, many important contributions to metazoan immunity have been made by nearly a score of American workers.

Development of Parasitology in America. In concluding this historical section a brief résumé of parasitology in America is in order. The only early naturalist in America who took an interest in this subject was Joseph Leidy; during the last half of the nineteenth century he made many and valuable contributions. He is said to have become so absorbed in the study of a worm that he entirely forgot an obstetrical case he had engaged to attend. If Joseph Leidy can be called the grandfather of American parasitology, H. B. Ward may be considered the father of it. He not only made numerous contributions of his own over a period of 50 years, but he also stimulated interest in a host of others. His position in American parasitology can best be appreciated when it is recalled that among the students who started their scientific careers under him at the University of Illinois were Ackert, Cort, Faust, Hunter, LaRue, Manter, Miller, Stunkard, Thomas, and Van Cleave. The only other university which even approaches such an output of senior present-day parasitologists is Harvard, among whose sons are Kofoid, Pearse, Sawyer, Smillie, Tyzzer, Wenrich, and Ward himself. A large proportion of the ever-increasing number of the younger generation of parasitologists in America today are the scientific grandchildren of H. B. Ward.

Importance of Minor Contributions. The discoveries mentioned in this brief résumé of the history of parasitic diseases are but a few of the more conspicuous milestones on the path of progress of modern medicine as related to animal parasites. They may be likened to the posts of a fence, while the hundreds of other discoveries, less striking in themselves, perhaps, but nevertheless necessary, correspond to the pickets. The posts are useless without the pickets, as are the pickets without the posts. Not one of the great outstanding discoveries in the field of parasitology and preventive medicine could have been made without the aid of numerous less illustrious accomplishments of hundreds of other investigators who, often without any semblance of the honor and recognition which they deserve, work for the joy of the working and feel amply repaid if they add a few pickets to the fence of scientific progress.

The formation of the American Society of Parasitologists in 1926 marked the weaning of parasitology as a science in the United States, but it was not until World War II that it really came of age and took its rightful place in the community of sciences in America. As the writer pointed out in 1946, parasitology touches upon or overlaps so many other sciences that a parasitologist probably has to stick his nose into more different fields of knowledge than any other kind of biologist. A parasitologist, like an orchid, requires long and careful nurturing, and develops slowly (about 85 per cent of parasitologists have a Ph. D. degree). But when he comes to flower he is a rare and beautiful object, scientifically speaking, and is usually slow in going to seed.

REFERENCES

The following is a list of references of a general nature and general books on parasitology in which students who are interested may find additional information or different viewpoints. Books and references dealing with more limited subjects are listed at the end of the appropriate chapters. These references are not intended to be complete; they include only a few important or comprehensive treatises, mostly recent, to help the student who desires to do so to pursue the subject beyond the hallway to which this book may lead him. Many of the references contain bibliographies of their own which should give an entree to the literature of the subject.

REFERENCES 11

ACKERT, J. E., *Laboratory Manual of Parasitology*, Minneapolis, 1937.

BELDING, D. L., *Textbook of Clinical Parasitology*, Springfield, Ill., 1942.

BENBROOK, E. A., *List of Parasites of Domesticated Animals in North America*, Minneapolis, 1946.

BENBROOK, E. A., and SLOSS, M. W., *Veterinary Clinical Parasitology*, Ames, Iowa, 1948.

BLACKLOCK, D. C., and SOUTHWELL, T., *A Guide to Human Parasitology for Medical Practitioners*, London, 1931.

CABLE, R. M., *An Illustrated Laboratory Manual of Parasitology*, Revised, Minneapolis, 1947.

CAMERON, T. W. M., *The Internal Parasites of Domestic Animals*, London, 1934. *The Parasites of Man in Temperate Climates*, Toronto, 1940.

CHANDLER, A. C., The Making of a Parasitologist, *J. Parasitol.*, **32**, 213–221 (1946).

CRAIG, C. F., and FAUST, E. C., *Clinical Parasitology*, 3rd ed., Philadelphia, 1943.

CULBERTSON, J. T., *Medical Parasitology*, New York, 1942.

DUBOIS, A., and VAN DEN BERGHE, L., *Diseases of the Warm Climates*, New York, 1948.

FAUST, E. C., Reflections of a Medical Parasitologist, *J. Parasitol.*, **35**, 1–7 (1949).

HALL, M. C., The Economic Importance of Veterinary Parasitology, Reprint, *U. S. Bur. Animal Ind.*, 1927.

The Glorification of Parasitism, *Science Monthly*, **33**, 45 (1931).

Parasitology in Its Relation to Other Sciences, *Puerto Rico J. Pub. Health and Trop. Med.*, **7**, 405 (1932).

HEGNER, R. W., ROOT, F. M., AUGUSTINE, D. L., and HUFF, C. G., *Parasitology*, New York, 1938.

HULL, T. D., *Diseases Transmitted from Animals to Man*, 3rd ed., Baltimore, 1947.

LEUCKART, R., *Die Parasiten des Menschen und die von ihnen herruhrenden Krankheiten*, Leipzig, 1879–1886.

MACKIE, T. T., HUNTER, G. W., III, and WORTH, C. B., *A Manual of Tropical Medicine*, Philadelphia, 1945.

MANSON-BAHR, P. H., *Manson's Tropical Diseases*, 12th ed., London, 1947.

MANTER, H., *A Laboratory Manual in Animal Parasitology, with Special Reference to the Animal Parasites of Man*, Minneapolis, 1938.

MÖNNIG, H. O., *Veterinary Helminthology and Entomology*, 2nd ed., London, 1941.

Notices biographiques, I, II, VII, VIII, IX, X, XVII, *Arch. Parasitol.*, **1**, 115, 420; **3**, 163, 269, 547; **4**, 5; **11**, 388 (1898–1906).

PEARSE, A. S., *Introduction to Parasitology*, Springfield, Ill., 1942.

RILEY, W. A., *Introduction to the Study of Animal Parasites and Parasitism*, 5th ed., Minneapolis, 1942.

SOUTHWELL, T., and KIRSCHNER, A., *A Guide to Veterinary Parasitology and Entomology*, 2nd ed., London, 1938.

STILES, C. W., and HASSALL, A., Index Catalogue of Medical and Veterinary Zoology, Authors, *U. S. Bur. Animal Ind.*, *Bull. 39*, Pts. 1–36, 1902–1912, and Revision, Pts. 1–10, 1932–1948.

STOLL, N. R., This Wormy World, *J. Parasitol.*, **33**, 1–18 (1947).

STRONG, R. P., *Stitt's Diagnosis, Prevention and Treatment of Tropical Diseases*, 7th ed., 2 vols., Philadelphia, 1944.

TALIAFERRO, W. H., *The Immunology of Parasitic Infections*, New York, 1929.

U. S. Dept. Agriculture, *Keeping Livestock Healthy*, Yearbook, 1942.

Volumen jubilare pro Professore Sadao Yoshida, Vol. II, Osaka, 1939.

WALTON, C. L., and WRIGHT, W. R., *Agricultural Parasitology*, London, 1927.

WHITLOCK, J. H., *Practical Identification of Endoparasites for Veterinarians*, Minneapolis, 1938.

ZELIFF, C. C., *Manual of Medical Parasitology, with Techniques for Laboratory Diagnosis and Notes on Related Animal Parasites*, State College, Pa., 1948.

CHAPTER 2

Parasites in General

Nature of Parasitism. The world of animal life consists of communities of organisms which live by eating each other. In a broad sense all animals are parasites, in that they are helpless without other organisms to produce food for them. Plants alone are able to build up their body substance out of sunlight and chemicals. Herbivorous animals, when they feed on vegetation, exploit the energy of the plants for their own use. Carnivorous animals, in turn, exploit the energies of the herbivorous ones, larger carnivores exploit the smaller ones, etc., the whole series thus constituting what ecologists call a food chain; many such chains can be traced in any animal community.

But animals and plants are not preyed upon alone by successively larger forms which overpower and eat them; they are also preyed upon by successively smaller forms which destroy only small, more or less replaceable portions, or even more subtly exploit the energies of the host by subsisting on the food which the host has collected with great expenditure of time and energy. Elton (1935) says, "The difference between a carnivore and a parasite is simply the difference between living upon capital and income, between the burglar and the blackmailer. The general result is the same although the methods employed are different." A man's relation to his beef cattle is essentially that of a tiger to its prey; his relation to his milk cattle and sugar maple trees is essentially that of tapeworms or hookworms to their hosts. There is every gradation between parasites and carnivores, e.g., hookworms, leeches, horseflies, bloodsucking bats, and tigers; there are also all gradations between parasites and saprophytes, or organisms which live on the wastes or leftovers, e.g., *Endamoeba histolytica*, feeding on the tissue of the host; *Trichomonas hominis*, feeding, in part, at least, on digested foods which would otherwise be converted into tissues; *Endamoeba coli*, feeding on still undigested particles and bacteria; and the coprozoic amebas, feeding on the waste fecal matter of the host.

General Relations to Hosts. The popular notion that parasites are morally more oblique in their habits than other animals, as if they were taking some unfair and mean advantage of their hosts, is, as Elton remarks, unjustified. Carnivores and herbivores have no interest in the welfare of their prey and ruthlessly destroy them; parasites, of

13

necessity, cannot be so inconsiderate, for their welfare is intimately bound up with the welfare of the host. " A parasite's existence," says Elton, " is usually an elaborate compromise between extracting sufficient nourishment to maintain and propagate itself, and not impairing too much the vitality or reducing the numbers of its host, which is providing it with a home and a free ride." A dead host is seldom of any use to a parasite in its adult state, though it may capitalize the death of an intermediate host as a means of attaining its destination in the definitive host. Food of the right kind and in sufficient quantity is the burning question in all animal society; for parasites this resolves itself into the question of what to do when the host dies; most internal parasites, as adults, are so specialized for a protected life in the body of the host that they are unable to take any steps to deal with this situation. The result is that they make no attempt to do so and resign themselves to dying with their hosts, leaving it to their offspring to find their way to another host in order to continue the race, and, since the offspring have to run enormous risks in order to succeed, they have to be produced in correspondingly enormous numbers, running into millions.

Parasites and Food Habits. Since food is the hub of the wheel of animal life, it is natural to find that many parasites have taken advantage of the food habits of their hosts in order to propagate themselves from host to host. Intestinal Protozoa, such as amebas and flagellates, usually solve the problem by entering into a resistant cystic stage in which they can survive outside the body until they can re-enter a host with its food or water; blood Protozoa, such as trypanosomes and malaria parasites, are adapted to live temporarily in bloodsucking insects which feed on the host and subsequently reinject them into another host; most flukes and tapeworms lay eggs which develop in the bodies of animals which the host habitually eats, or which is eaten by a third animal which is then eaten by the definitive host; some intestinal nematodes, such as the spiruroids, do likewise; others, such as Ascaris, follow the tactics of intestinal Protozoa; and still others, such as hookworms, produce self-reliant embryos which actively burrow into the skin of their hosts; most parasitic arthropods are able to migrate from host to host when these come in contact with each other, directly or indirectly; but the bloodsucking flies have no worries about this matter, and can go at will from host to host.

The result of the dependence of parasites to such a large extent on the food habits of animals is that the food habits largely determine the nature of the parasites harbored. Ascaris, Trichuris, intestinal Protozoa, etc., are abundant where unsanitary conditions favor fecal contamination of food or water; many fluke infections of man are abundant in localities in the Far East where fish is habitually eaten raw; Taeniae are abundant where pork or beef is eaten raw or partly cooked; guinea worms are common where infected Cyclops is ingested with drinking water; and spiruroid infections occur only accidentally in man because the human animal is nowhere habitually insectivorous in habit.

Origin of Parasitism. Parasitism, in the restricted sense of a small organism living on or in, and at the expense of, a larger one, probably arose soon after life began to differentiate in the world. It would be difficult, if not impossible, to explain step by step the details of the process of evolution by which some of the highly specialized parasites reached their present condition. Parasitism at times has probably grown out of a harmless association of different kinds of organisms, one of the members of the association, by virtue, perhaps, of characteristics already possessed, developing the power of living at the expense of the other, and ultimately becoming more and more dependent upon it.

It is easy to understand the general mechanism by which parasites of the alimentary canal were evolved from free-living organisms which were accidentally or purposely swallowed, and which were able to survive in the environment in which they found themselves, and to adapt themselves to it. It is also easy to see how some of these parasites might eventually have developed further territorial ambitions and have extended their operations beyond the confines of the alimentary canal. The development of some of the blood Protozoa of vertebrates, on the other hand, seems clearly to have taken place in two steps: first, adaptation to life in the gut of insects, and, second, adaptation to life in vertebrates' blood or tissues when inoculated by hosts with skin-piercing and bloodsucking habits.

Kinds of Parasites. Parasitism is of all kinds and degrees. There are facultative parasites which may be parasitic or free-living at will, and obligatory parasites which must live on or in some other organism during all or part of their lives, and which perish if prevented from doing so. There are intermittent parasites which visit and leave their hosts at intervals. Some, as mosquitoes, visit their hosts only long enough to get a meal; others, as certain lice, leave their hosts only for the purpose of moulting and laying eggs; and still others, as the cattle tick, *Boöphilus annulatus*, never leave except to lay eggs. Some parasites pass only part of their life cycles as parasites; botflies, for instance, are parasitic only as larvae, hookworms only as adults. There are permanent parasites which live their whole lives, from the time of hatching to death, in a single host, but in which the eggs, or the corresponding cysts in the case of Protozoa, must be transferred to a new host before a second generation can develop.   Such are many intestinal protozoans and roundworms.   The final degree of parasitism is reached, perhaps, in those parasites which live not only their whole lives, but also generation after generation, on a single host, becoming transferred from host to host only by direct contact.   Such are the scab mites and many species of lice.   Every gradation is found among all the types of parasites mentioned above, and a complete classification of parasites according to mode of life would contain almost as many types as kinds of parasites.

It is sometimes convenient to classify parasites according to whether they are external or internal.   External parasites, or ectoparasites, living on the surface of the body of their hosts, suck blood or feed upon hair, feathers, skin, or secretions of the skin.   Internal parasites, living inside the body, occupy the digestive tract or other cavities of the body, or live in various organs, blood, tissues, or even within cells.   No sharp line of demarcation can be drawn between external and internal parasites since inhabitants of the mouth and nasal cavities, and such worms and mites as burrow just under the surface of the skin, might be placed in either category.

Definitive and Intermediate Hosts.   Some parasites pass different phases of their life cycle in two or more different hosts; in a few kinds of flukes four may be involved.   According to a dictionary definition, the host in which the parasite reaches sexual maturity is the definitive host and those in which it undergoes preliminary development are the intermediate hosts.   Strict adherence to these definitions, however, leads to some peculiar situations among the Protozoa.   For example, since the malaria parasites undergo sexual reproduction in mosquitoes, the mosquito, according to the definition, is the definitive host and man is the intermediate host.   For trypanosomes, however, if Fairbairn and Culwick's work on sexual reproduction of blood trypanosomes is confirmed, tsetse flies are the intermediate hosts and man the definitive host.   But in the case of Leishmania, in which no sexual reproduction occurs, shall we consider man or sandfly the intermediate host?   Because of these difficulties, the writer prefers to use the terms definitive and intermediate for vertebrates and arthropods, respectively, in relation to protozoan parasites which alternate in their life cycles between these two types of hosts, irrespective of where the sexual reproduction, if any, occurs.

Man should be considered the primary host of malaria parasites (though possibly not the primitive one) since these parasites could conceivably live and multiply indefinitely in a human host as long as he lived, and could theoretically develop a method of transfer (e.g., venereal, as some trypanosomes have done) that would eliminate the insect host altogether, but no such thing could happen in the mosquito, in which the infection is self-limited and must be considered temporary.

Effects of Parasitism on Parasites. Aside from the toning down of their effects on the host, parasites are often very highly modified in structure to meet the demands of their particular environment. As a group, parasites have little need for sense organs and seldom have them as highly developed as do related free-living animals. Fixed parasites do not need, and do not have, well-developed organs of locomotion, if, indeed, they possess any. Intestinal parasites do not need highly organized digestive tracts, and the tapeworms and spiny-headed worms have lost this portion of their anatomy completely. On the other hand, parasites must be specialized, often to a very high degree, to adhere to or to make their way about in their particular host, or the particular part of the host in which they find suitable conditions for existence. Examples of specializations of external parasites are the compressed bodies of fleas, permitting them to glide readily between the hairs of their hosts; the backward-projecting spines of fleas, which are of much assistance in forcing a path through dense hair by preventing any backsliding; the clasping talons on the claws of lice; the barbed proboscides of ticks; and the tactile hairs of mites. In these same parasites can be observed marked degenerations in the loss of eyes and other sense organs, absence of wings, and sometimes reduction of legs. Internal parasites are even more peculiar combinations of degeneration and specialization. They possess all sorts of hooks, barbs, suckers, and boring apparatus, yet they have practically no sense organs or special organs of locomotion, a very simple nervous system, and sometimes, as said before, a complete absence of the digestive tube.

Still more remarkable are the specializations of parasites in their reproduction and life history to insure, as far as possible, a safe transfer to new hosts for the succeeding generations. Every structure, every function, every instinct of many of these parasites is modified, to a certain extent, for the sole purpose of reproduction. A fluke does not eat to live, it eats only to reproduce. The inevitable death of the host is the parasite's doomsday, against which it must prepare by producing all the offspring possible, in the hope that enough will survive to keep the race from extinction. The complexity to which the development of the reproductive systems may go is almost incredible. In some adult tapeworms not only does every segment bear complete male and female reproductive systems, but it may bear *two* sets of each. The number of eggs produced by many parasitic worms may run well into the millions. The complexity of the life history is no less remarkable. Not only are free-living stages interposed and intermediate hosts made to serve as transmitting agents, but also often asexual multiplications, sometimes to the extent of several generations, are passed through during the course of these remarkable experiences.

Mutual Tolerance of Hosts and Parasites. The effect of parasitism is felt by both parasite and host. A sort of mutual adaptation between the two is developed in proportion to the time that the relationship of host and parasite has existed. It is obviously to the disadvantage of internal parasites to cause the death of their host, for in so doing they destroy themselves. It is likewise to the disadvantage of external parasites, not so much to cause the death of their host, as to produce such pain or irritation as to lead to their own destruction at the hands of the irritated host. In well-established host-parasite relations the host succeeds in protecting itself against the injurious effects of the parasites, partly by developing antibodies which neutralize poisonous or injurious products of the parasites, partly by placing its blood-forming or tissue-repairing mechanisms on a plane of higher efficiency, and partly by less well-understood immune mechanisms, enforcing birth control or at least family quotas upon the parasites. The efficient parasite, as Swellengrebel pointed out, is one which is able to survive under these conditions, content to live in a restricted manner in a host which is in consequence not sufficiently aroused to put forth the effort necessary to eliminate it entirely. An African native living in a highly malarial district in apparently good health, in spite of having harbored malaria parasites approximately from birth, affords a good example.

It is a well-established fact that a disease introduced into a place where it is not endemic, i.e., does not normally exist, is more destructive than in places where it has long been present. In an abnormal host the delicate adjustment between host and parasite is missing and usually either the parasite fails to survive, or else the host is severely injured or destroyed; a high degree of pathogenicity of a parasite may be considered *prima facie* evidence of a recent and still imperfect development of the host-parasite relation. An organism and the parasites which are particularly adapted to live with it may, in a way, be looked upon as a sort of compound organism. Those parasites which live part of their lives in vertebrate animals and part in other parasites of these animals, as lice, ticks, and biting flies, are absolutely dependent for their existence on the relationships of the vertebrates and their parasites and form a sort of third party to the association.

Modes of Infection and Transmission. The portals of entry and means of transmission of parasites are of the most vital importance from the standpoint of preventive medicine. In the past few decades wonderful strides in our knowledge along these lines have been made, but much is yet to be found out.

Many parasites may be spread by direct or indirect contact with infected parts, e.g., the spirochetes of syphilis and yaws, the mouth amebas, itch mites, and, of course, free-moving ectoparasites. The parasites of the digestive system and of other internal organs gain entrance in one of two ways. They may bore directly through the skin as larvae, e.g., hookworms. More commonly they enter the mouth as cysts or eggs, e.g., dysentery amebas and Ascaris; as larvae, e.g., tapeworms; or as adults, e.g., leeches. Access to the mouth is gained in many different ways, but chiefly with impure water, with unwashed vegetables fertilized with night soil, with food contaminated by dust, flies, or unclean hands, or with the flesh of an animal which has served as an intermediate host. The parasites of the blood or lymphatic systems usually rely on biting arthropods (insects, ticks, and mites) to transmit them from host to host, and it is in this capacity, i.e., as transmitters and intermediate hosts of blood parasites, that parasitic arthropods are of such vast importance.

Geographic Distribution.   The distribution of parasites over the surface of the earth is dependent (1) on the presence of suitable hosts, and (2) on habits and environmental conditions which make possible the transfer from host to host. A human parasite which does not utilize an intermediate host is likely to be found in every inhabited region of the world, providing its particular requirements with respect to habits and environmental conditions are met, and if it can also live as a parasite in other animals it may occur even beyond the limits of human habitation. Parasites such as amebas, intestinal flagellates, pinworms, and itch mites, which require only slight carelessness in habits for their transfer, and are largely independent of external conditions, are practically cosmopolitan, but vary in abundance with the extent of the carelessness on which their propagation depends. Ascaris and Trichuris are only slightly more limited since they require some time outside the body to reach the infective stage, and are susceptible to heat and dryness. Hookworms are more limited, since they have to brave the dangers of the outside world as free-living organisms, unprotected by resistant egg shells; therefore, not only heat and dryness but also such factors as cold and the nature of the soil come into play.

When an intermediate host is involved, distribution is more limited, for not only must both hosts be present together, but the relations between them must be such as to favor the transfer of the parasites from one to the other.   Sleeping sickness never occurs outside the range of certain species of tsetse flies, malaria beyond the range of certain species of Anopheles, nor kala-azar outside the range of certain species of Phlebotomus.

Usually the distribution of the parasites is not as great as the distribution of their necessary intermediate hosts. A guinea worm not only requires both man and certain species of Cyclops, but it also requires conditions under which the Cyclops can be reached by the embryos and under which the infected Cyclops can be ingested by man. Even in the presence of both man and mosquitoes, filaria may not thrive, since it must have atmospheric conditions which give it time to penetrate human skin, after a mosquito has landed it there, before it dries up, and it has little chance in a place where houses and porches have mosquito-proof screens.   Clonorchis requires not only the simultaneous presence of man, certain snails, and certain fish, but it also requires unsanitary conditions making possible the access of eggs to the snails, a free association of infected snails and fish, and an established habit of eating raw fish.   Sometimes ability to infect other hosts than man may keep alive an infection even when human habits preclude the possibility of more than occasional or rare access to the human body.   No doubt the broad tapeworm would soon die out in the Canadian lakes if it were not that dogs and wild carnivores serve as reservoir hosts.

With modern transportation facilities, as remarked in the previous chapter, the possibilities of extension of the range of parasites are increased. With more frequent experimentation, parasites may find new suitable intermediate hosts, and the required environmental conditions, in new places.   Yellow fever has failed, during all the past centuries, to gain access to the Far East only because the long sea journey exceeds the incubation period of the disease and makes it possible to discover cases of yellow fever and prevent them, or mosquitoes which might have fed on them, from entering.   Today the danger is greater.   Sometimes altered environmental conditions cause some diseases to disappear and others to manifest themselves.   Thus, malaria disappears with adequate drainage and epidemic typhus with cleanliness.   On the other hand, Rhodesian sleeping sickness is the direct outcome of the civilization of East Africa and the creation of conditions under which *Glossina morsitans* more frequently bites man and less frequently the diminishing wild game.

Resistance and Immunity

It has been known for centuries that after a man or animal has recovered from certain diseases he, or it, is thereafter immune to those diseases; for ages the Chinese have practiced inoculation of their children from mild smallpox cases rather than risk their exposure during destructive epidemics. Pasteur, in the last half of the nineteenth century, put the matter on a more scientific basis, and since then the science of immunology has grown up.

Until recently most of the work on immunity has been done in connection with bacteria, and much has been found out about so-called "immune reactions" to bacterial and nonliving antigens; much less is known about actual functional immunity. We know that the presence of foreign proteins or antigens in the body results in the formation of antibodies in the blood which, under certain circumstances, cause them to dissolve if they are not already in solution, to clump or agglutinate if in discrete particles, and to precipitate as solid particles if in solution; that whenever there is a combination of an antigen with its antibody a certain enzyme-like constituent of the blood known as complement is used up or "fixed" (complement-fixation); that reactions are heightened so that there is a more rapid inflammatory process, with accumulation of phagocytic cells and a walling off of the site of invasion if it is localized; and that there is frequently, preliminary to the development of actual immunity, a state of general hypersensitiveness or allergy. In this allergic state inoculation of the antigen into the skin results in reactions which are easily seen and are highly diagnostic. All these reactions are usually so highly specific that even a different strain of the same species of organism may fail to elicit them.

In spite of a great mass of knowledge concerning these various "immune reactions," little is yet known about the true nature of antibodies or the role which the various reactions play in producing functional immunity. It is only in recent years that we have come to realize that the fundamental principles of immunity are the same for protozoan and metazoan parasites as they are for bacteria and proteins, though from the nature of the infections there are differences in degree or in details.

Natural Immunity. Natural immunity to particular parasites is the birthright not only of species of animals but also of races or even individuals. It is due to genetic and environmental factors affecting both host and parasite, such as mechanical barriers; phagocytosis; blood constituents; hormones; diet, especially vitamins; hydrogen-ion concentration; temperature; and probably many other factors not yet understood. It may also be due to specific factors in the metabolism of the parasite. Parasites adapted to live in a particular species of host often thrive better in that host than in any others, but after a number of generations they may adapt themselves better to some other

host (see p. 27). Natural immunity may often be broken down by
such means as removal of the thyroid gland or the spleen, dietary deficiencies, injury by other infections, or other debilitating factors.

Age Resistance. Age resistance is often in reality acquired immunity, or it may be due to increased speed of development of acquired
immunity. Culbertson in 1939 found that young animals had less
capacity to mobilize phagocytic cells or to produce antibodies, and that
the phagocytic cells, when present, failed to function as efficiently as
in older animals. However, that there is a true age immunity of some
animals to some infections cannot be denied. Sandground in 1928
wrote that he thought that age resistance is usually associated with
abnormal or imperfectly adapted hosts; any incompatibility between
host and parasite appears to become intensified with age. It is
significant that most cases of human infections with " foreign " worms,
belonging in other animals, are recorded in children. Ackert in 1938
found a tangible basis for age resistance of chickens to Ascaridia in the
increase with age of intestinal goblet cells, the mucin of which he
showed to have an inhibitory effect on the worms.

Premunition. It is a matter of common knowledge that protozoan
infections, after an acute attack, usually go into a chronic state in which
the parasites may be few and hard to find; such a chronic state is often
punctuated by relapses, due to the parasites taking advantage of a
temporary weakening in the defenses of the host, as the result of fatigue,
malnutrition, other diseases, etc. During the chronic stages of infection there is a high degree of resistance to superimposed infections, at
least with the same strain of the organisms. Resistance of this type,
dependent upon the presence of organisms from a prior infection, is
called premunition. In some cases, at least, there is no fundamental
difference between premunition and immunity; when immunity is of
short duration the presence of a few parasites has the effect of constantly renewing it. A chronic, symptomless malarial infection
behaves in this manner, but Boyd and Mathews in 1938 found a high
degree of resistance to a particular strain of malaria parasites might
still be present as long as seven years after the termination of the original infection. In some tapeworm infections, on the other hand, the
writer has shown the premunition to be due to a crowding effect;
resistance to reinfection disappears immediately with removal of the
parasites. This appears also to be true of some acanthocephalan
infections.

Acquired Immunity. As already noted, premunition to protozoan
infections is probably in most instances only a constantly renewed
acquired immunity. The fact that immunity is acquired from prior

exposure to protozoan and metazoan parasites, as well as to bacteria, is a comparatively recent observation, but it is now recognized as a very widespread phenomenon.

It has been possible for parasitologists to analyze the various factors involved in acquired immunity to a greater extent than bacteriologists have been able to do it. In the case of microscopic, multiplying organisms in parenteral situations, i.e., actually in the tissues, and not merely in the lumen of the alimentary canal, it is obvious that dying or disintegrating organisms must supply considerable amounts of antigen to which the body can react, and it is impossible to separate reactions to these body proteins from reactions against enzymes or metabolic products of the growing and assimilating organisms.

Taliaferro and Taliaferro in 1922 demonstrated that rats develop a reproduction-inhibiting antibody, or ablastin, as well as trypanocidal antibodies, to *Trypanosoma lewisi*. The trypanosomes are not injured in any way by the ablastin except that they are unable to reproduce, which, in the writer's opinion, is due to interference with nutrition and consequent growth; this antibody differs from others in not combining with its supposed antigen — the trypanosomes — when mixed with them. Later (1935), the writer found that nematodes (Nippostrongylus) in the intestines of rats likewise had their nutrition interfered with, so that they were unable to grow normally or to reproduce. In this case it is obvious that this immune reaction could not have been directed against the parasites' body substance, but only against enzymes or metabolic products of the parasites. That this is likewise true of the migrating larvae of this worm in the parenteral phase is suggested by two facts: (1) the observation made by Sarles, in collaboration with Taliaferro, that precipitates form at the mouth, anus, and excretory pore of the larvae, clearly an immune reaction to metabolic products; and (2) the far greater efficiency, in the production of immunity, of growing, migrating larvae than of injections of even very large quantities of worm substance. In the writer's opinion, Taliaferro's reproduction-inhibiting antibody against trypanosomes is probably of fundamentally the same nature, a reaction against metabolic products which interferes with nutrition but does not kill the parasites. If this is true there seems to be no good reason why it should not extend to other organisms as well, including bacteria; this may be the explana-. tion for the disappointing results in immunization with dead, as compared with living, vaccines.

Blacklock and Gordon showed in 1927 that, in reinfections in guinea pigs with the skin maggot, *Cordylobia anthropophaga*, most of the maggots which entered the skin failed to grow and died within 40 hours. This immunity they showed to be present not in the blood but in the skin, and to be local; i.e., a guinea pig with an immunized back could for a time still be infected in the abdomen, though gradually the maggot-killing property of the skin spread over greater areas. A similar local immunity was demonstrated by the writer in the Nippostrongylus work referred to above; it probably differs from general immunity only in the concentration and distribution of antigens. When the antigens are parenterally liberated they are distributed over the entire body, stimulating general immunity and formation of circulating antibodies. When produced by parasites in the skin or lumen of the intestine the antigens are for the most part taken up by the local tissues, which then develop local immunity. Good examples of local immunity have been observed in Coccidia, Trichinella, and Strongyloides infections.

Acquired immunity to helminthic infections has subsequently been demonstrated by numerous investigators, working with many different parasites. It may now be assumed that acquired immunity develops against all parenteral parasites, and for intestinal parasites that live in or feed on the mucous membranes or suck blood, such as amebas and Coccidia among Protozoa, and nematodes, trematodes, and *Hymenolepis nana* among helminths. On the other hand, at least some tapeworms (e.g., *Hymenolepis diminuta*), and Acanthocephala (e.g., *Moniliformis dubius*), seem *not* to stimulate their hosts antigenically, and refractoriness to reinfection is due entirely to crowding effects as shown by Chandler in 1939 and by Burlingame and Chandler in 1941.

Acquired immunity to protozoan parasites manifests itself by refractoriness to reinfection and by control of existing infections, the latter by limitation on reproduction and by destruction of parasites where exposed to antibodies. The parasites usually persist longest in brain tissue. In intestinal helminthic infections the first effect is failure of reinfection, and then elimination of already established parasites. The latter phenomenon was first observed by Stoll in 1929 in sheep infected with *Haemonchus contortus* (see p. 415) and was termed by him "self-cure." Heavy infections which undermine the health of the host, especially if accompanied by poor diet, inhibit the development of immunity and lead to still further infection, thus setting up a vicious cycle (Chandler, 1948).

Artificial and Passive Immunization. Artificial immunization with vaccines is possible against metazoan as against bacterial parasites but, as already noted, it is feeble compared with the immunity developed against living organisms, particularly in intestinal parasites. Passive transfer of immunity to metazoan parasites was first demonstrated by Miller in 1932 in larval tapeworms in rats; subsequently, Sarles and Taliaferro showed that resistance to Nippostrongylus infections in rats could be passively transferred if relatively enormous doses of serum were used, and Kerr got suggestive results with hookworms in mice and Ascaris in guinea pigs. In all these cases the passively transferable immunity is developed in response to the parenteral phase of development of the parasites.

Tolerance to Injurious Effects. In the foregoing paragraphs we have considered principally the immunity brought about by reactions against the parasites which result in their death or interference with their metabolism. In addition, however, there is a development of tolerance to the injurious products of parasites, or increased efficiency in repairing damage done by them, which protects the host without injuring the parasites. Persons losing blood from hookworm infections place their blood-forming mechanism on a plane of increased activity and efficiency; animals exposed to injury by the toxic products of screwworms develop the ability to neutralize these products and render them less harmful; and persons exposed to worm infections increase the number of the special white blood corpuscles called eosinophiles, which are somehow concerned with the neutralization of injurious products of the worms. This eosinophilia is a very characteristic feature of worm infections, particularly parenteral ones; failure to respond to parenteral invasions of worms by an increase in eosinophiles indicates that the defensive mechanism of the host is not functioning efficiently.

Host Specificity

Intimately bound up with the question of resistance of hosts and the mutual adaptation of host and parasite to each other is the question of limitation of parasites to particular hosts. In order for a parasite to live habitually in a host two conditions must be met: (1) a dependable means of transfer from individual to individual, and (2) ability to thrive in the individual when it gets there. It is the interplay of these two factors which determines in what hosts a parasite lives. Every parasite, of course, has at least one species of host, and sometimes several, in which these conditions are satisfactorily met, otherwise it would cease to exist. Usually there are other hosts in which one or both conditions are only occasionally met, in which case " accidental " parasitism results.

Lack of a dependable means of transfer relieves man from all parasitic infections in which the parasites encyst in the bodies of insects and wait for their insect hosts to be eaten in order to reach the definitive host, since no race of man is habitually insectivorous. If it were not for this there is little reason to doubt that there could be numbered among the common human parasites such forms as *Hymenolepis diminuta, Dipylidum caninum,* and many spiruroids and spiny-headed worms. On the other hand, man must commonly be exposed to infection with such parasites as bird malaria, animal schistosomes, dog and cat hookworms, and bird filariae, yet infection rarely or never occurs, because the parasites do not find suitable conditions for development in the human body. Such animals as rats, dogs, cats, and various domestic animals must very often be exposed to infection with human parasites, yet they habitually harbor very few of them.

The conditions in the body of one species of animal are never exactly the same as in another species; a parasite in its proper host has adapted itself to the particular set of conditions existing there, just as an insect or bird or plant has adapted itself to particular environmental conditions in its ecological niche in nature. Sometimes very slight modifications in an abnormal host make possible the survival of a "foreign" parasite. Cats, for example, would undoubtedly be common hosts of *Endamoeba histolytica* if food did not pass through the digestive tract so fast that cysts do not have time to hatch and the young amebas to apply themselves to the intestinal wall. If an operation is performed to stop the movement of the intestinal contents for even a few hours, infection of cats with this parasite is easy. Even then, however, the amebas could not thrive in cats alone, for the stimulus which causes them to form cysts, by means of which they are spread from host to host, appears to be lacking.

Many parasites perform migrations in the bodies of their hosts by which they ultimately reach their proper destination. They are so adjusted to their normal hosts that they are guided by a series of influences or stimuli which lead them in the right direction, and they only occasionally get lost. In strange hosts these road signs are misleading or missing, and the parasites become aimless wanderers in abnormal situations, unable to find their way to the localities in the body where they can successfully mature. Human hookworms, for instance, are guided by some condition in a human being to enter lymph or blood vessels in the skin, and so eventually reach the lungs and then the intestine; *Ancylostoma brasiliense* does likewise in its normal hosts but usually fails in man, and rambles in the skin, causing creeping eruption. Species of Gastrophilus, the horse bots, find their way to the digestive tract of horses, but in man the guiding influences are missing and they creep about under the skin. Gnathostomes and Lagocheilascaris are other worms which lose their way in the human host and end up in subcutaneous cysts, where they have no business.

Spread to New Hosts. All animals tend gradually to extend their range by adapting themselves to slightly different conditions; free-living animals continually try to occupy new territories which differ in climate, vegetation, or physical conditions from that to which they were accustomed, and parasites likewise attempt to utilize new hosts. But parasites are at a disadvantage compared with free-living animals; the latter are nearly always able to find intergrading conditions between two different types of habitat, whereas parasites cannot spread in this gradual manner; if they extend their range to a new host they must make the change in a single jump, for there is no middle ground where conditions are transitional. A song sparrow can find an infinite number of intergrading conditions between the damp, cool forests of the northwest and the dry, hot deserts of the southwest, but Ascaris can find no intergrading conditions between those found in the body of a pig and those in a human being.

Among free-living animals we have geographical subspecies or varieties; in parasites we have hostal races. When these varieties become distinct enough so that they can be morphologically distinguished, and especially if they become so well adapted to a particular environment that they are not easily transferred to others, and do not merge with other races, they should rightly be regarded as species. If, however, they have only average differences or none at all, even though they may after a few generations thrive better in one environment than in another, it seems more reasonable to regard them as races than as species, in parasites as well as free-living animals. Some parasitologists are inclined to consider extremely closely related parasites in different hosts as distinct species, to which separate species names are applied, until proved otherwise, whereas some tend to lump them all together.

Such difficulties arise in all groups of parasites — protozoans, worms, and arthropods. The mere fact that one form of parasite is more readily transferred from one individual to another of a single host species, than from species to species, does not seem to be sufficient basis for regarding it as a distinct species. Steiner has pointed out that certain soil nematodes, in the course of one or two seasons, involving a considerable number of generations, may thrive far better on a particular host plant than on others, and show a very decided preference, yet such adapted forms can be readapted to other host plants, and there is no question as to their specific identity. A similar condition appears to exist in such parasites as itch mites, hookworms, Ascaris,

Hymenolepis nana, Trichomonas, and many others. It has long been the custom of botanists and zoologists to recognize geographic races by subspecific or varietal names, and it would seem advisable for parasitologists to recognize hostal races, where morphological differences are slight or absent, and where interchanges are even occasionally possible, by similar varietal names.

The Names of Parasites

In all branches of natural history it has been found not only expedient but also necessary to employ scientific names, for there are estimated to be more than 10 million species of animals. Common names, like nicknames, vary from place to place, and often the same name is applied to quite different organisms in different places. Linnaeus, in the eighteenth century, devised a system of " binomial names " which consisted of the genus name, beginning with a capital letter, followed by a species name, in zoology beginning with a small letter, and both Latinized in form, since Latin came nearer to being a universal language than any other. Strictly, the genus and species names are followed by the name of the man who first gave the species name, in parentheses if the genus name is not the one he originally used, but in ordinary references to species this is omitted. The genus name may be likened to a surname and the species name to a given name, e.g., *Ascaris lumbricoides* is comparable to Smith, John.

Family names in zoology always have the ending " idae " attached to the root of the type genus, e.g., Muscidae from Musca, Ascarididae from Ascaris (root ascarid) ; superfamily names end in " oidea," but there is no standard ending for orders or classes. In botany the family ending is " aceae," e.g., Spirochaetaceae.

In order to avoid confusion there were adopted (in 1904) rules of nomenclature, known as the International Code of Zoological Nomenclature, which makes it impossible for any two animals to have the same name. A genus name can apply to only one genus in the entire animal kingdom, and a species name to only one species within a genus. The tenth edition of Linnaeus' *Systema Naturae* (1758) is accepted as the starting point for the names, no name proposed prior to that time having any standing. The first valid name given an animal is considered the correct one. Of course, if an animal is put in the wrong genus, it must be transferred to the right one. If a genus is split up, the animal may have to be placed in a new genus; for example, the old genus Oxyuris has been split into a number of genera. The oxyuris of the horse was the earliest one placed in the genus, therefore the *restricted* genus Oxyuris must contain this species and any others which fall into its subdivision of the old genus; since the human oxyuris falls into a different subdivision it comes out with the next available genus name, Enterobius. For the same reasons *Filaria bancrofti* is now *Wuchereria bancrofti*, etc. If two genera are combined, the older genus name applies to all the members of the merged genera. If the same animal is given different species names by different workers, the earliest name applies.

Although this system was established to prevent confusion, in many instances strict application of the rules has resulted in just the opposite. The number of possible errors and misinterpretations are disheartening, in consequence of which names, long recognized and accepted, have to be discarded for others, because someone shows that the established name was really first applied to another species, or an earlier name was overlooked, or for some other reason. Unfortunately, the commoner animals are the ones which suffer most, for they are the most likely to have been redescribed by various workers and to have been shifted about from genus to genus. Unfortunate as this situation is, it is better than having no rules at all, and steps are now being taken to make names which have been in common usage for many years inviolable. The synonymy, or list of aliases, of some of our common parasites is already deplorably long. In some instances there is a difference of opinion as to what the correct name should be.

Although the scientific names are sometimes barbarously long and at first may be very annoying and even terrifying, every student of parasitology, as of every other branch of biology, must overcome any childish aversion he may have for them, and become used to accepting and using them. They are not obstacles to be avoided, but valuable tools without which there would be hopeless confusion.

REFERENCES

BALL, G. H., Parasitism and Evolution, *Am. Naturalist,* **78,** 345 (1943).

BECKER, E. R., Host Specificity and Specificity of Animal Parasites, *Am. J. Trop. Med.,* **13,** 505 (1933).

VAN BENEDEN, P. J., *Animal Parasites and Messmates,* 5th ed., London, 1904.

CAULLERY, M., *Le parasitisme et la symbiose,* Paris, 1922.

CHANDLER, A. C., Speciation and Host Relationships of Parasites, *Parasitology,* **15,** 326 (1923).

The Nature and Mechanism of Immunity in Various Intestinal Nematode Infections, *Am. J. Trop. Med.,* **19,** 309 (1939).

Premunition in Tapeworm Infections, *Am. J. Hyg.,* **29,** D, 105 (1939); **31,** D, 17 (1940).

Factors Modifying Host Resistance to Helminthic Infections, *Proc. 4th Intern. Congr. on Trop. Med. and Malaria,* **2,** Sect. VI, 975–983 (1948).

CULBERTSON, J. T., *Immunity against Animal Parasites,* New York, 1941.

ELTON, C., *Animal Ecology,* Chap. 6, New York, 1935.

FAUST, E. C., The Nosogeography of Parasites and Their Hosts, *Puerto Rico J. Pub. Health and Trop. Med.,* **6,** 373 (1931).

HALL, M. C., The Wide Field of Veterinary Parasitology, *J. Parasitol.,* **16,** 195 (1930).

International Rules of Zoological Nomenclature, *Proc. Biol. Soc. Wash.,* **39, 75** (1926).

METCALF, M. M., Parasites and the Aid They Give in Problems of Taxonomy, Geographical Distribution and Palaeogeography, *Smithsonian Misc. Collections,* **81,** No. 8 (1929).

SMITH, THEOBALD, *Parasitism and Disease,* Princeton Univ. Press, 1934.

STRONG, R. P., The Importance of Ecology in Relation to Disease, *Science,* **82,** 307 (1935).

STUNKARD, H. W., Parasitism as a Biological Phenomenon, *Science Monthly,* **28,** 349 (1929).

TALIAFERRO, W. H., *Immunology of Parasitic Infections,* New York, 1929.
The Mechanism of Acquired Immunity in Infections with Parasitic Worms, *Physiol. Revs.,* **20,** 469 (1940).

PART I — PROTOZOA

CHAPTER 3
Introduction to Protozoa

Place of Protozoa in the Animal Kingdom. It is usual for zoologists to divide the entire animal kingdom into two great subkingdoms, the Protozoa and the Metazoa. These groups are very unequal in number of species. The Metazoa include all the animals with which the majority of people are familiar, from the simple sponges and jellyfishes, through the worms, mollusks, and the vast hordes of insects and their allies, to the highly organized vertebrate animals, including man himself. The Protozoa, on the other hand, include only microscopic or almost microscopic animals, the very existence of which is unknown to the average lay person. Although some Protozoa are readily visible to the naked eye there are others which approach the limit of visibility under light microscopes. There is no question but that in point of numbers of individuals the Protozoa exceed the other animals, millions to one; a pint jar of stagnant water may contain many millions of these minute animals. Over 15,000 species of Protozoa have been described, but it is probable that there are thousands more which are not yet known to science.

The distinction between the Protozoa and Metazoa is based on a characteristic of the most fundamental nature. The Protozoa are animals that perform all the essential functions of life within the compass of a single cell. The Metazoa, on the other hand, are many-celled animals, with specialized cells set apart to perform particular functions. A protozoan cell, even though sometimes living in a colony of individuals which are all bound together, can live its life and reproduce its kind quite independently of any other cells, having in itself the powers of digestion, respiration, excretion and secretion, sensibility, motility, and reproduction. Most metazoan cells, on the other hand, are so specialized for particular functions that, if separated from the other cells with which they are associated in the body, they die unless

31

provided with food and environmental conditions similar to those naturally provided by surrounding cells, as in tissue cultures.

The very fact of evolution makes it difficult to draw a sharp and fast line between two groups of organisms, even between such fundamentally different groups as the Protozoa and Metazoa. There are always borderline exceptions which make the work of the systematic zoologist at once difficult and interesting. In the case in hand there are colonial Protozoa in which all the cells are not exactly alike, but have at least the beginnings of specialization, and in which the colony may react as an individual. On the other hand, in the lowest Metazoa, the sponges, specialization of the cells is only very limited, and in the little-known Mesozoa differentiation is even less.

The distinction between Protozoa and bacteria, though involving the distinction between animals and plants, is much more difficult. As we descend the evolutionary scale of plants and animals the usual distinctions between them disappear, and it becomes difficult if not impossible definitely to place certain species in either the plant or animal kingdom. The possession of a distinct nucleus of some kind and some type of sexual reproduction are the characteristics which usually distinguish the Protozoa from the less highly organized bacteria. In a few Protozoa, however, there is no membrane-bound nucleus, and in many of them there is no sound evidence for any sexual phenomena. Until recently it was believed that a definite life cycle distinguished Protozoa from bacteria, but with the revelations that have been made in the life cycle of bacteria even this no longer holds as a valid means of separation. Chemical reactions, staining properties, and the like are sometimes resorted to, yet on this basis the spirochetes, now almost always placed with the bacteria, should be aligned with the Protozoa. The possession of a membrane-bound nucleus is probably the most valid distinction, and when this fails other signs of relationship must be relied on, as when a lizard lacks legs but is still not a snake.

The separation of Protozoa from the single-celled plants, Protophyta, is even more difficult. Calkins (1933) ejected the entire group of chlorophyll-bearing flagellates from their relatives among the Protozoa, in spite of the fact that some non-chlorophyll-bearing forms are obviously close cousins to the green forms and have secondarily lost their chlorophyll. From the nutritional standpoint a green flagellate, like Euglena, can be, and is, a plant by day and an animal by night. There are good arguments either for or against putting such forms with the colorless, motile Protozoa on the one hand, or with the green, nonmotile algae on the other. Between the higher plants and higher animals there is a broad no-man's land of single-celled organisms which might be segregated into a buffer state, for which the name Protista was suggested by Ernst Haeckel many years ago. The boundary between Protista and Metazoa is fairly sharply defined, but that between the Protista and the lowest forms of Metaphyta (algae and fungi) is much more arbitrary.

Structure. A protozoan, in its simplest form, conforms to the usual definition of a cell: a bit of cytoplasm containing a *nucleus*. The nucleus, bounded by a *nuclear membrane*, varies greatly in structure; it usually falls into one of two general types, *vesicular* or *compact*, though there are intermediate forms.

A vesicular nucleus (Fig. 13*A*) is filled with *nucleoplasm* which does not stain readily, and has the deep-staining *chromatin*, out of which the heredity-bearing chromosomes are made, arranged in a central body, in scattered granules, or encrusted on the inner surface of the nuclear membrane. Usually there is a well-defined, deep-staining body called an *endosome* (often also called a *karyosome*), which is usually a combination of chromatin and a chemically different substance called *plastin*, though it may be either one alone. The nucleus of some Protozoa, e.g., trypanosomes, has a very large endosome with a clear space between it and the periphery, while in other cases, e.g., *Endamoeba histolytica*, the endosome is very small and inconspicuous, and the chromatin is distributed in granules encrusted on the nuclear membrane. The nature of the endosome and distribution of the chromatin are sometimes of much value in identification, especially in the amebas.

The compact type of nucleus (Fig. 28*A*, *mac.n.*), on the other hand, contains closely packed chromatin granules with very little nucleoplasm; it is especially characteristic of the macronucleus of ciliates (see following paragraph). This type of nucleus is very variable in shape and may be divided into separate parts.

In most but not all cases division of the nucleus is accomplished by some form of mitosis or a process at least hinting at it; there is, however, no uniformity in the process as there is in Metazoa (see Fig. 1). Nature seems to have been experimenting with nuclear division in the Protozoa. Typical *chromosomes* are formed in some Protozoa, e.g., many amebas, but often there is no clear evidence of them. In Endamoeba mitosis takes place entirely within the nuclear membrane; a characteristic feature is the division of a *centriole* in the endosome into two, which migrate to opposite ends of the intranuclear spindle, but remain connected by a deep-staining strand called an *intradesmose* until division of the 6 or 8 chromosomes is completed (Fig. 1*A*). In the ciliates the nucleus divides, after sexual reproduction, into two functionally distinct parts. The smaller *micronucleus* (Fig. 2, *mic.n.*)

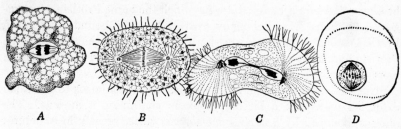

$$A \qquad\qquad B \qquad\qquad C \qquad\qquad D$$

Fig. 1. Mitosis in Protozoa. *A*, *Endamoeba histolytica*, early anaphase; note small number of chromosomes, intact nuclear membrane, and intradesmose. *B*, *Acanthocystis aculeata*, a heliozoan, in metaphase; note free "centroblepharoplasts" or centerioles and spindle, without nuclear membrane. *C*, *Trichonympha campanula*, a flagellate of termites, in anaphase; divided centroblepharoplast forms poles of spindle outside of nuclear membrane, which remains intact. *D*, *Endamoeba muris;* 2 sets of chromosomes undergo division — set 1 have already migrated to poles; set 2 in metaphase. (*A* and *C* after Kofoid and Swezy; *B* after Schaudinn; *D* after Wenrich.)

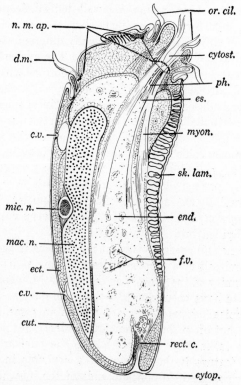

Fig. 2. A complex ciliate, *Diplodinium ecaudatum*, showing highly developed organelles; *cut.*, cuticle; *c.v.*, contractile vacuoles; *cytop.*, cytopyge; *cytost.*, cytostome; *d.m.*, dorsal membranelle; *ect.*, ectoplasm; *end.*, endoplasm; *es.*, esophagus; *f.v.*, food vacuoles; *mac. n.*, macronucleus; *mic. n.*, micronucleus; *myon.*, myonemes, strands for retracting esophagus; *n. m. ap.*, neuromotor apparatus; *or. cil.*, oral cilia; *rect. c.*, rectal canal; *sk. lam.*, skeletal laminae. × 750. (After Sharpe.)

is concerned only with reproduction; it contains an endosome, and divides by mitosis; the larger *macronucleus* (Fig. 2, *mac.n.*), though it arises originally from a micronucleus, becomes greatly modified in both form and function. It is of compact type; it divides without mitosis; and it disintegrates at the time of sexual reproduction. In a few Protozoa there is no nucleus as such, the chromatin being present in scattered particles as it is in bacteria.

The cytoplasm of a protozoan is usually more or less clearly divisible into an outer and inner zone, the *ectoplasm* and *endoplasm,* respec-

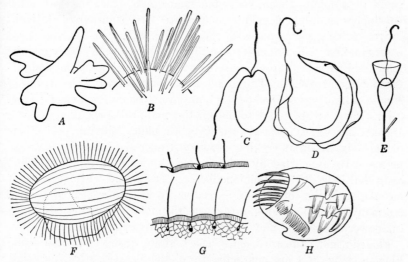

FIG. 3. Types of organs of locomotion in Protozoa; *A*, Amoeba with pseudopodia; *B*, a heliozoan with axopodia; *C*, Bodo with free flagella; *D*, Trypanosoma with flagellum attached to undulating membrane; *E*, choanoflagellate with flagellum and " collar "; *F*, Pleuronema with cilia and membranelle formed of fused cilia; *G*, modes of insertion of cilia; *H*, Aspidisca with cirri. (Figs. *F* to *H* from Calkins.)

tively (Fig. 2). The ectoplasm in simple forms like amebas is the less fluid and comparatively clear, while the endoplasm is more fluid and somewhat granular or vacuolated. The clearness of the differentiation between ectoplasm and endoplasm is sometimes useful in distinguishing species of Protozoa, especially amebas. The ectoplasm differs from the endoplasm in function as well as in appearance. The ectoplasm may be likened to the body wall and appendages of higher animals while the endoplasm may be compared with the viscera or internal organs. The endoplasm digests food and has the power of secretion and excretion, whereas the ectoplasm produces the various organelles for locomotion, food getting, oxygen absorption, and special senses. The term "organelle " is used in place of " organ " for structures which are only parts of a single cell. Whether or not Protozoa have a definite shape depends on the presence or absence of a limiting membrane or *pellicle*. Amebas have no outer membrane, and so, when relaxed in a fluid medium, they assume a spherical shape, which is modified in living forms by contractions, contacts, etc. Many forms have fine pellicles which allow change of shape but maintain a definite form other than the spherical one when the animal is relaxed, but in others the limiting membrane is so tough that the shape of the body is practically constant. Many Protozoa, particularly Sarcodina, produce shells of cellulose, chitin, cemented sand grains, silica, lime, or other substances, and some flagellates and ciliates have transparent chitinous loricas or tests, sometimes with collars (Fig. 3*E*).

Organelles. The organelles contained in a protozoan's body may be many and varied. Those connected with movement or locomotion differ in different groups. The simplest type of movement is by means of simple outflowings of the body cytoplasm known as *pseudopodia* (Fig. 3*A*). These are used both for locomotion and for the engulfing of food. In some species, e.g., the amebas, they are blunt, lobe-like projections of the body, but in others they are very slender and tapering; some are permanently supported by axial rods, in which case they are called *axopodia* (Fig. 3*B*). Pseudopodia are the characteristic organs of locomotion of the entire class Sarcodina, to which the amebas belong, but many flagellates and Sporozoa, e.g., the malaria parasites, also have the power of ameboid movement by means of pseudopodia.

Flagella and *cilia* are usually constant in arrangement and form. Flagella (Fig. 3*C*) are characteristic of the class Mastigophora, but they also occur in some stages in the life cycle of certain amebas and in the spermlike microgametes of Sporozoa. They are long whiplike outgrowths, capable of violent lashing or of rippling movements, and are composed of a fine filament, the *axoneme*, surrounded by a thin film of cytoplasm. Except in one group of flagellates, the Hypermastigida, which are mostly parasites of termites and more or less intermediate between flagellates and ciliates, the flagella are only from one to eight in number. They may be directed forward or trail behind, or may be attached to the side of the body by a delicate *undulating membrane* (Fig. 3*D*); if more than one is present they all may be alike, and perform similar functions, or they may be widely different.

A flagellum always arises from a minute deep-staining body called a *basal granule* or *blepharoplast* (Fig. 4). There has been much difference of opinion as to the origin and functions of the blepharoplast, which cannot be adequately discussed here. In many parasitic flagellates there is another deep-staining body, called the *parabasal*, believed by Kofoid to be a reservoir of kinetic material, very likely derived from the nucleus. The blepharoplast undoubtedly arises sometimes from a granule within the nucleus, and in some Protozoa it remains connected with it by a fiber called a *rhizoplast*. When a parabasal body is present this may also be connected with the blepharoplast by a fibril, or even by a cone of fibrils (Fig. 4*A*, *C*). The blepharoplast

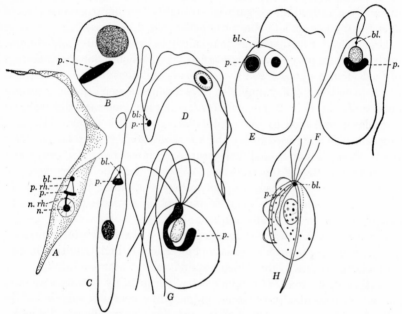

Fig. 4. Types of parabasal bodies. *A*, *Trypanosoma cruzi*, crithidial stage; *B*, Leishmania; *C*, Leptomonas; *D*, *Trypanosoma gambiense*; *E*, *Prowazekia cruzi*; *F*, *P. lacertae*; *G*, Polymonas; *H*, *Trichomonas tenax*. Abbrev.: *bl.*, blepharoplast; *n.*, nucleus; *n. rh.*, nuclear rhizoplast; *p.*, parabasal body; *p. rh.*, parabasal rhizoplast.

and parabasal together constitute a body which is called a *kinetoplast*, the function of which seems to be the control and coordination of movement.

Cilia (Fig. 3*F*), which are characteristic only of the Subphylum Ciliophora, have a structure similar to flagella, and like them arise from individual basal granules (Fig. 3*G*), but they are much shorter, more numerous, and beat rhythmically by a bending to one side. There is much more coordination of movement than in the case of flagella, and regular waves of beats of the cilia can be seen passing over the body of a ciliate. Sometimes rows of cilia are connected by a delicate cytoplasmic membrane into a *membranelle* (Fig. 3*F*), which functions somewhat like an undulating membrane, whereas in other cases, especially in creeping forms, brushes of cilia fuse together into stout organs called *cirri* (Fig. 3*H*).

Many Protozoa possess delicate contractile fibrils called *myonemes* (Fig. 2, *myon.*) which run in various directions in the ectoplasm or pellicle of the animal. In some flagellates and ciliates fibrils and minute deep-staining bodies have been described and have been interpreted as a more or less highly organized *neuromotor apparatus*, i.e., a definitely arranged and organized substance having a nervous control over the myonemes and cilia or flagella (Fig. 2, *n. m. ap.*).

Organelles for food-taking occur chiefly in the flagellates and ciliates. Such Protozoa may have a *cytostome* or cell mouth for the ingestion of food (Fig. 2, *cytost.*) and a *cytopyge* or cell anus for the elimination of waste matter. They may also have a delicate membranous *pharynx* and *esophagus* (Fig. 2, *ph., es.*) for leading the food material into the endoplasm, and *food vacuoles* into which the food is accumulated and in which it is circulated inside the body. In some protozoans, namely the Suctoria, a much modified group of ciliates, there are developed sucking tentacles for the absorption of food. In others there are tiny capsules in the ectoplasm, the *trichocysts*, containing minute threads which can be shot forth when stimulated, and used either for overpowering prey or for protection from enemies.

For the excretion of waste products of the body there is often present one or more *contractile vacuoles* (Fig. 2, *c.v.*), little cavities in the protoplasm of the body which expand with water containing urea and other waste matters conducted to them by tiny radiating canals, and which periodically contract, forcing their contents outside of the cell, sometimes through a definite excretory pore. Sense organs in the form of pigment spots sensitive to light, and outgrowths sensitive to chemical substances, giving, perhaps, a sensation comparable to taste, are present in some species, especially in free-living ones. Various supporting or skeletal organelles may occur. Shells and tests were mentioned on p. 36, but there may also be internal skeletal structures, such as the *central capsule* of Radiolaria or the supporting rod or *axostyle* of Trichomonas (Figs. 22, 23).

Although no protozoan possesses all these organelles, many possess a considerable number of them and exhibit a degree of complexity and organization almost incredible in a single-celled animal which is barely, if at all, visible to the naked eye.

Physiology and Reproduction. In their physiology and manner of life the Protozoa differ among themselves almost as much as do the Metazoa. Some ingest solid food through a cytostome or wrap themselves around the food; others possess chlorophyll and are nourished in a typical plant manner, and still others absorb nutriment by osmosis from the fluids or tissues in which they live. Ingested food particles are surrounded by fluid, forming *food vacuoles* (Fig. 2, *f.v.*), which circulate in the endoplasm. In ciliates they follow a regular course. Digestive fluids appear to be secreted into the vacuoles, and the vacuoles develop an acid reaction during digestion, later becoming neutral again. Undoubtedly the substances that can be digested vary widely with different Protozoa. Some species, e.g., *Endamoeba histolytica*, excrete substances which dissolve blood corpuscles and tissue cells outside the body, the soluble product being then absorbed through the body wall. Indigestible residue from solid food is extruded through the body wall; in forms having a pellicle this takes place through a definite cell anus or *cytopyge* (Fig. 2, *cytop.*). Reserve food material is stored as glycogen, fats, oils, and other substances. Many parasitic forms store food in the form of *volutin* or *metachromatic granules*, which stain like chromatin.

Metabolic wastes are either diffused through the body wall or are collected into one or more contractile vacuoles (Fig. 2, *c.v.*), which are more or less fixed in position in Protozoa with a pellicle; in some ciliates, e.g., Paramecium, they have radiating canals leading into them. Contractile vacuoles are always present in ciliates and in Sarcodina and flagellates inhabiting fresh water or soil, but marine and parasitic Sarcodina and flagellates and the Sporozoa, all of which are parasitic, lack them. The presence of a contractile vacuole is one feature by which free-living amebas capable of multiplying in feces can be distinguished from true inhabitants of the intestine.

Most free-living Protozoa are aerobic, using free oxygen in their respiration, but some, like certain bacteria, are anaerobic. These bring about their oxidations by chemical alterations, and may not be able to grow and multiply in the presence of oxygen; *Endamoeba histolytica*, for instance, grows well in cultures only if the oxygen supply is limited.

The multiplication or reproduction of Protozoa is of two quite distinct types, an asexual multiplication, more or less comparable with the multiplication of cells in a metazoan body, and sexual reproduction, comparable with a similar phenomenon in the higher animals. Several common asexual methods of multiplication occur amongst protozoans, namely, *simple fission*, or division into two more or less equal parts; *budding*, or separation of one or more small parts from the parent cell; and multiple fission or *schizogony*, which results from multiple or repeated division of the nucleus before the cytoplasm divides, thus producing a whole brood of offspring. In the flagellates simple fission is longitudinal, usually beginning with the blepharoplast, while in ciliates it is transverse. In flagellates the old flagella may be retained by one daughter, and new ones grow out from the blepharoplasts for the other, or the old ones may disappear and new ones form. Multiplication occurs in encysted forms in some species but not in others.

Protozoa which are in the phase of asexual multiplication are called *trophozoites*, in contrast to *gametocytes* which give rise to sex cells, and to *cysts*, which do not grow or multiply, although, early in their formation, the nuclei may multiply. The trophozoites of the Sporozoa, which multiply by schizogony, are called *schizonts*, and the daughters resulting from multiple division are called *merozoites*. After the sexual process a different form of multiple fission occurs called *sporogony*, ending in the formation of *sporozoites*. Cells intermediate between the parent cells and the merozoites or sporozoites may be formed, and these are called agametoblasts and sporoblasts, respectively.

Multiplication by one of the asexual methods may go on with great vigor for a long time, but sooner or later some modification of the process occurs. In many Protozoa a process comparable to sexual reproduction in higher animals occurs. In the ciliates this takes place by *conjugation*, i.e., a temporary union of two individuals during which time a daughter nucleus of one enters the other and fuses with a daughter nucleus, and vice versa; at the end of the process the two individuals separate, each being now a fertilized cell. In many other Protozoa two individuals, the *gametes*, unite permanently, and their nuclei fuse, a process which is known as sexual fusion. Sometimes the gametes are indistinguishable from ordinary asexually multiplying individuals, whereas in other instances the gametes are smaller cells produced by a special process of multiplication; the parent cell is then called a *gametocyte*. When there is no visible difference between the gametes, the process of fusion is called *isogamy*, whereas when the gametes differ in size, form, motility, etc., the process is called *anisogamy*, but there are all gradations between isogamy and a condition of anisogamy in which one gamete, the *macrogamete*, corresponds closely to an ovum, being large, immobile, and with a relatively large amount of cytoplasm charged with reserve food material, while the other, the *microgamete*, is relatively minute, is actively motile by means of flagella, and contains very little cytoplasm, being thus essentially similar to a spermatozoon. In many species of parasitic Protozoa, e.g., the malaria parasites, the sexual cycle takes place in an alternate host; in others, e.g., the Coccidia, it takes place outside the body of a host.

In many parasitic Protozoa, for example the parasitic amebas and the intestinal and blood flagellates, no sexual process has been observed with certainty, although Fairbairn and Culwick reported in 1946 what they interpreted as conjugation in trypanosomes. In those Protozoa which do not show true sexual reproduction, i.e, exchange of nuclear material between different individuals, resulting in mixing of hereditary characters and also in rejuvenation of the cells, it is likely that some process occurs which brings about the rejuvenation, even if not the exchange of hereditary characters. Protozoan cells tend to grow old after continued asexual multiplication and lose their youthful vitality and reproductive power, just as do the cells of a metazoan animal. In the Metazoa certain cells (sex cells) have the power of renewing their waning vitality by union with a cell of the opposite sex, thus beginning the cycle again; the same process occurs among Protozoa. It is not certain that in all Protozoa only specific cells can function as sex cells, as in the Metazoa, but in some forms there is evidence that this is so. But, just as rejuvenation may occur in Metazoa by parthenogenesis or sometimes by other methods, in place of sexual reproduction, so substitute methods may occur in Protozoa. Under favorable conditions Paramecium, for instance, can undergo a process of nuclear reorganization called endomixis, which rejuvenates just as if sexual reproduction had occurred. It seems possible that the complicated nuclear divisions of an excysting ameba, and perhaps the life cycle changes of hemoflagellates in their arthropod hosts, may have similar significance.

Encystment. A great many Protozoa, at some time in their life cycle, are able to form more or less impervious protective capsules around their bodies, enabling them to survive unfavorable environmental conditions such as desiccation, unfavorable temperatures, injurious chemicals, or lack of oxygen. This process is called *encystment*. It is by this means that many parasitic Protozoa are able to survive conditions outside the body and to pass through the inhospitable environment of the stomach to reach the intestine or other organs of new hosts. Most parasitic Protozoa that are not transmitted by intermediate hosts resort to cyst formation to gain access to new hosts, though a few, e.g., Trichomonas and Dientamoeba, manage without this.

In many Protozoa of water and soil, encystment occurs as a reaction to desiccation, but in the parasitic amebas and flagellates it is a normal phase in the life cycle, cysts being formed even when conditions are entirely satisfactory for continued multiplication of trophozoites. Encystment and excystment may both occur in the same culture medium, but each is favored by certain chemical and physical characteristics of the environment.

In the Sporozoa cyst formation is associated with sexual reproduction, the zygotes (fertilized gametes) being enclosed in *oöcysts* in which the sporogonic multiplication occurs, ending in the formation of from a few to thousands of *sporozoites*. The sporozoites may be free in the oöcysts, as in the Haemosporidia, to which the malaria parasites belong; they may be enclosed, singly or in groups, in capsules of their own called spores, as in the gregarines; or they may be enclosed in sporocysts inside the oöcysts, as in the Coccidia. Trophozoites of amebas, flagellates, or ciliates prepare to encyst by ceasing ingestion of food and extruding food residue, but they frequently store up considerable amounts of reserve food in the form of glycogen, volutin granules, or chromatoid masses. This is the precystic stage. Then the cyst wall forms, and in many species a multiplication of the nucleus ensues. Mature cysts of *Endamoeba coli*, for instance, have eight nuclei and those of *E. histolytica* have four, but in Iodamoeba cysts there is only one.

When an encysted organism arrives in a favorable environment it excysts and begins to multiply in the trophozoite stage. In some amebas there is a complicated series of nuclear divisions in the multinucleate individual that escapes from the cyst, before any unicellular amebas are set free.

Classification. It is little wonder that the varied assemblage of single-celled animals constituting the group Protozoa should be difficult to classify. Many undergo profound modifications in the course of their life cycles, and the entire life cycle must be considered in any scheme of classification.

For a long time it was customary to divide Protozoa into four classes: the Rhizopoda or ameba-like forms, the Mastigophora or flagellates, the Ciliata or ciliates, and the Sporozoa, or spore-forming parasitic forms. Doflein, however, modified this by first splitting the entire Phylum Protozoa into subphyla, the Plasmodroma and the Ciliophora, and this arrangement has been quite generally accepted by modern protozoologists. The classification, as now usually adopted, is shown in the following outline:

SUBPHYLUM PLASMODROMA. Movement by means of pseudopodia or flagella; sexual reproduction, where known, by fusion of entire gametes.
Class I. **Sarcodina.** Body without a cuticle, but in many free-living forms protected by shells; movement and food ingestion by means of pseudopodia during predominant phase of life cycle.
Class II. **Mastigophora.** Body usually with a definite cuticle; movement by means of one or more flagella; commonly known as flagellates.
Class III. **Sporozoa.** Parasitic forms without organs of locomotion in adult stage, and usually with complicated life cycle, the alternating sexual and asexual phases frequently in different hosts. All form spores except those

having sexual and asexual cycles in alternate hosts, which produce naked sporozoites.

SUBPHYLUM CILIOPHORA. Possess cilia, at least in some stage of life cycle.

Class I. **Ciliata.** Cilia present throughout life of trophozoites.

Subclass I. *Protociliata.* Two to many nuclei present, all of one type; sexual reproduction by fusion of gametes.

Subclass II. *Euciliata.* Two kinds of nuclei present, macronucleus and micronucleus; sexual reproduction by conjugation, accompanied by disintegration of the macronucleus.

Class II. **Suctoria.** Cilia present only in young stages, which later lose their cilia and develop sucking tentacles, usually becoming attached to objects.

Further classification of the classes Sarcodina, Mastigophora, and Sporozoa is given on pp. 83, 117, and 181, respectively.

The class Sarcodina includes mainly free-living forms inhabiting the ocean, fresh water, and soils. Many of the marine forms are furnished with calcareous shells which are largely instrumental in building up chalk deposits. Only a few are parasitic, and these are all typical amebas which produce pseudopodia from any part of the naked body.

The class Mastigophora includes a vast assemblage of organisms called flagellates, many of which bridge the gap between plants and animals. Here again the majority of the included forms are free-living; many of them possess chlorophyll and live like typical plants, and, in fact, are usually claimed by the botanists as well as the zoologists. Others have cytostomes through which they ingest solid food as do animals, and still others absorb dissolved subtances by osmosis through their cell walls. Some, like Euglena, physiologically may be plants in the daytime and animals by night. All the parasitic species are of animal nature, feeding either by ingestion or by osmosis. Formerly the spirochetes were associated with the flagellates because of a supposed relationship with the trypanosomes, but this idea has long since been exploded, and spirochetes are now placed in a group by themselves, associated with bacteria rather than Protozoa, though in some respects they show affinity to the latter.

The class Sporozoa includes a varied assemblage of parasitic forms, the relationships of which are discussed at the beginning of Chapter 9. They include numerous important agents of disease not only for all sorts of vertebrates, but also for invertebrates. Man is seriously afflicted only by the malaria parasites, but domestic animals are attacked by a number of different types.

The class Ciliata includes the most highly organized Protozoa. In the subclass Protociliata are placed the ciliates which have from two to several hundred nuclei all of one kind, and which reproduce by fusion of gametes, thus being intermediate between the Plasmodroma and the higher ciliates with functionally distinct nuclei and sexual reproduction by conjugation. Nearly all the members of this group are inhabitants of the large intestine of frogs and toads and do not concern us here. Members of the subclass Euciliata have the most complicated organization of any Protozoa. The majority are free-living forms found in abundance in foul water, hay infusions, etc., whence the name "Infusoria" sometimes applied to them. Many inhabit the digestive canals of herbivorous animals, but, since they prey on bacteria and debris in the intestine and do not attack the host itself, they may be regarded as commensals rather than parasites. A few are true pathogenic parasites, e.g., Balantidium (see p. 133), which parasitizes man, pigs, and other animals.

The class Suctoria, which lose their cilia and acquire suctorial tentacles as adults, are for the most part free-living organisms attached to various objects in water, but a few are parasitic on ciliates, and one, *Allantosoma intestinalis,* is of interest as a parasite of ciliates in the cecum of horses.

Parasitism and Host Specificity. It is very likely that parasitism among the Protozoa arose in the beginning by the ingestion of free-living forms by animals; some of these may be conceived of as having found conditions of life satisfactory in the digestive tracts of animals which devoured them; in the course of time such forms would become more and more perfectly adapted to the new environment, and eventually lose their power to live and reproduce in the outside world. Such parasitism would be expected to occur first in cold-blooded aquatic animals and subsequently to extend to warm-blooded land animals. It is significant that most of the common genera of intestinal Protozoa of man, e.g., Endamoeba, Chilomastix, Trichomonas, and Giardia, have representatives in the Amphibia, in some cases so closely similar to the human species as to have cast doubt on their specific distinctness.

Many of the blood Protozoa have undoubtedly arisen by a process only slightly more complicated. They first adapted themselves to the digestive tracts of invertebrates; in bloodsuckers they would then become adapted to living in the presence of the blood on which the invertebrates fed; having survived this probationary treatment, such parasites might then be capable, if inoculated into the blood stream or tissues of the vertebrates on which their invertebrate hosts habitually fed, of adapting themselves to life in this new environment, which had thus been approached in an indirect manner. There is little room for doubt that the leishmanias and trypanosomes of vertebrates arose in this manner.

The specificity of protozoan parasites for particular hosts is a much disputed question. The striking similarity between such parasites as the various amebas, Trichomonas, and Chilomastix in different species of mammals, together with the fact that nearly all the species from man are transferable to rats and other animals, throws grave doubt on the idea of fairly strict specificity which has been advanced by some protozoologists. Some intestinal parasites seem to have progressed in evolution to the point where they can inhabit only one or a few closely related hosts, but many have not evolved beyond the stage of hostal varieties, i.e., mere races of a single species, for the time being especially adapted to a particular host species by virtue of having lived in that host for a long time, but capable of transfer to a different host under favorable circumstances. Blood and tissue parasites, in general, show more specificity than intestinal parasites, but even among these there is much variation. The human malaria parasites are strictly confined to human beings, but the malaria parasites of birds show much less specificity. *Trypanosoma cruzi* is an example of a blood and tissue parasite that can infect such widely different mammals as opossums, armadillos, bats, rodents, dogs, and man. The question of host specificity is important from an epidemiological standpoint, since it involves the question of the extent to which other animals may act as reservoirs for human parasites.

Importance. The Protozoa are of prime importance as human parasites. Although Leeuwenhoek discovered the existence of Protozoa over 250 years ago, the first parasitic species, *Balantidium coli*, was not discovered until 1856. At the present time a large proportion of medical practice and disease prevention in tropical countries, and a considerable proportion in all countries, depends on our knowledge of the habits and life history of parasitic Protozoa, a large part of which has been gained since the beginning of the present century.

Protozoan vs. Bacterial Disease. The general course of the diseases caused by Protozoa is different in some respects from that of the majority of bacterial diseases. Most bacteria attract leucocytes and are attacked by them; when they invade the body there is an immediate sharp attack by the leucocytes, followed by mobilization of the larger phagocytic cells of the body. The battle usually continues unabated until either the host succumbs or the bacteria are completely destroyed, with not a survivor left. The waxy-coated acid-fast bacteria of tuberculosis and leprosy constitute an exception; after a preliminary struggle a sort of truce is struck and the disease settles down to a comparatively mild, chronic state in which there is a balance of power between invader and host, each one, however, ready to take advantage of the slightest circumstance which tips the balance in its favor.   This is essentially the course taken by most protozoan infections also.   Often, after an initial flare-up, there may be no symptoms whatever for a time, but the parasites are still present, suppressed but not destroyed, and ready to stage an insurrection the moment the resistance of the host is weakened by other invasions, or by exhaustion, malnutrition, etc.

A good example of the difference between a protozoan and a typical bacterial infection can be seen in the nature and course of amebic as compared with bacillary dysentery, the former with no pus and of long duration, the latter with abundant pus and of short duration.   The survival of protozoan infections in a chronic state seems to be due to immunity from attack by leucocytes, and the tendency of the other phagocytic cells of the body to relax their activity before their job is completed.

It is interesting, and perhaps suggestive, that spirochete diseases tend to be of the protozoan type, while the diseases caused by the Rickettsias and by the insect-borne filtrable viruses (yellow fever, dengue, and sandfly fever) are of the bacterial type.

It might also be noted that in most bacterial diseases stimulation of the natural defenses of the host by means of vaccines or serums is more effective than drug treatment, whereas in protozoan diseases treatment with specific drugs is necessary, e.g., emetin or carbarsone for amebiasis, antimony for leishmaniasis, and quinine, atebrin, etc., for malaria. Here again the acid-fast bacteria seem to be aligned with the Protozoa.

REFERENCES

CALKINS, G. N., *Biology of the Protozoa,* 2nd ed., Philadelphia, 1933.

CALKINS, G. N., and SUMMERS, F. M. (editors), *Protozoa in Biological Research,* New York, 1941.

CRAIG, C. F., *Laboratory Diagnosis of Protozoan Diseases,* 2nd ed., Philadelphia, 1948.

DOFLEIN, F., *Lehrbuch der Protozoenkunde,* 5th ed. revised by E. Reichenow, Jena, 1927–1929.

FAUST, E. C., SAWITZ, W., TOBIE, J., ODOM, V., PERES, C., and LINCICOME, D. R., Comparative Efficiency of Various Technics for the Diagnosis of Protozoa and Helminths in Feces, *J. Parasitol.,* **25,** 241 (1939).

HEGNER, R. W., *Host-Parasite Relations between Man and His Intestinal Protozoa,* New York, 1927.

The Evolutionary Significance of the Protozoan Parasites of Monkeys and Man, *Quart. Rev. Biol.,* **3,** 225 (1928).

HEGNER, R. W., and TALIAFERRO, W. H., *Human Protozoölogy,* New York, 1924.

KNOWLES, R., *An Introduction to Medical Protozoölogy,* Calcutta, 1928.

KUDO, R. R., *Protozoölogy,* 2nd ed., Springfield, Ill., 1939.

MORGAN, B. B., and HAWKINS, P., *Veterinary Protozoölogy,* Minneapolis, 1948.

PROWAZEK, S. VON, continued by W. NÖLLER, *Handbuch der pathogenen Protozoen,* 11 Lief., Leipzig, 1912–1925.

TALIAFERRO, W. H., Host Resistance and Types of Infection in Trypanosomiasis and Malaria, *Quart. Rev. Biol.,* **1**, 246 (1926).

THOMPSON, J. D., and ROBERTSON, A., *Protozoölogy, A Manual for Medical Men,* London, 1929.

WENYON, C. M., *Protozoölogy,* 2 vols., London, 1926.

WENYON, C. M., and O'CONNOR, F. W., *Human Intestinal Protozoa in the Near East,* London, 1917.

CHAPTER 4

Spirochetes

General Account. On the vague unsettled borderline between bacteria and Protozoa is a group of organisms, the spirochetes, some of which are waging a frightful war against human life and health. Some are free-living, some harmless commensals, some potentially pathogenic when the odds are weighted in their favor, and some are strictly parasitic and the cause of highly important human and animal diseases. Though long regarded as Protozoa allied to flagellates, they are now almost universally classed with bacteria. Most books in both protozoology and bacteriology discuss them, but in both they are usually passed over with less emphasis than they deserve. Until the bacteriologists are willing to assume full responsibility for them, it seems best that the protozoologists continue to give attention to this orphan group that Schaudinn left on their doorstep years ago, by confusing them with developmental stages of trypanosomes when he found them in an owl with a mixed infection.

Like bacteria, the spirochetes lack any distinct nucleus; their multiplication is by transverse division and is not longitudinal as in flagellates; they are not oriented into an anterior and posterior end; and the flexible cell wall or periplast is not like that of the Protozoa.

There are several different types of spirochetes. The true genus Spirochaeta (Fig. 5C) includes very long (200 to 500 μ) and relatively large organisms found in stagnant water, which have a central axis or filament around which the body is wound, like a piece of rubber tubing wound around a wire, as Wenyon expressed it. The body protoplasm has vacuoles in it, and a series of deep-staining granules which may or may not be chromatin. The genus Saprospira (Fig. 5B) contains large free-living forms with rather rigid undulating coils, forms found in both fresh and salt water, reaching about 100 μ in length. Internally they have transverse septa dividing the body into chambers. There are no flagella and no "crista." The genus Cristispira (Fig. 5C) includes large forms (45 to 100 μ long) found in the crystalline style of mollusks. The body is cylindrical and divided internally into short segments, somewhat like a bamboo stem; it is thrown into coarse spirals and has a flexible spiral membrane, the *crista,* appearing like a raised ridge along the concavity of the spirals.

48

The other spirochetes are relatively very small and slender, with flexible, spirally twisted bodies, like tiny corkscrews. Under an electron microscope they are seen to have a delicate cell wall or periplast, from which the denser cell substance may shrink away. At one or both ends the periplast is drawn out into a relatively coarse filament which earlier observers mistook for a terminal flagellum. The protoplasm is not homogeneous but is more or less mottled and contains scattered dense granules. Sometimes dense irregularly spherical bodies are seen attached to the cells along the sides; these have been interpreted as asexual sporelike bodies. Several authors have described and figured clusters of delicate flagella along the sides of the organisms,

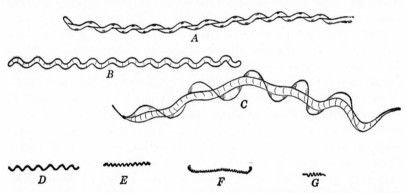

FIG. 5.   Types of spirochetes, drawn to scale.   A, Spirochaeta plicatilis (500 × 0.75 μ); B, Saprospira grandis (50 × 0.8 μ); C, Cristispira anodontae (60 × 1.8 μ); D, Borrelia recurrentis (15 × 0.25 μ); E, Treponema pallidum (10 × 0.25 μ); F, Leptospira icterohaemorrhagiae (15 × 0.2 μ); G, Spirella minus (3 × 0.25 μ). (Adapted from various authors.)

but Lofgren and Soule in 1946, studying relapsing-fever spirochetes, observed these only in much-manipulated specimens, and interpreted them as fragmentations or shredding of the periplast.

Spirochetes are very active in movement and dart swiftly back and forth across the field of a microscope, usually in straight lines if there are no obstructions. The movement is apparently by spiral wave motions passing through the body, though the possibility of flagella contributing to it must now be considered. Swiftly moving spirochetes show many small waves in their bodies, whereas the more slowly moving ones have larger and more graceful curls. Spirochetes are also able to bend their bodies, and to oscillate while adhering to some object by one end.

Spirochetes divide by a transverse division of the body, preceded by a fine drawing out of the periplast, like a glass tube drawn out after heating. Often two incompletely separated spirochetes twist about each other, giving the appearance of having split longitudinally. In healthy living spirochetes, when relaxed, the axis of the body is a straight line, but after being dried, as in blood films, they may become distorted, and the actual spirals be obliterated. Figure 6 shows the appearance of relapsing-fever spirochetes when living and after being dried and stained. A number of observers have described a breaking up of spirochetes into minute granules, and a subsequent growth of spirochetes from such granules, but the occurrence of this sort of phenomenon, though not impossible or even unlikely, has not been sufficiently confirmed.

The parasitic spirochetes fall into several natural groups, each of which has representatives found free-living in water as well as in the bodies of animals.

The first group contains spirochetes with relatively large graceful coils (Fig. 5D); it includes the blood spirochetes that cause relapsing fever, and a number of saprophytic or pathogenic forms found in the mouth or other parts of the body, or in sores. For these spirochetes the genus name Spirochaeta is commonly used, but, since they are certainly not congeneric with the mammoth free-living spirochetes to which this name was first applied, the genus name Borrelia is more properly applied to them. The second group, for which the name Treponema is used, includes a few slender species with short kinky coils (Fig. 5E) and is applied principally to the spirochetes of yaws, syphilis, and pinta. Actually there are many intergrading forms between these two groups, and their separation is of doubtful validity. The third group, placed in a genus Leptospira (Fig. 5F), includes excessively delicate forms in which the spiral ropelike windings are so minute as to be invisible in ordinary stained preparations, but visible under a dark-field microscope; these spirochetes show a few gross undulations of the body, which is usually bent hooklike at the ends.

The true spirochetes must be distinguished from the bacterial genus Spirillum, which contains organisms with rigid preformed spirals and with terminal flagella. The organism causing rat-bite fever (Fig. 5G), described by Japanese workers as *Spirochaeta morsus-muris*, was later thought to be a Spirillum, to which the name *Spirillum minus* was given. Zinsser and Bayne-Jones, however, think that it has more affinities with the spirochetes than with the spirilla, and favor its being retained in the spirochete group in the special genus Spirella, which was proposed for it in 1912. The organism differs from other spirochetes in being relatively rigid and in having at least one well-defined flagellum at each end.

The various species of spirochetes differ from one another in the length and coarseness of the body, in the number of spirals in a given length, and in the rounded or tapering form of the ends of the body. Many of the species described are indistinguishable morphologically, and are only recognizable by their pathogenic effects, places where found, immunological reactions, and methods of transmission. The relapsing-fever spirochetes, for instance, have been regarded by many workers as constituting many different species, separable on the basis of transmission by different species of ticks or by lice, cross-immunity tests between types, and pathogenicity for various laboratory animals. Likewise many different species have been described from normal and diseased conditions in the mouth, tonsils, lungs, intestine, skin ulcers, etc., which are not distinguishable morphologically. At present it is impossible to classify the species of spirochetes other than by their pathogenicity or otherwise, the types of infection produced, and the situations where they occur. The spirochetes of syphilis and yaws, for instance, cannot be distinguished with certainty from a form which occurs almost universally in normal mouths, on the tartar and about the roots of the teeth, and which is apparently perfectly harmless.

Spirochetes and Disease. Spirochetes are unquestionably responsible for several human diseases, among which are relapsing fever, syphilis, yaws, pinta, and infectious jaundice, and they are associated with many other diseased conditions for which they are in part, or at times, responsible. The mere presence of spirochetes in sores or diseased tissue, however, is not sufficient reason for believing that they are the direct cause of the disease condition, for, like many bacteria, they are often found in exposed sores which are known to be due to other causes. Spirochetes are often found associated in sores or ulcers with various kinds of bacteria; in Vincent's angina a spirochete and a fusiform bacillus appear to be jointly guilty, the two living together in a sort of symbiotic relationship.

In general the diseases caused by spirochetes may be divided into four main groups. First, there is the febrile type of disease marked by a series of remissions and relapses, in which the spirochetes live and multiply mainly in the blood or lymphatics. To this group belong the various forms of relapsing fever. Second, there is the type in which the spirochetes make a general invasion of the body and live primarily in the tissues, often localizing in particular tissues or organs after the preliminary general invasion. To this type belong syphilis and yaws. Third, there are local infections or lesions in which spirochetes may be present in large numbers, and may or may not be the sole or primary cause. To this belong Vincent's angina, spirochetal bronchitis, tropical ulcers, ulcerating granuloma, etc. Fourth, there are the Leptospira diseases, in which spirochetes of the genus Leptospira invade the body and localize primarily in the liver and kidneys. To this belong infectious jaundice and a number of related infections found primarily in dogs, pigs, cattle, and rodents, which are transmissible to man.

Relapsing Fever

In every continent in the world, with the possible exception of Australia, there occurs a form of relapsing fever caused by spirochetes in the blood. In Africa it ranks next to malaria and sleeping sickness as a scourge of that disease-cursed country. In India it is hardly less severe, but in eastern Europe and America it is a mild disease. Many great epidemics have swept Russian, Austrian, and Balkan cities.

Species, Transmitters, and Epidemiology. Spirochetes morphologically similar to those causing relapsing fever in man occur very extensively in other mammals and also in birds. The avian and mammalian spirochetes are not interchangeable, but the avian strains attack many different birds, and the mammalian strains are not at all " choosy " about their mammals; most of them are probably capable of causing infection in man, but some cause milder disease than others. A single strain may be infective for opossums, armadillos, rodents, shrews, bats, carnivores, pigs, monkeys, and even calves, though not all these can be considered reservoir hosts, since some have very light or inapparent infections. A form known as *Borrelia theileri* causes a symptomless infection in cattle, sheep, and horses. Probably all the mammalian strains except possibly some of the human louse-borne types are transmitted by particular species of Ornithodorus (see p. 538); the bird strains are transmitted by Argas. One form, *B. anserinum,* causes relapsing fever in chickens, ducks, and other birds.

Although it would probably be more nearly correct to consider the various types of spirochetes causing relapsing fever in man as strains of a single species, *B. recurrentis,* biologically modified by life in various vertebrate and transmitting hosts, many specific names have been applied to them. Attempts have been made to separate them on the basis of staining reactions, cross-immunity tests, protection tests, pathogenicity for various laboratory animals, their vertebrate hosts, and their vectors. Of all these criteria the last, i.e., the vectors by which they are transmitted, seems the most satisfactory, for as shown by Davis in 1941 most strains, if capable of infecting other vectors at all, cause very transient infections and are usually not transmissible by the bites although sometimes they are transmissible by injection for a few days.

Human relapsing fever in central Africa is primarily a human disease because the vector, *Ornithodorus moubata,* has become domestic and feeds primarily on man. This strain of spirochete, sometimes called *B. duttoni,* is virulent for rats and mice as well as for man, but hardly at all for guinea pigs. A strain in Dakar, Senegal, North Africa, and Spain, transmitted by *O. erraticus,* causes only sporadic infections in man because its vector usually feeds on shrews and wild rodents.

The frequency of human infections in other parts of the world, too, depends on the extent to which the local Ornithodorus vectors can and do attack man. In Panama and northern South America a strain carried by *O. rudis* fairly frequently infects man because its vector is carried into houses by rats. In California a strain carried by *O. hermsi* often causes annoying disease to people vacationing in the high Sierras because chipmunks move into vacated cottages during the winter; when they abandon these protected winter quarters upon the return of the summer residents, they leave behind some of their ticks, which are often infected with spirochetes. On the Mexican plateau human infection with a strain carried by *O. turicata* is fairly common since this tick has become semi-domestic there, and is frequently found in thatched huts, abattoirs, and especially pigsties. In the United States, from Texas to Kansas, where this species of tick is found in caves and burrows of animals, it causes only sporadic human cases.

Louse-borne strains undoubtedly arose, and perhaps repeatedly do so, from survival of the spirochetes in lice feeding on patients with spirochetes in their blood, originally derived from ticks. Nicolle and Anderson showed in 1926 that spirochetes derived from *O. erraticus* survived for 9 days in lice, since the macerated lice were infective when injected; this same strain survived 35 days in *O. savignyi* as shown by injection, but was not transmitted by the bites. That the louse-borne strains have, however, become completely independent of their tick connections is shown not only by their persistence in places far removed from the range of any species of Ornithodorus but also by failure of louse-borne strains in Ethiopia and China to be transmitted by ticks. Some tick strains survive in lice for some days but fail to multiply. *B. duttoni* was successfully transmitted by Heisch and Garnham in 1948 through four successive batches of lice but failed to develop the distinguishing characteristics of the typical louse-borne strain. Louse-borne strains have become established entirely independent of ticks in central and southeastern Europe, Iran, India, China, and parts of Africa, but have never become permanently endemic in the western hemisphere except at high altitudes in Mexico and Peru. After World War I a louse-borne infection started an epidemic in Upper Guinea which spread across to the Sudan and took about 100,000 lives in ten years, killing about 10 per cent of the population. The southward extension of the epidemic was limited by the absence of clothing on the central African natives.

Occasionally relapsing fever may be transmitted by other vectors than Argasid ticks and lice. There is one record of successful transmission of the North African strain by the dog tick, *Rhipicephalus sanguineus,* and of transmission to rats by fleas and rat lice. Bedbugs have often been suspected, but at most they play a minor role.

Geographic Distribution of Human Relapsing Fever. Human infection with tick-borne relapsing fever is most frequent in central and eastern Africa, from southern Sudan to Cape Province, due to the domestic habits of *Ornithodorus moubata,* as already noted. In the highlands of Ethiopia the disease is louse-borne. Cases are frequent in Iran, Palestine, Turkestan, and other parts of southwestern Asia, transmitted by *O. tholozani,* which is often brought into houses by rats. Sporadic cases transmitted by *O. erraticus,* as noted above, occur all along the African coast from Dakar to Libya, and also in Spain.

In the western hemisphere three tick-borne strains infectible for man occur in North America. One, carried by *O. turicata,* is fairly common in man on the Mexican plateau, but it also occurs sporadically in Texas, New Mexico, Oklahoma, and Kansas. Another, carried by *O. hermsi,* has been found in California, Nevada, Oregon, Idaho, and Colorado. A few cases from the Arizona mountains are also believed to be caused by this strain. The third, carried by *O. parkeri,* has been found in many far western states including California, Nevada, Oregon, Washington, Idaho, Montana, and also in British Columbia.

In Central America, Colombia, and Venezuela a strain transmitted by *O. rudis* quite frequently attacks man. Rare cases have been reported from Cuba and some small islands in the West Indies, but nothing is known of the vectors. In most parts of South America the disease is rare or absent; two louse-borne strains occur in Peru.

The Spirochetes. The spirochetes are usually from 10 to 20 μ in length, averaging about 15 μ, and have a series of regular, graceful spiral turns of the body, each occupying from 2 to 3 μ of the length. The ends of the body taper slightly. They may be extremely numerous in the blood, especially during the active phases of the disease, but they become very sparse, and often impossible to find, during the intermissions between relapses. When blood films are dried, the spirochetes become distorted and show irregular coarse spirals of quite a different nature from those present in the living organism (Fig. 6). During recovery from an infection, when antibodies are present in the blood, the spirochetes become immobilized and show degenerative changes, and are seen clumped together, with platelets and granules adhering to them. Some strains, at least, can be cultivated on artificial media, but often with difficulty. They can also be cultivated in developing chick embryos.

Immunological Strains. An interesting phenomenon is the immunological distinctness of the strains of the spirochetes which occur in the original infections and in relapses, first worked out in detail by Cunningham (1925) and added to by Meleney (1928). Cunningham *et al.* (1934) showed that in the louse-borne disease, in which there is usually

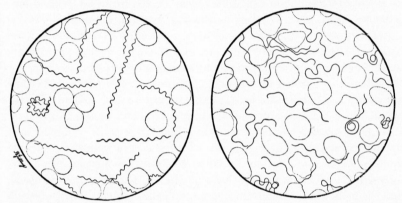

Fig. 6. *Borrelia recurrentis*, var. *duttoni*, showing appearance of spirochetes when living (left), and on a dried and stained slide (right). × 1000. (After Wenyon, *Protozoology*.)

only one relapse, the onset and relapse strains consist of single antigenic varieties, one giving rise to the other, but in occasional second relapses a total of seven additional varieties were found. Schuhardt, (1942, *Pub. 18, Am. Assoc. Advancement Sci.*), showed that in the tick-borne *Borrelia turicatae* strain the spirochetes developing at onset or at relapses consist of multiple antigenic varieties, which undergo further alteration in rats as antibodies are developed against them. The sequence of immunological changes is not, however, always the same in different rats, but in most rats the spirochetes seem ultimately to undergo all the possible variations, making the serum of a completely recovered animal effective against *all* varieties of the spirochetes. To what extent antigenic variations in spirochetes from different localities or vectors may differ or overlap has not yet been determined. Until it has, Brumpt's suggestion that the spirochetes be classified on the basis of their arthropod hosts may be a good one.

Life Cycle. There is still a difference of opinion as to whether the spirochetes have a granule stage, or even a filtrable stage, in their vertebrate or intermediate hosts; the data are conflicting, but the weight of evidence is swinging towards the nonoccurrence of any such stages.

When ingested by ticks the spirochetes persist in the stomach for about 10 days, but within 6 hours some of them have penetrated into the body cavity. Ticks once infective probably remain so for life, and the infection is transmitted to the offspring through the eggs. It can also occasionally be transmitted by copulation. There is a considerable variation in individual ticks in their ability to pass their infections on to their offspring, but the infection can persist for many generations, possibly indefinitely, without need for a vertebrate host. The ticks themselves are the principal reservoirs. Infection of vertebrates may occur directly by the bites or may be conveyed by the coxal fluid, which is exuded by most species while feeding or afterwards.

In lice the spirochetes leave the stomach very quickly, become numerous throughout the body cavity, even to the tips of the appendages, and remain present until about the end of the third week. Lice never transmit the infection by either their bites or their feces, but only when injured or crushed. In one case a man experimented upon in Algeria was bitten 30,000 to 40,000 times by gently handled infected lice without contracting the disease, but one louse crushed, and the body fluids brought in contact with the conjunctiva or a bite on the skin resulted in relapsing fever. Transovarial transmission by lice apparently does not occur.

The Disease. The most severe form of the disease is that of central Africa caused by *Borrelia duttoni*. The European louse-borne type is usually milder, but its severity varies in different epidemics. The sporadic cases caused by the *Ornithodorus erraticus* strain around the Mediterranean and by *O. rudis* in Central and South America are mild and usually occur in children. Mild strains may be used instead of malaria in fever treatment of neurosyphilis. The various types of the disease differ in the number and duration of the relapses and intervening periods, and in severity of the symptoms. After an incubation period lasting from about 3 to 10 days, the disease has an abrupt onset with nausea, headache, general pains, chills, and a rise of temperature, which lasts from about 2 or 3 days in mild cases to from 4 to 6 in severe ones. Then comes a crisis; the temperature falls rapidly to normal or below, and the patient recovers so rapidly and completely that he thinks it unnecessary to remain in the hospital any longer. Then, 4 to 8 days after the first crisis, comes a relapse, with a repetition of all the symptoms. A second crisis follows, and then a period of apparently normal health, which may be permanent or may be followed by more relapses. In general the louse-borne types have only one or two relapses, but some of the tick-borne types are likely to have four or five or even more, of shorter duration and more irregular in occurrence. The mortality is usually low, except in central Africa.

Immunity is of extremely variable duration, and sometimes more than one attack may occur within a year; but natives in endemic villages are usually immune, probably on account of repeated inoculations which keep up an immunity once developed. Immunity to one strain of the spirochete confers no immunity to other strains. Artificial immunity can be conferred, at least temporarily, by injections of killed cultures of mixed passage and relapse strains of the spirochetes.

Treatment and Prevention. Spirochetes in general, including those of relapsing fever, are susceptible to the effects of arsenic compounds, principally arsphenamines and mapharsen (see p. 68), and to penicillin, an antibiotic substance purified from secretions of certain molds of the genus Penicillium. Spirochetes in the blood and general visceral tissues are easily killed by either of these types of treatment, but the diseases tend to relapse because the spirochetes invade the central nervous system, particularly the brain, where they are ordinarily uninfluenced by peripherally injected drugs. After cessation of treatment, reinvasion of the blood and viscera may occur. Applied heat or fever induced by malaria not only directly affects spirochetes in the central nervous system but also enhances the action of drugs, presumably by favoring their penetration into the nervous tissues.

In the treatment of relapsing fever neither the arsenicals nor penicillin have proved reliable. Schuhardt and Hemphill in 1946 found that intraperitoneal injection of penicillin into mice with relapsing fever fails to kill the spirochetes in the brain. Moreover, they found that brain invasion practically always occurs, and within the first few days. That the brain spirochetes reinvading the blood stream are actually the cause of relapse seemed evident from the fact that mice given 1000 units of penicillin into the cranium, as well as an adequate dose into the peritoneum, failed to relapse. There is no doubt that penicillin is of real value in relieving symptoms of relapsing fever by destroying the blood and tissue spirochetes, even though permanent cure may not result.

Eradication of vermin from person and home and avoidance of places where infected parasites might be acquired are the most important protective measures in places where a louse-borne epidemic is raging. Methods for the control of ticks are discussed on p. 540, and of lice on p. 582.

Treponematoses — Syphilis, Bejel, Yaws, and Pinta

The slender, kinky-coiled spirochetes of the genus Treponema are the cause of a series of human diseases found in one form or another throughout the world. Syphilis occurs in all temperate and cold climates but is relatively rare in the tropics, where it is replaced by yaws in most hot moist climates, and in more local areas by bejel or pinta. There has been unending discussion as to whether these diseases, particularly syphilis and yaws, are separate entities or manifestations of infection by the same parasite, modified by climate and race, and adapted to contagious or venereal transmission. The spirochetes of these several diseases are indistinguishable morphologically and are very much alike biologically; to some extent, at least, the diseases produce immunity to each other, though this seems not to be true of pinta and syphilis; in general the diseases run a similar course, tending to have early and late stages separated by a latent period, and some of the same pathological effects recur in the various diseases. Hudson (1946) believes that there is only one pathogenic species, which, according to circumstances, can be propagated by either venereal or nonvenereal routes. According to this view, treponematosis in the tropics retains its primitive character as a contagious or insect-transmitted skin disease of children, while in cooler and drier climates it changes to a venereal disease of adults.

That there is a close relationship between the spirochetes of syphilis, yaws, bejel, and pinta there can be no doubt, nor can there be any opposition to the idea that they have evolved from some common ancestor which probably, as Hudson suggests, had its origin as a tropical skin parasite. They are all antigenically similar, and respond to the same serological tests, and they also respond to treatment with arsenicals and penicillin, but these facts cannot logically be advanced as arguments for their identity.

Clinically the several diseases named show numerous differences; they have very different geographic distributions; and they differ in their modes of transmission. Whether one was originally evolved from another, or whether under suitable conditions the alteration can still occur, are largely academic questions. Practically, syphilis, yaws, and pinta are recognizably distinct diseases, and it is therefore reasonable to consider the spirochetes that cause them distinct. Perhaps they should be considered strains rather than species, but there would be no practical advantage in reducing the species names they have been given to the rank of varieties, and burdening the literature with longer names. We shall, therefore, refer to the spirochete of syphilis as *Treponema pallidum*, to that of yaws as *T. pertenue*, and to that of pinta as *T. carateum*. The bejel parasite has not received a distinct name; Hudson, who described the disease, considered it a form of syphilis.

All these spirochetes are slender, kinky-coiled organisms (Fig. 7), varying in length from about 4 to 14 μ; they usually have from 6 to 14 very regular, short, sharp coils, each occupying about 1 μ. They are very active and dart rapidly across a slide, threading their way between

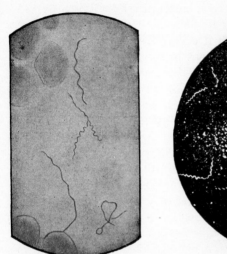

FIG. 7. Left, spirochetes from a syphilitic lesion; the two in the center are *Treponema pallidum*, the others *T. refringens*. (From Schaudinn and Hoffman.) Right, *T. pallidum* appearing as bright refractile objects under dark-field illumination. (After Park and Williams, from Gershenfeld's *Bacteriology*.)

cells or other objects in their way. Attempts to cultivate the treponemas have been unsuccessful.

In addition to the species causing the diseases mentioned above there are also harmless saprophytic forms which are very common in mouths, even in perfectly healthy ones. One common mouth species is called *T. microdentium*. Similar saprophytic forms are sometimes found in other locations in the body or in sores.

Syphilis

History. Syphilis is one of the commonest, most insidious, and most deceptive diseases afflicting man in temperate parts of the world. Rosenau says, "civilization and syphilization have been close companions"; the one has followed in the wake of the other like the guerillas behind an army. Opinions differ as to the origin of syphilis among civilized nations. An oft-repeated but not widely accepted story is that it was acquired by Columbus' crew in Haiti and carried back to Spain by them, whence it rapidly spread all over Europe, causing an unusually intense outbreak of venereal disease.

In spite of the importance of syphilis to the human race, little progress in knowledge of its cause, diagnosis, treatment, or control was made until early in the twentieth century, but since then advances in all these aspects of the disease have been steadily made. Today syphilis is no longer the dreaded incapacitator and killer that it was 50 years ago — at least it need not be. In 1902 the disease was successfully transmitted to animals in which it could be conveniently studied; in 1905 Schaudinn discovered the causative organism, *Treponema pallidum* (Fig. 7); in 1906 Wassermann demonstrated the possibility of detecting latent syphilis by the reaction which bears his name; in 1910 Ehrlich made the epoch-making discovery of his famous drug, " No. 606," or Salvarsan; in 1913 the direct relation of syphilis to insanity, paralysis, and other diseased conditions of the central nervous system was demonstrated by the discovery of the organisms in the cerebrospinal fluid; in 1943 penicillin was found to have remarkable curative value; and in 1949 promise of a cure by a single injection (see p. 69), in contrast to the 18-month regime of 10 years earlier, gives hope that syphilis may not long remain a top-ranking scourge of mankind. In some countries syphilis has been brought under control like other communicable diseases; in our own, the first great step in this direction was made by Parran in 1936, when he broke the conspiracy of silence which made even mention of syphilis taboo, and gave it a public coming-out party that may well lead to its ultimate downfall. Its suppression, however, has been slower than that of other communicable diseases because of the moral and social questions with which it is involved.

Prevalence. Syphilis is a deplorably common disease. Sir William Osler placed it third or fourth of the killing diseases. In the United States the death rate from syphilis was over 16 per 100,000 in 1937, but it has steadily declined until it was a little over half that (8.7) in 1947. The improvement in syphilitic infant mortality has been even better, declining from 79 per 100,000 births in 1933 to only 25 in 1945. The case rate, however, is still very high, especially in the southern states, mainly because of the large Negro population; it is lowest in Utah and the Dakotas. In 1947 there were 373,296 reported cases (262.8 per 100,000), of which about 29 per cent were primary or secondary cases and about 33 per cent congenital. Probably as many more cases were not reported, but relied for treatment on drugstores, quacks, or the grace of God.

The best statistics on actual cases were obtained from the incidence of positive serological tests in draftees in World War II. Among the first million registrants there were about 46,000 positive cases, but the rate varied from 1 per cent in whites in some northern states to 30 per cent in Negroes in some southern states. In California the incidence ran close to 4 per cent both in draftees and in labor unions. In Negroes between 36 and 40 years of age it ran over 43 per cent in one southern state. Venereal disease ranked first as a cause of disability among the armed forces in the United States during World War II, and about 18 per cent of it was due to syphilis. After mobilization syphilis increased in both military and civilian personnel, but, even so, it was lower in the armed forces than in any previous war.

It can probably be assumed that there are over 500,000 new victims of syphilis yearly in the United States, most of whom do not seek proper treatment until the disease is in its late stages. No other infectious disease of major importance except gonorrhea even approaches such a figure. A few thousand cases of infantile paralysis or diphtheria create a panic, but 500,000 cases of syphilis are almost ignored!

Although the disease invades both the penthouse of the millionaire and the hovel of the tramp, all classes of society are not equally attacked. In general, the prevalence of syphilis increases as we descend in the social scale. The disease is acquired primarily between the ages of 15 and 30; over half the reported cases are under 25 years of age, and 20 per cent under 20 years.

Distribution of Spirochetes in the Body. The causative spirochete, *Treponema pallidum*, can readily be found in the primary stage of the disease; the organisms are abundant in the lymph under the raised rim of the initial sore or chancre and in enlarged neighboring lymph glands. During the second phase of the disease and also toward the end of the first phase, the spirochetes make a general invasion of the entire body but are not always readily found. They occur in variable numbers in the blood but may become abundant in " mucous patches " in the throat and sometimes in the skin. Very early they make their way into the cerebrospinal fluid of the brain and spinal cord. At first it was thought that invasion of the central nervous system was exceptional and occurred only late in the disease, but actually 80 per cent of syphilitics show pathological changes in the spinal fluid, due to invasion by spirochetes, from the date of the primary sore, and are therefore possible candidates for syphilis of the nervous system.

During the latent period that follows the second phase the spirochetes are difficult if not impossible to find, even when the patient remains infective. In the tertiary stage the parasites usually show some special predilection for certain tissues or organs. The gummy sores or " gummas " which often break out during this third stage of the disease have

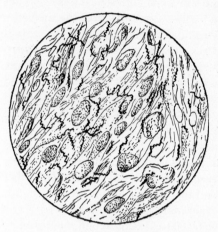

usually been considered noninfective, but the parasites have been found in some of these lesions also. In congenital syphilis the parasites often multiply in enormous numbers in the unborn child, penetrating practically every organ and tissue of the body. The liver especially is often found literally teeming with spirochetes (Fig. 8).

FIG. 8.   *Treponema pallidum* in liver tissue of a congenital syphilitic.

Treponema pallidum in nature attacks only human beings, but monkeys and rabbits can be experimentally infected; the course of the disease in these animals is milder, and there are no lesions of the viscera or central nervous system. Mice can be infected in the brain, but show no symptoms at all; brain material from such mice is said to be infectious even when there are no demonstrable spirochetes.

Transmission. Syphilis, at least in temperate climates, is fundamentally a venereal disease, transmitted by sexual intercourse, and over 90 per cent of cases are undoubtedly of such origin. It is a common belief that this is the only way in which the disease can be acquired, and sometimes an unjust stigma is attached to an innocent case of syphilis. However, because of the delicacy of the spirochetes and their inability to survive more than a very brief time, usually a few minutes, outside the body, the disease is usually acquired only by intimate contact, such as sexual intercourse or kissing. It is closely associated with promiscuous sexual relations, but is often transmitted to a husband or wife, or from parents to children before or at birth, or by nursing.

Kissing is the commonest method of transmission next to sexual intercourse, since " mucous patches " swarming with spirochetes often develop in the throat during the secondary stage of the disease. An instance is on record where seven young women at a church social acquired syphilis from kissing a young man who had a syphilitic sore on his lip. Another case was traced to the eating of apples sold by an Italian who was in the habit of spitting on his fruits and rubbing them on his sleeve to shine them. This is the only instance known to the writer in which a venereal disease was transmitted by a food handler in line of duty, although many cities require evidence of freedom from venereal disease before providing health cards for food handlers. Unsanitary barbers and dentists sometimes spread infection, and dentists and physicians themselves may contract the disease by handling syphilitic patients, the spirochetes readily entering the smallest cut or abrasion of the skin. Midwives and wet nurses are likewise exposed to infection from diseased babies, as are the babies from diseased nurses. The fragility of the spirochetes and short life outside the body make transfer by towels, bed linen, eating utensils, or hands improbable.

Bejel. In the tropics syphilis is relatively uncommon and is less consistently venereal, being commonly acquired in childhood, with resultant immunity later in life. Hudson (1938), for example, describes this type of syphilis as practically universal among the Syrian Arabs, by whom it is called " bejel "; like yaws, it is a contagious disease of children, but differs strikingly from that disease in the frequency of oral mucous patches. The children, instead of prostitutes and their clients, serve as a reservoir. Hudson believes the difference in epidemiology is due to different levels of personal hygiene; when people live in squalid huts or caves in warm countries, half-starved, nearly naked, unwashed, huddled together when sleeping, eating from a single utensil, careless with excreta, and attacked by hordes of ectoparasites, the delicate spirochetes are easily transmitted during childhood, but a slight rise in hygienic level results in sexual intercourse alone supplying sufficiently intimate contact for the safe passage of the spirochetes, which are far more delicate than most bacteria. It is certainly possible, however, that the spirochetes of bejel, like those of yaws, represent a distinct strain.

The Disease. Syphilis is a disease which has no equal in its deceptive nature, which largely accounts for the many tragedies resulting from its ravages. Its effects on the individual are often bad enough, leading to disease of almost any tissue or organ in the body, but it is only when judged in the light of the additional damage that is done to the innocent wife or husband, as the case may be, and to the next generation, that the true meaning of syphilis can be measured.

Syphilis may remain latent and unsuspected for twenty years or more, and the carrier may remain infective, or return to an infective state, for as long as five years. The semen and vulval or vaginal secretions, as well as the throat, may be infective when there are no visible lesions. Meanwhile the carrier, perhaps in ignorance of his condition, may infect a hitherto sound person whom he has taken for a life companion, and cause her, or him, to be ravaged by the disease. His chances of having healthy children are small. About 45 per cent of those who later become victims of general paralysis from syphilis never can have any children, either on account of sterility or repeated abortions. The author of the statement in the Bible that "the sins of the fathers shall be visited upon the heads of the children unto the third and fourth generations" may well have had in mind the hereditary effects of venereal diseases, but he might have stated further that often there is no third or fourth generation.

The only pity of it is that this is not always true, for those who are brought into the world are often hopelessly handicapped either mentally or physically. About 15 per cent of blindness is due to syphilis. Mental disease is very common, and 20 per cent of the inmates in insane asylums are syphilitic. There is some reason for believing that the hideous, mentally deficient children known as mongols are the result of syphilis in parents. And finally, as if all this were not enough, the carrier of latent syphilis may later develop general paralysis or some other disease of the nervous system, heart disease, or other conditions, which will render him an ineffectual social unit, and make him and his family a burden to the community.

The spirochetes are believed to be able to penetrate any mucous membrane, and will go through even a microscopic abrasion in the

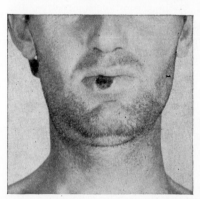

FIG. 9. Chancre on lip. (U. S. Army Institute of Pathology photo 44845.)

skin. Once under the surface they multiply rapidly and migrate by way of the lymph glands and then, within 12 hours, spread over the entire body. For this reason application of chemical prophylactics after exposure is progressively less reliable after the first hour or two.

In the majority of cases the disease begins with a small hard sore on the skin or mucous membrane known as the "primary chancre" (Fig. 9). This usually appears at the point of infection in from 10 days to 6 weeks, usually about 4 weeks, after the infection occurs. It has raised edges with reddish serum-encrusted center, and feels like a movable cartilaginous button. Although nearly always present except in congenital syphilis and in pregnant women, it is frequently inconspicuous and is easily overlooked. In nonpregnant women it may be located on the cervix or more rarely in the vagina, where it is difficult to find; it is also difficult to find when it is in the mouth. The chancre is most frequent on the genital organs, but may appear on lips, tongue, fingers, or other parts of the body. It is believed to be an allergic reaction.

The chancre gradually heals up and the second stage begins, in which constitutional symptoms appear, such as fever, anemia, and a general run-down condition during which the patient is very susceptible to other diseases, such as tuberculosis. Often there is an extensive breaking out on the body, production of scaly patches of skin, and inflammation of the mucous membranes of the mouth and throat. Headache, rheumatic pains, and enlarged glands are common.

Following the secondary stage there is usually a latent period lasting several months to many years, usually 2 to 3 years, before the deeper lesions become prominent. Often there is a revival of the secondary symptoms before the appearance of the tertiary ones.

From this point on the course of the disease depends on what particular tissues or organs the spirochetes especially attack, for although the parasites, as said before, may produce disease almost anywhere in the body, in any given case there is usually a localization. It seems that certain strains of the parasites have special preference for certain tissues. The differences in this respect have been shown by Nichols to hold good through many transfers from animal to animal, and visible differences in the parasites have been claimed. In about 40 per cent of cases in temperate climates syphilis settles in the nervous system, causing a great variety of evil effects, such as mental disturbances, tabes or locomotor ataxia, general paralysis, epilepsy, insanity, and moral defectiveness. During 1945 there were nearly 75,000 hospital admissions in the United States for psychoses due to syphilis. Among tropical natives, on the other hand, neurosyphilis is practically unknown; it has been suggested that this may be due to malaria or other fevers, which have been shown to have curative effects on syphilis of the central nervous system.

Another very common and even more fatal localization is in the aorta or heart. It is often not diagnosed until too late; it is responsible for one third of all fatal cases of syphilis. Syphilis often settles in the skin and mucous membranes, producing the gummy sores or " gummas " which were formerly supposed to be the usual tertiary stage of syphilis. It may select the bones, muscles, reproductive system, or any other part of the body, in each case producing a different set of symptoms. A form of " malignant syphilis " occurs in adults in which ulcerating sores appear early and gradually eat away large portions of the skin.

Unborn babies are not subject to such specialized attacks as are adults, but they often have all the organs and tissues in the body invaded by the spirochetes.

An active attack on one tissue or organ of the body seems to have an inhibiting effect on other attacks and therefore usually prevents reinfection. Treatment of skin syphilis is sometimes followed by a flare-up of the disease in the nervous system, where the spirochetes were not destroyed by the treatment; on the other hand paralytics with an active attack on the central nervous system seldom shows any other symptoms. After treatment reinfections are possible but infrequent; they occur more commonly after rapid treatment methods in early syphilis than in more prolonged methods which permit some degree of immunity to develop.

It is an odd fact that pregnancy tends to suppress or prevent the effects of syphilis; often the first suspicion of a conceptional infection is a miscarriage or premature stillbirth of a syphilitic fetus. Even the fetus is protected for three months; miscarriages earlier than that are not due to syphilis, and no evidence of fetal syphilis can be found short of four months. Beck and Daily suggest that the protection may be due to the corpus luteum hormone. It is presumably because of the protective effect of pregnancy that the incidence of serious late manifestations of syphilis is far more frequent in men than in women. Pregnancy may actually be helpful in the treatment of late syphilis. It is because of the frequent lack of symptoms that positive Wassermann reactions during pregnancy have often been considered false.

Diagnosis. The modern methods of diagnosing syphilitic infection have revolutionized our knowledge of the disease and have done much toward placing its treatment and control on a scientific basis. In at least 50 per cent of late syphilitic cases no symptoms can be attributed positively to syphilis, but we now have tests which make it possible to detect syphilis in practically any phase. In the chancre stage, examination of expressed serum for spirochetes, under a dark-field microscope, is very reliable and much better than any of the staining methods; of the latter the Fontana stain is the best. Often spirochetes can be demonstrated, on a dark field, in material obtained from puncture of an enlarged lymph gland.

A few weeks later, and invariably during the secondary stage, syphilis causes a " reagin " to appear in the blood which can be detected by a number of serological methods, comparable with the tests for specific antibodies in other diseases. The reagin is nonspecific only in the sense that it does not react with the spirochetes causing the disease, but with lipoidal extracts from animal tissues; extract of beef heart is used in the tests. When serum containing the reagin due to a syphilis infection is brought into contact with a lipoidal extract, called the antigen, the mixture has the property of combining with or " fixing " the enzyme-like " complement " of fresh serum, and under certain conditions a visible precipitation is produced.

The serological tests for syphilis are based on detection of the reagin by either a complement fixation or a precipitation test. The former is known as the Wassermann reaction; it has been perfected and standardized by Kolmer. To determine whether or not the complement has been fixed, a suspension of red corpuscles and specific antibodies for the corpuscles, called hemolytic amboceptor, is added. If the complement is still present, as it should be if the tested serum is not syphilitic, the sensitized corpuscles are dissolved, whereas if the complement has been fixed, showing the presence of reagin and therefore syphilis, the corpuscles remain intact.

The most widely used precipitation test is the Kahn test, but other valuable ones are the Kline and Hinton tests. Any of these tests require skill, care, and good judgment in their performance; they are by no means foolproof. In expert hands they are practically 100 per cent specific, except in cases of yaws and a few other tropical infections which should easily be ruled out. False positives are not the fault of the patient but of the technician. Even in expert hands, however, the tests are not as sensitive as they should be; only from 65 to 90 per cent of known syphilitic cases are detected. Unfortunately, in public and private laboratories the results are not always so good. In any case the serological findings should be very carefully checked if they do not fit with clinical observations.

In cases of neurosyphilis the spinal fluid also usually contains reagin, sometimes even when the blood does not, and should be tested. In babies born of syphilitic mothers serological tests are not always reliable during the first month or two, and examination of scrapings of the umbilical cord for spirochetes is desirable.

Although not infallible, the serological tests for syphilis constitute one of the most valuable and dependable means of diagnosis known in medicine. With a little further standardization, and improvement in the care and skill of technicians, their value will be still further enhanced.

Treatment. Some quack doctors still practice the same inefficient methods of curing syphilis that were in vogue several centuries ago. Syphilitic sores are powdered and cauterized and cured, and the patient is given to believe that his disease is cured. Unfortunately, as we have seen, the course of the disease is such that the doctor's claim of having cured may be borne out for months or years before the insidious disease appears again, this time in a much more destructive and perhaps incurable state. Superficial treatment of syphilis sores, accompanied perhaps by a few " tonic " pills, in no way destroys the virulence of the parasites or alters the future course of the disease. It merely makes the chance of correctly diagnosing the disease more difficult, and it frequently results in an unsuspecting victim's carrying the disease untreated to a stage where it has wrought irreparable damage to himself, his life-mate, and his children.

The first widely used drug for treatment of syphilis was mercury, which was administered in many different ways. Its toxicity, however, made it impossible to use enough of it to prevent relapses. Since about 1920 it has been almost entirely displaced by bismuth, which is more effective, less toxic, and not painful when injected into the muscles. In 1910 Ehrlich, after years of experimentation, produced a preparation, his No. 606, which was named Salvarsan; chemically it is an arsphenamine. It ranks with quinine and sulfonamides among the great therapeutic triumphs of medicine. Many modifications of the original drug have been developed, the most generally used being Neosalvarsan, which is somewhat slower in its effects but less toxic.

More recently Mapharsen, an arsenoxide, into which the arsphenamines decompose in the body, has come into extensive use. In the doses used it is less toxic than the arsphenamines and ranks between Salvarsan and Neosalvarsan in effectiveness. Spirochetes are said to disappear from active lesions in less than 24 hours after its injection. It is widely used in early and secondary syphilis, but like the arsphenamines is much less effective against late syphilis, and practically useless without heat treatment in neurosyphilis. These arsenical drugs act by some indirect method, being inactive outside the body.

Some success has been attained in lowering the toxicity of arsenical drugs. Abundant vitamin C is helpful, and methyl chalcone of hesperidin, a purified vitamin P made from lemon peel, has been shown to lower the toxicity of Mapharsen to rabbits when given intravenously before and with the drug. For the effect of p-aminobenzoic acid on pentavalent compounds like tryparsamide, see p. 170.

Penicillin was reported by Mahoney, Arnold, and Harris in 1943 to be highly effective in early syphilis; since then it has proved itself extremely valuable, either by itself or in conjunction with arsenicals or bismuth, in the treatment not only of early and secondary syphilis but also of milder forms of neurosyphilis.

One of the great drawbacks in the treatment of syphilis, as of other spirochete diseases (see p. 57), is the tendency to relapse because of failure of drugs to kill spirochetes in the central nervous system, and subsequent reinvasion of the blood and visceral tissues. Until recently either the treatment had to be continued over a long period of months or years, or massive doses of the drugs had to be given, with corresponding danger to the patients. Before the advent of penicillin the course of treatment recommended for early and secondary syphilis was weekly arsenic and bismuth injections for 18 long months. If the treatment began in the chancre stage and was never interrupted, about 85 per cent of the patients were cured. In congenital cases in infants, acetarsone, which can be given by mouth, was a beneficial substitute.

It is not surprising that 75 per cent of patients with early syphilis lapsed in their treatment before they were cured. In consequence, determined efforts have been made to speed up the treatment, at first by giving massive doses of arsenicals over shortened periods of time, either by a continuous "intravenous drip" method of injection of 1200 mg. of Mapharsen in 5 days, or by multiple injections over a period of 6 to 8 weeks. The 5-day method gave about 80 per cent of cures, but about 4 per 1000 died, which was about 12 times as many as died by the standard prolonged method. Early in World War II, and with the advent of penicillin, 50 publicly supported hospitals for rapid treatment of early syphilis were established, and various treatments with penicillin alone or combined with arsenicals or bismuth were used. It was found that with penicillin alone, after 40,000 units every 2 hours for 7½ days or 200,000 units every 2 hours for 3 days in primary or secondary stages of the disease, about 95 per cent of the patients were still in satisfactory condition after a year or more. Attempts to shorten the treatment further by giving 300,000 units every 2 hours for only 2 days did not give as reliable results. In 1948 a new penicillin product, procaine penicillin G in oil with 2 per cent aluminum monostearate, was developed; it permits slow absorption, so that a single injection gives a satisfactory level of penicillin in the blood over a period of several days. As a satisfactory blood level for 3 days cures 95 per cent of early syphilis cases, it now appears probable that a single injection of between 500,000 and 1,000,000 units will be all that is necessary. What an amazing change from ten years earlier when, as Wright and Nicholson (1949) put it, the best the medical profession could offer was 18 months of nauseating, painful and dangerous injections. Penicillin treatment during pregnancy is particularly spectacular; of 150 women observed, only 1 gave birth to a syphilitic child, and she began treatment only 2 weeks before term; the women, however, are not always cured.

Although penicillin is effective in some forms of neurosyphilis, general paralysis is still best treated by fever, induced either by malaria or by artificial means. The effectiveness is greatly enhanced when accompanied by injection of arsenicals, of which either Mapharsen or Tryparasamide may be used. According to Simpson, Kendall, and Rose (1942) twelve 3-hour sessions of 105°–106° temperature over a period of 4 weeks, each accompanied by 0.06 gram of Mapharsen, may be enough. Formerly ten 5-hour sessions at weekly intervals, or twelve malarial paroxysms, were considered necessary. Monkey malaria, caused by *Plasmodium knowlesi* (see p. 186), is frequently used, especially for Negroes, because of the large number who are more or less immune to human malaria.

One difficulty with syphilis treatments at present is that there are not adequate facilities for taking care of all who need treatment, or for the follow-up of treated cases to determine whether they were cured. Provision of such facilities is a necessary part of a successful campaign against this disease.

Prevention. Since syphilis can easily be diagnosed as soon as it reaches an infective stage and can be rendered noninfectious by treatment, this disease is theoretically more amenable to control than many other communicable diseases, yet in our own country it has been allowed to continue its depredations unchecked — shunned, ignored, even mention of it tabooed — because of its sexual form of transmission and its association with promiscuous sexual relations. Even doctors have been reluctant to suspect it, and unwilling to treat it. It has even been urged by ultramoralists that we are interfering with the hand of God when we attempt to abolish his just retribution for sin!

Without public knowledge of the prevalence of syphilis and the tragedy it brings, there could be no public enthusiasm for its control. Until Parran launched his campaign in 1936, syphilis was never mentioned in newspapers, magazines, radio, pulpit, cinema, or schools, but now public consciousness of it has been sufficiently aroused to make an attack possible and to treat syphilis as other transmissible diseases are treated. In Sweden an active governmental campaign reduced the cases of syphilis from 6000 new ones in 1919 to 431 in 1934, and a fourth of these were contracted outside the country. In a similar number of inhabitants in upper New York State there were 11,000 cases.

Results similar to those in Sweden were obtained in other countries prior to World War II, notably Norway, Denmark, England, and Canada. In Sweden control was enforced by laws similar to those that are sanctioned in every civilized country for such diseases as measles and smallpox. Every person must submit to treatment, but he has the right to obtain it free. Every physician treating a new case must try to obtain information as to the source of the infection and to give the information to public health officials; persons aware of infection and carelessly causing transmission are subject to punishment. Every marriage partner must sign a statement certifying to his or her freedom from venereal disease. Local health authorities publish information about clinics for diagnosis and treatment. Along with this, medical inspection of prostitutes was abolished, it having been found, as it has elsewhere, to be useless.

The basic principles of venereal-disease control are (1) the seeking out and enforced treatment of every infected person, and (2) the provision of adequate facilities for diagnosis and thorough treatment without expense to the patient and with a minimum of inconvenience. To be successful this requires public funds and experienced personnel, and an enlightened public opinion which will make possible the cooperation of doctors, patients, and health officers in local communities. The Public Health Service has drafted the following recommendations for state or local venereal disease control: (1) a well-trained public health staff; (2) enforced reporting of all cases, with follow-up of those delinquent in coming for treatment, and finding of sources of infection and contacts; (3) premarital medical certificates, making serological tests a legal requirement; (4) diagnostic services freely available to every physician without charge; (5) treatment of good quality available free at convenient times and places, and hospital beds for patients needing them; (6) state distribution of antisyphilitic drugs to physicians for treatment of all patients; (7) wider use of routine serological tests, e.g., in every pregnancy, every hospital admission, and every complete physical examination; (8) vigorous program of information among physicians and health workers; and (9) persistent, intensive, public education, reaching especially the 15 to 30 age group.

The accomplishment of these ends requires the expenditure of considerable public funds, but the amounts required are but a fraction of the public cost of the disease. The care of 61,700 cases of general paresis, nearly one-third of them in state institutions, alone cost $31,400,000 prior to World War II. Cost of syphilitic blindness added another $1,500,000. To this was added the maintenance of the wives and children of patients; the cost of home care for thousands of cases not in hospitals or institutions; the care of 160,000 cases of heart disease, and the support of the families of 40,000 of these who die each year; the public care of thousands of congenitally infected children; and the reduction of life expectancy of syphilitic white males between

30 and 50 to less than 20 per cent of that of the general population. It is in truth a costly disease, and public funds used to bring it under control may well be considered a profitable investment.

Many states now prohibit the marriage of persons with venereal disease, but without serological tests and with present laxity in notification of syphilitic cases the prohibition is of little value. This may soon be corrected, but in the meantime even the remote possibility of a diseased mate and of stillborn, insane, or hopelessly handicapped children should be enough to induce every man and woman to take every precaution to avoid such a tragedy.

Sanitary laws are less important in the case of syphilis than of many other diseases because of the delicacy of the spirochetes and their short survival outside the body. One possible source of infection, however, though more for gonorrhea than for syphilis, is the improperly constructed toilets in public schools, which are usually built so high and are of such a type that school children, little girls especially, are exposed to possible infection every time they use them.

. Personal preventive measures by the use of medical applications within an hour or two after exposure to infection were found to be fairly successful in military life, but when self-applied in civil life they are very unreliable; the intelligence required for proper application is lacking in those who need it most — immature boys, drink-befuddled men, defective girls, and the average prostitute. Private physicians, dispensary officers, and the health department staff are the persons qualified to employ medical treatment designed to prevent infection after exposure to it; avoidance of exposure constitutes the best and only safe preventive measure.

One of the first moves against syphilis should be abolition of open brothels. This has been shown to cause a marked decrease in venereal disease in army camps. Under peace conditions from 50 to 90 per cent of male infections are acquired from professional prostitutes. Even when not in brothels many infectious individuals can be located and placed under treatment by eliciting information from infected persons. Such contact work, to be successful, requires interviewers who not only are trained in medical and public health work, but who also have an abundance of tact and persuasiveness.

Such a program will, of course, result in some increase in clandestine prostitution and amateur promiscuity. Although this will probably never be entirely abolished, it can be minimized by improvement in living conditions; moderation in use of alcohol, especially by adolescents; provision of wholesome exercise and sports; minimum wage laws for women; and sex education.

Yaws

A common feature of nearly all tropical countries is the disease known as yaws or frambesia. The spirochete, *Treponema pertenue*, is morphologically indistinguishable from that of syphilis but produces somewhat different lesions in rabbits from those produced by *T. pallidum*. The fact that syphilis and yaws are never both prevalent in one locality is undoubtedly due to the reciprocal immunity conferred by these diseases on each other. Yaws is widespread throughout the tropics, being especially common in the West Indies, tropical America,

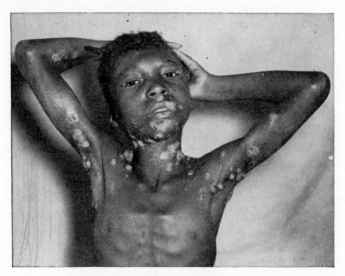

Fig. 10.   A case of yaws.   (U. S. Army Institute of Pathology photo.)

equatorial Africa, southeast Asia, and the East Indies. In many places practically 100 per cent of the natives suffer from the disease in childhood.

After an incubation period of 3 or 4 weeks, with indefinite symptoms, a papule appears at the site of inoculation. This develops into a raspberry-like tumor which bleeds easily and has a dirty, yellow crust. Six weeks to 3 months later a whole crop of such lesions appears, especially on the face and perineal region (Fig. 10). When on the palms or soles the eruptions are very painful; they give the thick skin a moth-eaten appearance and cause a peculiar gait which gave rise to the name " crab yaws." As in syphilis, after a latent period tertiary lesions of skin, joints, or bones may occur, but the viscera, eyes, and nervous system seem usually to escape.

Yaws attacks the epidermis primarily, in contrast to the mesodermal predilections of syphilis. A disease known as gangosa, prevalent in many places in both the East and West Indies and in Africa, causing a horrible ulceration of the entire nose and palate area, is believed to be due to yaws, but this mucous-membrane involvement is due to direct spread from the skin in contrast to the primary mucous lesions in syphilis. Yaws is very seldom a fatal disease except in young children.

Transmission. Yaws is spread by contagion, often by either biting or nonbiting flies, but the spirochetes always enter through some abrasion of the skin, such as ground itch from hookworm, leech or insect bites, scabies, vacination wounds, and scratches.

There is a considerable bulk of evidence incriminating eye flies (see p. 653) as vectors of the disease in various parts of the world, including the West Indies, Brazil, Assam, and Samoa. Workers in several West Indian islands have suspected *Hippelates flavipes* of being a prime factor in yaws transmission, and Kumm and Turner (1936) succeeded in transmitting the infection to rabbits by the bites of infected flies. It has also been shown that the spirochetes can successfully pass through houseflies.

Treatment and Prevention. Care of the general health of yaws patients and conditions leading to the free eruption of the yaws aid much in shortening and alleviating the course of the disease. The disease responds more readily to arsphenamine and also to penicillin treatment than does syphilis, probably because the central nervous system is less consistently invaded. In the majority of cases two or three injections of Neosalvarsan is curative during the eruption stage, but penicillin seems equally effective and is less toxic and so it will probably replace the arsenicals entirely in the treatment of this disease.

The suppression of yaws in communities where it is common consists largely in isolating patients and in preventing them by proper care and treatment from spreading the disease by contagion. Treatment campaigns, using one or two injections of an effective drug to reduce the number of actively contagious cases, rather than to effect complete cures, are being tried, but the danger is in the possibility of a great increase in the number of latent and tertiary cases.

Pinta (Mal-de-Pinto)

Pinta, long thought to be caused by a fungus, was shown in 1938 to give positive Wassermann and Kahn reactions, and to be caused by a spirochete indistinguishable from those of syphilis and yaws. It is characterized by changes in the pigmentation of the skin, at first blue or slaty freckles or patches, later by complete loss of pigment on large spots or areas with deeper pigmentation in other places. In dark-skinned people, who are almost exclusively affected, it produces un-sightly disfigurement. Sometimes, as in yaws, painful thickenings of the soles and palms occur; this is much commoner in Cuba than in Mexico. There are usually no subjective symptoms or any impairment of the general health, except sometimes in late stages when tertiary symptoms may appear, such as hypertension, heart lesions, and changes in the cerebrospinal fluid, as well as atrophy of the epidermis. The disease is not a cutaneous form of syphilis, since it can be inoculated into patients who have that disease in latent form.

It responds well to antisyphilitic drugs in early stages, but when loss of pigment is complete, the white spots are permanent. The spiro-chete has been named *Treponema carateum;* it can easily be found in lymph from the affected areas.   Infection is believed to be acquired by contact, but certain species of Simulium have been suspected as possible vectors.

This unsightly affliction is particularly common in southern Mexico, where there are estimated to be 270,000 cases, and in Colombia, but it is also found in Central America, Ecuador, Peru, and some West Indian Islands.   In 1943 three cases were reported in the United States, where it is probably commoner than is supposed, since loss of pigment is sometimes ascribed to syphilis or to unknown causes.   Loss of pig-ment also occurs in leprosy but in that disease it is usually accompanied by loss of sensation.

Spirochetes in Local Infections

Saprophytic spirochetes of several types occur very commonly in the human mouth and sometimes in the intestine.   One of the commonest is *Treponema refringens,* found in the mouth, mucous membranes, genitals, and often in association with *T. pallidum* in syphilitic lesions. Whether these apparently harmless spirochetes, so often present in entirely normal individuals, are identical with the spirochetes which secondarily invade diseased tissues, and perhaps aggravate them, it is impossible to say.

Vincent's Disease, Tropical Ulcer, etc.   One of the most important of these secondarily developing conditions is Vincent's disease, which appears to be caused by two entirely different organisms living in a symbiotic partnership, one a spirochete which has been named *Borrelia vincenti,* and the other a large, cigar-shaped, fusiform bacillus.   It affects either mucous membranes or subcutaneous tissue; in the mouth it causes " mal-de-boca " and " noma "; in the throat it usually follows a streptococcus infection and causes a diphtheria-like ulceration of the tonsils and throat known as Vincent's angina; in the skin of debilitated people it produces lesions called tropical ulcers or by the more impressive name, tropical sloughing phagedena (Fig. 11). A severe and very common form of the infection known as Naga sore occurs in Assam: the gangrenous process erodes tendons, muscles, and even bone,

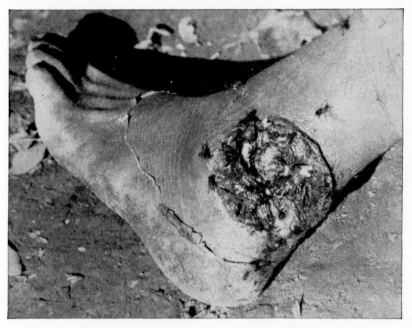

Fig. 11.   A tropical ulcer (U. S. Army Institute of Pathology photo C43–1.)

and a horrible, yellowish slough is formed which has a characteristic fetid odor.   Ulcerations are not infrequent in the genital organs also. In Ethiopia noma is frequently fatal.

The organisms concerned are not primarily pathogenic, for they are frequently found in healthy mouths and also about the genitals, and are often secondary invaders of various diseased tissues.   Smith (1932) calls them opportunists; only when normal health or resistance of tissues is lowered are they capable of invasion.   That vitamin deficiencies may play a part is suggested by the response of the disease to relatively large amounts of niacin.   The spirochetes are 12 to 25 μ long with 6 or 7 loose coils to every 10 μ, and are always accompanied by the cigar-shaped bacilli, and often by spirilla and vibrios also.

Penicillin has a spectacular effect on Vincent's infections, and all lesions actually due to the spirochetes and the accompanying fusiform bacilli heal after 2 or 3 days of penicillin treatment followed by good diet.

Bronchial Spirochetosis. Spirochetes sometimes become very abundant in the trachea and bronchial tubes, causing cough, blood-stained sputum, pain in the chest, and sometimes chronic pulmonary hemorrhages suggestive of tuberculosis. The spirochete is very variable in size and form. It has been named *Borrelia bronchialis,* but may be one of the mouth spirochetes invading tissue that for some reason has lost its normal resistance, or it may be *B. vincenti,* unaccompanied by the fusiform bacilli. Wenyon and some others are very skeptical of the pathogenic nature of the spirochetes; he thinks it would be as logical to consider every mouth abnormality as due to mouth spirochetes when these can be found there as to accuse the bronchial spirochetes of being the cause of the diverse pulmonary disorders in which they have been found present. The fact, however, that in acute uncomplicated cases immediate relief, accompanied by a disappearance of the spirochetes, has been effected by injections of arsphenamine and other spirocheticidal drugs is hard to explain if the spirochetes are mere saprophytic invaders without pathogenic power.

Infectious Jaundice and Other Leptospira Diseases

The genus Leptospira contains extremely delicate spirochetes in which the body consists of a very fine filament with tapered ends, so closely and regularly coiled as to resemble a rope (Fig. 12). They are very active, and they often have the ends of the body hooked over in a characteristic manner; other spirochetes, it should be recalled, tend to keep the bodies extended in a straight line while swimming. When examined with a dark-field microscope the leptospiras look like brilliantly refractile swimming bits of rope, but after being dried and stained the fine rope-like coils are usually not visible, and the organisms appear like tiny threads with hooked or looped ends. They grow readily in artificial cultures.

Some workers recognize no less than 19 distinct parasitic species of Leptospira, separable by antigenic differences; of these, 14 occur in man frequently or occasionally, and 5 have been found only in animals. These various " species " are supposed to differ in geographic distribution, clinical symptoms, animal hosts, pathogenicity for various animals, and epidemiology. Some of these special types have been found only in a few cases in a localized area. In a study in Belgian Congo in 1946, 21 strains of Leptospira were isolated and found to belong to 8 different antigenic groups, 2 of them new. No correlation of antigenic strains with clinical types of disease or virulence for guinea pigs was observed. A considerable degree of overlapping of antigenic types occurs, i.e., serum of an animal or man recovered from one strain reacts with other strains than the homologous one, though not at the same titer. The majority of human Leptospira infections are derived from water, in which the organisms may survive for a

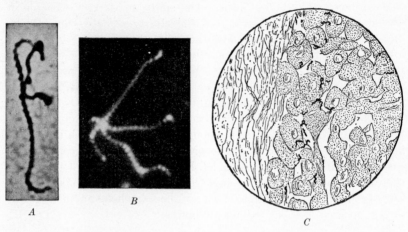

A

B

C

FIG. 12. *A* and *B*: Photomicrographs of *Leptospira icterohaemorrhagiae*; *A*, a silver-stained specimen; *B*, three living specimens as seen under dark-field examination. (After Noguchi in *J. Exptl. Med.*) *C*: *L. icterohaemorrhagiae* in liver of patient who died of Weil's disease on sixth day. × 200. (Sketched from figure by Inada *et. al.*)

number of weeks. The parasitic forms appear not to be identical with the saprophytic aquatic leptospiras, which are usually referred to as *L. biflexa,* but there can be little doubt of their original water origin. It seems quite possible that repeated passage through different animal hosts may be one factor that leads to different strains. Of the commoner human Leptospira infections, *L. icterohaemorrhagiae* is primarily a parasite of rats, *L. canicola* of dogs, *L. pomona* of pigs, *L. bovis* of cattle, sheep, and goats, and *L. grippotyphosa* and most of the others of field mice or other rodents.

Infectious Jaundice. The commonest, most widespread, and longest-known Leptospira infection is infectious jaundice or Weil's disease, caused by *L. icterohaemorrhagiae.* The organisms are extremely slender, 5 to 25 μ long, with 10 to 12 coils in 5 μ of length. They occur in a large proportion of brown rats, *Rattus norvegicus,* in all parts of the world, being especially common where the rats live near water. Schüffner (1934) found an average of 45 per cent infected in Holland. A high percentage of dogs (in the United States probably 25 to 50 per cent) also are temporary or permanent carriers of this species or a related one, *L. canicola* (see below). In past years few cases of infectious jaundice have been reported in this country, but since about 1940 increased use of agglutination tests has shown that it is not rare.

The leptospiras invade the body through mucous membranes, eyes, or skin abrasions, but probably not through unbroken skin. The infection is spread most frequently by urine of infected animals, especially when water is contaminated by it. The leptospiras may live several weeks in contaminated water, even when brackish. In Holland Schüffner has obtained evidence that human infection commonly results from swimming in dirty water frequented by rats. During World War I infection often developed in trenches where the soil was polluted by rats. People working along water fronts and in slaughterhouses, granaries, mines, etc., are also especially subject to infection. In Lisbon an epidemic occurred from drinking water taken from a public fountain. In Germany the frequency of the disease in people bathing in stagnant water has led to the name "slime fever."

The disease is characterized by sudden onset, after an incubation period of 1 to 2 weeks, with chills, fever, headache, muscular pains, vomiting, and sometimes diarrhea. After a few days jaundice develops in severe cases, but this is not as characteristic a symptom as is sometimes thought, being absent in about 40 per cent of cases. Red eyes, due to flushing of the conjunctiva, especially under the eyelids, is a very characteristic symptom.

The fever subsides in from 6 to 10 days. Small hemorrhages often appear in skin, mucous membranes, and internal organs. The urine usually contains both albumin and bile. Meningeal symptoms are not infrequent in the second week. A secondary rise in temperature often occurs after about 3 weeks from the onset. In experimental animals after the acute stage the descending convoluted tubules in the kidneys are crowded with leptospiras, demonstrable by silver staining. The mortality varies from 4 to 48 per cent.

In early stages the disease may easily be confused with typhus, yellow fever, or dengue, but it does not have the characteristic rash of typhus and can be distinguished from the other two diseases by leucocytosis. The leptospiras may be found by dark-field examination of the blood during the first few days, and in the urine after about 10 days. After the first week agglutination tests are valuable, using cultured leptospiras preserved in 0.5 per cent formalin as an antigen. Guinea pigs inoculated with 3 to 5 cc. of plasma from early cases, or urine later, usually show leptospiras in the peritoneal fluid after a few days, and die with jaundice in 10 or 12 days.

Many drugs have been tried in the treatment of infectious jaundice, but penicillin is the only one that is reasonably successful. If given early in the disease, it alleviates the symptoms and sometimes cures, but often there are relapses. Serum from patients who have recovered from homologous strains is beneficial.

Other Leptospiral Infections. A strain closely related to that of Weil's disease is *L. canicola*, which commonly affects dogs in Europe and America. Dogs are also susceptible to *L. icterohaemorrhagiae*, but *canicola* rarely if ever occurs in rats and only rarely infects man. Coffin and Stubbs (1942) have reported over 50 per cent mortality in cases in dogs in Pennsylvania. The symptoms are mainly gastrointestinal, with fever and acute collapse. In Europe this strain rarely produces jaundice, although it not infrequently does so in America.

Another strain, *L. grippotyphosa*, called mud, swamp, or field fever in various parts of Europe, causes disease outbreaks among agricultural people working in marshes, especially during floods, in later summer and autumn. It has a reservoir in field mice. It causes fever, headache, and sometimes stiff neck, suggestive of meningitis, but no jaundice, and its virulence is low. Another European strain is *L. pomona*, which has been shown to cause symptomless infections in pigs, in whose urine the leptospiras are excreted. It is believed to be the cause of "swineherd's disease" in Switzerland. In Palestine, Russia, and Australia a strain has been found in cattle, sheep, and goats which produces symptoms in these animals varying from mild fever to jaundice and bloody milk, and is sometimes fatal. It is believed to infect man since the sera of some human cases with jaundice and kidney disease agglutinate this strain. It is not pathogenic for rats or guinea pigs.

In the Far East, besides typical Weil's disease, a variety of other leptospiral diseases are caused by organisms differing only in their serological reactions. One strain, *L. hebdomadis*, causes a dengue-like "7-day fever" in Japan, Malaya, and India and is harbored by a field mouse, *Microtus montebelloi*. This strain produces very little jaundice. Another strain, *L. autumnalis*, causes a similar but more virulent disease in the Far East. In the Dutch East Indies and Malaya, eight or more serological strains have been described. A common form of the disease in Java in which jaundice is infrequent has been called pseudo-dengue and is caused by a strain named *L. pyrogenes*. Two other strains, *L. bataviae* and *L. javanica*, are often acquired by cats.

The distinctness of many of these strains may justifiably be doubted, and there is evidence that their immunological characteristics, which overlap somewhat, may be altered by cultivation and passage through animals.

REFERENCES

Syphilis, Yaws, and Pinta

AM. ASSOC. ADVANCEMENT SCIENCE, Syphilis (Symposium by Medical Section), Pub. 6, edited by F. R. Moulton, Lancaster, Pa., 1938.

EAGLE, H., and HOGAN, R. B., An Experimental Evaluation of Intensive Methods for the Treatment of Early Syphilis, *Venereal Disease Inform.*, **24**, 33, 69, 159 (1943).

HELLER, J. R., The Treatment of Syphilis with Penicillin, *Proc. 4th Intern. Congr. Trop. Med. and Malaria*, Sect. 3, 1949.

HUDSON, E. H., Treponematosis, *Oxford Loose Leaf Medicine*, Chap. 27-C, 9–122 (1946). (reprint).

KUMM, H. W., and TURNER, T. B., The Transmission of Yaws from Man to Rabbits by an Insect Vector, *Hippelates pallipes Loew.*, *Am. J. Trop. Med.*, **16**, 245 (1936).

LIEBERTHAL, E. P., Pinta (Mal-de-Pinto, Carate) in Continental United States, *J. Am. Med. Assoc.*, **123**, 619 (1943).

MOORE, J. E., *The Modern Treatment of Syphilis*, 2nd ed., Springfield, Ill., 1941.

NELSON, N. A., and CRAIN, G. L., *Syphilis, Gonorrhea and the Public Health*, New York, 1938.

RIETZ, E., The Prevention of Venereal Diseases in Sweden, *Am. J. Publ. Health*, **26**, 357 (1936).

SCHAFFER, L. W., Present Status of the Intensive Arsenotherapy of Early Syphilis, *Venereal Disease Inform.*, **24**, 108 (1943).

SIMPSON, W. M., KENDALL, H. W., and ROSE, D. L., The Treatment of Syphilis with Artificial Fever Combined with Chemotherapy. A Critical Review, *Venereal Disease Inform.*, Suppl. **16** (1942).

Standard Treatment Procedure in Early Syphilis, Coop. Clin. Studies in the Treatment of Syphilis, *Venereal Disease Inform.*, **15**, No. 4, April, 1934.

THOMAS, E. W., *Syphilis, Its Course and Management*, New York, 1949.

TURNER, T. B., Studies on the Relationship between Yaws and Syphilis, *Am. J. Hyg.*, **25**, 477 (1937).

TURNER, T. B., et al., Yaws in Jamaica, *Am. J. Hyg.*, **21**, 483–521, 522–539 (1935).

WRIGHT, R. D., and NICHOLSON, F. P., Treatment as a Factor in the Control of the Venereal Diseases, *Bol. oficina sanit. panamer.*, **28**, 462–468 (1949).

Other Spirochetes

AM. ASSOC. ADVANCEMENT SCIENCE, A Symposium on Relapsing Fever in the Americas, Pub. 18, 1942.

BLANK, H., Tropical Phagedenic Ulcer (Vincent's Ulcer), *Am. J. Trop. Med.*, **27**, 383–398 (1947).

BRUMPT, E., MAZZOTTI, L., and BRUMPT, L. C., Étude épidémiologique de la fiévre récurrente endémique des hauts plateaux mexicains, *Ann. parasitol. humaine et comparée*, **17**, 275 (1939).

CHUNG, H. L., and WEI, Y. L., Studies on Transmission of Relapsing Fever in North China. II. Observations on Mechanism of Transmission of Relapsing Fever in Man, *Am. J. Trop. Med.*, **18**, 661 (1938).

COFFIN, D. L., and STUBBS, E. L., Observations on Canine Leptospirosis in the Philadelphia Area, *Univ. Penna. Vet. Ext. Quart.*, **87**, 3 (1942).

COLES, A. C., Observations on the Life History of the Spirochetes of Relapsing Fever, *J. Trop. Med. Hyg.*, **39**, 77 (1936).

CUNNINGHAM, J., THEODORE, J. H., and FRASER, A. G. T., Further Observations on Indian Relapsing Fever. Part I, *Indian J. Med. Research*, **22**, 105 (1934); Part II (Cunningham and Fraser), *ibid.*, **22**, 595 (1935).

DAVIS, G. E., Ticks and Relapsing Fever in the United States, *Pub. Health Repts.*, **55**, 2347 (1940).

The Spirochetes, *Ann. Rev. Microbiol. for 1948*, 281–334 (1948).

HAVENS, W. B., BUCHER, C. J., and REIMANN, H. A., Leptospirosis: A Public Health Hazard, *J. Am. Med. Assoc.*, **116**, 289 (1941).

KEMP, H. A., MOURSUND, W. H., and WRIGHT, H. E., Relapsing Fever in Texas, *Am. J. Trop. Med.*, **13**, 425 (1933); **14**, 159, 163, 479 (1934); **15**, 495 (1935).

MEYER, K. F., EDDIE, B., and ANDERSON-STEWART, B., Canine, Murine and Human Leptospirosis in California, *Proc. Soc. Exptl. Biol. Med.*, **38**, 17 (1938).

PACKCHANIAN, A., Positive Agglutination Tests in Inspected Cases of Weil's Disease, *Pub. Health Repts.*, **56**, 2145 (1941).

SCHÜFFNER, W., Recent Work on Leptospirosis, *Roy. Soc. Trop. Med. Hyg.*, **28**, 7 (1934).

SMITH, D. T., *Oral Spirochetes and Related Organisms in Fusospirochetal Disease*, Baltimore, 1932.

VAN THIEL, P. H., Diagnosis and Treatment of Leptospirosis, *Proc. 4th Intern. Congr. Trop. Med. and Malaria*, **1**, Sect. III, 321–327 (1948).

The Leptospiroses, Leiden, Netherlands, 1948.

WHEELER, C. M., Relapsing Fever in California, *Am. J. Trop. Med.*, **18**, 641 (1938).

CHAPTER 5
Amebas

Amebas are animated bits of naked protoplasm, familiar to every freshman biology student who peers through a microscope with appropriate marvelings at the simplicity of animal life in its most primitive state. The vast majority are free-living animals inhabiting soil, water, and decaying organic matter everywhere, and play an important role in the control of bacteria in some of these situations. In view of their wide adaptability and the frequent contamination of food or drinking water by their cysts, it is not surprising that some species of them have adapted themselves to living out the active phase of their lives in the intestines of animals. The majority even of these are harmless commensals, content to use the intestine as a haven of refuge where food is abundant and enemies scarce, but a few have developed a taste for live meat, and have taken to feeding upon the wall of the intestine that shelters them.

Classification. The position of the amebas among the Protozoa of the class Sarcodina may be seen from the following outline.

Class **SARCODINA.** Protozoa which move and ingest food by means of pseudopodia during the predominant phase of their lives, though some may have a transitory flagellated phase. No cuticle, but may have shells.

Subclass I. **RHIZOPODA.** Have temporary pseudopodia (lobe-like, filamentous, or branching) constantly extended and retracted.
Order 1. **Amoebida.** Lobe-like pseudopodia, and no shells or "tests."
Family 1. *Amoebidae.* Free-living amebas, usually with contractile vacuoles and no flagellated stage. Includes many "coprozoic" forms found multiplying in stale feces.
Family 2. *Endamoebidae.* Parasitic forms, without contractile vacuoles or flagellated stages. Includes all the amebas which become permanently established in the alimentary canal of higher animals.
Other Families (2). Have flagellated phases.
Other Orders (4). Forms with filamentous or branching pseudopodia, some with chitinous or calcareous tests. Include slime molds, Testacea, and Foraminifera.

Subclass II. **ACTINOPODA.** Have more or less permanent pseudopodia supported by axial rods (axopodia).
Order 1. **Heliozoa.** More or less spherical with radiating axopodia (Fig. 3B).
Order 2. **Radiolaria.** With perforated capsule separating cytoplasm into two parts, and usually with skeletal structures also.

The true amebas differ from other members of the Sarcodina by producing lobe-like pseudopodia which do not branch or anastomose, and in having no shells or tests. The parasitic amebas (Endamoebidae) are characterized mainly by their mode of life, by the absence of any flagellated phase in the life cycle, and by having no contractile vacuoles. Because of their small size, simple life cycles, and scarcity of good variable characteristics their further classification into genera and species requires a great deal of care and patience. The members of the family are separated into a number of genera on the basis of minute structural differences in the nuclei, and the species within the genera on still finer nuclear differences and on variations in the structure of the cysts.

Habits of Trophozoites. All the parasitic amebas, as far as known, inhabit the large intestine of their hosts, with the exception of *Endamoeba gingivalis* which makes itself at home in the mouth. *E. histolytica* and perhaps some of the others occasionally invade the lower part of the small intestine just above the ileocecal valve, and they can frequently be found in the appendix. They all multiply in the active or trophozoite phase by simple fission; in most species this is initiated by a division of the nucleus, but in one genus, Dientamoeba, the nuclear division usually occurs shortly after cell division, resulting in a high proportion of individuals with two nuclei. Most of the species are mere scavengers, feeding on bacteria, cysts, and various debris in the contents of the large intestine, but *E. histolytica,* and to some extent *E. gingivalis,* are more fastidious. *E. histolytica* while living in the intestine never contains anything but red blood corpuscles in its food vacuoles; in cultures, however, it " goes native " and feeds on bacteria and starch grains like other kinds of amebas. *E. gingivalis* occasionally picks up a bacterium or other types of food, but in its natural habitat in the mouth it lives mainly on leucocytes or their nuclei.

Encystment. Most of the parasitic amebas form cysts, which are better able to withstand conditions outside the body than are the trophozoites, but *Endamoeba gingivalis* and *Dientamoeba fragilis* manage to survive without them. When preparing to encyst, the amebas eliminate all food vacuoles, round up, and shrink somewhat, probably by a condensation of the cytoplasm, so that the nucleus becomes relatively large. This is the precystic stage. A delicate cyst wall develops to protect the organism during its hazardous existence outside the body while waiting for an opportunity to infect a new host. As long as the amebas are alive the cyst walls are relatively impervious to many substances, including dyes and weak disinfectants. They are unaffected by either chlorine or dilute silver ions in the proportions used for killing bacteria in drinking water. The fact that living cysts are not ordinarily stained by dilute eosin, whereas dead cysts are, has been used extensively as a test of the viability of cysts in experimental work, but there is some question of its reliability. In some species glycogen is stored during encystment in more or less well-defined vacuoles, and there may be deep-staining " chromatoid bodies " also; their true nature is doubtful, but they probably constitute reserve food material. They gradually disappear as the cysts grow older.

In most of the species of amebas some multiplication of the nucleus takes place during the formation of the cysts, but in Iodamoeba the nucleus remains single. In *E. histolytica* and *Endolimax nana* four nuclei are normally produced, and in *Endamoeba coli* eight. The exact conditions under which cysts are produced in natural infections are still uncertain. It was formerly thought that cysts were formed as a reaction to unfavorable environmental conditions in a host, but in cultures cysts are produced when conditions are highly favorable for continued multiplication. Nevertheless, there is evidence that certain chemical or physical stimuli produced by the food or secretions of the host are necessary for encystment. Cysts are not found in dysenteric or liquid stools and are never formed in tissues or liver abscesses. Encystment should be considered a naturally recurring phenomenon in the life cycle, analogous to the formation of gametocytes by malaria parasites, although there is no evidence that any sexual phenomenon is involved. The sole purpose of encystment seems to be the safe transfer of the parasite from one host to another.

Excystment. The conditions which lead to excystment are also little understood, but most cysts " hatch " in the small intestine above where the trophozoites ultimately settle down. The amebas escape from their cysts through a perforation in the cyst wall. The process was first described by Dobell in 1928 for *Endamoeba histolytica*. The four-nucleated ameba draws itself in and out of the cyst several times before escaping. It then undergoes a complicated series of nuclear and cell divisions, resulting ultimately in eight little amebulas with a single nucleus each.

Species Found in Man. Prior to the appearance, in 1919, of Dobell's book, *Amoebae Living in Man*, the amebas found in man were in a terrible muddle, and most of the earlier literature cannot be relied upon as far as species are concerned. Since the publication of this valuable work there have been a number of suggested modifications or additions, but none of them has stood the test of time; today six species of amebas living in man are recognized and are separated into four genera, just as Dobell arranged them. All protozoologists recognize the following genera and species; *Endamoeba gingivalis*, inhabiting the mouth; *E. histolytica*, a pathogenic intestinal form; *E. coli, Endolimax nana,* and *Iodamoeba williamsi*, harmless intestinal forms; and *Dientamoeba fragilis*, an intestinal form which is at least sometimes pathogenic.

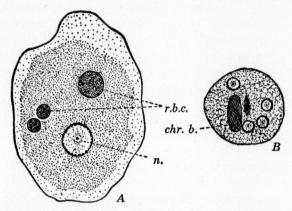

Fig. 13. *Endamoeba histolytica.* × 1650. *A*, stained trophozoite; *B*, cyst with four nuclei; *n.*, nucleus, showing peripheral chromatin granules and central endosome; *r.b.c.*, ingested red blood corpuscles; *chr. b.*, chromatoid body. (After Dobell.)

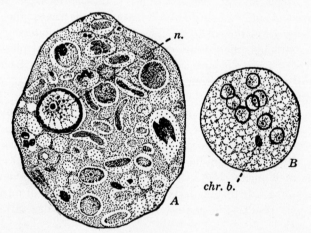

Fig. 14. *Endamoeba coli.* × 1650. *A*, stained trophozoite; *B*, cyst, with eight nuclei; *n.*, nucleus, showing coarse peripheral chromatin granules, chromatin granules in " clear zone " between periphery and endosome, and eccentric endosome; *chr. b.*, remnant of chromatoid body. Note large number of food vacuoles in trophozoite. (After Dobell.)

In at least some of the species of human amebas there are races or strains which differ in the size of the cysts they produce, sometimes of the trophozoites also. It has long been observed that the races of *E. histolytica* that produce small cysts are not associated with dysentery or liver abscesses in man and are relatively mild in their effects on cats and dogs. They are often found in symptomless cases, but they are sometimes associated with mild symptoms which disappear after treatment. A number of European parasitologists consider these small amebas to constitute a separate species, *E. dispar*. Some American and British workers, on the other hand, thought there were from 3 to 5 different size races. Sapero, Hakansson, and Louttit in 1942, however, found good evidence for the existence of only two distinct races, a small one with cysts less than 10 μ in diameter (9 μ after fixation), averaging 7 μ, and a large one with cysts over 10 μ in diameter, averaging 11.5 μ. The amebas of the small race do not ingest red blood corpuscles, are less actively motile, and are not so easily cultivated. Most workers have considered these size races constant,

FIG. 15. *Endolimax nana.* × 1650. *A*, two stained trophozoites, showing nuclei with large irregular endosome, and numerous food vacuoles. *B*, cyst with four nuclei. (After Dobell.)

but Meleney and Zuckerman reported an increase in size of a small-cyst strain after 5 years in culture.

Differentiation of Genera. The outstanding characteristics of the genera of amebas which occur in human beings are as follows:

Endamoeba: nucleus vesicular with chromatin arranged in a peripheral layer of bead-like granules of fairly uniform size, and a small compact endosome; a capsule-like structure can usually be seen surrounding the endosome. Cysts, if produced, with normally 4 or 8 nuclei similar in structure to those of the free forms, and including also glycogen masses and refractile " chromatoid " bodies, though these masses and bodies commonly disappear before or soon after the cysts become mature. (See Figs. 13 and 14).

Endolimax: nucleus vesicular without a distinct peripheral layer of chromatin. A fairly large compact mass of chromatin (endosome) in the interior, usually more or less eccentric and connected by threads or processes with one or more smaller masses. Mature cysts oval, with 4 nuclei in the known species, similar in structure to those of the free forms. The cysts contain, in addition to the nuclei, a number of small refractile granules of a substance known as volutin. The young cysts also contain masses of glycogen. (See Fig. 15.)

Iodamoeba: nucleus vesicular with moderate-sized central endosome and well-developed membrane without a distinct peripheral zone of chromatin, but with a single layer of rather large granules between the endosome and the outer membrane; cysts very characteristic, formerly known as iodine cysts or I. cysts, often of irregular shape, containing, besides a single nucleus, a number of brightly refractile granules and a relatively large, clearly defined solid mass of glycogen which stains very deeply in iodine. The nucleus is peculiar in that the endosome comes to lie peripherally in contact with the nuclear membrane. (See Fig. 16.)

Dientamoeba: mature individuals with 2 similar nuclei; these are vesicular with the endosome represented by a cluster of small granules near the center; nuclear

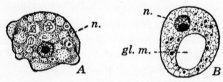

FIG. 16. *Iodamoeba williamsi.* × 1650. *A*, stained trophozoite, showing numerous food vacuoles and nucleus (*n.*), the latter with large central endosome and a single layer of granules between endosome and nuclear membrane. *B*, cyst, showing nucleus (*n.*) with peripheral endosome, and glycogen mass (*gl. m.*) or " iodophilic body," from which these cysts received the name " Iodine or I. cysts." (After Dobell.)

FIG. 17. *Dientamoeba fragilis.* × 1650. *A*, stained trophozoite, showing two nuclei with granular endosomes, and food vacuoles; *B*, living ameba, showing leaflike pseudopodia. (*A* after Dobell; *B* after Jepps and Dobell.)

membrane very delicate without distinct peripheral chromatin; cysts not found. (See Fig. 17.)

Host Specificity. There has been much discussion about the identity of the human species of amebas and morphologically identical ones found in other animals. Strict host specificity on the part of intestinal amebas can no longer be accepted, although some protozoologists have grimly adhered to belief in it in spite of growing evidence against it. The genus Endamoeba is an excellent one to illustrate the situation. In man there are two universally recognized intestinal species, *E. coli* and *E. histolytica.* The latter species can be successfully transferred to a variety of animals such as monkeys, rats, guinea pigs, rabbits, cats, dogs, and pigs. *E. coli* has been transferred to monkeys, cats, and rats. In various species of lower primates, from spider monkeys (Ateles) to apes, indistinguishable forms of one or both of these types of amebas have been described. Kessel in 1928 showed that identical diseases were caused in cats by monkey and human *E. histolytica,* by either of these after being established in pigs, or by the *histolytica*-like amebas naturally harbored by pigs.

Five of the species of human amebas (and four human flagellates) have been found by Kessel in Macacus monkeys, differing in no morphological or physiological respect from the corresponding Protozoa in man. Although these might have been acquired from contact with human beings, this is probably not true of 44 wild Philippine monkeys, obtained where they probably had had no chance to be contaminated by their protozoa-infested human compatriots, and which Hegner found to harbor eleven different species of human intestinal, oral, and vaginal protozoa. One was a veritable zoological garden for human Protozoa, harboring eight different species, and none had less than two.

Natural infections with *E. histolytica* occur in most of the animals in which experimental infections have been produced. Kessel's successful experiments in 1923 on the transfer of five different species of human intestinal amebas to rats demonstrated that in spite of environmental changes the morphological characters of species and strains remain strikingly constant.

Intestinal amebas are much less common in carnivores than in herbivores, but cats and dogs artificially (or rarely spontaneously) infected with *E. histolytica* are the only animals other than man and monkeys in which amebic infections are definitely known to be pathogenic. Amebas belonging to the same genera as those found in man occur also in birds, cold-blooded vertebrates, insects, and other invertebrates. The type species of the genus Endamoeba lives in roaches. Some parasitologists do not think this ameba belongs to the same genus as *histolytica* and *coli*, so they place these in a separate genus, Entamoeba. Mouth amebas are commonly found around the teeth and gums of monkeys, dogs, and horses.

Coprozoic Amebas. Cysts of free-living amebas and flagellates, and sometimes even ciliates, may enter the body with food and pass through the alimentary canal unhatched and undigested. Some of these find conditions satisfactory for rapid multiplication in the feces after passage, and may confuse an unwary laboratory technician. All such amebas, however, are distinguishable by the presence of one or more contractile vacuoles. Another rhizopod sometimes found in stale human feces is *Chlamydophrys stercorea*, a chitin-shelled member of the order Testacea. There is no evidence that these coprozoic forms can ever establish themselves and multiply in the intestines; they become progressively more abundant in stale feces, whereas the trophozoites of the true intestinal species die out very rapidly, usually within a few hours after leaving the intestines.

Diagnosis. Diagnosis depends upon (1) finding the organisms in the feces and (2) making a correct identification of them. Cysts are rarely found in liquid or dysenteric stools, whereas trophozoites, except those of Dientamoeba, are seldom found except in purged or naturally diarrheic stools. Cysts of intestinal amebas are voided intermittently, so a single examination cannot be relied upon to bring to light all infections. Sawitz and Faust (1942) showed that a combination of a simple smear and zinc sulfate flotation methods (see p. 91) demonstrates only about 20 per cent of existing *Endamoeba histolytica* infections and about 45 per cent of other Protozoan infections whereas four or five such examinations at intervals of 2 or 3 days over a period of 10 days will reveal 75 to 90 per cent of all infections. Marsden (1946) pointed out that, for a reasonable chance of finding one cyst from a patient passing 1000 per day, 220 examinations would have to be made, and that therefore there is no practical way of detecting more than a minority of patients voiding 10,000 or less per day. Examination of four stools at intervals of a week allows for a better chance of success than examination of a greater number on consecutive days. Examination of more than one preparation from a single stool increases the chances of detection so slightly as to be not worth while.

Formed stools to be examined for cysts can be kept in the icebox for 2 or 3 days before examination, but trophozoites in liquid stools degenerate very rapidly and should be searched for as soon as possible after being passed, while the stool is still warm. If the stools are kept at body temperature the trophozoites are usually still identifiable for about 30 minutes. A higher percentage of infections can be found in a single purged or diarrheic stool examined for trophozoites than in a single formed stool examined for cysts. Oil-purged stools are useless for examination.

Direct smear examinations are made by comminuting a small amount of feces in saline, to which may be added 1:1000 aqueous eosin to stain the debris pink, leaving the living trophozoites and cysts unstained. After spreading over the width of two cover glasses, apply a cover to one side for examination of living organisms; to the other side, before covering, add a small drop of D'Antoni's iodine (1.5 grams iodine in 100 cc. standardized potassium iodide, filtered after standing 4 days). The iodine will stain nuclei, chromatoid bodies, etc., well enough for identification. Additional aqueous instead of saline smears facilitate diagnosis by destroying fungus and Blastocystis and by showing certain characteristics of Dientamoeba. Permanent preparations showing minute details of structure can be made by fixing the films in Schaudinn's fluid (equal parts sat. $HgCl_2$ and 95 per cent alcohol) at body temperature and staining with iron hematoxylin, but success requires careful technique. Brooke and Goldman (1949) showed that addition to the fixative of 5 per cent elvanol, a polyvinyl alcohol, permits drying of the slides and subsequent staining without harm to anything but large cysts. In unstained preparations the details of nuclear structure, and in *E. histolytica* even the nuclei themselves, are invisible under an ordinary microscope, but these minute details can be seen without staining under a phase contrast microscope.

Faust *et al.* (1939) worked out a method of concentrating both the cysts of Protozoa and eggs of worms by making up a 1 to 5 suspension of feces in physiological salt solution, straining through cheesecloth or wire gauze, and then centrifuging 2 cc. in a Wasserman tube with water added (45 seconds at 2640 rpm.). The supernatant fluid is then poured off, zinc sulfate of specific gravity 1.180 (331 grams of U.S.P. granular zinc sulfate in a liter of distilled water) added, the sediment stirred up, and the tube centrifuged again. The surface film is then removed by means of a 5-mm. wire loop, or enough more zinc sulfate is carefully added to form a meniscus to which the surface of a clean slide is touched. The number of positives was nearly twice as great as with simple smears in Faust's series. This method is, however, good only for cysts and should be supplemented by a direct fecal smear stained with iodine or iron hematoxylin.

Endamoeba histolytica

Distribution and Incidence. Because of its great though often latent capacity for causing disease, its wide geographical distribution, and its discomforting frequence as a resident of the human colon, *Endamoeba histolytica* must be ranked as one of the most important human parasites. Although it once had the reputation of being mainly a tropical parasite, it is by no means so limited. It has world-wide distribution, and is almost as frequently present, though fortunately not so frequently pathogenic, in the land of apples and apoplexy as it is in the lands of mangoes and mañana. The only reason that this ameba often inhabits more people in tropical than in temperate localities is that the people in the tropics take less pains to avoid devouring its cysts with contaminated food or water. One of the most remarkable records is the finding of a 60 per cent infection in 900 people examined in the Kola Peninsula of Russia, a locality lying entirely within the Arctic Circle.

When routine examinations are made by competent microscopists, seldom less than 5 to 10 per cent of the entire population, even in northern Europe and the United States, are found to be infected. In a state-wide survey of Tennessee, Meleney *et al.* in 1932 found more than 11 per cent of the rural population infected, and in one group of counties above 22 per cent; these findings on one examination indicate probably twice as great actual incidence. In one group of 27 individuals in 5 backward families, 23 were carriers of *E. histolytica*. The Chicago outbreaks of 1933 and 1934 show how well this parasite can prosper far from the native haunts of dark skins and palm trees. In some examinations in tropical America more than 50 per cent of the population have been found infected; a group of club servants, waiters, and cooks in Colombia revealed the disconcerting incidence of 60 per cent. In Peiping, China, Kessel and Svensson found 30 per cent of adult Chinese and 25 per cent of adult foreigners infected.

With respect to age, young children are much less frequently infected than adults, but the incidence increases rapidly during childhood; the highest incidence is in young adults, which suggests the development of some degree of immunity after continued or repeated infections. For some unexplained reason males are more commonly infected than females. In Tennessee, Meleney found no significant difference in degree of infection between whites and Negroes.

A relatively high percentage of people harboring *E. histolytica* also harbor one or more other species of amebas, as might well be expected, since conditions favoring transmission of one favor that of others also, and the passage through the stomach of the thicker-walled cysts of the other species is probably easier than that of *histolytica* cysts.

Morphology. The trophozoites of *Endamoeba histolytica* (Fig. 13*A*) are relatively large; they usually vary in diameter from about 20 to 30 μ, but larger forms occur, and smaller ones, even down to an average of 10 to 12 μ, are sometimes found. About one third of the ameba consists of clear, refractile ectoplasm, the rest being a finely granular endoplasm. In the fresh state, when warm, the amebas are very active, and travel along in a straight line in a manner which Dobell describes as suggesting a slug moving at express speed; in this condition the rapidly advancing end of the body consists of a single clear pseudopodium, while ingested red corpuscles flow and roll about as though in a mobile liquid. Other amebas have more tendency to stay in one place, where they extend and retract their pseudopodia without making much headway.

Ingested red corpuscles, which usually number from 1 to 10 but sometimes up to 40, are very characteristic and are in contrast to the miscellaneous food ingested by other amebas. Sometimes when the stools are not bloody the amebas may not contain them, but they do not contain bacteria or other debris, although rarely there may be tiny fragments of tissue cells. Any ameba found in a dysenteric stool and containing only blood corpuscles may safely be regarded, without further investigation, as *E. histolytica*.

After stools have been passed and allowed to cool the amebas begin to become abnormal and to die almost immediately, and they then present very different appearances, which has resulted in much confusion, for more often than not the stools are several hours old when an examination is made. The amebas under these circumstances no longer travel, but remain in one place, throwing out large, dome-shaped, clear pseudopodia from different parts of the body; the endoplasm becomes full of vacuoles, and bacteria invade the dying body. The nucleus also disintegrates and presents abnormal appearances in both fresh and stained preparations. Even in this condition the large amount of clear ectoplasm serves as a means of differentiation from *E. coli*.

The nucleus is so delicate in structure that it is practically invisible in fresh active forms. After being fixed and stained with iron hematoxylin the nucleus has a characteristic structure. The nuclear membrane is encrusted with uniform fine granules of chromatin, and a small dotlike central endosome is surrounded by an indefinite, clear halo. Between the endosome and the nuclear membrane is a clear area devoid of chromatin granules, marked by a linin network which often has a spoke-like radial arrangement. *E. coli*, on the other hand, has coarser and more irregular peripheral granules and a larger endosome, eccentric in position, with a more definite halo and with usually a few chromatin granules strung on the linin network surrounding the halo; the nucleus of this species is visible as a bright refractile ring in fresh, living organisms. When stained with iodine the nuclear membrane and endosome of *E. histolytica* show as refractile bodies, and the cytoplasm of the ameba stains a greenish yellow.

E. histolytica multiplies by simple fission and a modified form of mitosis in which, according to Kofoid and Swezy, six chromosomes are formed (see Fig. 1*A*). When preparing to encyst, the amebas become smaller and rounded, lose their ingested blood corpuscles, and then lay down the delicate cyst wall. The relatively large nucleus then divides into two and then four progressively smaller ones, but with the same morphology as the nucleus of the trophozoite. Rarely *E. histolytica* overshoots the mark and produces eight nuclei in a cyst.

Most precystic or young cystic amebas (Fig. 13*B*) lay down in the cytoplasm one or two bar-shaped "chromatoid bodies" which are refractile in living or iodine-stained cysts and which stain deep black with iron hematoxylin; these chromatoid bodies are quite different from the less massive splinter-like ones found in *E. coli*. In most young cysts there is some stored glycogen, usually in less well-defined vacuoles than in the cysts of *E. coli*. Both the chromatoid bodies and the glycogen vacuoles disappear as the cysts grow older. In fresh preparations the cysts have a faintly greenish tint and are refractile; if a preparation containing numerous cysts is viewed with a low-power objective slightly out of focus the cysts appear as little shining spheres. The size of the cysts varies from about 5 to 20 μ in diameter; as noted on p. 87 at least two races of the ameba exist which differ in the average size of the cysts. Races with small cysts are rarely pathogenic to man.

The mature 4-nucleated cysts of *E. histolytica* are characteristic enough for any trained technician to be able to identify them. Their differentiation from those of *E. coli* and *Endolimax nana*, with which they are most likely to be confused, is indicated by the table:

	Endamoeba histolytica	Endamoeba coli	Endolimax nana
Size	5–20 μ	10–33 μ	$4 \times 5 \mu - 10 \times 14 \mu$
Shape	round	round	usually oval
Nuclei, number	usually 4	usually 8	usually 4
Nuclear structure	membrane encrusted with fine chromatin granules; small central endosome	membrane encrusted with coarser granules; larger, usually eccentric endosome; a few scattered chromatin granules	chromatin in a single or lobed mass, large relative to size of nucleus
Chromatoid bodies (when present)	bar-like	splinter-like	absent or dot-like
Glycogen vacuoles (when present)	usually diffuse, ill-defined	may be fairly well defined	none

Habits and Biology. Like most other parasitic amebas, *Endamoeba histolytica* is normally an inhabitant of the large intestine, frequently invading the appendix and occasionally venturing into the lower part of the small intestine. Although amebic ulcers may be found anywhere along the 6 ft. of the large intestine from ileocecal valve to anus, they are most frequent in the cecum and ascending colon, and next most frequent at the opposite end, in the sigmoid flexure and rectum. These are the regions where the contents of the intestine are usually allowed a temporary halt in their otherwise rough and restless journey through the alimentary canal.

Unlike any of the other intestinal amebas, *E. histolytica* does not feed on bacteria or other contents of the intestine of the host, but nourishes itself on the living cells and tissues. In cultures, however, as noted on p. 84, it reverts to more primitive habits and feeds on bacteria and starch grains. The amebas produce a toxic substance which causes tissue cells to dissolve, whence the name *histolytica*, which means "tissue dissolving." They undoubtedly nourish themselves in part on the liquefied tissues as well as on ingested blood corpuscles. They multiply rapidly by simple fission.

Some think that *E. histolytica* is invariably a tissue invader, but James (1928) called attention to the fact that it is incredible, as is usually taught, that the majority of the trophozoites live in the tissues,

for the number of amebas found in dysenteric stools is out of all proportion to the number found in the tissues at autopsy, and there are
often enormous numbers of motile or encysted forms in the stools during intervals between symptoms.   The majority seemingly apply themselves to the surface of the mucous membrane and superficially dissolve
the cells without burrowing in.   The earliest lesions of amebic infection
are not ulcers, but superficial erosions.   Often no ulcers can be found
in human or monkey " carriers." Westphal (1948) thinks that the
amebas primarily inhabit the lumen, but that penetration into the
tissues is facilitated by bacterial intestinal infections.

The motile forms, or trophozoites, live for only a few hours after
leaving the body even if the feces are kept warm, and they are killed
immediately by drying, acids, or other unfavorable conditions.

Cysts have never been found in the tissues except in the liver of dogs
fed with raw liver or liver extract.   They apparently form in the lumen
of the large intestine, and are often passed before they have fully
matured, but they are capable of completing their development outside the body if the cyst wall has been formed.   The cysts are rarely
found in liquid stools, in which the trophozoites frequently abound, but
they are usually the only forms present in normal formed stools.

The cysts, if kept moist and cool, will live for a number of weeks
outside the body.   They may remain viable for a week or two in feces
if kept cool, and for as long as 10 days in water at room temperature.
In a refrigerator they can be kept alive in water for 6 or 7 weeks. They
will not stand desiccation, however, and have been found to die in from
5 to 10 minutes when dried on the hands.   They will live from 24 to
48 hours in the intestines of either flies or roaches.   Although cold is
favorable for their survival (this in itself is enough to throw suspicion
on their limitation to the tropics), they are susceptible to moderately
high temperatures, even as low as 115° to 120° F.   They are therefore
killed by pasteurization of milk and by heating of water; heating and
filtration are the only practicable methods yet known for destroying
them in drinking water.   Their specific gravity is only about 1.06, so
they settle very slowly in contaminated water; it is estimated that it
would take them 4 days to settle 10 ft. in perfectly quiet water.

Cultivation. *Endamoeba histolytica* was first successfully grown in
culture by Boeck and Drbohlav in 1925; since then many modifications
have been suggested.   The most successful cultures are made with
autoclaved liver-infusion agar slants or slants of whole egg diluted
with Ringer's solution and overlaid with horse, beef, or human serums
diluted with 6 parts of Ringer's solution. Balamuth (1946) devised
an all-liquid medium made of dehydrated egg yolk in a buffered saline

solution, which is also good for other intestinal amebas and flagellates (except Giardia). Another simple medium, devised by Nelson (1947), is prepared from alcoholic extracts of egg yolk, liver, or other tissues made into agar slants and overlaid with buffered saline. This medium has the advantage of preventing growth of the fungus Blastocystis, which is often a nuisance in cultures. All human parasitic amebas grow in the original culture, but only *E. histolytica* and flagellates survive in transfers. To all these media a little sterile rice starch is added, on which the amebas feed gluttonously. The cultures are inoculated with feces, and the amebas grow abundantly, producing cysts as well as trophozoites. They may begin encysting in 18 to 24 hours and may begin excysting again as soon as the cysts mature. They are, however, fastidious about the bacteria which accompany them, and they often fail to grow if "foreign" bacteria are not kept out by sterile methods; these "gate-crashers" somehow render the medium unsuitable for encystment or even multiplication. To keep a culture going, transfers must be made every 4 to 10 days, the first subculture usually sooner.

Numerous attempts have been made to grow *E. histolytica* free of bacteria. Jacobs in 1947 and Shaeffer and Frye in 1948 successfully grew it in a medium containing fluid in which bacteria had been grown. This fluid contained products of their growth but few remaining bacterial bodies; the further growth of these bacteria was inhibited by penicillin. Efforts to find out what bacterial product the amebas require have so far been unsuccessful.

Pathogenicity. 1. Nondysenteric Infections. Although amebiasis is usually thought of as the cause of dysentery with blood and mucus stools, or of liver abscesses, these conditions are actually the exception rather than the rule, and some workers have reported that as high as 90 per cent of cases in temperate climates are apparently symptomless. Faust (1941) found *E. histolytica* in 13 (6.5 per cent) of 202 autopsies of persons who had suffered sudden accidental death in New Orleans, but in only 5 of these were amebic lesions demonstrated, and these were superficial, confined to the mucosa. Craig, on the other hand, stated that in his experience 65 per cent of so-called "carriers" have symptoms referable to their infection, which disappear after eradication of the parasite. Sapero (1939), in a study of 216 nondysenteric cases, found symptoms in 100 of them, in many cases trivial, but often severe enough to require hospitalization. The commonest symptoms are abdominal pain, nausea, flatulence, and bowel irregularity, with headaches, fatigability, and nervousness in a minority of cases. The symptoms resemble those of many other gastro-intestinal disorders, particularly appendicitis and peptic ulcer. Appendicitis, or pains simulating it, are frequent enough so that Craig (1944) believes that in all cases of suspected appendicitis an examination for *E. histolytica* should be made and, if found, amebic treatment should be given before resorting to operation. A high percentage of obscure gastro-intestinal ailments are probably due to amebic infection but are seldom diagnosed as such.

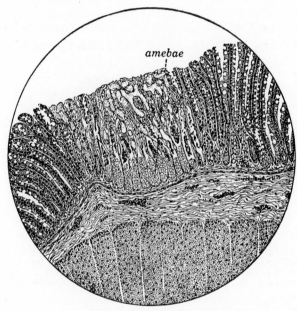

Fig. 18. Section of colon of cat showing an amebic ulcer limited to the mucous membrane. Note broken-down and necrotic epithelium of invaded glands, extravasated blood, and masses of amebas at bottom of glands. (Drawn from slide prepared by Meleney.)

2. Amebic Dysentery. Since the amebas feed only on red blood cells or dissolved tissue cells, it is not likely that they are ever entirely harmless. At first they erode the superficial mucous membranes, either along the whole large intestine or locally in the cecum or other parts. Eventually eating into the tissues (Fig. 18), especially if aided by trauma or injurious accompanying bacteria, they reach the submucosa and then extend their flask-shaped ulcers (Fig. 19). The abcesses extrude their contents into the intestine as necrosis becomes complete, causing the edges of the injured mucous membrane to cave in, giving a craterlike effect. Sometimes several undermining abscesses coalesce under the surface. Fortunately, the muscular coats of the

intestinal wall usually act as a barrier, but sometimes this layer is
penetrated by way of the connective tissue sheaths, and the amebas
reach the serous membrane, causing extensive adhesions or dangerous
perforations. The ulcers vary greatly in number and size; in severe
cases almost the entire colon is undermined. When not invaded by
bacteria, the ulcers show no signs of inflammation, but invasion by
bacteria often occurs. Sometimes amebic granulomata form in the
colon and may be confused with cancerous growths.

The ulceration of the bowel, as noted previously, may produce severe
dysentery, though it does so in a minority of cases. In the tropics
dysentery occurs in perhaps 10 per cent of amebic infections, but in

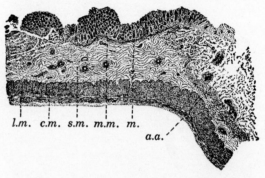

Fɪɢ. 19. Section of human colon showing deep amebic ulcer broken through into the
submucosa. Note abnormal thickness (edema) of submucosa and pus-like contents of
ulcer: *l.m.*, longitudinal muscle layer; *c.m.*, circular muscle layer; *s.m.*, submucosa;
m.m., muscularis mucosae; *m.*, mucosa; *a.a.*, amebic abscess. (Drawn from slide prepared
by Meleney.)

temperate climates far less often. The reason for this has been the
subject of much speculation, and although, as already noted, some
authors have attributed it to the existence in temperate climates of fixed
races of very low virulence, others, notably Brug, believe that a
tropical climate in itself favors the production of dysenteric symptoms.
Diet is another factor. McCarrison found that a diet deficient in
vitamins would cause infected monkeys to break down with acute
dysentery whereas those kept on an adequate diet remained healthy.

In amebic dysentery the stools, usually acid, consist of almost pure
blood and mucus, in which swarms of amebas, laden with blood corpuscles, are usually present. The patient is literally "pot-bound,"
owing to the rectal straining and intense griping pains, with the passage
of blood and mucus stools every few minutes. In uncomplicated cases
there is little or no fever, a point which is sometimes useful in differentiating amebic from bacillary dysentery. Recurring symptoms some-

times manifest themselves over a period of 30 or 40 years or even longer, and there may be latent periods lasting for at least 6 or 8 years.

3. Abscesses in Liver, Lung, etc. It is clear that the amebas, actively dissolving the tissues, may frequently be drawn into the portal circulation. Such amebas are carried to the liver and sometimes settle there, attacking the liver tissue. In view, however, of the frequency with which amebas are undoubtedly carried to the liver from intestinal ulcers it is evident that this organ must have a high natural resistance to infection. Nevertheless, small or temporary amebic infections of the liver are probably much commoner that we usually think; sometimes liver abscesses develop without any preceding attack of dysentery. The abscesses are usually sterile so far as bacteria are concerned, although they are sometimes secondarily infected; they may become very large and filled with a slimy, bloody, chocolate-colored material resembling pus, but made up of dead amebas, blood, and fibrous tissue left by the amebas, with active amebas in the enlarging walls. The patient has pain in the liver region, fever, and a high leucocyte count, and his face presents a sorrowful aspect of weariness and apathy, with sallow skin, sunken cheeks, and dark-circled eyes.

Amebas which have escaped into the blood stream are not necessarily halted in the liver but may be carried to any part of the body. Lung abscesses are fairly frequent; these are usually caused by direct extension from a liver abscess through the diaphragm; such an abscess may rupture into the pleural or pericardial cavity, but it usually works directly into the lung tissue where the lung adheres to the diseased diaphragm. The lung abscess in turn usually ruptures into a bronchial tube and discharges a brown mucoid material which is coughed out with the sputum. Next in frequency are abscesses of the brain. Abscesses elsewhere are rare. Skin infections, however, may develop about the incisions made for surgical treatment of amebic abscesses.

Factors Determining Pathogenicity. There is no doubt that chronic infections with indefinite symptoms are the rule, with the amebas localized in the large intestine or liver. Whether an amebic infection produces acute dysentery, a chronic state of vague discomfort, or no obvious symptoms at all probably depends on several factors. Undoubtedly natural resistance varies, possibly dependent upon general health, vitamin sufficiency, and perhaps other dietary factors which affect the bacterial flora and intestinal acidity. But there is also a striking difference in the pathogenic powers of different strains of amebas, which remain fairly constant even after long artificial cultivation and passage through different kinds of animals (see Meleney and Frye, 1936). As already remarked on p. 87, the harmlessness to man

of small-cyst strains has led a number of European workers to postulate a separate nonpathogenic species, which they named *Endamoeba
dispar.*

Meleney and Frye doubt that accompanying bacteria play any
important part in determining the pathogenicity, but others think
that pathogenic bacteria present in the intestine or obtained along
with the amebas under unsanitary conditions are an important factor.
Nauss and Rappaport showed that irritation of the intestinal mucosa
definitely facilitates invasion by amebas. Westphal (1948) in a
study of intestinal disturbances in German troops in north Africa
found evidence that amebic infections tended to remain chronic, non-
dysenteric, lumen infections until resistance to tissue penetration was
lowered by intercurrent bacterial infections. In his experience tissue
invasion occurs in about one third of *E. histolytica* carriers who acquire
bacillary intestinal infections.

There is some evidence that the longer and more frequent the exposure to infection the greater the danger of clinical dysentery.

Infection in Other Animals. Animals other than man suffer from
amebic dysentery. In kittens experimental infections are very severe
and usually fatal, but if recovery occurs the infection dies out instead
of becoming chronic. A peculiarity of the infection in cats is the
failure of the amebas to produce cysts. Dogs also can be experimentally infected and not infrequently become naturally infected, but
normally they do not produce cysts and so are not involved in the
spread of the infection. Pigs, which harbor amebas morphologically
like *Endamoeba histolytica* as well as many other Protozoa morphologically like those of man, may play a role in transmission. Rats can
be experimentally infected and have been found spontaneously infected.
Monkeys are even more extensively infected in nature than man;
these animals are probably the only important reservoir of the infection among lower animals. Gordon Ball, however, was unable to
produce infections in capuchin monkeys.

Mode of Infection and Epidemiology. Since only the cysts can
survive outside the body, these alone are concerned in transmission.
The trophozoites are rarely capable of passing through the human
stomach and intestine to reach their promised land in the colon. Since
dysenteric cases rarely pass cysts, they are not usually concerned in
transmission; persons who are cyst-passers with few or no symptoms
are principally concerned. Even the cysts probably find the stomach
a dangerous hazard. Tsuchiya found that *Endamoeba histolytica*
cysts fed to rats on an empty stomach passed through to the intestine
much more rapidly and produced a much higher percentage of infec-

tions than did cysts fed on a full stomach. This suggests that *E. histolytica* cysts, like typhoid organisms, may cause infection more readily when ingested with water than with food because of the greater rapidity with which they pass the stomach. It also throws light on the relative frequency of amebic infections in individuals with abnormally low stomach acidity. According to Tsuchiya, cysts of *E. coli* and Giardia were not similarly affected by a sojourn in the stomach, possibly because of their thicker cyst walls. He suggests that this may account for the higher incidence of *E. coli* than of *E. histolytica* in most human populations.

Since amebic cysts survive for considerable periods outside the body if not desiccated, it is obvious that if they get into drinking water or moist foods they are in an advantageous position both from the standpoint of length of life and of opportunities to "thumb a ride" into a human alimentary canal. Polluted water is undoubtedly one of the most important means of transmission, and wherever unprotected or untreated ground water is used for drinking in areas where there is widespread soil pollution, amebic infections will be common. Such conditions prevail over vast portions of the tropics and in the rural areas of our own southern states.

Even when a purified water system prevails, accidents may lead to widespread outbreaks of water-borne infections. One hazard is in defective plumbing. The basements of hotels and public buildings frequently contain a veritable maze of pipes, gradually built up, repaired, and replaced throughout a generation or more, and it is not as surprising as it seems at first that errors in plumbing should be made. This was strikingly demonstrated by an outbreak during the Chicago World's Fair in 1933 in which defective plumbing caused almost 1000 known cases of amebiasis and 58 deaths scattered over 206 cities. The plumbing hazards included back siphonage from sanitary fixtures into water lines, leakage of sewer pipes into basements, and even cross connections between sewer pipes and water pipes made by careless and muddled plumbers. Such faults in plumbing seem to be surprisingly common, but only exceptionally do they cause explosive epidemics. Chlorination of water in most cities prevents sewage-tainted supplies from causing typhoid or other bacterial infections, but it has no effect on protozoan cysts. Sand filtration, properly carried out, seems to remove the cysts very well. It seems probable that amebic infections might be acquired from dirty swimming pools if very much of the water is swallowed.

Raw vegetables grown in polluted soil, particularly where night soil is used, or freshened with contaminated water, are potential cyst carriers, but the chance of cysts conveyed by them passing through the stomach unharmed is less than that of cysts in water or unpasteurized milk.

Although it has been shown that cysts survive for only a few minutes on hands, except under long, closely fitting fingernails, and that the chances are against transmission by soiled hands of food handlers on any single occasion, nevertheless there is no doubt that oft-repeated exposure of one's food to handling by careless infected food handlers is dangerous. Although cyst-passing cooks, dairy workers, icemen, waitresses, etc., must all occasionally transmit amebic infection, probably housewives and mothers are most important, since the frequency of exposure is greatest. However, the fact that food handlers do not transmit infection as readily as was once supposed is comforting news for those whose gastronomical needs are ministered to by native servants, public food handlers, or rural southern hospitality.

Diagnosis. This should always be based on the finding of *Endamoeba histolytica* in the stools by the methods described on pp. **89–90.** In examining dysenteric stools for trophozoites, special attention should be paid to flakes of blood or mucus. When clinical manifestations of infection are present, a high percentage of cases can be diagnosed by a single examination of a stool or of the rectum by a proctoscope. The presence of whetstone-shaped " Charcot-Leyden " crystals in feces is usually indicative of *E. histolytica* infection.

Craig has demonstrated that a complement fixation reaction, using an alcoholic extract of an ameba culture as antigen, is highly specific and sometimes demonstrates otherwise unrecognized cases in hospitals, but it requires extreme care in technique. It may be a very useful adjunct to diagnosis, particularly in occasional cases of liver infections when the amebas are no longer present in the intestine.

Some workers favor the cultural method of diagnosis. If the investigator is not an expert microscopist who can accurately detect Protozoa by means of a 16-mm. lens, the culture method may have advantages, but few if any expert examiners would substitute it for the direct microscopic examination. Usually the percentage of cases that are detected by one method and not the other is small.

Experience in identifying Protozoa is required. As great danger lies in making a false positive diagnosis as a false negative one, for to inexperienced workers an ameba is an ameba, and often even epithelial cells and other objects are amebas. Many a patient, unfortunate enough to have an undiscriminating technician mistake leucocytes in a bacillary dysentery stool or find an innocent *E. coli* or *Endolimax nana,* has had to submit to a course of treatment which was useless if not injurious to himself and quite innocuous to the amebas. Dobell in 1917 wrote: " The errors committed by an examiner with little or no previous experience are such as I could not have believed possible if I had not actually encountered them; and in cases where the health of the patient is at stake, it is, I believe, almost better that no examination at all should be made, than that it should be made by an incompetent and inexperienced person."

Treatment. Like many other protozoan diseases, amebiasis if left untreated tends to become chronic and to persist indefinitely. Since the amebas are found both on the surface of the mucosal cells in the lumen and buried in the tissues, permanent cure requires a drug or drugs that will reach them in either situation.

Three groups of drugs are extensively used in the treatment of amebiasis — emetin, iodine compounds, and arsenic compounds. In addition two antibiotics, bacitracin and aureomycin, have been shown to have curative value. Emetin, usually given by subcutaneous injection since it produces severe nausea when given by mouth, is an alkaloid obtained from a Brazilian herb, ipecacuanha. It must be given with care, for it is toxic to the heart muscle. It is marvelously effective in checking acute dysentery, often within 1 or 2 days, and is the only drug useful in liver infections; but it seldom succeeds in eliminating an infection entirely, presumably because it fails to kill amebas that are not actually buried in the tissues. A daily injection of 1 grain is given for 7 to not more than 12 days. In dysentery a switch to one of the iodine or arsenic compounds is indicated as soon as the acute symptoms subside. Shrapnel (1947) reported that emetin could be given by mouth in enteric-covered tablets without causing nausea or toxic effects, and that clinical cures were obtained in all of 25 adults and 5 children with intestinal infections, only 1 case subsequently relapsing. In later efforts to repeat this, however, toxic effects have developed, so further investigation is necessary before this method can be recommended. Some workers recommend emetin bismuth iodide in hard gelatin capsules as a substitute or supplement for emetin, but it often produces unpleasant symptoms.

Of the iodine compounds, which Craig (1944) considers the safest and most effective, Chiniofon (Yatren), Diodoquin, and Vioform are most esteemed. Chiniofon, 4 tablets (16 grains) given 3 times daily for 7 to 10 days cures 90 per cent of cases but may cause severe diarrhea, so it is well to begin with a smaller dose. Diodoquin is nontoxic and causes no ill effects except a rare headache, so is recommended by Craig for symptomless carriers and also as a prophylactic for people traveling in places where there is danger of infection. In these cases

2 or 3 tablets are given 3 times a day after meals for 20 days; for symptomatic cases the dose is increased to 10 or 12 tablets a day. Vioform (1 capsule 3 times a day for 10 days) is also effective, but the course may have to be repeated after a week's rest.

For occasional cases not responding to iodine treatment, arsenicals are tried; the best is Carbarsone. One capsule (4 grains) given twice a day for 10 days cures 90 per cent of cases but is mildly toxic and should not be used where there is liver or kidney disease. For a method of detoxification see p. 170.

In dysentery cases Neoprontosil (1 to 3 tablets 3 times a day for 5 to 7 days) is a useful adjunct to the iodine drugs to relieve abdominal distress and inhibit secondary infections.

For children the dose of the iodine and arsenic drugs mentioned above is about one eighth the adult dose per 20 lb. of weight.

Although carriers and early cases sometimes respond to single courses of treatment, a series of courses is often necessary, using a variety of different drugs.

Emetin is highly effective for treatment of liver abscesses and frequently cures them without puncture or aspiration. The latter should never be done until at least 5 or 6 emetin injections have been given to kill the amebas. Conan in 1948 reported successful treatment of hepatic amebiasis with chloroquine (see p. 207), 0.3 gram twice a day for 2 days, then 0.3 gram a day for 12 more days. Symptoms disappeared promptly in all of 6 cases, and no recurrences were observed in from 2 to 12 months. Emetin is said not to be so effective in the treatment of lung abscesses, but it is the only drug on which any reliance can be placed.

Bismuth subnitrate or subcarbonate is often a useful adjunct to treatment in controlling dysentery or diarrhea. Dunn, in China, tells of some dysentery patients of his who, after a prolonged course of unsuccessful treatment, were relieved of all medication and other forms of treatment and put on a full diet rich in vitamins; almost like magic they began putting flesh on their emaciated forms, and all symptoms vanished.

Prevention. The essentials in the prevention of amebic infection are sanitation and protection of water and vegetables from pollution. Soil pollution, especially by use of night soil, is dangerous in places where unfiltered water is used for drinking, even if it is chlorinated. Clark showed that there was a great falling off of amebic dysentery in Panama after a good water system was installed in 1914–1915. Between 1905 and 1914, 4.25 per cent of 4000 autopsies showed amebiasis, whereas from 1914 to 1923 there were only 0.28 per cent among

2800 autopsies. In view of the plumbing hazards discovered in Chicago in 1933 it seems evident that public health officials and city governments should spend sufficient money for inspection of hotels and public buildings, but for the most part they have not done so.

Vegetables such as lettuce, radishes, and strawberries, grown in ground fertilized by night soil or even in ground subject to ordinary pollution, are dangerous. It is customary for Europeans in India to soak uncooked vegetables in a potassium permanganate solution for an hour, but usually several cooks have to be discharged before one is found who will actually carry out what he considers a silly notion rather than risk being caught not doing it. Even then he feels that if he sets a head of lettuce in an inch of " red water " he has sufficiently carried out instructions. Immersion for 30 seconds in water at about 150° F. has also been recommended.

Although transmission by the hands may not be so easy as was once supposed, Craig believes that food handlers constitute the most important means of transmission in sanitated cities. The tendency for the infection to spread in families indicates transmission from person to person, probably as a rule from the servant or housewife who prepares the food. Continually repeated exposure may be dangerous when occasional exposure is not. A careful washing of the hands with soap and water after using a toilet would probably eliminate most of the danger. James recommends that Europeans in the tropics should insist on all servants cleaning their hands thoroughly with scrubbing brush, antiseptic soap, and water several times a day, especially before preparing or serving food. This is excellent advice, but in India, at least, one would have to stand over each servant with both eyes wide open during the entire process of each washing and would very likely have to render assistance!

Animal carriers probably do not contribute to human infection, but flies and roaches may do so. Pipkin in 1942 found viable cysts in the regurgitations of flies up to half an hour after ingestion, and in fecal droppings for several hours. A fly-borne epidemic was described by Craig in 1916.

Other Intestinal Amebas

The other amebas which inhabit the human intestine, with the exception of *Dientamoeba fragilis*, would be of very little consequence if it were not for the danger of confusion between them and *Endamoeba histolytica*. They are never tissue parasites, and there is no good evidence that a human being is any worse off for harboring these guests in his intestine. They ordinarily live free in the lumen of the intestine, at least so far as is known at present, and fail to show the fastidiousness with respect to food that *E. histolytica* shows. Instead, they feed on bacteria, small cysts, starch grains, and all sorts of debris found in the semifluid medium in which they live. In other respects, such as life cycle, mode of encystment, resistance in the cyst stage, mode of transmission, transferability to other kinds of animals, etc., they appear to be similar to *E. histolytica*.

Endamoeba coli. This is the commonest species of ameba in the human intestine and has been stated to occur probably in 50 per cent of human beings; its distribution is world-wide; according to Dobell " no race, nor any country, has yet been discovered in which infections with this species are not common." In surveys made in the United States the incidence of infection usually varies between about 18 and 30 per cent, roughly about three times the incidence of *E. histolytica*. As already noted, the higher incidence of *E. coli* infections is probably due to the thicker cyst walls of this species (see p. 101). Walker and Sellards obtained 17 successful infections by feeding cysts to 20 human volunteers. Andrews in 1934 found a 62 per cent infection among a group of Mexicans in a mining town in Mexico.

The motile forms are found especially in the upper part of the large intestine, and the precystic and cyst forms lower down. Although this species is undoubtedly a harmless commensal, there is some evidence that it may rarely invade injured tissues. Occasional ingestion of blood corpuscles is to be expected since it displays little selection in its diet.

The outstanding characteristics of *E. coli* (Fig. 14) have been mentioned in connection with its differentiation from *E. histolytica*, but they may advantageously be summarized again. The living forms are usually 20 to 30 μ in diameter and are never as small as the smallest races of *histolytica*. The body usually has very little ectoplasm, and even the ponderous pseudopodia are usually composed mainly of endoplasm, although clear ones are occasionally produced. Unlike *histolytica* this ameba tends to move about sluggishly in one place without making much headway in any one direction. The body is usually crammed with food vacuoles, for it is a voracious feeder. Knowles says he has several times seen this ameba with an ingested starch grain almost as large as itself, apparently half-paralyzed with lethargy after such an enormous meal. The nucleus is visible in living specimens as a refractile ring.

In stained specimens the contained food and the nucleus distinguish it from *histolytica*. The nucleus has a coarser peripheral layer of chromatin, a larger and eccentrically placed endosome, and usually dots of chromatin strung on the linin network.

Encystment occurs precisely as in *E. histolytica,* except that 8 instead of 4 nuclei are produced. The precyst stages are the most difficult to distinguish from those of *histolytica:* the distinction can be made only by observation of the nuclear structure in good specimens. The cysts have thicker walls than those of *histolytica;* the 2-nucleated stage usually has a very large glycogen vacuole, which nearly fills the cyst, lying between the nuclei, but it begins to become diffuse even by the time the cyst becomes 4-nucleated. The mature cysts, which are most commonly found in fresh stools, are from 15 to 22 μ in diameter, have 8 nuclei of the typical *coli* type, more granular cytoplasm than in *histolytica,* and either no chromatoid bodies or else a few flakes like splintered glass, but never the heavy bars found in *histolytica.* According to Hegner, the cysts hatch as entire 8-nucleated amebas.

Endolimax nana. This little ameba is almost as frequent an inhabitant of the human intestine as is *Endamoeba coli,* and is commonly found in from 15 to 30 per cent of cases in routine examinations in this country. Its principal characteristics are those given under the genus Endolimax on p. 87 and shown in Fig. 15. It is a very small ameba, varying from 6 to 12 or 15 μ in diameter, but usually averaging only about 7 to 9 μ. It creeps sluggishly like *E. coli* and, like that species, often contains numerous food vacuoles filled with bacteria. The 4-nucleated cysts (Fig. 15*B*) might be confused with those of *E. histolytica* but are distinguishable by their small size (usually 6 to 10 μ by 5 to 8 μ), their usually oval shape, and the peculiar structure of the nuclei, described on p. 87. Although frequently found associated with *E. histolytica* in dysenteric patients, there is no evidence that this species is at all pathogenic. Like *E. coli,* it cannot be eliminated by emetin or any other drug, although it temporarily disappears during emetin treatment. Its exact habitat in the intestine is not known, but it is certainly not a tissue parasite. *Endolimax nana* also occurs in monkeys, and probably identical forms occur in rats and pigs; a form from a guinea pig differing only in its smaller size has also been described. Other probably different species occur in frogs, lizards, and fowls.

Iodamoeba williamsi (or **bütschlii**). This small ameba is usually larger than Endolimax and smaller than the Endamebas. Usually the amebas average about 9 to 11 μ in diameter, but specimens varying from 4 to 19 μ have been found, and Wenrich (1937) believes that there are large and small races. The characteristic features of the nucleus are mentioned on p. 87, and shown in Fig. 16. The living trophozoites are sluggish but move about by the extrusion of clear ectoplasmic pseudopodia; the nucleus is not usually visible but there are usually ingested food particles. In stained specimens the body does not usually show any clear ectoplasm and often has a vacuolated appearance.

The cysts of this ameba (Fig. 16B) are peculiar in several respects. They are about the same size as the trophozoites and are of irregular shape, as if formed under pressure. The endosome moves to an eccentric position almost in contact with the nuclear membrane, and the granules between it and the periphery usually cluster into a crescent-shaped mass on the inner side of it. Usually the nucleus remains single, but Wenrich states that occasionally cysts with two or even three nuclei are formed. The most striking feature of the cysts, however, is a large, sharply defined vacuole filled with glycogen and therefore staining brown in iodine. When first discovered these cysts were thought to be of vegetable nature and were called " iodine cysts." In fixed and stained specimens the glycogen dissolves out and leaves a large cavity.

Iodamoeba williamsi infests a very high percentage of monkeys and pigs. Cauchemez estimated that 50 per cent or more pigs in France are infected, and Feibel found 20 per cent of pigs slaughtered in Hamburg harboring it. The pig may, in fact, be considered the normal host in temperate climates. This is another example of the close parasitological relations between pigs and man. This ameba is not so common in man as those hitherto described; in most surveys in this country it occurs in from 2 to 6 per cent, especially of adults. Incidences of 10 to 16 per cent have, however, been recorded from Mexico and China.

Dientamoeba fragilis. This is another small ameba, usually ranging in size from 3.5 to 12 μ; the average is usually around 9 μ, but in diarrheic stools it may be 11 μ. This ameba (Fig. 17) is peculiar in that, in most populations of it, about 80 per cent have two nuclei, and occasionally supernucleate forms appear. This is due to the fact that, unlike other amebas, the nucleus divides shortly after cell division instead of just before it. The nucleus has in its center a cluster of four to eight deep-staining granules, one of which stains more deeply than the others and is designated the endosome. The cytoplasm has a granular or frothy appearance, with or without food vacuoles, and often the ectoplasm is sharply demarcated from the endoplasm by a deep-staining zone. This and other characters of the nucleus and cytoplasm have led both Dobell and Wenrich to suggest relationships to the flagellate Histomonas (Fig. 27); Dobell says that " Dientamoeba is, indeed, a typical flagellate except for the important circumstance that it possesses no flagella." No cysts are formed by Dientamoeba.

In living or iodine-stained specimens the nuclei are not visible. In saline suspensions the trophozoites remain in a sort of dazed, immobile state for 5 or 10 minutes, appearing rounded and granular; they then extrude broad, flat, leaflike pseudopodia of clear ectoplasm. In tap water they swell up and explode, leaving a hollow shell of ectoplasm.

Dientamoeba has a world-wide distribution, and its incidence is probably as high as or higher than that of *Endamoeba histolytica,* in spite of the fact that in many surveys it is not reported at all, partly because methods suitable for its detection are not used and partly because many technicians fail to recognize it when they see it. According to Wenrich (1944), " When properly trained observers employ appropriate techniques, the incidence of Dientamoeba will be found to be much higher than present survey results indicate." Wenrich and his co-workers found it in 4.3 per cent of 1060 students at the University of Pennsylvania and in 3.9 per cent of 190 Philadelphia food handlers, when only a single stool was examined; with more examinations an incidence of 7.4 per cent was obtained in the latter group. In some institutions incidences of 36, 42, and 50 per cent have been obtained. In contrast to these findings Wenrich found that, in 19 surveys in the United States between 1934 and 1944, 65,253 persons were examined without this evasive organism being found in any of them! The organism is best recognized in smears fixed with picro-formol-acetic in the proportions of 75:15:10, and stained with iron hematoxylin. In the group of 1060 students mentioned above, over 60 per cent of the Dientamoeba infections were recognized on stained slides alone.

There is strong evidence that Dientamoeba may sometimes be pathogenic, so, unlike the other amebas except *Endamoeba histolytica,* it is of interest to the medical practitioner as well as to the parasitologist in an ivory tower. Wenrich *et al.* in 1936 reported a higher incidence of gastro-intestinal disturbances among students playing host to this ameba than among those harboring *Endamoeba histolytica,* and Sapero (1939) recorded that 27 per cent of Dientamoeba cases had complaints as compared with 43 per cent of those with *E. histolytica,* and 7 per cent of those devoid of intestinal protozoa or harboring only *Endamoeba coli,* Endolimax, or Iodamoeba. Wenrich calls attention to frequent eosinophilia in Dientamoeba cases; the commonest symptoms associated with it are diarrhea and colicky pains, but symptoms indicative of lowered vitality, such as quick tiring and low resistance to colds, are frequently reported, suggesting toxicity. Though none of the evidence is absolutely conclusive, the case against Dientamoeba as a potentially harmful parasite is very strong.

Some Dientamoeba infections are transitory, but they frequently last months or years. How it is transmitted is still an unsolved problem, since the organism usually dies in from a few hours to a day or two in feces, and explodes in water. Dobell failed to infect either himself or two monkeys by means of swallowed cultures, although the infection does occur in monkeys. Dobell's belief that Dientamoeba is related to Histomonas suggests the possibility that it may be transmitted by the eggs of parasitic worms, since Histomonas is transmitted in this manner (see p. 132).

Dientamoeba infections usually respond to Carbarsone and other drugs effective against *E. histolytica*. This in itself is suggestive of its being a pathogenic parasite, for the species of amebas that are content to live a saprophytic life in the lumen of the intestine are unaffected by these drugs.

Mouth Amebas (Endamoeba gingivalis)

In contrast to all other amebas living in man, or even in animals, there is one species of Endamoeba, *E. gingivalis*, which inhabits the mouth instead of the large intestine. The same or a similar species has been found in pyorrheal pus from the mouths of dogs and cats, around the teeth of horses, and in a high percentage of captive monkeys. Dogs with inflamed gums or pus pockets can be infected with the human mouth ameba. In man it can be found in a high percentage of individuals, increasing with advancing age until, according to Kofoid, 75 per cent or more of people over 40 harbor it.

Endamoeba gingivalis markedly resembles *E. histolytica*. It is about 12 to 20 μ in diameter and has crystal-clear ectoplasm (Fig. 20). The vacuolated endoplasm is usually crowded with food particles which seem to float in the center of large, fluid cavities. The pseudopodia are normally broad and rounded, like large blisters, and the ameba normally progresses rapidly in various directions. The nucleus has the peripheral chromatin in rather uneven granules, and the endosome consists of several closely associated granules. Whereas the *E. histolytica* nucleus has a clear halo around the endosome and a finely granular outer zone between the halo and the nuclear membrane, *E. gingivalis* has a granular, cloudy halo, especially dense around the endosome, and a clear outer zone, through which a few spoke-like strands of linin run (Fig. 20*C*).

Unlike its close relatives this species fails to form cysts; apparently the ease and rapidity with which infections can spread from one human mouth to another do away with the biological necessity for cysts. As would be expected of an organism inhabiting the mouth, it is rather more adaptive to changing environmental conditions than are the intestinal amebas. It will survive for 20 minutes at a temperature of 45° C. and shows remarkable resistance to low temperatures. Miss Koch in 1927 showed that some amebas were still alive after 48 hours at 15° C. and some survived for 18 hours at the freezing point. They survive the shock of exposure to a wide range of hydrogen-ion concentration, and they are not at all fastidious as to the chemical constituents of a culture medium. They survive on a slide for 3 minutes

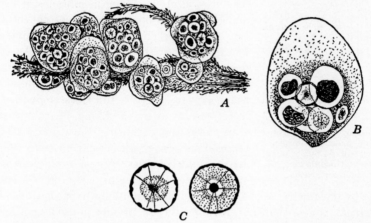

FIG. 20. *Endamoeba gingivalis.* *A*, cluster of amebas on filamentous mass of Leptothrix, containing large numbers of food vacuoles with remnants of nuclei of leucocytes; *B*, an ameba in locomotion with characteristic single broad pseudopodium; *C*, comparison of nuclei of *E. gingivalis* (left) and *E. histolytica* (right). (After Kofoid and Swezy.)

after all visible moisture has disappeared, the minute amount of water retained by tiny particles of coagulated egg from the culture being enough to keep them alive.

The food vacuoles of *Endamoeba gingivalis* sometimes contain bacteria, but they most often contain what are unquestionably the nuclei of leucocytes, in various stages of digestion (Fig. 20). Goodey and Wellings in 1917 concluded that these were " salivary corpuscles," i.e., nuclei of disintegrating leucocytes, which are abundant in saliva, but Child in 1926 found undoubted evidence of the ingestion of whole leucocytes as well as remnants of dead ones, and in cultures Miss Howitt in 1926 found that they ingest both red blood corpuscles and leucocytes. She also observed that red corpuscles lying near them faded from view in a few minutes, indicating histolytic action, which may also be effective against leucocytes and tissue cells.

Pathogenicity. Although the presence of amebas in the mouth has been known for many years, no one took much interest in them until

Bass and Johns in 1914 and Barrett in 1915 demonstrated an apparent relation between these mouth inhabitants and the presence of pus pockets between the teeth and gums, a disease known as pyorrhea,

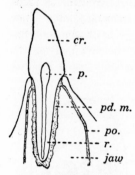

FIG. 21. Sketch of tooth showing peridental membrane, where *Endamoeba gingivalis* attacks, and where pyorrhea develops; *cr.*, crown; *p.*, pulp; *pd. m.*, peridental membrane; *po.*, periosteum; *r.*, root.

from which a high percentage of human beings suffer. These little pockets erode the delicate peridental membrane surrounding the roots of the teeth (Fig. 21), which corresponds in a general way to the periosteum of the bones. The erosion of the living membranes of teeth and gums is accompanied by a constant formation of pus and a proneness of the gums to bleed, often without provocation. As the ulceration of the membrane continues, the tooth is gradually loosened from the gum. Just as meadow mice girdle fruit trees, so pyorrheal infections eat away the living " bark " of the teeth, eventually causing them to fall out. Over 50 per cent of all permanent teeth which are lost fall out as the result of pyorrhea.

Whether the formation of pus pockets is initiated by the amebas or by other organisms is not known, but *Endamoeba gingivalis* is nearly always, perhaps always, present in the lesions, and at the very bottom of them, often buried in the inflamed tissues.

After this ameba had had the spotlight turned on it for two or three years on account of its apparent association with pyorrhea, it fell into obscurity again with almost as dramatic suddenness because a number of workers, including Craig, Dobell, and others, vigorously denied its claim to prominence. Their arguments were based principally on the frequent occurrence of the ameba in apparently normal mouths, its occasional absence in cases of pyorrhea, and particularly the failure of emetin, which acts so powerfully against *E. histolytica*, to bring about improvement in the disease, and the assertion that the ameba feeds only on dead and disintegrating tissues.

Interest in this little parasite was revived by Kofoid and some of his students. From a survey of 350 individuals by Hinshaw in 1926, using the cultural method of diagnosis, which is more accurate than microscopic examination, it was concluded that protozoan parasites do not occur in normal mouths, whereas *E. gingivalis* occurs in most, if not all, cases of incipient to advanced pyorrhea. The further demonstration that this ameba ingests both red corpuscles and leucocytes, and perhaps even excretes a tissue-dissolving enzyme, leaves the burden of proof with those who believe in its innocence.

The amebas are often very localized in the mouth and are only present in the pus pockets. They do not tolerate association with putrefactive bacteria of decaying debris and so cannot be regarded as scavengers. Apparently they cluster about on the strands of filamentous bacteria which are involved in the formation of tartar, and prey upon the nuclei of the swarming leucocytes, without invading the adjacent gum tissue (Fig. 20A). The bony tissue between the teeth and below the level of the tartar is extensively eroded without accompanying evidence of infection by either bacteria or amebas. The host reacts to the stimulus of this combination of bacteria, amebas, and tartar by an active and continuous accumulation of leucocytes and resulting flow of pus. Even if the amebas do not actually initiate the ulcerations but merely find a pleasant field of activity in them after bacteria have started them, one must be very generous to absolve them from complicity in their extension. The amebas exhibit a peculiar adhesive quality and frequently drag along behind them large clumps of bacteria; such transportation of bacteria to the depths of the pus pockets may in itself be injurious, even if the amebas do not directly attack other tissues than the leucocytes.

Pyorrhea is not the only pathological condition with which *E. gingivalis* is associated. The parasite was found by Smith, Middleton, and Barrett to be a common invader of the crypts of infected tonsils, where, as in the mouth, it may be presumed to do some mechanical injury if it does not actually attack the living tissues. The same authors suggested a possible relation, through injury to the tonsils, to certain types of goiter.

Treatment and Prevention. Ordinary cleanliness of the mouth by frequent brushing of teeth, rinsing of the mouth and care of imperfect teeth is the most important factor in protecting the gums against the formation of pus pockets, but such methods are of little or no avail after the disease has started. No good remedy is known for amebic infections of the mouth.

Though it is still uncertain to what extent, if at all, amebas are involved in causing or aggravating pyorrhea, it would seem to be the course of wisdom to avoid them as far as possible. They are undoubtedly spread not only directly from mouth to mouth, as in kissing, but also by minute droplets expelled in coughing or sneezing, and by means of drinking glasses, spoons, etc., on which it is evident that they can live as long as a trace of moisture remains. It is probably impossible, however, to avoid occasional infection with *E. gingivalis*. One cannot always make a protozoological examination of a mouth before indulging in a kiss, nor can one be sure that a cook has not coughed during the preparation of a meal.   If, however, the mouth is kept scrupulously clean and in as near perfect condition as possible, the amebas may be less likely to find a congenial place to settle down; in most mouths, on the other hand, plenty of hospitality is offered to them.

REFERENCES

ANDREWS, J., The Transmission of *Endamoeba histolytica* and Amebic Disease, *Southern Med. J.*, **35**, 693–699 (1942).

BALAMUTH, W., Improved Egg Yolk Infusion for Cultivation of *Endamoeba histolytica* and Other Intestinal Protozoa, *Am. J. Clin. Path.*, **16**, 380–384 (1946).

BOECK, W. C. and DRBOHLAV, J., The Cultivation of *Endamoeba histolytica*, *Am. J. Hyg.*, **5**, 371 (1925).

BROOKE, M. M., and GOLDMAN, M., Polyvinyl Alcohol-Fixative as a Preservative and Adhesive Solution for Staining Protozoa in Dysenteric Stools and Other Liquid Materials, *J. Parasitol.*, **34**, Suppl. 12 (1948).

CHINN, B. D., JACOBS, L., REARDON, L. V., and REES, C. W., The Influence of the Bacterial Flora on the Cultivation of *Endamoeba histolytica*, *Am. J. Trop. Med.*, **22**, 137–146 (1942)

CRAIG, C. F., *Etiology, Diagnosis and Treatment of Amebiasis*, Baltimore, 1944.
 Some Unsolved Problems in the Parasitology of Amebiasis, *J. Parasitol.*, **22**, 1 (1936).

D'ANTONI, J. S., Amebiasis, Recent Concepts of its Prevalence, Symptomatology, Diagnosis and Treatment, Reprint from *New Intern. Clinics*, **1**, ser. 5, 101–109 (1942).

DOBELL, C., *The Amoebae Living in Man*, London, 1919.
 Researches on the Intestinal Protozoa of Monkeys and Man, I, II, *Parasitology*, **20**, 357 (1928); III, *ibid.*, **21**, 446 (1929); IV, *ibid.*, **23**, 1 (1931); V, *ibid.*, 436 (1933); VIII, *ibid.*, **28**, 541 (1936); IX, *ibid.*, **30**, 195 (1938).

DOBELL, C., and O'CONNOR, F. W., *The Intestinal Protozoa of Man*, London, 1921.

FAUST, E. C., The *Endamoeba coli* Index of *E. histolytica* in a Community, *Am. J. Trop. Med.*, **10**, 137 (1930).
 The Prevalence of Amebiasis in the Western Hemisphere, *Am. J. Trop. Med.*, **22**, 93–105 (1941).

FAUST, E. C., SAWITZ, W., TOBIE, J., ODOM, V., PEREZ, C., and LINCICOME, D. R., Comparative Efficiency of Various Technics for the Diagnosis of Protozoa and Helminths in Feces, *J. Parasitol.*, **25**, 241 (1939).

FRYE, W. W., and MELENEY, H. C., The Cultivation of *Endamoeba histolytica* in Erlenmeyer Flasks, *Science*, **81**, 2091 (1935).

HAKANSSON, E. G., *Dientamoeba fragilis*, A Cause of Illness, *Am. J. Trop. Med.*, **16**, 175 (1936).

JAMES, W. M., Human Amebiasis due to Infection with *Endamoeba histolytica*, *Ann. Trop. Med. Parasitol.*, **22**, 201 (1928).

KOFOID, C. A., The Protozoa of the Human Mouth, *J. Parasitol.*, **15**, 151 (1929).

MELENEY, H. E., and FRYE, W. W., The Pathogenicity of *Endamoeba histolytica*, *Trans. Roy. Soc. Trop. Med. Hyg.*, **29**, 369 (1936).

NELSON, E. C., Alcoholic Media for the Diagnosis and Cultivation of *Endamoeba histolytica*, *Am. J. Trop. Med.*, **27**, 545–552 (1947).

SAPERO, J. J., Clinical Studies in Non-Dysenteric Intestinal Amebiasis, *Am. J. Trop. Med.*, **19**, 497 (1939).

SAPERO, J. J., and JOHNSON, C. M., An Evaluation of the Role of the Food Handler in the Transmission of Amebiasis, *Am. J. Trop. Med.*, **19**, 255 (1939).

SAWITZ, W. G., and FAUST, E. C., The Probability of Detecting Intestinal Protozoa by Successive Stool Examinations. *Am. J. Trop. Med.*, **22**, 131–136 (1942).

SHRAPNEL, B. C., Oral Emetine in the Treatment of Intestinal Amebiasis, *Am. J. Trop. Med.*, **27**, 527–544 (1947).

WENRICH, D. H., Studies on *Dientamoeba fragilis* (Protozoa)—IV. Further Observations, with an Outline of Present-Day Knowledge of this Species, *J. Parasitol.*, **30**, 322–328 (1944).

——— Studies on *Iodamoeba bütschlii* (Protozoa) with Special Reference to Nuclear Structure, *Proc. Am. Phil. Soc.*, **77**, 183 (1937).

WENRICH, D. H., STABLER, R. M., and ARNETT, J. H., *Endamoeba histolytica* and Other Intestinal Protozoa in 1060 College Freshmen, *Am. J. Trop. Med.*, **15**, 331 (1935).

WESTPHAL, A., Zur Epidemiologie und Pathogenese der Amöbenruhr in Nordafrika, *Z. Hyg. Infektionskrankh.*, **128**, 73–86 (1948).

CHAPTER 6

Intestinal Flagellates and Ciliates

Flagellates in General

The flagellates (class Mastigophora) surpass all other Protozoa in numbers of individuals and in variety of environments successfully occupied. Free-living forms range from the " red snows " of the polar regions and Alpine summits to the ooze of the ocean's depths. They swarm in seas, lakes, rivers, puddles, and soil; they abound in decaying organic matter, and in feces and sewage, and play a part in the transformations attendant upon putrefaction and decay; they inhabit the bodies of the majority of species of animals and many plants, and invade most organs and tissues, even to the innermost recesses of the human brain. They may nourish themselves as plants do by utilizing sunlight and chlorophyll, as animals by actively devouring living or dead organisms, as bacteria or fungi by absorbing dissolved organic matters, or as parasites by preying on living animals which harbor them. They afford valuable material for the study of many fundamental biological problems.

Classification. The classification of this great group of primitive organisms is still in an uncertain state. They are usually divided into two subclasses: Phytomastigina and Zoömastigina. The former include plantlike forms which possess chromatophores bearing green or yellow pigments by means of which they are capable of photosynthesis, and a few obviously related forms which have evidently lost their chromatophores, just as some insects have lost their wings. Calkins eliminated these forms from the Protozoa altogether and placed them in the plant kingdom, which seems too much like splitting a town that happens to be situated on a state line. It emphasizes the rationality of recognizing a group " Protista " to include all unicellular animals, as suggested on pp. 32–33.

The Zoömastigina are the only forms that concern us here. Kudo (1939) divided them into four orders, but Kirby recognized an additional order, Trichomonadida, for a group characterized by a certain type of parabasal body and nucleus and the presence of an axostyle. The division into families is a matter on which hardly two texts agree;

116

the system followed in Craig and Faust's *Clinical Parasitology* (1943) is as logical as any as far as families are concerned, and so it is adopted here.

Order 1. **Rhizomastigida.** Body with both pseudopodia and flagella.
Family 1. *Rhizomastigidae.* Includes Histomonas (see p. 131).
Order 2. **Protomonadida.** One flagellum, no cytostome or axostyle.
Family 1. *Trypanosomidae.* Includes hemoflagellates (see Chapter 7).
Order 3. **Polymastigida.** Two or more flagella; no axostyle.
Family 1. *Embadomonadidae.* Ovoid body, anterior nucleus, cytostome, 1 anteriorly directed and 1 posteriorly directed flagellum, the latter in cytostome. Includes only Embadomonas (see p. 130).
Family 2. *Cercomonadidae.* One or more anterior flagella, and 1 posterior, adhering to body part of length. Includes Enteromonas (see p. 131), and the coprozoic forms, Bodo and Cercomonas (see p. 119).
Family 3. *Chilomastigidae.* Oval or pear-shaped, 3 anterior flagella, 1 posteriorly directed; one in cytostome. Includes only Chilomastix.
Family 4. *Hexamitidae* (*Octomitidae* in Craig and Faust). Six to eight flagella in pairs, and body bilaterally symmetrical with 2 nuclei. Contains Giardia and Hexamita (see pp. 127 and 132).
Order 4. **Trichomonadida.** Three to five anterior, and 1 trailing flagellum; axostyle present; parabasal body and nucleus of Trichomonas type.
Family 1. *Trichomonadidae.* Undulating membrane and costa present. Includes Trichomonas (see p. 119).
Order 5. **Hypermastigida.** Highly specialized bodies with numerous flagella; parasites or symbionts of termites and other insects.

For convenience we can divide all the flagellates found in man and domestic animals into two groups, the hemoflagellates and the intestinal flagellates. The hemoflagellates live in the blood, lymph, and tissues of their vertebrate hosts and usually pass one phase of their life cycle in the gut of insects. All these belong to the family Trypanosomidae and will be considered in the next chapter. The intestinal flagellates will be considered in the present chapter, along with the allied forms found in the mouth and vagina. At the end of the chapter we shall also present a brief discussion of intestinal ciliates, only one species of which is a true parasite of man, though many are commensals in the alimentary canals of large herbivorous animals. The coccidians, some of which are important parasites of the digestive tracts of many birds and mammals, will be reserved for consideration in Chapter 10, along with other Sporozoa.

Intestinal Flagellates

The human "intestinal" flagellates which are commonly recognized belong to five genera, of which Trichomonas lives in the mouth, large intestine, and vagina; Chilomastix, and probably the rarer

Embadomonas and Enteromonas, live in the large intestine; and Giardia lives in the small intestine. In addition to these we shall briefly consider Histomonas, a parasite of the intestine, ceca, and liver of turkeys, and Hexamita, in the intestine of various birds.

In some respects nearly all the flagellates which make their home in the digestive tracts of animals resemble one another. Nearly all of them, with the conspicuous exception of Trichomonas, secrete for themselves cyst walls which protect them from drying up or from the presence of an unfavorable medium; it is in the encysted state that transfer to a new host is usually accomplished. None of the human intestinal flagellates requires a second host to transmit it as do the blood-dwelling parasites. While outside the body they remain dormant in their cysts for weeks or months until they can again gain access to a host through food or water.

All the intestinal flagellates except Giardia are easily cultivated in artificial media and are less fastidious about their culture media than *Endamoeba histolytica*, although any medium satisfactory for this ameba will also grow the intestinal flagellates. A simple and successful culture consists of a long slant of 1.5 per cent nutrient agar, without a butt, half covered with a sterile Ringer solution with 1/20 part of horse serum added. For *Trichomonas vaginalis* the slant should be three-quarters covered, the pH lowered to 5.5 to 6, and 0.2 per cent dextrose added. It has been customary to subculture every few days, but Wenrich found that, if the nutrients and evaporated water are replaced as needed, cultures will live possibly for years.

Some of the intestinal flagellates appear to be harmless commensals; such are Chilomastix, Embadomonas, and Enteromonas. Trichomonas and Giardia, on the other hand, unquestionably have pathogenic propensities, although some authors tend either to minimize or exaggerate them.

There is still much doubt as to the extent to which intestinal protozoans are confined to particular hosts. Some workers believe that each animal has its own species peculiar to it, and that these species do not normally infect other hosts. Evidence is accumulating, however, to show that many intestinal protozoans of man are able to live in such animals as monkeys, rats, and hogs.

Naturally these parasites are seldom discovered except when there is some intestinal ailment, since in normal health feces are seldom submitted for examination. Where routine examinations have been made regardless of physical condition, it has been found that a large percentage of people in unsanitary places are infected. Stiles, in a town in one of our southern states, found that from 50 to 100 per cent of the children were infected with intestinal protozoans; and it would probably be easily within the bounds of truth to say that 75 per cent of all people in warm countries, living in places where unsanitary conditions prevail, are subject to infection with one or several species of intestinal protozoans.

It is important to remember that free-living, coprozoic flagellates not infrequently appear in stale specimens of feces or urine, and may be a cause of confusion to unsuspecting technicians. Especially common are species of Bodo and Cercomonas, 5 to 10 μ long, both of which have two flagella, one anterior and one trailing. Bodo has an indistinct cytostome and parabasal body, which Cercomonas lacks.

Trichomonas

General Morphology. The trichomonads (Fig. 22) are all spindle- or pear-shaped organisms easily recognizable by their free anterior flagella, which are from three to five in number, and their undulating membrane. The latter has a flagellum and an accessory fibril along its outer margin, giving it a double appearance, and a deep-staining basal rod or costa along its attachment to the body. The body is supported by a stiff axostyle often protruding posteriorly like a tail spine. The anterior nucleus is round or oval with varying amounts of chromatin. In most species there is a sausage-shaped parabasal body anteriorly, close to the nucleus, with a posteriorly directed parabasal fiber. In *T. hominis* the parabasal seemed to be lacking, but Kirby (1945) noted a small rounded one in a slightly different position. The anterior flagella, when three or four in number, arise together from an anterior blepharoplast; when a fifth is present it arises separately and is posteriorly directed. A cytostome is present, in some species well developed, in others vestigial; in the latter there are few or no food vacuoles. All these structures are shown in Figs. 22 and 23.

Species. Many vertebrates, including fish, frogs, reptiles, birds, and mammals, harbor species of Trichomonas. Some of these species habitually have three, some four, and some five anterior flagella. By some authors these have been placed in separate genera, Tritrichomonas, Trichomonas, and Pentatrichomonas, respectively. There has long been a belief that the human intestinal species, *T. hominis*, unlike other forms, may have either three, four or five flagella, and there is still some uncertainty about it, since two or more of the clustered anterior flagella tend to adhere to each other. Kirby (1945) thinks the five-flagellated form is the common if not the only form, but Wenrich (1947) hesitates to accept this view. The common five-flagellated form differs from other species not only in having the additional independent flagellum, but also in having a full-length undulating membrane and costa, free posterior flagellum, and a different type of parabasal body. These characteristics are sufficient to warrant separating these five-flagellated intestinal forms into a separate genus Pentatrichomonas. They occur not only in man but also in monkeys, cats, dogs,

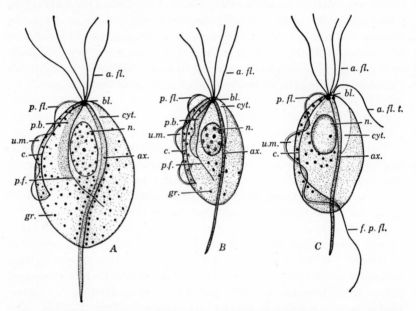

Fig. 22. Trichomonads of man. *A*, *T. vaginalis;* *B*, *T. tenax;* *C*, *T. hominis.* Abbrev.: *a. fl.*, anterior flagella; *a. fl. t.*, trailing anterior flagellum; *ax.*, axostyle; *bl.*, blepharoplast; *c.*, costa; *cyt.*, cytostome; *f. p. fl.*, free posterior flagellum; *gr.*, metachromatic granules; *n.*, nucleus; *p.b.*, parabasal body; *p.f.*, parabasal fibril; *p. fl.*, posterior flagellum with accessory fibril; *u.m.*, undulating membrane. (After Wenrich.)

and rats. Wenrich, however, prefers to be conservative and retain the name *Trichomonas hominis* for the intestinal group until the status of four- and five-flagellated forms is determined.

Many forms of Trichomonas show distinctive morphological and physiological characters, which warrant their recognition as distinct species. There is, however, no justification for recognizing new species simply because they are found in new hosts, since, to the annoyance of those who adhere to a belief in fairly close host specificity for intestinal Protozoa, many trichomonads are remarkably promiscuous about their hosts. *T. gallinae*, for instance, a common pathogen of pigeons, can establish itself in chickens, turkeys, hawks, parakeets, and sparrows, and *T. hominis* can be established in monkeys, cats, and rats.

Trichomonads are more finicky about their habitats in the body than they are about their hosts. *T. hominis* and *T. gallinarum* inhabit the lower alimentary canal; *T. gallinae* the throat, esophagus, and crop; *T. tenax, canistomae,* and *equibuccalis* the gums about the roots of the teeth; *T. vaginalis* the vagina and prostate; and *T. foetus* the vagina and uterus of cows and the preputial cavity of bulls. One three-flagellated species, *T. faecalis,* recovered repeatedly from the feces of a single human being, grew in fecal and hay infusions and was successfully established in frogs and tadpoles. Wenrich suspects that this species may be identical with *T. batrachorum* of Amphibia.

Trichomonads vary in pathogenicity from the harmless coprozoic form *T. faecalis* to highly pathogenic species like *T. foetus* and *T. gallinae* (see pp. 125–126). Fortunately the pathogenicity of the species found in man is relatively low.

There has been much dispute as to whether the three species in man — *vaginalis, hominis,* and *tenax* — are distinct species, but it is now definitely established that they are, since they differ in both morphology and physiology, and are not transferable from one habitat to another. *T. vaginalis* and *T. tenax* resemble each other more than they resemble *T. hominis.*

Miss Bonestell in 1936 succeeded, as have others, in establishing *T. hominis,* but not *vaginalis* or *tenax,* in the large intestines of kittens, and she could establish *tenax,* but not the others, in the mouths of kittens. *T. vaginalis* has not been established elsewhere than in the human vagina, probably because here alone it finds suitably high acidity (*p*H 4 to 5). Stabler *et al.* (1941, 1942) in a series of 151 trials failed to implant *T. hominis* in human vaginas; in most cases they disappeared in a few hours and in no case survived for 48. *T. tenax* also failed to establish itself permanently, though in two cases it survived for 7 and 18 days respectively.

Biology. Trichomonads swim with a characteristic wobbly or rolling motion; sometimes they use their flagella to whirl their bodies about while anchored to a bit of debris by the axostyle. In worming their way through devious passages they can squeeze their bodies, especially the fore part, into distorted shapes. The intestinal forms feed extensively on bacteria and all sorts of debris, but the vaginal and buccal forms taken from their natural environment seldom contain any solid food except leucocytes or their remains, although in cultures they contain bacteria. Probably all species feed in part by absorption of dissolved substances.

Multiplication is by simple fission, but when it is rapid the division of the cytoplasm may fail to keep pace with growth and nuclear division, so that large multinucleate bodies are occasionally formed. No sexual phenomena have been observed.

No evidence exists that any of the species encyst. The trophozoites are apparently hardy enough to live outside the body long enough to be transferred to new hosts. *T. hominis* lives in undiminished numbers for several hours, and in some individuals for days, in the feces, and will survive a day or two in water or milk. *T. tenax* will live for several days in tapwater at room temperature; in mixed material Stabler *et al.* found *T. tenax*, but not *T. vaginalis*, to survive when held at 16° to 18° C. for 48 hours before incubating at 37° C. *T. vaginalis* survives less readily than the others, and its means of transfer from host to host is somewhat of a mystery, although it is often transmitted venereally, and for brief periods by contaminated toilet seats, etc. Most species of Trichomonas can be grown readily on various culture media containing serum or blood. *T. vaginalis* does best on liver infusion agar overlaid with 5 per cent human serum in Ringer's solution at a *p*H about 5.5 or by the method described on p. 118. Johnson, Trussell, and Jahn (1945) succeeded in obtaining bacteria-free cultures of *T. vaginalis* with the help of penicillin. *T. foetus* and *T. gallinae* can also be cultivated free of bacteria, but not *T. hominis*.

Trichomonas vaginalis (Fig. 22A). This is a very common human parasite. Various authors in many parts of the world have reported it in from 20 to 40 per cent or more of women where unselected series of examinations have been made, whereas in series of cases with leucorrheic conditions the organism is commonly found in from 50 to as many as 70 per cent of patients examined. The incidence is nearly twice as high in Negro women as in white.

This is the largest of the trichomonads found in man; it varies in length from about 10 to 30 μ, but most individuals are usually between 15 and 20 μ long. There are four anterior flagella and a short undulating membrane which seldom reaches beyond the middle of the body. The axostyle projects as a slender spike at the posterior end, and the organism is frequently seen to anchor itself to debris by this structure. The nucleus is oval and contains rather scanty chromatin scattered in granules. Deep-staining granules are also abundant in the cytoplasm, many of them in rows beside the axostyle or along the costa. The cytostome is very inconspicuous, and the body contains few food vacuoles, although leucocytes or their remains are occasionally seen. A parabasal apparatus is also present, in the form of a sausage-shaped, rather faintly staining body lying beside the nucleus, and a more slender but deeper-staining fibril reaching to near the middle of the body.

T. vaginalis inhabits the vagina primarily, but also invades Skene's glands in the urethra; it is only occasionally found in other parts of the female urinogenital system. It also occurs in the urethra and prostate of from 4 to 15 per cent of men. Repeated reinfection from the sexual partner has frequently been found to account for infections in women that seemed refractory to treatment. *T. vaginalis* often grows in abundance in the upper part of the vagina around the cervix but seems to show no tendency to invade the uterus as does *T. foetus* in cattle (see p. 125). It occasionally occurs in the urinary bladder, but care must be taken not to confuse it with coprozoic flagellates (see p. 119), which are frequently found in carelessly collected or stale urine.

The presence of *T. vaginalis* in the vagina is associated with a characteristic acid, creamy-white, frothy discharge which may be very abundant, and which to the experienced eye is usually sufficient for a diagnosis of the infection. The discharge often persists for months or years. The vulva becomes red and chafed, and the mucosa of the vagina and cervix is congested, with a deep red mottling. Some patients complain of itching or irritation in the genital region, but many seem to have no symptoms other than the discharge. That Trichomonas is actually the cause of these symptoms has been proved by inoculation of bacteria-free cultures. Of 29 women, 9 became infected and 7 showed symptoms. The incubation period was from 5 to 20 days.

Bland, Wenrich, and Goldstein in a series of 250 cases found a significantly higher morbidity rate in childbirth in infected than in uninfected women, and they think that pregnant women with obvious infections should be treated and if possible freed of the parasites in the prenatal period.

Karnaky believes that *T. vaginalis* infections are associated with a lowered acidity of the vagina, along with a thinner epithelium and less glycogen in the cells. The normal high acidity of the mature human vagina is due to the presence of a flourishing culture of Döderlein bacilli, which are probably identical with *Bacillus acidophilus*. The bacteria feed on glycogen stored in the vaginal epithelial cells, and produce considerable amounts of lactic acid. It is this acid condition which makes the vagina normally unsusceptible to gonorrheal infection after puberty, although it is susceptible in children.

On the theory that Trichomonas will not thrive in a normally acid vagina, and that pathological conditions lower the acidity, decrease the thickness of the epithelium, and reduce the stored glycogen, Karnaky has recommended treatment with capsules containing (1) glucose and lactose to stimulate growth of the Döderlein bacillus; (2) boric acid to create an immediate acidity; (3) Floraquin, a proprietary mixture of Diodoquin (see p. 103), dextrose and lactose, to kill the parasites; and (4) corn starch as a carrier. The vagina is washed out with tincture of green soap followed by a boric acid douche, after which a Floraquin capsule is inserted once or twice a day for 2 or 3 weeks. Douches of diluted vinegar are also recommended. Karnaky claims a higher percentage of cures by this method than by any other and also recommends it for gonorrheal vulvovaginitis in children. Other methods consist of douches of 1 per cent picric acid, 0.5 per cent lactic acid, or various antiseptics; drying and blowing with kaolin, corn starch, etc., with or without arsenicals; packing with cotton treated with powders; etc. When the parasites penetrate into glands, however, surface treatments fail to cure, and no effective treatment via the general circulation has yet been reported.

Trichomonas tenax. This form of Trichomonas (Fig. 22*B*) resembles *T. vaginalis* very closely in most respects, but is smaller, usually only 6 to 10 μ in length. The nucleus has much more chromatin and often stains almost solid black, and the granules in the cytoplasm are scattered and less conspicuous. Formerly this was regarded as a rather uncommon parasite, but Hinshaw, using cultural methods, found it in 40 per cent of the people whom he examined who were above 30 years of age, but most of these had pyorrheic conditions. Beatman (1933) found it in more than 22 per cent of 350 examinations of adults in Philadelphia; the incidence was 26.5 per cent in diseased mouths and 11.4 per cent in apparently normal mouths. It is probably this species which is occasionally found in bronchial and pulmonary infections. The same or similar forms are found in the mouths of monkeys and also dogs.

Although this parasite has been found suspiciously associated with advanced inflammatory pyorrhea, its pathogenicity has not yet been proved. Along with *Endamoeba gingivalis* (see p. 110) it may well play some role, even if a minor one, in this disease. As already remarked (p. 113), there are no special means of treatment or prevention of this parasite; only oral cleanliness is of any value.

Intestinal Trichomonads. The question of whether there is more than one species of Trichomonas inhabiting the human intestine has not yet been settled to the satisfaction of all, but most parasitologists are now coming to the view that there is only one, *Trichomonas* or *Pentatrichomonas hominis*, which usually if not always has five anterior flagella.

T. hominis (Fig. 22*C*) is easily separable from *T. vaginalis* and *T. tenax* by the fact that the undulating membrane extends the full length of the body, the flagellum along its margin continuing free at the posterior end. The parabasal apparatus and chromatic granules are not usually in evidence, but there is a distinct cytostome and the body commonly contains food vacuoles. In size this species is intermediate, being commonly from 8 to 12 μ in length.

Although the pathogenicity of *T. hominis* has not been proved to the satisfaction of those who are skeptical about it, the infection is often associated with persistent diarrhea, for which some investigators

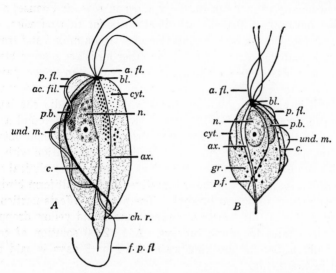

Fig. 23. *A, Trichomonas (Tritrichomonas) foetus* of cattle; *B, Trichomonas gallina*; of pigeons and other birds. Abbrev.: *ac. fil.*, accessory filament; *a. fl.*, anterior flagella; *ax.*, axostyle; *bl.*, blepharoplasts; *c.*, costa; *ch. r.*, chromatic ring; *cyt.*, cytostome; *f. p. fl.*, free posterior flagellum; *gr.*, metachromatic granules; *n.*, nucleus; *p.b.*, parabasal body; *p.f.*, parabasal fibril; *p. fl.*, posterior flagellum; *und. m.*, undulating membrane. (*A* after Wenrich and Emmerson, *J. Morphol.*; *B* after Stabler, *J. Morphol.*)

believe it responsible. Kessel in 1928 reported pathogenic effects in naturally and artificially infected kittens in China, but Hegner and Eskridge failed to confirm this in experiments in the United States. Treatment of intestinal trichomoniasis is considered on p. 135.

Trichomonads in Domestic Animals. Three important Trichomonas infections occur among domestic animals. *Trichomonas foetus* (Fig. 23*A*) is a world-wide common and injurious parasite in the genital tract of cattle; it can be experimentally established in sheep also. It is a venereal disease, transmitted from infected bulls to heifers, in which it attacks the mucous membrane of the vagina and invades the uterus, causing abortions, stillbirths, delayed conceptions, and other damage. After a number of months the animals overcome the disease and are immune to further infection. Bulls are usually infected in the preputial cavity and remain infected for life. Morgan in 1947 reported promise in the treatment of bulls with sodium iodide, but it has unpleasant effects, and after several injections both the bulls and the owners are uncooperative, so other chemotherapeutic agents are being tested.

Trichomonas gallinae of young pigeons and other birds (Fig. 23*B*) attacks the mucous membranes of the throat region and esophagus, and occasionally of ducts in the liver and pancreas, and causes a considerable mortality. Pigeons are ideal hosts for this parasite, since they feed their squabs by regurgitation of " pigeon milk " and transfer the parasites at the same time. Many other birds are susceptible, but chickens and pheasants are usually refractory. In an active state the infection causes caseation and necrosis of tissues in the mouth and throat and is called " canker." Birds which do not die continue to harbor the organisms for a long time. Stabler (1947) found a wide variation in the virulence of different strains in pigeons and obtained a high degree of immunity to severe strains by inoculation with relatively harmless ones. No treatment does much good for clinical cases.

T. gallinarum affects the lower digestive tract of galliform birds but is particularly injurious to turkeys. The parasite affects particularly the liver and ceca. It causes droopiness and liquid yellow droppings, and is often fatal to young turkeys. A 1 : 2000 solution of copper sulfate substituted for drinking water for 2 or 3 days is said to be helpful in treatment.

Chilomastix mesnili

This organism, often confused with Trichomonas by careless observers, inhabits the large intestine of about 3 to 10 per cent of human beings. Closely similar forms are found in all groups of vertebrates. They are common in both rats and frogs. Chilomastix (Fig. 24) is an unsymmetrical, pear-shaped animal which has its posterior end drawn out into a sharply pointed tail. It varies in length from 6 to 20 μ, but the usual length is from 10 to 15 μ. The body is less plastic than in Trichomonas, so there is less variability in shape. It has three slender anterior flagella which, like those of Trichomonas, function as two groups, two of them lashing back against the left side of the body, and one against the right. The relatively enormous cytostome is an oval groove half or more the length of the body, the lips of which are supported by a complicated system of fibers. Lying in this groove is a fourth flagellum, attached to the left lip by an undulating membrane; by its flickering movements this " tongue " wafts food

particles into the depths of the groove, where they pass into the body
to be enclosed in food vacuoles, with which the body is often literally
crammed. The nucleus lies in the fore part of the body just behind
the free flagella.

The animals do not move as rapidly as Trichomonas, and proceed
by a sort of jerky spiral movement unlike the continuous wobbly
progression of Trichomonas.

The ordinary multiplication is by simple fission, but sometimes large
multinucleate forms are produced. Unlike Trichomonas, Chilomastix
forms lemon-shaped cysts, narrower at the anterior end. The cysts

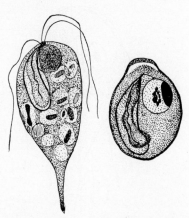

are usually about 7 to 9 μ long; they
have thin walls except where thickened at the anterior end, and the
fibers of the cytostome, practically
unaltered in form, lie alongside of or
overlapping the nucleus. Occasionally the nuclei and cytostomal fibers
are duplicated in the cysts, which
then presumably give rise to two
individuals when they hatch. The
cysts are very resistant and live for
months in water at room temperature, and for several days in the
intestine of flies. Boeck found that
a temperature of 72° C was necessary
to kill them.

Fig. 24.   *Chilomastix mesnili.* Left,
trophozoite; right, cyst.   × 3000. (After Boeck.)

There is little evidence that Chilomastix is pathogenic. Westphal
(1939), in experiments on himself, found this parasite and also *Enteromonas hominis* to fluctuate with the condition of the intestine, and considers their presence a result rather than the cause of intestinal
ailments with which they may be associated.

Giardia

Giardia, long known as Lamblia, is one of the commonest inhabitants of the human intestine, especially in children, and probably
affects at least 15 per cent of all human beings. Giardias also occur
extensively in various kinds of mammals and birds, and also in
amphibians. Most of those found in warm-blooded animals have only
minute, and for the most part average, differences, and their specific
distinctness is still open to question. Even within a single species,
e.g., *Giardia lamblia* of man, there are races which show slight morphological differences.

Morphology. Giardia is a most fantastic little animal in appearance. It is bilaterally symmetrical, with nucleus and all other parts reduplicated on the right and left sides. It is analogous to two Chilomastix-like flagellates fused together in the middle line. As Knowles remarks, the student's first sight of a dead Giardia, in its motile phase, is likely to give him a shock, for it is as if a wizened monkey face were looking up at him from the other end of the microscopic tube. The outline of the body is strikingly that of a tennis racket without the handle. In side view it is shaped like a pear split lengthwise in two

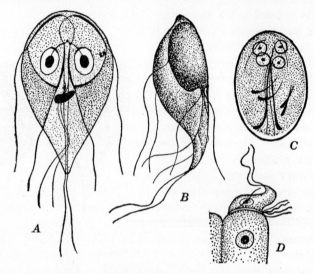

Fig. 25. *Giardia lamblia.* *A*, face view of trophozoite; *B*, semiprofile view; *C*, cyst; *D*, position of trophozoite resting on epithelial cell. *A*, *B*, and *C*, × 3000; *D*, × 1000. (*A* after Simon; *D* after Grassi and Schewiakoff; *B* and *C* original.)

parts, with the flat surface in the broadest part gouged out as a large concave sucking disc, with slightly raised margins. The finely tapering posterior end is usually turned up over the convex back. There are eight flagella, one pair attached posteriorly, the others emerging from the body at various points as shown in Fig. 25. They may be thought of as corresponding more or less to eyebrows, moustaches, and beard. The body is from 10 to 18 μ in length. The two nuclei have large central endosomes. Between them, running longitudinally through the body, are two slender rods, the axostyles, to which the nuclei are anchored by slender fibrils. There is a complicated system of basal granules and fibrils connecting with the flagella and the rods supporting the sucking disc, as shown in Fig. 25. Two deep-staining, rather variable comma-shaped bodies lying just behind the disc have been interpreted as parabasal bodies.

During encystment a thick wall is secreted, and the cyst assumes an oval form, measuring 8 to 14 μ in length, commonly about 10 μ; usually the contents shrink away a little from the posterior end, leaving an empty space. At first the cyst contains a sort of " shadow outline " of the motile animal, the two nuclei situated anteriorly, the axostyle rods lying more or less diagonally, and a pair of curved, deep-staining parabasals. Division takes place in the cyst, first of the nuclei and then of the fibrils, and there may be even further multiplication. Usually the four nuclei, now spherical, are clustered at one end, but they sometimes come to lie in pairs at opposite poles. Division is not completed until after the cysts hatch.

Biology. Unlike any of the other intestinal flagellates, Giardia ordinarily makes its home in the small intestine, especially in the duodenum, although Faust (1931) found it to develop frequently in the large intestine in dogs infected through the rectum. Hegner, however, found Giardias of both rat and human origin to localize only in the upper part of the small intestine of rats, and showed that they were attracted by bile salts.

In life these grotesque little creatures fasten themselves by their hollow faces to the convex surfaces of epithelial cells in the small intestine, their flagella streaming like the barbels of a catfish (Fig. 25D). Sometimes large areas of epithelium are practically covered with them, each one perched on a separate cell. Their vast numbers can be judged from the fact that in one instance Miss Porter estimated the number of cysts in a single stool to exceed 14,000,000,000. The number of cysts in an average stool in a case of moderate infection she estimated at over 300,000,000. The motile forms are not normally found in the stools, but in cases of diarrhea dead ones may be present in considerable numbers. They do not ingest solid food, nor do they appear to dissolve tissue cells; possibly they feed on the abundant secretion of mucus which their presence seems to stimulate.

Multiplication occurs by division into two in a plane parallel with the broad surfaces, and occasionally multiple fission occurs as in other intestinal flagellates. The cysts are formed intermittently; enormous numbers may be found on one day and then none for several days, when a shower of them again appears. Occasionally fecal examination fails to reveal them even when they are present in the duodenum in large numbers. The cysts remain alive in feces for 10 days or more and survive many days in the gut of roaches. The parasite is a very persistent one; infections sometimes last for many years, possibly in some cases for life.

Pathogenicity. There is no longer any doubt of the pathogenicity of Giardia. Véghelyi in 1939 found evidence of mechanical interference with absorption, particularly of fats, from the intestine by the layer of parasites adhering to its wall. It is obvious that this might lead to vitamin deficiencies, particularly of the fat-soluble ones. The presence of large amounts of unabsorbed fats in the stools causes a persistent or recurring diarrhea, often with large amounts of yellow mucus. The symptoms may resemble those of celiac disease, sprue, or chronic gall bladder disease. Epigastric pains, vague abdominal discomfort, loss of appetite, apathy, headache, etc., may be present. In some cases, on the other hand, there are no evident symptoms.

Occasionally the parasites are found in the bile ducts and even in the gall bladder. It is possible that they may cause some irritation in the bile ducts and predispose them to chronic infection, but the evidence for this is inconclusive. For treatment, see p. 135.

Other Intestinal Flagellates

A few other flagellates may be residents of the human intestine, but they are relatively rare and of little importance.

Embadomonas intestinalis. This little slipper-shaped animal, which Wenrich believes should be called *Retortamonas intestinalis*, was first discovered in Egypt but has subsequently been found in many parts of the world, though always rare. The fact that members of the same genus occur in various insects, especially aquatic ones, and in frogs and turtles, suggests that the infections of man and other mammals in which they have been found may perhaps be derived from the swallowing of cysts of some insect or aquatic species with water. Its rarity makes it doubtful that it is normally a human parasite.

Embadomonas (Fig. 26A and B) is very small, only 4 to 9 μ in length and 3 to 4 μ in breadth; it has two flagella, a long, slender, anterior one, and a shorter, thicker one which lies partly in a large, elongated cytostome the borders of which appear to have supporting fibers. The nucleus is anterior in position. The cysts are whitish, opalescent, pear-shaped bodies, 4.5 to 6 or 7 μ long when living. When stained they show what appears to be the endosome of the nucleus, sometimes dumbbell-shaped, and fibers which Wenyon interprets as the marginal fibers of the cytostome.

Faust described another species, *E. sinensis*, from China; it is larger and is said to have the two flagella alike, but Wenyon believes it to be identical with *E. intestinalis*. It was found in 9 cases with diarrheic stools, and was again reported from 2 cases in China by Watt in 1933. It has been successfully cultivated, and seems to be a valid species.

Enteromonas hominis. This small flagellate, also called *Tricercomonas intestinalis* (Fig. 26C and D), is an oval or pear-shaped organism, 4 to 10 µ in length and 3 to 6 µ broad, slightly flattened on one side, where a flagellum is attached until it becomes free at the posterior end. There is also a cluster of three anterior flagella. Small oval cysts 6 to 8 µ long are formed which have well-developed cyst walls, giving them a double outline, and from one to four nuclei, visible only when stained. In cysts with two or four nuclei these are arranged at opposite ends. The parasite has been reported from many parts of

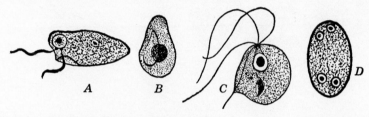

FIG. 26.   *A* and *B*, *Embadomonas* (or *Retortamonas*) *intestinalis*, trophozoite and cyst; *C* and *D*, *Enteromonas* (or *Tricercomonas*) *intestinalis*. × 3000. (After Wenyon and O'Connor.)

the world, but it is always rare and probably accidental. There is no evidence that it is pathogenic, and it persists in the human intestine for only a few days or weeks.

Intestinal Flagellates of Domestic Animals

Although all species of vertebrate animals are probably parasitized by a number of species of flagellates, pathogenic effects are produced in only a few cases. Certain species of Trichomonas (see p. 125) are exceptions. Giardia has been reported as sometimes causing severe damage to rabbits and dogs, and the writer has seen dogs with intermittent attacks of diarrhea of the type associated with Giardia infections. Other important flagellates are *Histomonas meleagridis* and *Hexamita* spp.

Histomonas meleagridis. This important parasite of galliform birds (Fig. 27A, B, C) causes " blackhead " in turkeys. It is found both in the ceca and liver, and occasionally in the kidney. It is an ameboid organism 8 to 10 µ in diameter, with a small eccentric nucleus with a blepharoplast on or near the nuclear membrane. From this arise from ' one to four flagella in the intestinal forms, often, however, not extending beyond the cell wall.   Organisms in the tissues have no flagella. The organism fails to produce cysts and lives for a very short time when passed in the droppings, but it has developed an excellent means of transfer to new hosts by becoming enclosed inside the eggshells of cecal worms, Heterakis (see p. 428). When embryonated eggs of Heterakis are fed to turkey poults a high mortality from blackhead results.   In nature turkeys are infected by worm eggs passed from healthy chicken carriers; this is the principal reason why it is usually

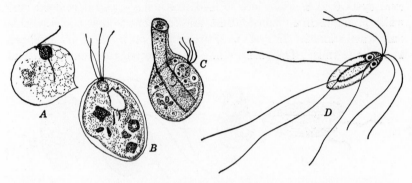

Fig. 27.   *A–C, Histomonas meleagridis;* *A,* tissue form with one flagellum and cytoplasmic fibril; *B,* lumen form with four flagella; *C,* lumen form with cytoplasmic process engulfing bacteria; *D, Hexamita meleagridis.*   (*A* and *B* after Tyzzer; *C* after Wenrich; *D* after McNeil, Hinshaw, and Kofoid.)

disastrous to try to raise chickens and turkeys together.   According to Barger and Card (1943) Mapharsen shows some promise in treatment.

Hexamita spp. A number of species of Hexamita occur in various vertebrates. They are more or less elongated flagellates with two anterior nuclei, four anterior flagella in pairs, and two which arise anteriorly but pass posteriorly through the body to emerge near the posterior end (Fig. 27*D*).   These parasites cause a severe diarrhea in young turkeys and pigeons. Quail, partridges, and chicks suffer less. According to McNeil, Hinshaw, and Kofoid (1941), *H. meleagridis* of turkeys and *H. columbae* of other birds are two distinct species. *H. columbae* was not transferable to turkeys, and *H. meleagridis* caused only temporary infections in chickens and ducks.

Intestinal Ciliates

All the intestinal ciliates of warm-blooded animals belong to the Subclass Euciliata (see p. 43). Amphibia, on the other hand, have the rectum inhabited by many species of Opalinidae, which belong in the Subclass Protociliata.

The Euciliata are divided by Kudo into four orders as follows:

Order 1. **Holotricha.** No adoral zone of flattened cilia or membranelles. Includes Paramecium and many coprozoic ciliates, but no parasites of higher vertebrates.

Order 2. **Spirotricha.** Adoral zone of membranelles winding clockwise to cytostome, the peristome (mouth region) not protruded. Two suborders contain parasites of vertebrates: *Heterotricha,* with body covered with cilia, includes Balantidium; *Oligotricha,* with body nonciliated, but with adoral and other zones of membranelles, includes numerous species in stomach of ruminants and colon of horses.

Order 3. **Chonotricha.** Like Order 2, but peristome protruding like a funnel. No vertebrate parasites.

Order 4. **Peritricha.** Body not entirely ciliated; anterior region disclike with counterclockwise adoral zone of membranelles. Example, Vorticella. None parasitic in vertebrates.

The stomachs of ruminants and the large intestine of horses harbor numerous species of commensal ciliates belonging to the suborder Oligotricha. They may play some part in the digestion of cellulose in these animals. One of the species from ruminants is shown in Fig. 2 (p. 34).

Balantidium coli. This is a parasite of the large intestine of man, monkeys, and pigs. A parasite in rats identical with *B. coli* was reported from Moscow; and rats can be experimentally infected. McDonald, in 1922, believed that the pig harbors another species, a *B. suis,* which is not infective for man, but Hegner, in 1934, doubted this.

B. coli (Fig. 28), as found in man, is much larger than any of the other protozoan inhabitants of the human intestine and usually measures from 50 to 80 μ in length, with a breadth between two thirds and three fourths as great. In pigs it sometimes reaches a length of 200 μ. It is shaped like an egg or pear, and has at the anterior end an obliquely arranged depression, the peristome, which may appear wide open or slitlike, and in the bottom of which is the cytostome. The whole body is covered with fine cilia arranged in rows, with a special row of longer " adoral " cilia surrounding the peristome. The macronucleus is only very slightly curved, usually with a slight concavity on either side. It usually lies obliquely near the middle of the body and is about two-fifths the length of the body. The micronucleus is very small and inconspicuous. There are two contractile vacuoles, and food vacuoles circulate in the endoplasm. Like other ciliates, Balantidium divides by transverse fission, a new cytostome being formed by the posterior daughter.

A process of conjugation occurs, similar in its general features to that

of Paramecium.   Thick-walled cysts are formed in which single individuals are usually enclosed.   Slow-moving cilia are at first visible on
encysted ciliates, but later all structures except the nuclei and sometimes one or more refractile bodies disappear.   No multiplication
takes place in the cysts.

Pigs are usually regarded as important sources of human infection.
Such infections are rather infrequently reported, but they may be
locally common.   Young (1939) reported 7 cases, all with marked
diarrhea, among 142 insane hospital patients examined in South Carolina.   A smaller species, *B. minutum,* was described from man by
Schaudinn in 1899, but Watson in 1945 believed this to have been a

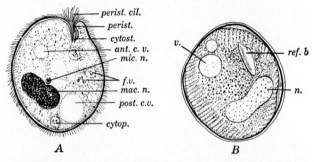

FIG. 28.   *Balantidium coli.*   *A,* trophozoite;   *ant. c. v.,* anterior contractile vacuole;
cytost., cytostome; *cytop.,* cytopyge; *f.v.,* food vacuoles; *mac. n.,* macronucleus; *mic. n.,*
micronucleus; *perist.,* peristome; *perist. cil.,* peristomal cilia; *post. c. v.,* posterior contractile vacuole.   *B,* cyst; *n.,* nucleus; *ref. b.,* refractile body; *v.,* vacuole.   × about 500.
(*A* original; *B* after Dobell and O'Connor.)

free-living coprozoic ciliate, *Balantiophorus minutus,* the cysts of
which infect stools after passage.   Other species occur not only in
many kinds of vertebrates but also in insects and lower invertebrates.
They are common in frogs and toads.

In man *B. coli* is known to be a pathogenic parasite, though in pigs
it appears to be harmless.   In man it may cause ulceration of the
large intestine and invade the tissues of the walls.   A post-mortem
may show the colon to be in a horrible condition, ulcerated from end
to end, with shreds of mutilated or dead tissue hanging from the walls.
Nevertheless, the majority of cases suffer only from diarrhea and may
show no symptoms at all; only a small number develop severe or fatal
dysentery.

Another ciliate recorded as a human parasite is *Nyctotherus faba,*
found by Schaudinn in the same case as *B. minutum.*   It is a flat
kidney-shaped ciliate with a cytostome situated in the notch in the
middle of the body.   There have been a few subsequent discoveries

of this or supposedly related organisms about which little is known. Cockroaches commonly harbor a species of Nyctotherus.

Like amebas and flagellates, coprozoic ciliates are common and have misled more than one parasitologist.

Treatment and Control of Intestinal Flagellates and Ciliates

Considerable success has attended the use of the amebicidal arsenic and iodine compounds against intestinal Trichomonas and Balantidium. Young and Burrows in 1943 had good results in a series of Balantidium cases, using Carbarsone as recommended for *Endamoeba histolytica* (see p. 104), but in some cases a second course was necessary. Chiniofon is said to be the most effective of the iodine compounds, but Shunshin in 1947 cured all of 10 cases of balantidiasis with injections of $\frac{1}{24}$ to $\frac{1}{2}$ grain of mercury biniodide. Some writers have recommended enemas containing quinine, ipecac, or thymol along with Carbarsone for balantidiasis. For Giardia infections, atebrin and chloroquine, valuable antimalarial drugs, have proved highly effective when given at the rate of 0.1 gram 3 times a day for about 5 days. Cysts cease to be passed after the second or third day.

Another method of approach toward control of at least some flagellates has been suggested by the work of Hegner and his students on the effect of diet on flagellates in rats and other animals. Hegner found that a diet rich in carbohydrates favored an abundance of Trichomonas, whereas a protein diet inhibited them. A similar relation has been found for Balantidium in both pigs and rats. Ratcliffe (1928) concluded that the number of Trichomonas was inversely proportional to the abundance of proteolytic anaerobic bacteria, which are favored by a protein diet. A survey of known infections in carnivorous animals demonstrates the rarity of flagellate and ciliate infections in carnivorous animals as compared with their abundance in herbivorous ones, such as ungulates, rodents, and primates.

A few cases of treatment of human "flagellate diarrhea" with a carnivorous diet have been recorded and were succesful. Giardia cases respond less quickly than Trichomonas, as would be expected in view of their situation in the small intestine, where bacterial changes are less easily induced. It is possible that the greater frequency of flagellate diarrheas and of protozoan dysenteries in the tropics may be due in part to diets high in carbohydrates and low in proteins.

Since infection depends on the ingestion of cysts or, in the case of Trichomonas, motile forms passed in the feces of infected man or animals, avoidance of infection depends on precisely the same factors as with amebas: sanitary disposal of feces, protection of food and water from contamination, and cleanliness on the part of infected individuals who might spread the infections by means of soiled hands. Since, as with the amebas, such animals as pigs, rats, and dogs can become infected with human flagellates and ciliates, the possible role of these animals in the spread of the infections must not be lost sight of.

REFERENCES

BALL, G. H., Observations on the Life History of Chilomastix, *Am. J. Hyg.*, **16**, 85 (1932).

BARGER, E. H., and CARD, L. E., *Diseases and Parasites of Poultry*, Philadelphia, 1943.

BEATMAN, L. H., Studies on *Trichomonas buccalis*, *J. Dental Research*, **13**, 339 (1933).

BISHOP, A., *Histomonas meleagridis*, *Parasitology*, **30**, 181, (1938).

BLAND, P. B., GOLDSTEIN, L., WENRICH, D. H., and WEINER, E., Studies on the Biology of *Trichomonas vaginalis*, *Am. J. Hyg.*, ·**16**, 492 (1932).

BOECK, W. C., Studies on *Tricercomonas intestinalis*, *Am. J. Trop. Med.*, **4**, 519 (1924).

BREUER, A., Die Symptomatologie und die Behändlung der Lamblien-Infektion des Menschen, *Arch. Schiffs- u. Tropen-Hyg.*, **42**, 201 (1938).

DOBELL, C., Researches on the Intestinal Protozoa of Monkeys and Man, VI, VII, *Parasitology*, **26**, 531 (1934); **27**, 564 (1935).

DOBELL, C., and O'CONNOR, R. W., *The Intestinal Protozoa of Man*, London, 1921.

GEIMAN, Q. M., Cytological Studies of the Chilomastix of Man and Other Animals, *J. Morphol.*, **57**, 429 (1935).

HEGNER, R. W., A Comparative Study of the Giardias Living in Man, Rabbit, and Dog, *Am. J. Hyg.*, **2**, 442 (1924).

The Relations Between a Carnivorous Diet and Mammalian Infections with Intestinal Protozoa, *ibid.*, **4**, 393 (1924).

HEGNER, R. W., and CHU, H. J., A Comparative Study of the Intestinal Protozoa of Wild Monkeys and Man, *Am. J. Hyg.*, **12**, 62 (1930).

HINSHAW, C., On the Morphology and Mitosis of *Trichomonas buccalis*, *Univ. Calif. Pub. Zool.*, **29**, 159 (1926).

JOHNSON, G., TRUSSELL, M., and JAHN, F., Isolation of *Trichomonas vaginalis* with Penicillin, *Science*, **102**, 126–128 (1945).

KIRBY, H., The Structure of the Common Intestinal Trichomonad of Man, *J. Parasitol.*, **31**, 163–175 (1945).

KOFOID, C. A., The Protozoa of the Human Mouth, *J. Parasitol.*, **14**, 151 (1929).

LEVINE, N. D., BOLEY, L. E., and HESTER, H. R., Experimental Transmission of *Trichomonas gallinae* from the Chicken to Other Birds, *Am. J. Hyg.*, **31** (C), 23–32 (1941).

McNEIL, E., HINSHAW, W. R., and KOFOID, C. A., Hexamita sp. nov. from the Turkey, *Am. J. Hyg.*, **34**, 71–82, 1941.

MORGAN, B. B., *Bovine Trichomoniasis*, Minneapolis, 1944.

NELSON, E. C., Cultivation and Cross-Infection Experiments with Balantidia from Pig, Chimpanzee, Guinea Pig, and *Macacus rhesus*, *Am. J. Hyg.*, **22**, 26 (1935).

REES, C. W., Observations on Bovine Venereal Trichomoniasis, *Vet. Med.*, **33** (July, 1938).

STABLER, R. M., *Trichomonas gallinae,* Pathogenic Trichomonad of Birds, *J. Parasitol.,* **33,** 207–213 (1947).

STABLER, R. M., FEO, L. Q., and RAKOFF, A. E., Implantation of Intestinal Trichomonads (*T. hominis*) into the Human Vagina, *Am. J. Hyg.,* **34** (C), 114–118 (1941); Survival Time of Intravaginally Implanted *Trichomonas hominis, Am. J. Trop. Med.,* **22,** 633–637 (1942); Inoculation of the Oral Trichomonad (*T. tenax*) into the Human Vagina, *ibid.,* **22,** 639–642 (1942).

TRUSSELL, R. E., *Trichomonas Vaginalis and Trichomoniasis,* Springfield, Ill., 1947.

TYZZER, E. E., Studies on Histomoniasis, or "Blackhead" Infection in the Chicken and Turkey, *Proc. Am. Acad. Arts Sci.,* **69,** 189–264, 1934.

WEHR, E. E., and CHRISTENSEN, J. F., Internal Parasites of Poultry, Protozoan Parasites, *U. S. Dept. Agric. Yearbook for 1942,* pp. 1014–1022.

WENRICH, D. H., Observations in the Morphology of Histomonas (Protozoa, Mastigophora) from Pheasants and Chickens. *J. Morphol.,* **72,** 279–303 (1943) The Species of Trichomonas in Man, *J. Parasitol.,* **33,** 177–188 (1947).

WESTPHAL, A., Beziehungen zwischen Infektionsstärke und " Krankheitsbild " bei Infektionen mit *Chilomastix mesnili* und anderen Dickdarmflagellaten, *Z. Hyg. Infektionskrankh.,* **122,** 146–158 (1939).

WICHTERMAN, R., The Present Status of Knowledge Concerning the Existence of Species of Nyctotherus Living in Man, *Am. J. Trop. Med.,* **18,** 67 (1938).

CHAPTER 7

Hemoflagellates—I. Leishmania and Leishmaniases

The Trypanosomidae

The term "hemoflagellates" is used for those flagellates which habitually live in the blood or tissues of man or other animals. There are only two kinds of these which occur in man, namely, the leishman

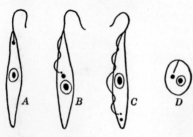

FIG. 29. Diagram of forms assumed by Trypanosomidae, either as adults or as developmental forms; *A*, Leptomonas; *B*, Crithidia; *C*, Trypanosoma; *D*, Leishmania. (After Wenyon.)

bodies, belonging to the genus Leishmania, and the trypanosomes, belonging to the genus Trypanosoma. These two types of organisms, however, are only two of a number of genera which all belong to one family, Trypanosomidae, in the order Protomonadida (see p. 42). Other members of the family occur as gut parasites of insects, and still others as parasites of plants. Since both the hemoflagellates and the plant parasites undergo cycles of development in the gut of insects, it is safe to presume that this entire group of flagellates were originally and primitively parasites of the guts of insects.

Four distinct morphological types of these parasites are found in the bodies of insects, as follows:

1. The Leptomonas type (Fig. 29*A*). This is the most primitive type, in which the body is more or less elongate or pear shaped: it contains a nucleus near the center, a parabasal body near the anterior end, and a single long slender flagellum which arises from a basal granule closely associated with the parabasal body. All the other types of Trypanosomidae may be considered as having arisen from this.

2. The Crithidia type (Fig. 29*B*). This differs in that the flagellum arises from a kinetoplast (basal granule and parabasal body) which has shifted back to a position just in front of the nucleus and is connected with the body, up to the anterior end, by an undulating membrane.

138

3. The Trypanosoma type (Fig. 29C). In this the kinetoplast has moved far behind the nucleus to a point near the posterior end of the body, and the flagellum is attached to the body for most of its length, with or without an undulating membrane.

4. The Leishmania type (Fig. 29D). This is a rounded-up form which contains a nucleus and a kinetoplast, but is entirely devoid of a flagellum. Any of the other three types may assume this form and, conversely, may be developed out of it.

Any or all of these forms may occur in the digestive tracts of insects, but only the leishmania and trypanosome forms occur in the blood of vertebrates.

The fact that some flagellates never develop farther than the leptomonas form, and others never, so far as known at present, farther than the crithidia form, whereas the trypanosomes go through all the stages, makes a study of this group of flagellates very confusing. When a leptomonas or crithidia type is found in an insect gut, it is impossible to say, without further investigation, whether it is an adult animal which never undergoes any further development, or is only a developmental phase of a trypanosome of a vertebrate animal. A number of crithidias which were supposed to be purely insect parasites with no trypanosome stage have been found to develop into trypanosomes in the blood of certain vertebrates, so it may be that most of the crithidias are really developmental stages of these parasites.

The Trypanosomidae are divided into a number of genera on the basis of the morphological forms they assume and on whether they are transmissible to vertebrate animals or to plants. The following genera are usually recognized:

1. **Genus Leptomonas.** Species having only leptomonas and leishmania stages, and confined to invertebrate hosts. They are common in various kinds of bugs, larvae and adults of fleas, various Diptera, and other insects. They live in the hind-gut, where they attach themselves to the epithelial cells by their flagellar ends, the free flagella being very short or lacking. Often they occur in rosettes of dozens of individuals. They produce resistant cystlike forms resembling ordinary leishmania forms but apparently protected by cyst walls.

2. **Genus Leishmania.** Species having only leptomonas and leishmania stages, but transmissible to vertebrates. Unlike Leptomonas, they develop mainly in the stomach and fore gut, and form no resistant cystlike bodies. In vertebrates they develop intracellularly and entirely in the leishmania phase, whereas in artificial cultures or in insects they assume the leptomonas form and are extracellular.

3. **Genus Phytomonas.** Similar to Leptomonas, but transmitted to plants, particularly Euphorbia and milkweeds, where they multiply in the latex. In some, at least, the organisms are said to be inoculated by the bites of insects, and cystlike forms are not found in the feces.

4. **Genus Crithidia.** Strictly insect parasites in which leptomonas, leishmania, and crithidia stages occur, and in which cystlike forms are voided in the feces of the host. As noted above, many of these have proved to be developmental stages of trypanosomes.

5. **Genus Herpetomonas.** Strictly insect parasites having leptomonas, leishmania, and crithidia stages, and also a stage in which the kinetoplast is at the posterior end of the body as in trypanosomes, but with the flagellum passing along the body like a rhizoplast, instead of being attached to an undulating membrane as in true trypanosomes. Cystlike forms are produced in the feces of the host (Fig. 30).

6. **Genus Trypanosoma.** Species which have both vertebrate and invertebrate hosts, and may go through all the stages of development. Some of the more

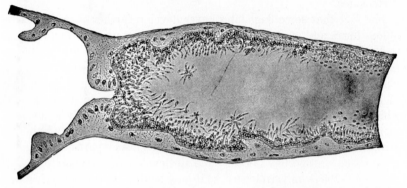

Fig. 30. Longitudinal section of the intestine of a dog flea, showing leptomonads lining the hind-gut. × 170. (After Wenyon, *Protozoology*.)

primitive forms, e.g., *Trypanosoma cruzi* and *T. lewisi*, have both trypanosome and leishmania forms (the latter intracellular) in their vertebrate hosts, and may go through all the phases in the invertebrate hosts, where they multiply in the hind-gut like typical insect flagellates. More specialized ones, e.g., the African species transmitted by tsetse flies, occur exclusively in the trypanosome form in their vertebrate hosts, free in the blood and lymph, and may exist only in the crithidia and trypanosome forms in their insect hosts, where they develop in anterior parts of the digestive system (see Fig. 41).

Leishman Bodies and Leishmaniasis

In India in 1903 two British scientists, Leishman and Donovan, working independently, discovered the parasites now known as *Leishmania donovani*, or leishman bodies, in the spleen of victims of one of Bengal's major scourges, kala-azar or dum-dum fever. In 1904 the leishman bodies, first suspected of being developmental stages of trypanosomes, were found to develop in cultures into flagellates identical with the leptomonads of insects, which had long been known. Years later Patton (1907) found that they developed into a flagellated stage in bedbugs also. Patton's discovery was an unfortunate one, since it started investigators on a false trail in the search for the **transmitting** agent and led to a dozen years of futile work.

Types of Leishmaniasis. Leishmania infections are usually classed in two general types, visceral and cutaneous, but there are several types of each, and intermediate conditions exist. Visceral leishmaniasis, or kala-azar, is a generalized and often fatal disease, accompanied by fever and enlargement of spleen and liver. Cutaneous leishmaniasis is limited to development of one or more local sores usually without fever or generalized symptoms. These sores may be confined to the skin, as in Oriental sore of the Old World, or may spread to mucous membranes of the nose and mouth, as in espundia of tropical America. This mucocutaneous form of the disease is evidently caused by parasites that are intermediate in invasive power.

Several types of leishmaniasis are known. In Sudan a form occurs in which skin sores are frequent and mouth sores sometimes occur. It is less amenable to treatment than Indian kala-azar. Kirk (1942) suggested that this form might be caused by a distinct strain of the parasite, perhaps of intermediate or variable virulence. In central Asia pinhead papules of the skin appear in children several months before the development of kala-azar. Around the Mediterranean and in western and middle Asia there is an infantile form of kala-azar which is largely confined to children under the age of two, although during World War II a considerable number of cases developed in adults.

Typical Oriental sore is common from the Mediterranean to central and northern India, in some localities intermingling with kala-azar but transmitted by different vectors. In Turkestan a U.S.S.R. commission reported two types of cutaneous leishmaniasis, one a seasonal rural infection of which wild rodents (gerbils and marmots) serve as reservoir hosts, and a nonseasonal urban disease transmitted from man to man (see p. 151).

Mucocutaneous leishmaniasis, or espundia, is widespread in Central and South America, from Yucatan to Agentina. Possibly the Peruvian " uta " is a distinct type, since it is characterized by multiple skin sores, and it may be that typical Oriental sore also occurs in South America.

Species of Leishmania. The parasites of these various types of disease are not distinguishable from each other in their morphology either in disease tissue or in cultures. They behave similarly in cultures and are difficult to separate by immunological reactions. Some differences in effects in experimental animals, however, have been observed.

Visceral strains produce generalized infections in monkeys, dogs, hamsters, and mice, and sometimes rats, but cats, rabbits, and guinea pigs are relatively insusceptible. Cutaneous inoculations sometimes produce only local skin sores in monkeys and dogs. Cutaneous strains, on the other hand, produce only local infections in dogs, cats, monkeys, rats, and guinea pigs, whereas in mice they often produce generalized infections, often with skin lesions as well. Geiman (1940) found that *Leishmania tropica* of Oriental sore develops readily in the chorioallantoic fluid of a 5- to 9-day-old chick embryo, whereas *L. brasiliensis* does not, though the original organisms may survive to a second passage.

The difference between visceral and cutaneous types seems clearly to be one of virulence; the body defenses, except in mice, are capable of localizing the cutaneous strains of Leishmania, thus confining them to the skin or testicles where inoculated, whereas they are unable to exert a similar restraining action on the visceral strains. In addition to these differences in virulence, the visceral and cutaneous parasites, at least in the Old World, differ in the species of sandflies (Phlebotomus) concerned in their transmission; little is known about this phase of it in America.

The prevailing opinion is that *all* visceral leishmaniasis in man is caused by a single species of parasite, *L. donovani*, although the parasites of infantile kala-azar were at one time distinguished as *L. infantum*, those of South American kala-azar as *L. chagasi*, and those of canine kala-azar in China as *L. canis*. The parasite of Oriental sore is given recognition as a separate species, *L. tropica*. The parasites of the more intractable South American cutaneous leishmaniasis are usually allowed the distinction of a separate name also, and are called *L. brasiliensis;* it is by no means certain, however, that all forms of South American leishmaniasis are caused by identical strains of parasites.

Leishmania donovani and Kala-azar

Kala-azar is a disease that is insidious in origin, slow in development, and fearful in effects. In 1890–1900 an epidemic swept Assam which depopulated whole villages and reduced populations over large areas. In 1917 another epidemic started in Assam and Bengal, reached its height about 1925, and then mysteriously subsided until, by 1931, it was almost gone. In 1937 a new outbreak began in Bihar. In other parts of the world it is less subject to such vacillations. A few decades ago kala-azar brought terror and persecution in its path. Today, knowledge of its epidemiology, diagnosis, and treatment has shorn it of much of its power for evil.

Distribution. In the Old World typical kala-azar occurs in India, particularly in Assam, Bengal, and Bihar, in North China, and in Sudan. Around the Mediterranean and in western and middle Asia

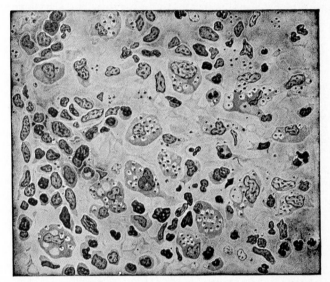

FIG. 31. Section of human spleen showing numerous leishman bodies in the cells. × 750. (After Nattan-Larrier, from Wenyon, *Protozoology*.)

the infantile type of the disease occurs, along with numerous infections in dogs; adults are rarely infected. Extensive use of the "viscerotome" for examination of livers for detection of yellow fever demonstrated the fact that kala-azar is widespread in South America, particularly in northeast Brazil and in the Chaco region of northern Argentina and Paraguay, but cases have also been reported in Bolivia and Venezuela. Cases are more frequent in dogs and cats than in man; human infections are commonest in children.

Leishmania donovani. The parasite of kala-azar, as it occurs in the human body, is usually a minute round or ovoid body only 2 to 4 μ in diameter (Fig. 31). It has a rounded nucleus, usually applied to one side of the body, and a kinetoplast which appears either as a minute dot beside the nucleus or as a tiny oblique rod. Torpedo-shaped parasites are also found, especially in the spleen. They multiply by simple fission; sometimes rosette-like clusters of individuals occur as the result of rapid, repeated division. These bodies are widely distributed in the body, but the special habitat seems to be the large endothelial cells of blood vessels and lymphatics. They are especially abundant in the spleen, liver, and bone marrow, but they are by no means confined to these organs. They are found both inside and outside of the tissue cells, and are present in limited numbers in the circulating blood, usually inside of monocytes, but occasionally free.

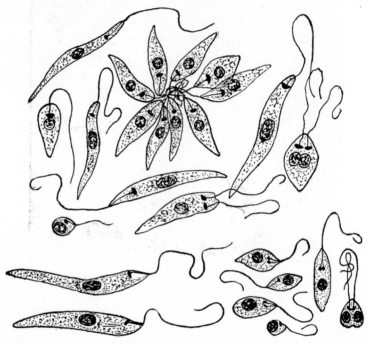

FIG. 32. *Leishmania donovani*. Upper figures, forms found in cultures. (Original.) Lower, forms found in mid-gut of *Phlebotomus argentipes;* at left, forms found in lumen; at right, forms found attached to walls. × 1600. (Sketched from figures by Shortt, Barraud, and Craighead.)

Often the cells containing the parasites enlarge to many times their normal size and may contain dozens of parasites. The parasites may be abundant in reticulo-endothelial cells in the intestinal wall, oral and nasal mucosa, and skin, even when no evident lesions exist. They have been found in nasal secretions, feces, and urine.

In cultures or in the digestive tracts of insect intermediate hosts, the parasites transform into active, flagellated leptomonads (Fig. 32). Typically these are spindle-shaped, about 14 to 20 μ long and from 1.5 to 3.5 μ broad. The round or oval nucleus is in the center, and the usually oval parabasal lies transversely near the anterior end; in front of it is a light-staining area called the " eosinophile vacuole," over or around which runs the root of the flagellum. The flagellum is as long as, or longer than, the body. The flagellates divide by longitudinal fission. In young cultures many stumpy, pear-shaped, or oval forms are found, and the body tends to become relatively more slender as the culture matures. Row described " O " bodies which he thought were reversions of the flagellates to resistant, nonflagellated infective forms, but most workers believe that these are merely dying and degenerate flagellates.

Transmission. Few problems in parasitology have caused more fruitless effort, more blasted hopes, more false conclusions, or more unfounded speculation than the transmission of kala-azar, but the final piece was fitted into the puzzle in 1942. Kala-azar is a house and site infection, and for this reason it was believed for a time that infection spread by way of contaminated soil. Then Patton in 1907 discovered that the parasites transform into flagellates and multiply as such in the mid-gut of bedbugs. In the following 18 years Patton, Cornwall, Adie, and others endeavored to prove that the bedbug was the natural vector of kala-azar, but, as Knowles put it, although the bedbug started as a hot favorite, it never reached the winning post. Shortt and his colleagues of the Indian Kala-azar Commission finally concluded, in 1925, that the bedbug has nothing to do with the transmission of kala-azar, which any careful observer of the epidemiology might have guessed. In the Mediterranean region fleas fell under strong suspicion, but their case was thrown out of court by Nicolle and Anderson in 1924.

In 1921 a Kala-azar Inquiry was set up in Calcutta, and in 1924 a Kala-azar Commission began work in Assam. Guided by an observation of Sinton's that the distribution of *Phlebotomus argentipes* in India coincides closely with that of kala-azar, Knowles, Napier, and Smith found epidemiological reasons for suspecting this sandfly as a transmitter in Calcutta, and in the same year, 1924, made the important discovery that a high percentage of these flies became infected when fed on kala-azar cases. This was quickly corroborated by Christophers, Shortt, and Barraud in Assam, and soon thereafter many important details were added concerning the development of the flagellates in the sandfly, including demonstration of occasional massive infections of the pharynx and proboscis.

Then followed years of patient but largely fruitless effort to prove actual transmission by sandflies. In the course of hundreds of trials, only four successful infections were obtained, all in hamsters; transmission to human volunteers failed.

After 1930, when the Assam epidemic had subsided, work on the problem was largely discontinued but was revived again in 1939 when the disease assumed epidemic proportions in Bihar. There Smith, Halder, and Ahmed made the interesting discovery that if sandflies, after an infective meal, were fed on raisins instead of additional blood meals, the flagellates frequently grew so numerous that they blocked the pharynx as do plague germs in fleas (Fig. 33). These authors then subjected five hamsters to bites of flies fed on raisins after their infective blood meal, and every one developed kala-azar; of five others fed on by flies given repeated blood meals, at least four failed to become infected (one escaped). In confirmation of this remarkable result,

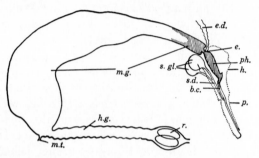

Fig. 33. Gut of sandfly, showing " blocking " of pharynx and fore part of mid-gut (shaded area) by *Leishmania donovani*; *b.c.*, buccal cavity; *e.*, esophagus; *e.d.*, esophageal diverticulum; *h.*, head; *h.g.*, hind-gut; *m.g.*, mid-gut; *m.t.*, Malpighian tubule; *p.*, proboscis; *ph.*, pharynx; *r.*, rectum; *s.d.*, salivary duct; *s. gl.*, salivary glands. (After Shortt, Barraud, and Craighead.)

Swaminath, Shortt, and Anderson (1942) then succeeded in infecting every one of five human volunteers in Assam. Thus to a successful end came 20 years of patience, perseverance, labor, and ingenuity.

This work, taken in conjunction with the epidemiology and the success of experimental infection of sandflies in various parts of the world, leaves no further doubt that sandflies are an important factor in the transmission of kala-azar. Nevertheless, other methods of transmission are possible. As already noted, the parasites occur in nasal secretions, urine, and feces, and they may live some hours in contaminated soil. Infection by mouth is possible in experimental animals. Archibald and Mansour (1937) infected monkeys by swabbing or spraying the nose with infected nasal secretion and also by confining them in an insect-proof room with infected comrades.

In nature dogs are commonly infected, though apparently much more frequently in the areas where infantile kala-azar occurs than in India or Sudan. In South America, too, canine infections are common. In these places dogs constitute an important reservoir of the disease, and it is probable that transmission from dog to man is more frequent than

from man to man. A similar situation exists between cutaneous leishmaniasis of dogs and man. Cats are sometimes infected, and occasionally horses, sheep, and bullocks. Experimentally monkeys, mice,
hamsters, and ground squirrels are susceptible.

All the suspected transmitters of kala-azar in the Old World
(*P. perniciosus* and *P. major* around the Mediterranean, *P. argentipes*
in India, and *P. chinensis* in China) belong to the *P. major* group of
Phlebotomus flies. With the discovery of *P. langeroni* in Sudan and
Ethiopia, members of this group are known to occur in all places where
kala-azar is found in the Old World. Naturally infected sandflies have
repeatedly been found in infected localities. In South America *P. intermedius* and *P. longipalpis* readily become infected with visceral
leishmaniasis when fed on infected dogs. Whether any species of
Phlebotomus in the United States can serve as transmitters is not yet
known.

Adler and Theobald think that the frequent occurrence of kala-azar
in dogs and infants in the Mediterranean region and not in India or
China may be due to the fact that the Mediterranean vectors, *P. perniciosus* and *P. major*, may infect their victims very frequently by
direct inoculation into the skin at the time of biting, whereas the Indian
and Chinese vectors, *P. argentipes* and *P. chinensis*, respectively, less
frequently inoculate the parasites by their bites but cause infection by
being crushed. Since dogs and babies are not so adept at slapping the
flies as are adults they escape infection.

The Disease. *Leishmania donovani* seems primarily to invade the
reticulo-endothelial or macrophage system of cells in the body, living
and multiplying in the very cells which in most diseases constitute one
of the principal means of defense. The parasites are probably picked
up by the macrophages as are other invading bodies, but instead of
being digested they grow and multiply, causing the host cells to become
enormously enlarged. The macrophages increase to an amazing
degree, so that the organs in which they are abundant, such as the
spleen and liver, become tremendously enlarged. The parasites are
found wherever there are macrophages, and in proportion to their
number, in the spleen, liver, bone marrow, skin, submucosa, and lymph
glands. Monocytes circulating in the blood also frequently harbor
them.

The disease often comes on with symptoms suggestive of typhoid,
malaria, or dysentery, and may actually be precipitated by these
diseases, for there is now evidence that there is a high natural resistance to kala-azar and that probably the parasites are held under
control in many latent infections, and no symptoms appear until resist-

ance is lowered. In a case that Adler experimentally infected by inoculation of a massive dose of cultured Leishmania, no symptoms appeared over a period of 9 months, although numerous parasites were found post-mortem. The incubation period is usually at least several months.

After onset there is an irregular fever with enlargement of spleen and liver, rheumatic aches, anemia, and a progressive emaciation. The leucocytes are reduced in number, and the skin is often edematous. Untreated cases usually die in from a few weeks to several years, usually from some intercurrent disease which the patient cannot fight with his macrophage system converted into a Leishmania breeding ground. Often in patients who have been treated and have recovered from the systemic disease, whitish spots develop in the skin and eventually grow into nodules the size of split peas; they occur mainly on the face and neck. This condition is called post-kala-azar dermal leishmanoid. Apparently the parasites are able to survive in the skin after the viscera have become too " hot " for them. A number of cases of extensive lesions in the mouth have been seen in Sudan, in which the parasites were found in abundance in the oral lesions, although they could not be found in the enlarged liver and spleen. Such cases probably represent intermediate conditions of parasite virulence and host resistance between typical kala-azar and cutaneous leishmaniasis.

The Mediterranean type of the disease in infants and dogs runs a similar course but may be of shorter duration.

Diagnosis. Though the clinical symptoms are highly suggestive in endemic localities, diagnosis should be confirmed either by finding the parasites or by serological tests. Puncture of liver, spleen, or lymph glands is useful in finding the parasites. Some workers recommend sternal puncture but Shortt considers this less effective and more unpleasant for the patient. Shortt et al. have been able to find parasites in over 75 per cent of cases by examination of a thick edge left after making a blood smear. Another method is to make a smear from the dermis exposed with as little bleeding as possible. Inoculation of NNN culture medium with spleen juice, blood, or bits of excised dermis is a reliable procedure. Shortt particularly recommends seeding 3 or 4 NNN culture tubes with the top of the sediment obtained by centrifuging 2 to 5 cc. of blood added to four times its volume of citrated saline. The tubes are incubated at 22 to 24° C. and flagellates appear in 7 days or later in 90 per cent of untreated cases.

A number of simple serological tests have been recommended. One of the first was Napier's aldehyde test, in which a drop of strong formalin is added to 1 cc. of serum; in positive cases the serum gels and turns milky white; a mere gel is not diagnostic. Precipitates are also formed with organic antimony compounds, resorcinol, alcohol, peptonate of iron, lactic acid, and even distilled water, under conditions in which they are not formed by normal serum. The multiplication of apparently unrelated serum tests was becoming very confusing until Chorine (1937) showed that they are all due to increase in euglobulin and decrease of albumin in kala-azar serum.

Treatment. Before the discovery of the striking effectiveness of antimony compounds for all forms of leishmaniasis, the death rate in kala-azar cases was about 95 per cent; now it is less than 5 per cent. Two groups of compounds are used: trivalent ones such as sodium and potassium antimonyl tartrates and sodium antimonyl gluconate, and pentavalent ones, the most extensively used being Neostibosan, Neostam, Solustibosan, and urea stibamine. Some trivalent compounds, such as anthiomaline and fuadin, which are very useful in schistosomiasis and filariasis, are ineffective against leishmaniasis. The pentavalent compounds have the advantage of being less toxic, more quickly effective, and most of them injectable intramuscularly as well as intravenously, but they are more expensive.

The great trouble with treatment is the long time that has been required for complete cures. Of the tartrates at least 25 or 30 doses daily or on alternate days, totaling at least 2500 mg., is needed. Of the pentavalent compounds, only about 10 or 12 doses, totaling 2700 to 4000 mg., is required. Kirk and Sati in 1947, however, reported excellent results in Sudan kala-azar cases using sodium antimonyl gluconate in large daily doses (100 mg. antimony per cc., 6 cc. per dose) for only 4 days, and then 2 to 6 more doses, usually after an interval of 2 weeks. They got immediate clinical response; usually gland and spleen punctures were negative after the first four injections. They claimed toxic effects to be negligible.

Since about 1940 another group of drugs, the aromatic diamidines, have proved very effective, but they are also very toxic. They are useful when, because of drug fastness or allergies, the antimony compounds fail.

Prevention. Protection against kala-azar involves avoidance and control of sandflies, which is discussed on page 624. Infected houses and people should be avoided after dusk, when sandflies are biting, unless repellents are used. In Assam it was considered best to burn or destroy native habitations where cases had occurred and to prevent erection of a new hut on the same site, since isolation of a few hundred yards seems enough to prevent spread of the disease. Now, however, DDT spraying gives as good results. Some control can be obtained locally by the establishment of free clinics and treatment of all cases. In endemic regions where the canine disease occurs, Sergent *et al.* recommend destruction of all dogs showing evidence of infection by symptoms or blood tests, and of all stray dogs; control of movement of dogs into and out of infected areas; and prevention of contacts between children and dogs. Destruction of the majority of dogs in Canea on the island of Crete in 1933 led to a markedly lower incidence of human kala-azar in the following year.

Oriental Sore

Distribution. One of the commonest sights in many tropical cities, particularly those of the eastern Mediterranean region and south-western Asia, is the great number of children, usually under three years of age, who have on the exposed parts of their bodies unsightly ulcerating sores, upon which swarms of flies are constantly feeding. In some cities infection is so common and so inevitable that normal children are expected to have the disease soon after they begin playing outdoors, and visitors seldom escape a sore as a souvenir. Since one attack gives immunity, Oriental sores appearing on an adult person in Baghdad brands him as a new arrival, and the same is true in many other tropical cities. Dogs frequently suffer from cutaneous leishmaniasis also, especially on the nose and ears, and undoubtedly constitute an important reservoir. Many other animals develop local lesions when inoculated (see p. 142).

The disease is more or less prevalent from the shores of the Mediterranean to central Asia and the drier parts of central and western India, and also in parts of China and in many parts of Africa. It is possible that true Oriental sore has been introduced into South America also, but here it is obviously difficult to distinguish it from the native South American infection.

The Parasites. *Leishmania tropica* is morphologically indistinguishable from *L. donovani* in either lesions or cultures, but its clinical effects in man and animals are entirely different, and immunity to one of these species fails to protect against the other.

The parasites are found in the dermal tissues of the sores, where greatly increased numbers of large monocytes and other reticulo-endothelial cells are literally packed with them. Torpedo-shaped parasites (Fig. 34) are more commonly found than in kala-azar. Growth in culture is identical with that of *L. donovani*, and similar development takes place in infected sandflies.

The Disease. Oriental sore (Fig. 35) begins as a small red papule, like an insect bite, which gradually enlarges to a diameter of an inch or more. The covering epithelium eventually breaks down and granulation tissue is exposed, but no pus is evident unless the sore is secondarily infected by bacteria. In uncomplicated cases the ulcer remains shallow and sharply defined by raised edges. It persists from a few months to a year or more. The incubation period varies from a few days to several months. In an outbreak among fresh troops in Quetta the incubation period was over 3 months in more than half the cases.

There may be one sore or several, sometimes many, probably due to multiple infective bites. Neighboring lymph glands may be invaded and become large and painful, but general invasion of the body does

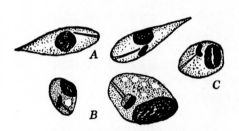

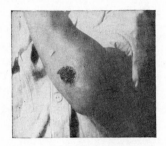

FIG. 34. *Leishmania tropica* from an Oriental sore; *A*, torpedo-shaped forms found outside the cells; *B* and *C*, intracellular forms. × 4000. (After Wenyon.)

FIG. 35. Oriental sore on arm. (From Army Institute of Pathology, photo 79107.)

not occur; generalized symptoms and changes in the blood are lacking unless there are secondary infections. In Turkestan rural infections (see p. 141) are characterized by rapidly ulcerating moist sores developing 2 to 3 weeks after infection and lasting 3 to 6 months, but urban infections have an incubation period of several months, and develop into a chronic sore of " dry " type which persists for a year or even several years. In experimental infections of the ears of mice with *L. tropica* cultivated from human ulcers of the " moist " type, Russian workers observed that the parasites first multiply profusely outside the cells, causing inflammation. Then macrophages are attracted and ingest the parasites, which then continue to multiply intracellularly and destroy the cells. After 2 or 3 months the epidermis disintegrates and the ulcer appears. Then antibodies destroy the extracellular parasites on a large scale, eventually eliminating them, and scar tissue forms.

Transmission. Although the parasites may occasionally be inoculated into broken skin by contact or by flies that have just fed on other sores, the disease is usually transmitted by Phlebotomus flies. The pupiparous fly, *Hippobosca canina* (see p. 656), may act as a mechanical transmitter among dogs.

Either *Phlebotomus papatasi* or *P. sergenti* or both occur wherever Oriental sore occurs; both are readily infected after feeding on infective material, are frequently found naturally infected, and produce infection when crushed and rubbed into scarified skin. According to Adler, however, some strains of *L. tropica* seem better adapted to *P. sergenti* and others to *P. papatasi*. Early attempts to produce infection by the bites of sandflies were unsuccessful or at least inconclusive, but, by altering the method of infecting the flies, Adler and Ber (1941) produced human infections by the bites of *P. papatasi* with what they called ridiculous ease.

Treatment and Prevention. If only one or a few sores are present, they can be treated by local injections around or into the sores of a 1 to 2 per cent solution of atebrin, or 20 minims of 2 to 5 per cent emetin, or 2 cc. of a 1 per cent solution of berberine sulfate, repeated at 7- to 10-day intervals. Multiple or chronic sores are best treated by injections of antimony compounds as for kala-azar, although in such cases intramuscular injections of the milder compound, fuadin, are satisfactory. Usually, if the sores are protected, they heal in 15 to 30 days. Other local treatments with carbon dioxide snow, x rays, and various antiseptic ointments have favorable influence but are not as effective as the methods mentioned above.

Control probably lies largely in keeping the sores on either man or dog protected so that sandflies or other biting insects cannot get at them. It is not likely that insects can become infected from sucking blood elsewhere, since blood cultures are never positive. Inoculation with cultures into unexposed parts of the body is recommended in endemic areas.

American Mucocutaneous Leishmaniasis (Espundia)

Distribution. A form of cutaneous leishmaniasis which is frequently followed by horrible, spreading ulcers of the mucous membrances of the nose and pharynx occurs over a vast area in tropical America, from Yucatan and Campeche in Mexico, through Central and South America to northern Argentina. It is particularly common in Brazil, Paraguay, northern Argentina, and eastern Peru. It goes by a variety of names: chiclero ulcer in Mexico and Guatemala, Bay sore in British Honduras, Bosch yaws, forest yaws, and pian bois in the Guianas, espundia in Brazil and eastern Peru, uta in other parts of Peru, and buba in Paraguay. Shattuck (1936) pointed out that heat and moisture characterize the climate of all the endemic foci, with the possible exception of the mountain valleys in Peru where uta occurs.

It is almost always contracted, as is jungle yellow fever, in virgin forests, usually among men gathering chicle, rubber, or maté, or constructing railways through the forests. It has been reported in 11 per cent of chicle gatherers in low-lying rain forest areas in Yucatan, being most prevalent from August to January when the collecting season is at its height. Exceptions to the usual distribution were outbreaks in Rio de Janeiro in a residential section provided with gardens and shrubbery, and in Peruvian villages in the Andes, studied by Strong and by Townsend in 1915.

Dogs are sometimes found naturally infected, but not as commonly as with Oriental sore in the Old World. Monkeys and dogs can be experimentally infected, and Fuller and Geiman in 1942 found that squirrels, especially Texas ground squirrels, are susceptible to cutaneous but not to intraperitoneal inoculation, and develop ulcerating sores. Hamsters are less easily infected but may develop nodular skin lesions that do not ulcerate.

The Parasites. The organisms causing the disease are not distinguishable from those of other forms of leishmaniasis, but because of peculiarities in the course of the infection in man they are given a distinctive name, *Leishmania brasiliensis.* It is, however, by no means certain that only a single type of cutaneous leishmaniasis occurs in tropical America. Townsend in 1915 found it difficult to believe that the mild leishmanian skin sores known as uta occurring in the Peruvian Andes at an elevation of 4500 to 7500 ft. are identical with the severe espundia of the steaming Brazilian forests.

The Disease. In typical cases the infection begins precisely as in Oriental sore and frequently follows a similar course, but there is a greater tendency for the sores to spread over extensive areas and for more numerous sores to appear. In one instance 248 sores were reported. The ears, face, forearms, and lower legs are the favorite sites for the original lesions, but laborers naked to the waist may get ulcers on the trunk, and occasionally on the genitals or elsewhere. In Yucatan the lesion appears on the ear in over 60 per cent of cases and may cause loss of a large part of this organ by sloughing, but it does not spread to the mucous membranes.

Sometimes the sores show a mass of raw granular tissue raised above the surface; at other times they become extensively eroded, with sharply defined, raised, purplish edges and a surrounding red inflamed area. The foul-smelling fluid which exudes sometimes crusts over, but may be inoculated into abrasions elsewhere and cause secondary ulcers.

Secondary infections with bacteria, spirochetes, fungi, or maggots are frequent. The rarity of leishmanias in late stages suggests that secondary infections may play an important role, though the prompt healing which follows antimony treatment shows that the leishmanias still play a leading part. There is nothing about the sores to distinguish them with certainty from others caused by blastomycosis, syphilis, tropical ulcers, or even in some cases yaws, so it is little wonder that there has been much confusion about their distribution and etiology.

The most striking feature of the disease is the secondary development of ulcerations in the nasal cavities, mouth, and pharynx, which may

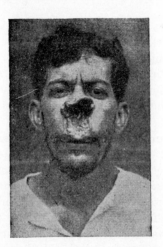

Fig. 36. A case of espundia before and after treatment with tartar emetic. (After d'Utra e Silva.)

occur in 20 per cent or more of the cases, though much more commonly in some geographic regions than in others. In rare cases ulcers occur in the vagina. According to Villela *et al.* small incipient lesions can be found in the nose in many cases in which no obvious lesions are present, and scrapings of the mucosa frequently reveal Leishmania even when it is perfectly normal in appearance. The mucous membrane ulcerations may appear before the skin lesions have healed, but usually they develop from several months to several years later. Ordinarily they commence as tiny itching spots or swellings of the mucous membrane, usually in the nose, the infected membrane becoming inflamed, and marked either with small granular sores or with blister-like swellings. The lymph glands in the infected regions become swollen and turgid. A granular ulceration begins in a short time, invading all the mucous membranes of the nose and spreading by means of infective fluid which flows down over the upper lip into the mouth cavity, attacking the hard and soft palate.

Advance of the lesion is obstinate and slow, and gives rise to serious complications. The nostrils become too clogged to admit the passage of sufficient air and the patient has to keep his mouth constantly open to breathe. His repulsive appearance and fetid breath help to make his life miserable. Affections of the organs of smell and hearing, and even sight, may supervene, and the voice is weakened or even temporarily lost. The digestive tract becomes upset from the constant swallowing of the exudations mixed with saliva or food. A spreading of the nose due to the eating away of the septum is a characteristic feature. Although in late stages of the disease the entire surface of the palate and nasal cavities is attacked and the septum between the nostrils destroyed, the bones are left intact, a feature which readily distinguishes a leishmanian ulcer from a syphilitic one. Usually the victim of espundia, if untreated, dies of some intercurrent infection, but he may suffer for years and eventually succumb to the disease itself.

Diagnosis is usually made by finding the leishmanias in the lesions, but a skin test described by Montenegro in 1926 is sometimes helpful. Dead cultured flagellates are injected into the skin; in positive cases an allergic inflammation develops within 48 hours.

Transmission. Little is definitely known about the transmission of the disease, though by analogy with other forms of leishmaniasis it is highly probable that bites of Phlebotomus flies are usually responsible. Support for this view is provided by instances in which typical sores developed at the site of bites of *P. lutzi* in Brazil. Aragão in 1922 found leptomonads in some wild *P. intermedius* captured in a locality in Rio de Janeiro where a local outbreak occurred, and in five of the flies that had fed on espundia sores 3 days before, he found similar flagellates. When emulsions of these flies were inoculated into the nose of a dog, an ulcerating sore containing leishmanias developed 3 days later. Pessôa et al. (1940, 1941), in an endemic region in Brazil, found natural infections in a small percentage of *P. migonei* and *P. pessoai,* and think the epidemiology definitely incriminates sandflies.

According to Shattuck (1936) it is probable that species of Phlebotomus occur wherever the disease exists in tropical America, with the possible exception of Peru. Here Townsend obtained some experimental evidence that two species of midges of the genus Forcipomyia (see p. 627) are the transmitters, but this work needs confirmation.

Treatment. Most cases respond well to injections of antimony compounds, but some respond better to Neosalvarsan. Treatment should be accompanied by removal of scabs from ulcers, even on nose, lips, or mouth, and cleansing to get rid of bacterial infections. Local treatments are helpful, using antimony tartrate applied as a powder or in 1 or 2 per cent solutions, or the methods described for Oriental sore can be employed.

REFERENCES

ADLER, S., and BER, M., The Transmission of *Leishmania tropica* by the Bite of *Phlebotomus papatasii*, *Ind. J. Med. Research*, **29**, 803 (1941).

ADLER, S., and THEODOR, O., Investigations on Mediterranean Kala-azar, *Proc. Roy. Soc. (London)* **B108**, 447; **110**, 402; **116**, 494; **125**, 491 (1931-38).

ARCHIBALD, R. G., and MANSOUR, H., Some Observations on the Epidemiology of Kala-azar in the Sudan, *Trans. Roy. Soc. Trop. Med. Hyg.*, **30**, 395 (1937).

CHAGAS, E., *et al.*, Leishmaniose Visceral Americana, *Mem. inst. Oswaldo Cruz*, **32**, 321 (1937).

CHORINE, V., Les réactions sérologiques dues aux euglobulines, *Ann. inst. Past.*, **58**, 78 (1937).

CHUNG, H-L., On the Relationship between Canine and Human Kala-azar in Peiping and the Identity of *Leishmania canis* and *Leishmania donovani*, *Chinese Med. J.*, **57**, 501, 661 (1940); **59**, 301, 540 (1941); **61**, 19, 73, 77 (1942).

GEIMAN, Q. M., A Study of Four Peruvian Strains of *Leishmania brasiliensis*, *J. Parasitol.*, **26**, Suppl., 22–23 (1940).

HOARE, C. A., Cutaneous Leishmaniasis (Critical Review of Recent Russian Work), *Trop. Diseases Bull.*, **41**, 331 (1944).

The Relationship of the Haemoflagellates, *Proc. 4th Intern. Congr. Trop. Med. and Malaria*, **2**, Sect. VII, 1110–1118 (1948).

HOEPPLI, R., The Epidemiology of Kala-azar in China, *Chinese Med. J.*, **57**, 364–372 (1940).

KIRK, R., *et al.*, Studies in Leishmaniasis in the Anglo-Egyptian Sudan, *Trans. Roy. Soc. Trop. Med. Hyg.*, **33**, 501, 623 (1940); **34**, 213 (1941); **35**, 257 (1942); **38**, 61, 489 (1944–45).

LEAGUE OF NATIONS, On the Diagnosis, Treatment, and Epidemiology of Visceral Leishmaniasis in the Mediterranean Basin. *Quart. Bull. Health Organisation*, **4**, 789 (1935).

NAPIER, L. E., *et al.*, The Treatment of Kala-azar by Diamidine Stilbene, *Indian Med. Gaz.*, **77**, 321 (1942).

PESSÔA, S. B., *et al.*, Leishmaniasis in São Paulo, *Arquiv. hig. e saúde públ.*, **5**, 15, 23, 45 (1940); **6**, 15, 23, 103, 125, 141 (1941).

REPORTS OF THE INDIAN KALA-AZAR COMMISSION, No. 1 (1924–1925), *Indian Med. Research Mem.*, **4**, 1926; No. 2 (1926–1930); *ibid.*, **25**, 1932. (Contains numerous papers by Calcutta and Assam workers.)

SHATTUCK, G. C., The Distribution of American Leishmaniasis in Relation to that of Phlebotomus, *Am. J. Trop. Med.*, **16**, 187 (1936).

SMITH, R. O. A., HALDER, K. C., and AHMED, J. (Transmission of Kala-azar), *Indian Med. Gaz.*, **75**, 67–69 (1940); Editorial, *ibid.*, 97–98; *Ind. J. Med. Research*, **28**, 575–591 (1940); **29**, 783, 789, 799 (1941).

SWAMINATH, C. S., SHORTT, H. E., and ANDERSON, L. A. P., Transmission of Indian Kala-azar to Man by the Bites of *Phlebotomus argentipes*, Ann. and Brun., *Ind. J. Med. Research*, **30**, 473 (1942).

CHAPTER 8

Hemoflagellates—II. Trypanosomes

One of the blackest clouds overhanging the civilization of tropical Africa is the scourge of trypanosome diseases which affect both man and domestic animals. The ravages of sleeping sickness, which is the final phase of trypanosome infection in man, were well known to the old slave traders, and the presence of " lazy niggers " lying prostrate on wharves and docks with saliva drooling from their mouths, insensible to emotions or pain, was a familiar sight. It did not take these astute merchants long to find that death was a frequent outcome of the disease, and they soon recognized swollen glands in the neck as an early symptom and refused to accept as slaves Negroes with swollen glands. Nevertheless sleeping sickness must often have been introduced with its parasites into various parts of North and South America, as it frequently is even at the present time, and only the absence of a suitable means of transmission has saved the western hemisphere from being swept by it. Fossil remains of tsetse flies have been found in Colorado, belonging to the Oligocene period, and it has been suggested that the extinction of prehistoric camels and horses in North America, which cradled them in the early days of their evolution, may have been brought about by tsetse-borne trypanosome diseases.

History. Although trypanosomes were first discovered in **1841,** which is very ancient history in parasitology, the first connection with disease was the discovery in **1880** that they were the cause of surra in horses and other animals in India. In **1895** Bruce showed that nagana of domestic animals in Africa was caused by a trypanosome which now bears his name. In **1902** Forde and Dutton discovered the presence of trypanosomes in human blood in a case of " Gambia fever," the preliminary stage of sleeping sickness. In **1903** Castellani found trypanosomes in the cerebrospinal fluid of cases of sleeping sickness in Uganda.

The transmission of nagana by tsetse flies was known even before the cause of the disease was discovered, but it required the labors of many workers to elucidate the details of the process. It was Kleine, in **1909,** who showed that the tsetse fly was no mere mechanical transmitter but a true intermediate host. In that same year there was dis-

157

covered a new type of human sleeping sickness in Rhodesia, and Chagas described an entirely different human trypanosome infection in South America.

The Parasites. The general relationships of trypanosomes have been discussed on pp. 138–140. They may be regarded as having developed in the course of evolution from the crithidias of invertebrates, adapted to living in the blood of vertebrates on which the invertebrates habitually feed. They thus bear the same relation to Crithidia that Leishmania bears to Leptomonas.

Trypanosomes exist as parasites in all sorts of vertebrates — fish, amphibians, reptiles, birds, and mammals — living in the blood, lymph, or tissues of their hosts. A great number of different species have been named; usually any trypanosome found in a new host is named after the host as a tentative label until more is found out about it. Though

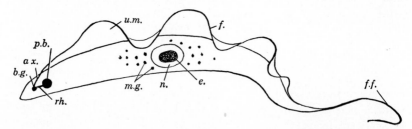

Fig. 37. *Trypanosoma gambiense*, slender form; *ax.*, axoneme; *b.g.*, basal granule or blepharoplast; *e.*, endosome; *f.*, flagellum; *f.f.*, free flagellum; *m.g.*, metachromatic granules; *n.*, nucleus; *p.b.*, parabasal body; *rh.*, rhizoplast; *u.m.*, undulating membrane.

this procedure is not in accordance with rules of naming animals, it is better than the alternatives of having numerous nameless trypanosomes to deal with, or of identifying them with species from which they may subsequently be found to differ.

In form most trypanosomes are active wriggling little creatures somewhat suggesting diminutive dolphins or eels, according to their slenderness (Fig. 37). They swim in the direction of the pointed end of the body, being propelled by the wave motions of the undulating membrane. The body is shaped like a curved, flattened blade, tapering to a fine point anteriorly, from which a free flagellum often continues forward. This flagellum continues nearly to the posterior end of the body, and is connected with the body by an undulating membrane, like a long fin or crest; in some species it is thrown into numerous graceful ripples; in certain others, e.g., *Trypanosoma cruzi*, it is only slightly rippled. The body contains a nucleus which varies in its position in different species and under different circumstances. Near the posterior end, or sometimes at the tip, there is a parabasal body (rarely absent) and a basal granule from which the flagellum arises. Many species also contain scattered, deep-staining granules in the cytoplasm.

Life Cycles. In the vertebrate hosts most trypanosomes usually multiply by simple fission. The kinetoplast is the first structure to divide; next a new flagellum begins to grow out along the margin of the undulating membrane; then the nucleus divides; and finally the body splits from the anterior end backwards.

The African polymorphic trypanosomes of man and animals are mainly parasites of the lymphatic and intercellular fluids, but multiplication also occurs in the blood stream; *T. equiperdum* thrives in edematous fluid of sex organs and skin; and some trypanosomes of birds apparently live mainly in the bone marrow. *T. cruzi*, however, multiplies intracellularly in a leishmania form (Fig. 43), changing to the trypanosome form before being liberated from the cells; the free trypanosome forms get into the lymph and blood but do not multiply there (see p. 173). Because of these peculiarities some workers, notably Dias, prefer to place this species in a separate genus, Schizotrypanum, intermediate between Leishmania and Trypanosoma. In many cases the favorite habitat of trypanosomes is unknown, only the blood forms having been recognized. In some species at least, e.g., *T. lewisi* of rats and *duttoni* of mice, an immune response which inhibits reproduction soon develops, in which case the " coefficient of variation " of the parasites quickly drops to a low level, but in some species dividing forms are found even late in the course of an infection. Trypanosomes are commonly spoken of as polymorphic or monomorphic; polymorphic forms are those in which some individuals have a free flagellum and others do not, e.g., *T. gambiense, brucei,* and *rhodesiense,* while monomorphic forms may always have a free flagellum, e.g., *lewisi, cruzi, vivax, evansi, equinum,* and *equiperdum,* or may always lack one, e.g., *congolense, suis.*

It has been generally accepted that trypanosomes have no sexual phase, but Fairbairn and Culwick (1946) claim that a polymorphic trypanosome as found in the blood exhibits six different types, with different electric charges and different morphology, and that the parasites undergo syngamy (sexual fusion) in the blood. This work requires confirmation.

Although at least one trypanosome, *T. equiperdum,* has become completely independent of its ancestral invertebrate hosts and is transmitted directly from horse to horse during copulation, and although other trypanosomes can live and multiply indefinitely in vertebrate hosts if artificially injected by the soiled proboscis of biting flies, the majority of them, when they reach a suitable invertebrate host, hark back to the traditions of their remote forebears and go through a cycle of development more or less like that of typical crithidias. Some, such as *T. cruzi* and *T. lewisi,* finding themselves in the ancestral home, revert almost completely. After being sucked into the stomach of an insect they assume the crithidial form, attach themselves to the epithelial cells or enter them, and multiply. Gradually they move backwards towards the rectum, and the infective forms are voided with the feces. Infection occurs either by contamination of the bite with the feces, which is probably the usual way in *T. cruzi;* by ingestion of the feces of the insect when licking the bites, as in the case of *T. lewisi;* or by ingestion of the whole insect. The reversion of *T. cruzi* to the crithidial condition is still more complete in that the infection sometimes passes from insect to insect.

Those trypanosomes which develop thus in the hind-gut of invertebrates are said to develop in the posterior station; they are the conservatives. The trypanosomes of this group use a variety of invertebrates as intermediate hosts; for example, *T. lewisi* of rats develops in fleas, *T. melophagium* of sheep in sheep ticks (keds), *T. theileri* of cattle in tabanids, *T. cruzi* of man and other animals in triatomid bugs, and African reptilian trypanosomes in tsetse flies. There are other trypanosomes, however, the radicals, which after ingestion by their insect vectors develop in the anterior part of the alimentary canal and infect by way of the proboscis. They form an evolutionary series: first the *T. vivax* group, which develop only in the proboscis; then the *congolense* group, which develop first in the stomach and then move forward to the pharynx; and finally the *brucei* group, which, after some development in the stomach, move forward and invade the salivary glands, where the cycle of development is completed. So far as known at present this specialized procedure occurs only in tsetse flies, which serve as transmitters of African mammalian trypanosomes, and in leeches, which transmit the trypanosomes of aquatic animals. These trypanosomes are said to develop in the anterior station. The infective trypanosomes that appear at the end of the cycle in insects, whether in the anterior or posterior station, are called metacyclic forms; they resemble the blood forms but are smaller.

Identification of Mammalian Trypanosomes. The following key indicates the principal differences between some of the commoner mammalian trypanosomes:

I. Polymorphic forms; undulating membrane convoluted; kinetoplast usually not terminal; body with metachromatic granules. Invade salivary glands of tsetse flies.

1. Nucleus nearly always central or slightly posterior; low virulence for domestic and laboratory animals (Fig. 38, *1* and *2*)........*T. gambiense.*
2. Nucleus sometimes posterior, especially in small laboratory animals (Fig. 38, *3*); highly virulent in laboratory and domestic animals.
   a. Man not susceptible.....................................*T. brucei.*
   b. Man infectible......................................*T. rhodesiense.*

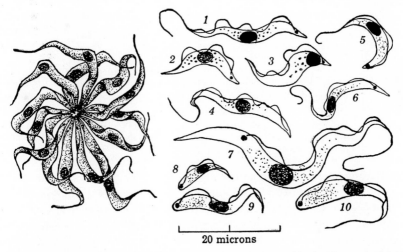

20 microns

Fig. 38.   *Left:* Agglomeration of trypanosomes, *T. lewisi,* in blood of immunized rat. (After Laveran and Mesnil.)   *Right:* Mammalian trypanosomes: *1, brucei* or *gambiense,* with free flagellum; *2,* same, without free flagellum; *3, brucei* or *rhodesiense,* form with posterior nucleus; *4, equinum; 5, cruzi; 6, lewisi; 7, theileri; 8, congolense; 9, simiae; 10, vivax.*

II.   Monomorphic forms with free flagellum.
   1. Undulating membrane only slightly convoluted.
      a. Kinetoplast small, not terminal; nucleus anterior; length about 25 μ; parasite of rats; develops in fleas (Fig. 38, *6*)................*T. lewisi.*
      b. Kinetoplast large, egg-shaped, usually terminal; nucleus central; body stumpy; length about 20 μ; parasite of various small mammals and man; develops in triatomids (Fig. 38, *5*)....................*T. cruzi.*
   2. Undulating membrane moderately or strongly convoluted.
      a. Size large, usually 50–70 μ long; kinetoplast distant from posterior end.
         (1) In cattle; develops in tabanids (Fig. 38, *7*)...........*T. theileri.*
         (2) In sheep; develops in sheep-tick................*T. melophagium*
      b. Size moderate (18–30 μ).
         (1) Posterior end swollen and rounded; undulating membrane moderately convoluted; kinetoplast terminal or nearly so; highly pathogenic for domestic animals, but laboratory animals insusceptible; develops in tsetse fly in proboscis only (Fig. 38, *10*)
         ....*T. vivax*
         (2) Posterior end pointed.
            (*a*) Kinetoplast usually normal; undulating membrane well convoluted; closely resembles flagellated phase of *brucei* (Fig.

38, *1*); highly pathogenic for horses, dogs, and camels (causing surra), and for laboratory animals; milder in cattle and elephants; transmitted by biting flies without developmental cycle ....*T. evansi.*

(*b*) Similar to *evansi,* but no parabasal body in kinetoplast; causes mal-de-caderas in horses in South America (Fig. 38, *4*) ....*T. equinum.*

(*c*) Similar to *evansi,* but milder in dogs; causes dourine in horses; venereally transmitted, with no insect intermediary ....*T. equiperdum.*

III. Monomorphic forms with no free flagellum.

1. Small, 9–18 μ long; kinetoplast terminal or nearly so; produces chronic wasting disease in domestic animals, especially injurious to cattle; not highly virulent for laboratory animals; develops in stomach and pharynx of tsetses, not in salivary glands (Fig. 38, *8*)..............*T. congolense.*

2. Larger, 14–24 μ long; highly virulent for pigs; monkeys, sheep, and goats also susceptible, but usually not other domestic or laboratory animals (Fig. 38, *9*)................................*T. simiae* (or *suis*).

Pathogenicity and Immunity. The very name trypanosome suggests deadly disease, yet at least the majority of trypanosomes are harmless to their hosts. Wenyon in 1926 went so far as to say: " As a general statement, it is safe to regard all trypanosomes as nonpathogenic to their natural hosts." The so-called pathogenic trypanosomes of man and domestic animals he regards as owing their injuriousness to their being in unnatural hosts; in the wild game animals of Africa, which he regards as the natural hosts, they are harbored without ill effects. *T. gambiense* has undoubtedly arisen from a *brucei*-like ancestor and may have adapted itself to man sufficiently to have lost some of its infectiveness for game animals, but has not yet reached a stage of equilibrium with its new host where it can exist without creating a disturbance. It is significant that where human infections have existed longest the disease tends to assume a mild chronic form.

The pathogenicity of trypanosomes depends largely on ability of the hosts to develop trypanocidal antibodies and in some cases reproduction-inhibiting antibodies (Taliaferro, 1926). Vitamin deficiencies may increase their harmfulness; Becker *et al.* in 1947 showed that the usually benign *T. lewisi* may become pathogenic in pantothenate-deficient rats. The serum of a recovered animal contains protective antibodies against the particular trypanosome involved, and shows the usual immune reactions, such as complement fixation and lysis. It also causes the trypanosomes to clump together in rosettes, attached by their posterior ends (Fig. 38, left), and to adhere to leucocytes and platelets in the blood. Serum of naturally immune animals protects against infection when injected but is not destructive *in vitro.*

African Trypanosomiasis and Sleeping Sickness

Two distinct types of trypanosomes cause human disease, one type in Africa, the other in South and Central America. The African trypanosomes belong to a group of closely related polymorphic forms. One of these, *Trypanosoma brucei*, is found in many African wild animals, is highly virulent for domestic animals, especially horses and camels, is infective for almost every kind of mammal except baboons and man, and is transmitted by *Glossina morsitans*. This is without doubt the parent form from which two species or strains capable of infecting man have arisen, namely *T. gambiense* and *T. rhodesiense*. Some authorities consider both of them distinct species, some think that *gambiense* but not *rhodesiense* is distinct from *brucei*, and some, notably Strong, think that all of them are mere strains of a single species modified by life in different tsetse flies or different vertebrate hosts.

It seems evident that here again, as in the case of spirochetes, amebas, and leishmanias, we have run up against the difficulty in classification that comes from the fact that pathogenic organisms are not immutable things that can be described like simple chemical compounds, but are constantly undergoing adaptation and change. Their evolutionary possibilities are great because of their rapid multiplication, and are further enhanced by the isolation and variety of environmental conditions afforded them by life in a variety of intermediate and definitive hosts.

Aside from minor and inconstant differences in behavior in tsetse flies and in effects on laboratory animals, the only difference between *T. gambiense* and *T. rhodesiense* is the fact that the latter, like *T. brucei*, when developing in small laboratory animals produces a small percentage of forms in which the nucleus is displaced to the posterior end of the body. Even this is not a constant difference, and it is possible that it results from unusually rapid multiplication, and may be only an indication of virulence of the parasite or susceptibility of the host.

Although these two forms of African trypanosomes may really be strains rather than species, most writers refer to them by their species names, so for convenience these are retained here.

Morophology and Habits. The African polymorphic trypanosomes vary in length from about 15 to 30 μ, with exceptionally longer or shorter forms. They show the characteristic slender forms with free flagellum, stumpy forms without a free flagellum, and intermediate forms, in any single blood or gland smear (Fig. 39). They are nearly always sparse in human blood, and are usually more abundant in the juice of enlarged lymph glands. They also occur in the spleen, which is often enlarged. Later, usually after 3 months, they appear in the cerebrospinal fluid and even in the tissues of the brain and spinal cord. Throughout the infection they live between the cells and are only found inside the cells when they have been ingested by phagocytes.

These trypanosomes are not easily cultured in the usual artificial media, but thrive when inoculated into developing chick embryos.

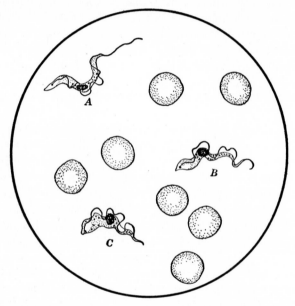

Fig. 39. *Trypanosoma gambiense* with blood corpuscles, showing *A*, long form with free flagellum; *B*, intermediate form; and *C*, short form without free flagellum. × about 1200.

Trypanosoma gambiense is readily inoculated into certain kinds of monkeys and less readily into small laboratory animals, unless first passed through a monkey. Various antelopes and other herbivorous animals, and also dogs, are susceptible. The Situtunga antelope is an important natural reservoir in some places, and domestic animals, particularly pigs, may also serve in this capacity.

T. rhodesiense parasitizes wild game and domestic animals as well as man. Normal human serum is toxic to all kinds of trypanosomes except *T. gambiense* and *T. rhodesiense*, but whereas *T. gambiense* apparently never loses this immunity, *T. rhodesiense* may do so after being kept in culture or in laboratory animals for a long time. This suggests that *T. rhodesiense* is a strain that has not become as thoroughly acclimated to human blood as *T. gambiense*. The rather sporadic appearance of human cases or outbreaks also supports the view that *T. rhodesiense* is merely a recurring strain of *T. brucei* which has been able to adapt itself to living in the presence of human serum. The less perfect adaptation of this form as a human parasite is also indicated by its greater virulence.

Distribution. Human infections with *Trypanosoma gambiense* occur in a wide area in tropical western Africa from Senegal to Loanda, extending inland along the rivers, particularly the Congo and Niger. The affected areas have been extended to Lake Tanganyika and southern Sudan by white settlement and consequent movement of infected natives. Stanley's expedition to reach Emir Pasha in 1888 probably introduced the disease to virgin territory in Uganda and the Great Lakes region, where it gave rise to a terrible epidemic that in one district reduced the population from 300,000 in 1901 to 100,000 in 1908. Some whole villages and islands were depopulated.

In more recent years the severity of the disease has been reduced in many parts of Africa by preventive measures and treatment, together with a natural decrease in virulence in many areas. In Nigeria alone from 1931 to 1937 over 2,000,000 examinations were made, with detection and treatment of 300,000 cases. The infection rate in Nigeria is now only one-tenth of what it used to be. However, in many endemic areas in Africa from 5 to 30 per cent or more of the natives are still infected.

T. rhodesiense infection was first reported in Rhodesia in 1909. Since then many more cases have occurred over a fairly wide area in eastern Africa from Kenya to southern Rhodesia and northern Mozambique, and inland across Tanganyika to Uganda and eastern Congo. A few outbreaks that might be termed epidemics have occurred, including one in Uganda in 1940–1943, but in general the infection in *T. rhodesiense* areas is markedly sporadic.

The occurrence of this strain of trypanosomes since 1909 is probably correlated with reduction in amount of wild game and concomitant increase in domestic animals around human settlements, thus drawing *Glossina morsitans,* the principal vector of *T. brucei,* in from the drier, game-inhabited, and relatively nonpopulated areas to the vicinity of villages and farms. The resulting closer relation of this fly to man would obviously facilitate the development of a strain of *T. brucei* which is infective for humans.

Transmission. The entire group of polymorphic trypanosomes is transmitted by tsetse flies; they differ from other tsetse fly-transmitted trypanosomes by invading the salivary glands of the flies. The species of tsetse flies involved vary with the strains. The principal vector of *brucei* and *rhodesiense* is *Glossina morsitans*, although in one part of Tanganyika *G. swynnertoni* is also an important carrier. In the Uganda epidemic of *T. rhodesiense* in 1940–1943, *G. pallidipes* seemed to be the principal transmitter. The principal vector of *gambiense* is *G. palpalis*, but in northern Nigeria and Cameroons *G. tachinoides* seems to be the important transmitter. These species of Glossina are discussed on pp. 649–652. Experimentally *T. brucei* and *rhodesiense* can also be transmitted by *G. palpalis* and other tsetses, and *T. gambiense* by *G. morsitans*.

There are two methods by which tsetse flies can transmit trypanosomes — by direct inoculation, or by inoculation after a cycle of devel-

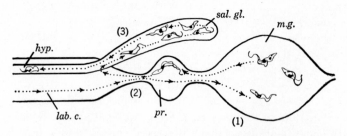

Fig. 40. Course of development of *T. gambiense* in tsetse flies. (1) Multiplication in mid-gut in trypanosome form; (2) long, slender trypanosomes in proventriculus; (3) passage to salivary glands and development there of crithidial and then infective trypanosome forms; hypopharynx and labial cavity used for passage only; *hyp.*, hypopharynx; *lab. c.*, labial cavity; *m.g.*, mid-gut; *pr.*, proventriculus; *sal. gl.*, salivary gland.

opment. As Duke has shown, when natives push off from the jungly shore of a lake to fish, a swarm of tsetse flies is likely to follow, and if one of these, when biting an infective native, is not allowed to finish its meal in peace, it is likely immediately to try its luck on another individual, injecting trypanosomes which are still in the labial cavity. Duke thinks that particularly virulent strains are built up by such mechanical transfer, and that these may then produce severe local outbreaks, whereas the "cyclical" transmission keeps up the disease in endemic form.

Stomoxys or tabanids may also transmit trypanosomes mechanically, though this must be relatively rare, at least as far as man is concerned. It is, however, the usual method by which *Trypanosoma evansi*, the cause of surra, is transmitted to horses and other domestic animals in the Far East.

Development in Tsetse Flies. When cyclical development occurs, the ingested parasites multiply first in the middle intestine, producing forms with more anteriorly placed kinetoplasts (Fig. 41*B*). After the tenth to fifteenth day long slender forms (Fig. 41C) are developed, and these move forward to the proventriculus. These slender trypanosomes have long snouts and differ most strikingly from the earlier forms in the appearance of the nucleus. After several more days the

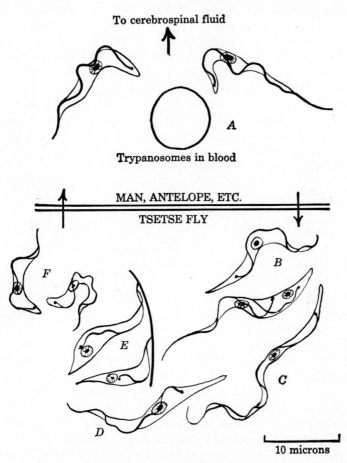

To cerebrospinal fluid

Trypanosomes in blood

MAN, ANTELOPE, ETC.

TSETSE FLY

10 microns

FIG. 41. Life cycle of *T. gambiense*. *A*, long and short forms in human blood; *B*, trypanosomes in mid-gut of tsetse 48 hours after blood meal; *C*, slender proventricular forms, 10th to 15th day; *D*, trypanosome newly arrived in salivary glands, 12th to 20th day; *E*, crithidias in salivary glands, 15th to 25th day; *F*, infective trypanosomes in salivary glands, 20th to 30th day. (Constructed from figures by Robertson.)

trypanosomes make their way to the fly's salivary glands, to the walls of which they attach themselves by their flagella (Fig. 41E) and, rapidly multiplying, undergo a crithidial stage. As multiplication continues free-swimming trypanosome forms are again produced which very closely resemble the parasites in vertebrate flood (Fig. 41F) and which are now capable of infecting a vertebrate host. The whole cycle in the fly usually occupies from 20 to 30 days. A temperature between 75° F. and 85° F. is necessary for the full development of the parasite in the fly, ending in invasion of the salivary glands.

In nature not more than 1 or 2 per 1000 wild tsetses are found infected with trypanosomes of the *brucei* group although 20 to 30 per cent of the game on which they feed are infected. Miss Robertson believed that there is a recurring " endogenous " cycle of development in the vertebrate host and that at certain periods the blood is not infective even though numerous trypanosomes are present. Many flies appear to be completely refractory to infection, as Huff has shown to be true of mosquitoes and malaria. On the other hand, individuals gifted with susceptibility are often found to be infected with more than one species of trypanosome. Strains of trypanosomes vary in their ability to infect the salivary glands of tsetses, and some lose their power of cyclical transmission entirely after prolonged cultivation of passage through animals.

Trypanosome Fever and Sleeping Sickness

The course of the disease caused by trypanosome infection is insidious and irregular. The Gambian and Rhodesian diseases are essentially alike in their symptoms and in the course they run, except that the latter is usually more rapid in development and more virulent in effect, as a rule causing death within 3 or 4 months after infection. The variety of the Gambian disease found in Nigeria is comparatively mild and of long duration.

The bite of an infected tsetse fly is usually followed by itching and irritation near the wound, and frequently a local, dark-red, button-like lesion develops, occasionally increasing to considerable size. After a few days, fever and headache develop, recurring at irregular intervals for weeks or even months, accompanied by increasing weakness, enlarged glands, and usually some edema, and a markedly lowered resistance to other diseases. Often a peculiar tenderness of the muscles is complained of also. Usually an irritating rash breaks out during the early stages of the disease. Sometimes for long intervals trypanosomes are so sparse in the blood that they can be detected only by animal inoculation. Loss of ambition and vitality usually figure prominently, and childbirth is seriously interfered with.

It is possible that after weeks or months or years of irregular fever and debility the disease may spontaneously disappear and never become more than trypanosome fever. Usually, however, the parasites ultimately succeed in penetrating to the cerebrospinal fluid of the brain and spinal cord, and "sleeping sickness" results.* In the Rhodesian disease the central nervous system is usually invaded early, but in the Gambian disease this is a late manifestation and may appear from a few months to at least 7 years after the onset of symptoms. The invasion is accompanied by a striking accumulation of round cells in and around the walls of vessels in the brain and by characteristic increases in the cells of the cerebrospinal fluid.

Sleeping sickness is ushered in by an increase in the general physical and mental depression. The victim wants to sleep constantly and lies in a stupor; his mind works very slowly, and even the slightest physical exertion is obnoxious. Eventually the sleepiness gets such a hold on him that he is likely to lose consciousness at any time and even neglects to swallow his food. After weeks of this increasing drowsiness his body becomes emaciated, a trembling of the hands and other parts of the body develops, with occasional muscular convulsions and sometimes maniacal attacks. He finally passes into a state of total coma ending in death, or death may end the unhappy condition earlier during an unusually intense convulsion or fever, or through the agency of some complicating disease. If untreated, death is the inevitable outcome. A large percentage of infections occurs among people of middle age; old people are significantly few in number in sleeping-sickness districts.

Diagnosis. Diagnosis should be confirmed by finding the parasites in blood or gland juice in early cases, or in cerebrospinal fluid when symptoms or increased cells suggest involvement of the central nervous system. Often the parasites are very scanty, and inoculation of laboratory animals may have to be resorted to. Blood can be examined by centrifuging it twice, just enough to throw down the red cells each time, removing the supernatant and leucocyte cream, and recentrifuging this at high speed for a long time, then examining the sediment. Sometimes the parasites are detectable by their movement in fresh, fairly thick preparations, or they may be found in Giemsa-stained thick smears.

Examination of gland juice obtained by puncturing an enlarged gland with a dry needle is usually more reliable in early cases, and in late cases centrifuged cerebrospinal fluid is more frequently positive than is the blood. Marrow obtained by sternal puncture is sometimes positive, but less often than in leishmaniasis.

Treatment. When the trypanosomes are still confined to the blood and lymph systems, in the first stage of trypanosomiasis, successful

*It should be noted that the so-called sleeping sickness of the United States is a totally different disease, caused by a filtrable virus.

treatment is possible by a number of drugs, but most of these drugs are ineffective against trypanosomes that have invaded the central nervous system in the second stage of the disease, and must be supplemented by drugs that will penetrate into the cerebrospinal fluid.

Among the many drugs that have been found effective against trypanosomiasis in its first stage are various arsenic and antimony compounds, particularly atoxyl and tartar emetic; a urea derivative, Bayer 205, also called Antrypol, Germanin, Suramin, etc.; and certain aromatic diamidines, especially stilbamidine and pentamidine. Bayer 205 and pentamidine have been most favored, as they are relatively low in toxicity. They render the patient noninfective for tsetse flies after only one or two doses. They provide permanent cures in a high percentage of cases, and they protect against reinfection for several months. Bayer 205 is usually given in 4 to 10 intravenous injections of 1 gram each at intervals of 3 or 4 days, whereas pentamidine is injected in daily doses of 0.1 gram for ten days. Bayer 205 is very well tolerated except by a few people who show idiosyncrasies to it. The diamidines sometimes cause initial alarming symptoms, especially a marked fall in blood pressure, but these pass away in 10 to 30 minutes.

To combat trypanosomes which have invaded the central nervous system, the only effective drug known up to about 1945 was a pentavalent arsenic compound, tryparsamide, which has marked disadvantages because it is dangerously toxic and because strains of trypanosomes that are resistant to the drug have cropped up all over Africa. According to Friedheim (1949), the Sleeping Sickness Service of the Belgian Congo reported that, in 1947, 80 per cent of all second-stage cases of trypanosomiasis detected were resistant to tryparsamide. Unlike the 10- to 14-day treatments possible with other drugs, tryparsamide treatment requires a series of once-a-week injections of 0.04 grams per kilo for 10 or 12 weeks, usually repeated once or even twice after 3-month intervals, so that a completed treatment takes as long as a year. The drug sometimes injures the optic nerve and may cause blindness. According to Sandground and Hamilton, p-aminobenzoic acid, if administered with or just prior to the drug, has protective action against the toxic effects of this and other pentavalent arsenic and antimony compounds, such as Carbarsone, atoxyl, and Stibosan.

In 1946 Weinman obtained promising results from treatment with a trivalent arsenic compound, Melarsen Oxide, which has low toxicity, can be given either by mouth or by injection, and is curative in all stages of the disease in a reasonably short time. Friedheim (1949) stated that even advanced second-stage cases have been cured by 2 series of 7 daily injections of 1.5 mg. per kilogram, with a month of rest between. Friedheim also reported very favorable preliminary results with a related drug, Mel B, and recommended 2 series of 4 daily doses of 3.6 mg. per kilogram, separated by a week.

Thus far no method of dealing with drug-fast strains of trypanosomes has been found except the use of a variety of different drugs, for the parasites obstinately retain their resistance even after passage through tsetse flies, just as malaria parasites do after sexual reproduction in mosquitoes. As long as tryparsamide was the only drug available for treatment of the sleeping sickness stage of the disease, the situation was very discouraging.

Prevention. The ultimate control of sleeping sickness resolves itself into the question of controlling or locally exterminating the particular tsetse flies which serve as intermediate hosts; this is discussed in detail on pp. 652–653. Great numbers of people now live safely in fly-protected areas that were formerly almost uninhabitable. In the meantime other methods for controlling, if not entirely eliminating, the disease have been utilized with more or less success. These consist in reducing, as far as possible, contacts between tsetse flies and man, by the careful selection of sites for camps and villages, local clearing of brush from river edges, and large-scale examination and treatment of cases. In some places inhabitants have been removed on a wholesale scale from badly infected localities, and in other places quarantine and spraying of conveyances have been employed to prevent extension to new areas.

In the Belgian Congo prior to World War II, almost astronomical numbers of people (over 3 million) were examined annually. As a result of treatment of these at dispensaries the incidence was reduced from about 12 to 6 per 1000. In Nigeria, as already noted, the incidence has been reduced about 90 per cent. Even if treatments are insufficient to effect complete cures, giving enough drug to eliminate the trypanosomes from the peripheral blood protects other members of a community. A single injection of 1 gram of Bayer 205 or tryparsamide appears to be protective against infection for 3 to 6 months, and an injection of pentamidine is said to guarantee against natural infection for 6 months or longer. According to Lester (1939), however, there is little hope of complete eradication of the disease by treatment methods.

Chagas' Disease

A different type of human trypanosome infection was found by Chagas in 1909 in the state of Minas Geraes in Brazil. He discovered that the houses of the natives were infested with large bloodsucking bugs, *Panstrongylus megistus*, which the natives called barbeiros, and that these bugs were infected with flagellates which, when inoculated into monkeys and guinea pigs, caused acute infections. On further investigation he found that in the infested houses there were frequent cases, especially among infants and young children, of an acute disease characterized by fever, enlarged glands, anemia, and disturbances of the nervous system. In one of these cases trypanosomes were found in the blood, and in others they were demonstrated by injection of animals.

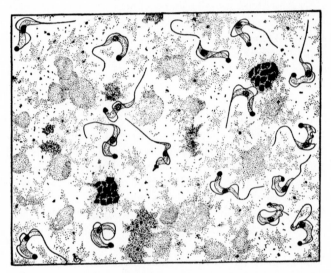

Fig. 42.   *Trypanosoma cruzi* in dehemoglobinized thick drop of blood from experimentally infected mouse.   (After Brumpt.)

These trypanosomes, named *Trypanosoma cruzi* or *Schizotrypanum cruzi* (see p. 159), have since been found to parasitize many small mammals, and to be common in bugs of the family Triatomidae all the way from the pampas of Argentina to the deserts and canyons of southern California and Arizona, and the scrub woods and farms of southern Texas.   A similar parasite has been found in Asiatic monkeys. Fortunately, human infection is far less widely distributed.

In 1944 another trypanosome, *T. rangeli*, was found in a clean triatomid bug, *Rhodnius prolixus*, fed on a child in Venezuela; in 1948 it was isolated from a number of human cases in Venezuela, and dogs were found to be reservoirs.   A trypanosome reported from man and from *R. prolixus* in Guatemala and called *T. guatemalensis* is probably also *T. rangeli*.   As yet there is no evidence that this trypanosome is pathogenic.

The Parasite. *Trypanosoma cruzi* is a curved, stumpy trypanosome about 20 μ long, with a pointed posterior end, an elongated nucleus in the center of the body, a large egg-shaped kinetoplast close to the posterior end, a narrow and only slightly rippled undulating membrane, and a moderately long free flagellum (Fig. 42).

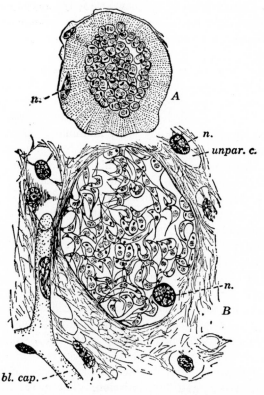

Fig. 43. *Trypanosoma cruzi.* *A*, cyst containing Leishmania forms in muscle fiber of guinea pig, cross section; *n.*, nucleus of muscle fiber. *B*, older cyst, containing trypanosome forms, in neuroglia cell in gray matter of cerebrum; *n.*, nucleus of parasitized cell; *bl. cap.*, blood capillary; *unpar. c.*, unparasitized cell. × 1000. (After Vianna.)

This species as found in the blood never exhibits stages in division. Greatly swollen cells, enclosing a mass of rapidly dividing trypanosomes, varying in number from just a few to many hundreds, were found in 1911 by Vianna in tissues of man and animals dead of the disease, especially in the heart and voluntary muscles, central nervous system, and various glands. During the stage of rapid intracellular multiplication the parasites are round in form and resemble leishman bodies (Fig. 43*A*), but as they grow older a flagellum grows out, and crithidial and eventually trypanosome forms develop (Fig. 43*B*). Then the loaded cell ruptures, liberating the parasites, which invade neighboring cells or are distributed to other parts of the body by the lymph or blood system, unless destroyed by immunological reactions before they reach the safety of another cell. It is only in the early acute stage of the disease that the parasites can live in the blood for long; in the chronic stage, when antibody reaction has occurred, the blood forms are rarely seen and can be demonstrated only by animal inoculation or culture, although parasites may still be abundant in tissue cells.

T. cruzi is a very versatile trypanosome. Its natural hosts appear to be armadillos, opossums, and rodents; it can thrive in monkeys, marmosets, guinea pigs, rats, rabbits, cats, dogs, and other mammals, but not birds or cold-blooded vertebrates. Man seems to be more resistant to infection than many other mammals. Dias *et al.* (1945) think that wild animals are not important reservoirs of infection as far as man is concerned, although cats and dogs may be of some importance. Where human infection is common, the transmitting triatomid bugs have adapted themselves to living in houses and the infection is essentially a residential one.

Probably a number of strains of the parasite exist, possibly differing in their infectivity for man. A strain found in bats can seldom be successfully inoculated into other animals. Mazzoti (1940) isolated a number of strains from triatomids in Mexico which differed in their virulence for guinea pigs. In French Guiana, different strains vary in their infectivity for particular species of triatomids.

T. cruzi can be cultivated in NNN medium or blood broth. Unlike some trypanosomes it does not multiply in the chorio-allantoic fluid of developing chick embryos, though it may survive for a number of days. It will, however, grow in chick embryo tissue cultures.

Intermediate Hosts, and Transmission. The insect transmitters of *T. cruzi* are the large and usually highly colored bugs of the family Triatomidae (see p. 561). More than 30 species of these bugs have been found infected, and it is not unlikely that all of them may be. There are, however, relatively few species that are important as transmitters to man; these are the ones that habitually invade houses. In parts of Brazil the most important one is *Panstrongylus megistus*, a fierce black and red insect infesting the thatched mud houses of natives, coming out at night to suck blood and skillfully secreting itself in the daytime. In almost all other parts of South America (Argentina, parts of Brazil, Uruguay, Bolivia, Chile) *Triatoma infestans* plays the leading part, but in the north (Venezuela, French

Guiana) the chief vector is *Rhodnius prolixus*. These transmitters are discussed on p. 565.

Experimentally bedbugs, ticks, and other arthropods can be infected, but they seem to play little or no part in transmission.

The development of *T. cruzi* in the intermediate host is similar to that of *T. lewisi* of rats, and takes place in the "posterior station." Within 24 hours the trypanosomes may pass into the intestinal portion of the mid-gut, where they transform into crithidias and multiply abundantly. Eventually crithidial forms pass to the rectum where small ones are found attached to the epithelium. In the rectum they give rise to "metacyclic" trypanosomes which resemble those in verte-

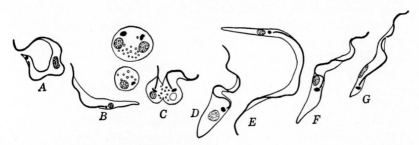

Fig. 44.   Development of *Trypanosoma cruzi* in digestive tract of *Triatoma megista*. *A*, freshly ingested trypanosome; *B*, crithidia, 6 to 10 hours after ingestion; *C*, leishmanias in mid-gut, 10 to 20 hours after ingestion; *D*, redevelopment of flagellum and undulating membrane, 21 hours after ingestion; *E* and *F*, crithidias in hind-gut, 25 hours after ingestion; *G*, metacyclic trypanosome in rectum, 8 days or more after ingestion. (*A*, *B*, and *G* after Wenyon; *C–F* after Brumpt.)

brate blood and are the infective forms. These appear about the sixth day in larval bugs, but not until the tenth to fifteenth in adults. As many as 3500 of these per cubic millimeter may be voided with the insect's excreta.

Normally the salivary glands do not become infective, but S. F. Wood in 1942 found trypanosomes in great numbers in the body cavity of dead bugs. Probably accidents of some sort caused the body-cavity invasions, which resulted in death of the bugs, but such bugs *might* transmit the infection by their bites before dying.

Transmission usually comes from contamination of mucous membranes or skin with infected excreta. Human infection seems most frequently to come from rubbing the eyes after a bite on the lids, presumably contaminating the mucous membranes or conjunctiva with feces deposited by the bug while feeding, or squeezed out by slapping. Animals can become infected by eating the bugs or licking their bites. Cats can be infected by eating infected rodents. The infection can also spread from bug to bug by cannibalism or ingestion of liquid feces (see p. 566). Once infected, a bug remains so probably for the rest of its life.

Human Infection. Human infection with Chagas' disease occurs all the way from Mexico to northern Argentina but is by no means evenly distributed. It is an odd fact that no natural human infections have been observed in the United States, in spite of the fact that *Trypanosoma cruzi* has been found in many species of triatomids and frequently in a high percentage of individual bugs even in houses (see pp. 566–567). That the Texas strain is infective for man is indicated by a single successful experimental transmission by Packchanian (1943). In South America the disease is most prevalent in areas where species of triatomids live like bedbugs in houses and habitually suck human blood. Since the bites of triatomids are not infective unless contaminated by the bugs' feces, only constant exposure to bites, especially during sleep, when they are unconsciously rubbed, is likely to lead to infection, and then only if the bugs regularly defecate during or immediately after a meal, as the " domestic " South American species do. It is possible that the nondomesticated species of triatomids in North America are not as quick to defecate after a meal and are therefore less prone to cause infection. This is known to be true of *T. protracta*.

Only a few cases occur in Mexico and Central America, and little is heard of the disease in Colombia, Ecuador, or Peru. It is common, however, in many parts of Venezuela, French Guiana, Brazil, Bolivia, northern Chile, Paraguay, Uruguay, and northern Argentina. In some areas in Brazil, Bolivia, Chile, and Argentina from 10 to 20 per cent of the inhabitants show evidence of infection. In Brazil it is particularly common in a goiterous area in the state of Minas Geraes.

There seems to be a rather high natural resistance to acute infections; these occur most frequently in infants and children in whom resistance is weakened by a goiterous condition, malnutrition, or chronic malaria or other chronic diseases. However, acute cases do occur in individuals who are otherwise apparently healthy. The occasional finding of parasites in the blood or by xenodiagnosis in unsuspected cases, high incidence of positive Machado reactions (see p. 178), and frequency of characteristic electrocardiographic changes indicate that the infection is much more frequent than was formerly thought. That the infection is often overlooked is suggested by the fact that until 1937 no case had been recorded in Uruguay. When looked for after a case was publicized, 18 cases were recorded in the course of a year. In the northern half of Chile 12 per cent of individuals examined harbored *T. cruzi*, and 17 per cent gave positive Machado reactions.

When Chagas first discovered human trypanosome infections in the regions of endemic goiter in Minas Geraes, he believed that the goiter, with all its sinister consequences — myxedema, infantilism, cretinism, etc. — was caused by the trypanosome infection, through a supposed toxic effect on the thyroid gland. But it is now evident that Chagas got the cart before the horse — trypanosome infections were the result of the goiter, not vice versa.

Prenatal infection has been reported in dogs, and one human case reported by Mazza was apparently acquired with the mother's milk.

The Disease. Acute cases of Chagas' disease are especially common in infants or young children. Frequently the disease begins with an endematous swelling of the eyelids and conjunctiva (Fig. 45) and sometimes other parts of the face, usually only on one side. This is accompanied by inflammation of the tear gland and swelling of lymph glands of the neck. These symptoms suggest that the eye may be the usual site of inoculation, the insect biting the lids, and the victim then rubbing infected excreta from the bug into his eye. The swelling, called a primary " chagoma," is caused by an inflammatory exudation in the locality where the parasites are colonizing in tissue cells, particularly in subcutaneous fat cells. Later other chagomata may appear in distant parts of the body; they may be conspicuous or only detectable by palpation. During early days of the dis-

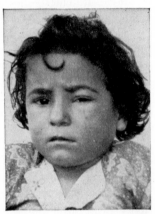

FIG. 45. Acute case of Chagas' disease in 5-year-old Brazilian girl, with trypanosomes easily seen in blood. (Photo by Emmanuel Dias.)

ease there may be severe headache and marked prostration, with more or less continuous fever. After this acute stage subsides the disease goes into a chronic stage, which many authors believe persists for life, but there may first be a long latent period with few or no symptoms, during which the disease is insidiously progressing. Characteristic symptoms in the chronic stage are extensive, hard edema, inflamed lymph glands, and enlarged liver and spleen. In protracted cases there is a progressive anemia and sometimes such nervous disturbances as delirium, convulsions, extreme lassitude, or paralysis. In severe cases death may occur in 2 or 3 weeks.

In animals the trypanosomes tend to localize in particular organs, especially the heart, lymph glands, or central nervous system, and they produce symptoms according to where they localize. Disturbance of the function of the heart is very common and according to Chagas is the commonest chronic manifestation in man. Nearly all fatal cases show injury to the heart muscle, which is one of the favorite tissues attacked by the parasite. The injury causes separation of the cells, inflammatory infiltration by phagocytic cells, and increase of fibrous tissue, which weakens the heart in chronic cases. Electrocardiograms show characteristic types of heart blocks and other abnormalities. The prevalence of chronic heart disease and frequent deaths from strokes in the parts of South America where Chagas' disease occurs is suspected by some to be the result of chronic trypanosome infection. As in certain parts of Africa where trypanosomiasis is prevalent, elderly people are few.

Diagnosis. In acute cases a diagnosis can usually be made by finding the parasites in direct blood smears, but in some acute and most subacute cases such slow or tiresome methods as blood cultures, large inoculations of blood into susceptible animals, or xenodiagnosis (feeding of uninfected bugs on the patient) have been resorted to. Muniz, however, showed in the late 1940's that a precipitin test is helpful in such cases, using a polysaccharide extract of cultured trypanosomes as antigen; this method is simple, rapid, and reliable, since no crossreactions are obtained in leishmaniasis cases. In chronic cases a complement fixation test, called the Machado reaction, is useful; negative reactions rule out all but very early stages of infection, and strongly positive results occur only in *T. cruzi* and Leishmania infections. The latter can be ruled out by clinical examination or by the formol-gel test (see p. 148), which is not positive in Chagas' disease.

Treatment and Prevention. No successful method of treatment of *Trypanosoma cruzi* infections has yet been found, except injection of Bayer 7602, reported by Mazza *et al.* to bring about much improvement in acute cases and severe cases with brain involvement, but it is doubtful that the infection is often completely eliminated. Chronic cardiac cases must be treated sympomatically.

Prevention of the disease consists largely in avoiding and exterminating the house-dwelling triatomids (see p. 567), but it is practically impossible to keep the bugs out of mud or thatched houses. For this reason the rebuilding of houses with other materials is being urged everywhere in Brazil, and with good results. The town of Belo-Horizonte, for example, is said to have been nearly freed from Chagas' disease by remodeling of the houses. People accidentally bitten by triatomids, if conscious of it, should avoid possible contamination of the bite by the feces of the bug.

Trypanosomiasis of Animals

Domestic Animals. As can be seen from the key on p. 161, many trypanosomes are pathogenic to domestic animals. In Africa *Trypanosoma brucei* is the most virulent; it causes a severe disease, nagana, in nearly all domestic and laboratory animals. Horses, camels, cattle, pigs, dogs, and monkeys (except baboons) are usually killed, the virulence being about in the order named. Sheep and goats are somewhat more resistant. *T. congolense* produces a chronic wasting disease in various domestic animals, especially cattle. *T. simiae* is highly virulent for pigs and monkeys, and slightly so for goats; almost all other animals are refractory. *T. vivax* is especially common in cattle, sheep, and goats, and less so in horses; goats sometimes survive, but other animals seldom do. For all these, African game animals serve as reservoirs, and tsetse flies as transmitters.

A new drug, antrycide, announced in 1948 as effective in a single dose both for treatment and prophylaxis of trypanosomiasis in animals, may make Africa one of the world's important meat-raising areas.

T. evansi, widespread in tropical parts of the world, causes a fatal disease, surra, in horses and dogs. In camels and elephants it is more chronic and these animals sometimes recover; cattle are still less susceptible. *T. hippicum* in Panama and *T. venezuelense* in Venezuela are closely related to *evansi* if not identical with it, but *hippicum* is transmitted by vampire bats and also venereally. *T. equiperdum* resembles *evansi* but is a venereally transmitted species causing dourine in horses. It is endemic in most parts of the world, including North America. Dogs develop severe infections when inoculated. *T. equinum* of South America, causing mal-de-caderas, also closely resembles *evansi*, but it lacks a parabasal body. All these appear to be transmitted by bloodsucking flies or ticks, especially tabanids, without cyclical development. They are probably strains of the polymorphic (*brucei*) group that have lost their ability to develop in tsetses as a result of continual direct passage from one vertebrate host to another.

T. theileri is a nonpathogenic species of cattle, with cyclic development in tabanids. It is so sparse in cattle blood that it can be demonstrated only by feeding of clean tabanids or by culture. It occurs in American cattle in some localities. The related *T. melophagium* of sheep, with cyclic development in sheep ticks, occurs in Europe.

Trypanosoma lewisi in Rats. Although of no economic importance, *T. lewisi* of rats is of interest because it is easily obtained and because interesting biological studies can be carried out with it. Numerous parasites appear in the blood of young rats about 5 or 6 days after infection; the number rises steadily for a few days, but because of the development of an inhibition of reproduction, followed by destruction of a high percentage of the parasites by a trypanolytic antibody (see p. 162), the parasites soon become sparse, and rats rarely suffer from the infection unless deficient in vitamins (see p. 162). *T. lewisi* can be cultured on blood-agar media. Rat fleas serve as intermediate hosts, the development being in the posterior station (see p. 160).

REFERENCES

BRUMPT, E., Le *Trypanosoma rhodesiense,* Revue critique, *Ann. parasitol. humaine et comparée,* **2,** 254 (1924).

La Maladie de C. Chagas, *Presse méd.,* **47,** 1013–1015, 1081–1085 (1939).

BUXTON, P. A., *Trypanosomiasis in Eastern Africa, 1947,* Colonial Office, London, 1948.

CHAGAS, C., Ueber eine neue Trypanosomiasis des Menschen, *Mem. inst. Oswaldo Cruz,* **1,** 158–218 (1909).

DIAS, E., LARANJA, F. S., and NOBREGA, G., Doença de Chagas, *Mem. inst. Oswaldo Cruz,* **43,** (3), 495–582 (1945).

DUKE, H. L., Some Recent Advances in the Biology of Trypanosomes of Sleeping Sickness, *Trans. Roy. Soc. Trop. Med. Hyg.,* **30,** 275 (1936).

FAIRBAIRN, H., and CULWICK, A. T., A New Approach to Trypanosomiasis, *Ann. Trop. Med. Parasitol.,* **40,** 421–452 (1946).

FRIEDHEIM, E. A. H., Mel B in the Treatment of Human Trypanosomiasis, *Am. J. Trop. Med.,* **29,** 173–180 (1949).

GASIC, L. G., Algunos hechos sobre clinica y epidemiologia de la enfermedad de Chagas en Chile, *Bol. oficina sanit. panamer.,* **22,** 327 (1943).

LESTER, H. M. O., Certain Aspects of Trypanosomiasis in Some African Dependencies, *Trans. Roy. Soc. Trop. Med. Hyg.,* **33,** 11 (1939).

MAZZA, S., *et al.,* Investigaciones sobre enfermedad de Chagas, *Univ. Buenos Aires: Missión de estudios de patologia regional Argentina* (Jujuy), *Pub.,* **42–63** (1939–1942).

MAZZOTI, L., Variations in Virulence for Mice and Guinea Pigs in Strains of *Trypanosoma cruzi* Chagas from Different Species of Bugs (Triatomidae) from Different Localities in Mexico, *Am. J. Hyg.,* **31** (C), 67 (1940).

PACKCHANIAN, A., Natural infection of *Triatoma gerstakeri* with *Trypanosoma cruzi* in Texas, *Publ. Health Rept.,* **54,** 1547–1554 (1939); Natural infection of *Triatoma heidemanni* with *Trypanosoma cruzi* in Texas, *Publ. Health Repts.,* **55,** 1300–1306 (1940).

Infectivity of the Texas Strain of *Trypanosoma cruzi* to Man, *Am. J. Trop. Med.,* **23,** 309–314 (1943).

TALIAFERRO, W. H., Host Resistance and Types of Infections in Trypanosomiasis and Malaria, *Quart. Rev. Biol.,* **1,** 246 (1926).

VEATCH, E. P., BEQUAERT, J. C., and WEINMAN, M. D., Human Trypanosomiasis and Tsetse-Flies in Liberia, *Am. J. Trop. Med.,* Suppl., **26** (5), 1–105 (1946).

WOOD, F. D., and WOOD, S. F., Present Knowledge of the Distribution of *Trypanosoma cruzi* in Reservoir Animals and Vectors, *Am. J. Trop. Med.,* **21,** 335 (1941).

CHAPTER 9

The Sporozoa. I. Malaria

The Sporozoa include a large and varied assemblage of Protozoa which have little in common except a parasitic mode of life, the lack of any organs of locomotion during most stages of their development, and the evolution of a complicated life cycle usually involving an alternation of generations and the production of resistant stages which in some cases are called spores. The term Sporozoa was originally proposed by Leuckart in 1879 for the Coccidia and a group of parasites found principally in invertebrates, called gregarines, but was later extended to include a host of related and unrelated parasitic spore-forming Protozoa. Doflein in 1901 separated the sheep from the goats, reserving the name Sporozoa for those which showed some evidence of relationship to the forms for which Leuckart originally proposed it, and lumping the others together in a class Cnidosporidia. Some protozoologists, apparently more for convenience than from conviction, still keep the true Sporozoa and the Cnidosporidia together, in which case the name Sporozoa is used for the entire class and the name Telosporidia for the true Sporozoa.

Since this is the arrangement adopted by Calkins, Hegner, Kudo, and Pearse in America, it is reluctantly adopted here. Following is a brief outline of the classification of the Sporozoa:

Class **SPOROZOA**

Subclass I. **TELOSPORIDIA** (or **SPOROZOA**, in restricted sense). Alternating sexual and asexual phases; zygotes produce oöcysts and sporozoites for infection of new hosts; sporozoites enter cells and subsequently either reproduce again and again by schizogony, some cells eventually becoming gametocytes, or become extracellular and grow without multiplication, thus all becoming gametocytes.

Order 1. **Gregarinida.** Asexual adults extracellular; usually do not multiply in this phase. Parasites of invertebrates and ascidians.

Order 2. **Coccidia.** All development intracellular. Schizogony in asexual phase. Usually parasites of epithelial cells of intestine or associated glands.

Suborder 1. *Eimeriidea.* (Fig. 53.) Gametocytes similar, not associated during development; microgametes numerous. Zygote not motile, forming resistant oöcysts which do not grow, but produce a number of sporozoites, usually in intermediary sporocysts. Usually no alternation of hosts. Contains ordinary coccidia (Eimeria, Isospora, etc.).

181

Suborder 2. *Adeleidea.* Gametocytes dissimilar, associated during development; microgametes few. Nongrowing oöcysts produced as in Suborder 1. No intermediate hosts. Mostly parasites of invertebrates.

Suborder 3. **Haemogregarina.** (Fig. 52, *5.*) Schizogony in fixed cells, or at least not in peripheral circulation; gametocytes in blood cells. Fertilization as in Adeleidea, but in an intermediate host in which motile zygotes develop into growing oöcysts, as in Haemosporidia. Includes hemogregarines and Hepatozoön.

Order 3. **Haemosporidia.** Asexual phase with intracellular schizogony. Usually parasites of blood cells. Fertilization in intermediate host; zygote motile; oöcysts grow during development, and large numbers of sporozoites are formed.

Family 1. *Plasmodiidae.* (Fig. 49.) Schizogony either in tissue cells (Haemoproteus and Leucocytozoön) or principally in red cells (Plasmodium). Gametocytes in circulating blood. Produce hemozoin pigment granules when in red cells. Includes malaria parasites.

Family 2. *Babesiidae.* (Fig. 52, *6, 7.*) Division into 2 or 4 cells in red blood corpuscles; no other schizogony known. No pigment. Includes Babesia, Theileria, and Aegyptianella.

Of uncertain position. Toxoplasma and Anaplasma. (Fig. 52, *4, 8.*)

Subclass II. **CNIDOSPORIDIA.** Ameboid and multinucleate in adult stage. Spores produced during life of trophozoite; each spore produced from several cells and provided with one or more polar capsules from which long filaments can be protruded. Parasites of invertebrates and fishes. Includes numerous Myxosporidia of fishes, and pathogenic Microsporidia of bees, silkworms, etc.

Subclass III. **ACNIDOSPORIDIA.** Spore-forming Protozoa of doubtful relationships. Spores without polar capsules.

Order 1. **Haplosporidia.** Grow into multinucleate plasmodia in cells or cavities of aquatic animals. Spores of various form but without polar capsules.

Until recently the Sarcosporidia were included as a second order in the Acnidosporidia, but Spindler demonstrated in 1945 that they are not Protozoa but fungi. They grow into large, chambered, cystlike bodies in the muscle cells of vertebrates and become filled with sickleshaped spores. Until 1923 Rhinosporidium, a fungus causing polyplike growths in the nose or eye of man and horses, was also included in this subclass of Protozoa.

In the present chapter we shall consider only the malaria parasites of the genus Plasmodium, and will discuss the other Haemosporidia as well as other Sporozoa of man and animals in Chapter 10.

Systematic Position of Malaria Parasites. The malaria parasites belong to one of the two recognized families of Haemosporidia (see above), the Plasmodiidae. There are three genera in the family. Plasmodium, containing the human malaria parasites, is the only genus in which schizogony takes place in the red blood corpuscles

(Fig. 49); it contains many species found in mammals, birds, and lizards. Haemoproteus, found in birds and reptiles, differs in that only the gametocytes develop in red corpuscles, the asexual forms always developing in reticulo-endothelial cells; the gametocytes (Fig. 52, *1*) curve around the nuclei of the red cells and are called "halteridia" because of their halter shape. Both Plasmodium and Haemoproteus produce blackish or brownish hemozöin pigment granules when growing in red cells. The third genus of the family is Leucocytozoön, found in mammals and birds. It resembles Haemoproteus except that the red cells infected with gametocytes are drawn out into a peculiar fusiform shape (Fig. 52, *2*) and there is no pigment. The gametocytes of haemogregarines and Hepatozoön, also found in erythrocytes (see p. 218), resemble those of Haemoproteus but lack pigment.

The genera Haemoproteus and Leucocytozoön are sometimes separated from Plasmodium into a distinct family Haemoproteidae because their schizogony occurs only in fixed cells and only the gametocytes occur in the blood, but, with the discovery that in many species of Plasmodium, if not all, schizogony may be exoerythrocytic as well as erythrocytic, the fundamental distinction between these families no longer exists. Huff in 1942 showed remarkable similarities among all three genera.

Malaria

Importance. Of all human diseases none is of more importance in the world today than malaria, and this in spite of the fact that we have a very full knowledge of its cause, the manner of its spread, its cure, and means of prevention. It has been estimated to be the direct or indirect cause of over one-half the entire mortality of the human race. It is found in all tropical and subtropical parts of the world, except some of the islands of the Pacific (Hawaii, Fiji, New Caledonia) where there are no Anopheles mosquitoes. It is also mildly or locally endemic in many places far from the tropics. Russell estimated in 1943 that there were 300 million cases in the world and 3 million malarial deaths a year. In an epidemic in Ceylon in 1934, in a population of 5 million, there were 1½ million cases and 70,000 deaths.

It seems evident that, although historians and economists have failed to recognize it, malaria must have played a large part in the history of the world and the progress of nations. With its powerful accomplice, the hookworm, it has been a major factor in the retardation of certain regions, among them parts of our own southern states. In Nyasaland it has been estimated that from 4 to 9 out of every 10 children die before they are 6 years old largely because of malaria. If they survive that long, malaria is not likely to harm them much more, provided they stay in the region and do not allow their immunity to lapse.

During World War II malaria was the Number 1 problem of non-immune troops and caused tremendous havoc in the Mediterranean, India-Burma, and South Pacific theaters of operation. At the fall of Bataan, when quinine ran out, 85 per cent of every regiment had acute malaria. In the South Pacific campaign, malaria caused more than five times as many casualties as did combat. In April 1942, the case rate on Efati was 2678 per 1000 per year, and on Guadalcanal in November 1942, two months after occupation, the rate was 1800 per 1000 per year. That was before the importance of malaria was realized, and before strict malaria discipline was developed. The prevalent attitude then was well expressed by one high-ranking officer who said, "We are out here to fight Japs, and to hell with mosquitoes." That was a good slogan, but not the way the officer meant it. When it became apparent that malaria had to be licked before the Japs could be, the job was successfully done by the combined efforts of entomologists, sanitarians, engineers, physicians, and occasional court martials, and malaria rates dropped to 10 to 50 per 1000 in some of the world's worst malarial areas.

Malaria in the United States. Opinions differ as to whether malaria existed in America in pre-Columbian days, but it developed soon thereafter and was a scourge during colonial and pioneering days. Of 45,713 patients admitted to Charity Hospital in New Orleans from 1814 to 1847, 43 per cent were classed as " fevers " and 20 per cent as " intermittent fevers." In the Civil War one command of 878 men below Savannah had 3313 cases of malaria in 14 months!

In contrast, Faust and DeBakey in 1942 apologized for considering malaria mortality in the United States as a matter of sufficient public interest to write a paper about it, at a time when a single case in Charity Hospital was considered worthy of exhibition to the students of two medical schools. The civilian malaria mortality decreased over 90 per cent in the decade from 1935 to 1945 and is still going down. Andrews in 1948 stated that the malarial death rate for 1946 and the reported case rate for 1947 were about one-fifteenth of their respective figures for 1920. Faust and Hemphill (1948) stated that in 1946 only 341 deaths from malaria were reported from residents of continental United States, as compared with 580 in 1944, 1422 in 1940, and 4435 in 1935. The decrease in morbidity is still more striking. The disease had had a tendency to rise and fall in 5- to 7-year cycles, but its last peak was from 1933 to 1936 in different states, and it has not had the vitality to rise again. It was feared that return of thousands of soldiers with relapsing malaria might cause a marked increase in the disease in the South and a revival of it in places which had long been malaria-free, but owing to careful planning by the U. S. Public Health Service, such outbreaks have been minimal. Reported cases in 1947 were about 17,000 as compared with 48,000 in 1946 and 136,000 in 1935.

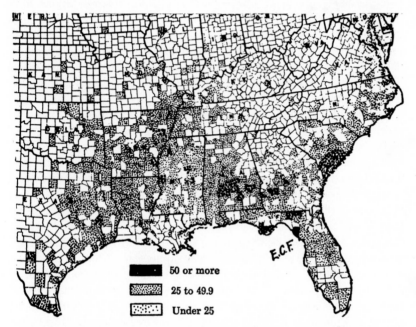

FIG. 46. Malaria mortality rates per 100,000 population in eastern United States in 1940. In 1948 the total malaria deaths were only about one-eighth as numerous.

Agricultural drainage, treatment, screening, better hygiene, and spray guns eliminated malaria from north and midwestern states where it was prevalent before the turn of the century; these factors, augmented by residual DDT spraying, may well banish it from the entire continental United States by 1960.

History. " Malaria," meaning bad air, was so named because of association of the disease with the odorous air of swamps, particularly at night, and the notion that damp night air causes malaria still exists. It was in 1880 that Laveran, a French army surgeon in Algeria, discovered the malarial organism. King in 1883 suggested the probability that malaria parasites were spread by mosquitoes, adducing much circumstantial evidence in support of his views, but it was not until 1898 that Sir Ronald Ross proved experimentally that malaria parasites are absolutely dependent upon certain species of mosquitoes for their transmission and worked out the details in the case of bird malaria. Immediately afterward Grassi and his pupils worked out the cycle of human malaria in Anopheles.

During the ensuing years a great mass of epidemiological knowledge was accumulated; the transmitters were discovered, their habits studied, and methods of control worked out. Striking demonstrations have been made in Havana, Ismailia, Panama, Malaya, and elsewhere. In 1920 Wagner-Jauregg discovered the value of malaria as a treatment for syphilitic paralysis of the insane, and since then a large mass of data has been accumulated from artificial infections. Taliaferro and his colleagues have contributed much to our knowledge of the mechanism of immunity to malaria.

Species of Plasmodium in Animals Other than Man. Numerous species of Plasmodium are found in lizards and birds. The majority of those in birds are, primarily at least, parasites of passerine birds, such as *praecox, cathemerium, elongatum, circumflexum, relictum,* and many others, but *gallinaceum* is primarily a parasite of chickens and other gallinaceous birds, and *lophurae* of pheasants and guinea fowls. Huff *et al.* (1947) have shown that the behavior of these various parasites differs considerably in different hosts, so that it may not be easy to decide which are the natural ones. In unnatural hosts there may be no development at all; more or less suppression of either the blood or exoerythrocytic stages or both; failure to produce gametocytes, or lack of sexual potency of the gametocytes. Interesting examples of these conditions have been given by Huff and Coulston (1946) and by Huff, Coulston, Laird, and Porter (1947). The bird species are transmitted by various species of Aëdes and Culex, and rarely by Anopheles.

Monkeys are the only mammals other than man that harbor malaria parasites, except for a species recently found in an Indian rodent. Several species have been reported from bats, but pigmented schizogonic forms are not found in their blood and no success has been achieved in infecting mosquitoes. Manwell in 1946 expressed the opinion that these bat parasites are more nearly related to Haemoproteus. The monkey parasites closely resemble the human species and are transmitted by Anopheles mosquitoes. One monkey species, *P. knowlesi,* which is usually fatal to rhesus monkeys in 12 days but produces relatively mild infections in man, has been used to some extent for malaria therapy of syphilis (see p. 70). It has an advantage over the human species in that Negroes in southern United States are not immune to it as they are to the human species.

The bird and monkey malarias have been very extensively used in connection with studies of the biology, life cycle, immunity, and treatment of malaria.   During the war many thousands of drugs were " screened " by testing them first on bird malarias in an effort to find better drugs than were available (see p. 206).

Species of Plasmodium in Man.   Four species of Plasmodium are capable of causing malaria in man.   One, *P. ovale*, is very rare, though it has been found in such widely separated parts of the world as

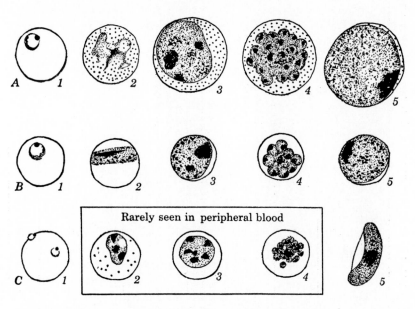

Fig. 47.   Comparison of the three species of malaria parasites, illustrating diagnostic characteristics in each stage.   *A, Plasmodium vivax; B, P. malariae; C, P. falciparum; 1*, " ring " stages; *2*, growing schizonts; *3*, grown schizonts with dividing nucleus; *4*, segmenting parasites nearly ready to leave corpuscle; *5*, female gametocytes.

West Africa, South America, Russia, Palestine, and New Guinea.   The other three species, *P. vivax, P. malariae,* and *P. falciparum,* are common and of wide distribution.

P. vivax is the commonest and most widely distributed species, being prevalent in both tropical and temperate zones.   It is the cause of " tertian " or " benign tertian " malaria, though a better term is " vivax " malaria.   It has a 48-hour cycle of development in man and is particularly likely to cause relapses.   *P. malariae* is also widely distributed in both tropical and temperate climates, but it has a spotty distribution and is usually much less common than either *vivax* or *falciparum*.   It is the cause of " quartan " malaria.   It has a 72-hour cycle and causes infections of many years' duration.   *P. falciparum*

TABLE OF COMPARISONS BETWEEN DIFFERENT SPECIES OF HUMAN MALARIA PARASITES

	P. vivax	P. malariae	P. ovale	P. falciparum
Rings	Coarse, about $\frac{1}{3}$ to $\frac{1}{2}$ diameter of corpuscle; rarely more than one in corpuscle.	Similar to vivax	Similar to vivax; Schüffner's dots may be present even in this stage.	Fine, about $\frac{1}{6}$ to $\frac{1}{5}$ diameter of corpuscle; doubly infected corpuscles common; often situated at edge of corpuscle; two nuclei frequent.
Corpuscles infected with schizonts	Enlarged and pale; contain Schüffner's dots.	Size and color normal; no Schüffner's dots.	Oval in shape, often fimbriated; not much enlarged; normal in color; contain Schüffner's dots.	Not seen in peripheral circulation; size normal; color dark, brassy; have reddish clefts called Maurer's dots, and may have bluish stippling.
Growing schizonts	Very irregular, sprawled out over cell; pigment in small brown granules, usually collected in a mass.	More compact and rounded, or drawn out band-like across cell; pigment blacker and in coarser granules.	Usually round, not ameboid; pigment brownish, coarse, somewhat scattered.	Usually compact, rounded; pigment coarse and blackish; not seen in peripheral circulation.
Segmenters	Nearly fill enlarged, dotted corpuscle; 15 to 20 merozoites, occasionally up to 32, irregularly arranged.	Nearly fill normal-sized corpuscle; 6 to 12 merozoites, commonly 8 or 9, arranged like daisy-head.	Occupy $\frac{3}{4}$ of dotted oval corpuscle; 8 to 10 merozoites, arranged like bunch of grapes.	Occupy $\frac{2}{3}$ to $\frac{3}{4}$ of corpuscle; number of merozoites very variable, from 8 to 32; not seen in peripheral circulation.
Gametocytes	Rounded, larger than corpuscles (10–14 μ in diameter); pigment granules fine, brown, evenly peppered throughout cytoplasm.	Rounded, smaller, nearly filling a corpuscle of normal size; pigment blacker and coarser than in vivax and more or less concentrated at center and periphery.	Rounded, filling $\frac{3}{4}$ of enlarged dotted corpuscle; pigment coarse, black, evenly peppered.	Crescent-shaped or bean-shaped with pigment granules clustered about nucleus at center; remnants of corpuscle often not in evidence.
Distinctions between microgametocytes and macrogametocytes.	Microgametocytes with pale cytoplasm; nucleus large, pink, often stretched across center of body. Macrogametocytes slightly larger, with deeper blue cytoplasm; nucleus small, red, usually lying at or near one side of body.	Same differences as in vivax.	Same differences as in vivax.	Microgametocytes short and squatty with pale blue cytoplasm and pink nucleus; pigment granules scattered except at poles. Macrogametocytes longer and more slender, deeper blue, with small red nucleus; pigment more concentrated near center.
Interval between sporulations.	48 hours.	72 hours.	48 hours.	48 hours.

is very prevalent in the tropics but does not thrive as far north as *vivax* does. It has a 40- to 48-hour cycle of development and is the cause of " malignant tertian," " subtertian " or " aestivo-autumnal " malaria, now preferably called " falciparum " malaria. It causes a much more dangerous disease than the other species but runs a shorter course without relapses, seldom lasting more than 8 to 10 months without reinfection. The principal morphological and physiological differences between the human species are indicated in the table on p. 188 and in Figs. 47 and 48.

In at least two of the human species, *vivax* and *falciparum,* there are races or strains differing in their clinical course, geographic distribution, and ability to produce immunity to each other.

1   2   3   4   5   6

Fig. 48. *Plasmodium ovale; 1,* normal corpuscle; *2,* ring stage; note corpuscle already full of Schüffner's dots. *3,* young schizont; note irregular shape of corpuscle and " fimbriated " appearance, also seen in *4* and *5; 4,* dividing schizont; note oval, fimbriated corpuscle and round parasite; *5,* segmenter; note only 8 merozoites around a central clump of pigment; *6,* female gametocyte; note similarity to quartan gametocyte except for shape of corpuscle and presence of Schüffner's dots. (Drawn from figures by James, Nicol, and Shute.)

There is no animal reservoir for any of these human parasites, although in rare instances apes have been experimentally infected. Malaria cannot, therefore, be acquired in uninhabited regions; for malaria to thrive there must be infected humans and plenty of man-biting Anopheles, and easy contact between the two.

Life Cycle. Although the general nature of the life cycle of all species of Plasmodium is similar, there are some marked differences between them which have very important practical consequences. The general course of the life cycle is shown in Fig. 49.

Exoerythrocytic Stages. It was long thought that the life cycle of malaria parasites involved only two phases, the sexual sporogonic cycle in mosquitoes ending in the production of sporozoites in the salivary glands, and the asexual schizogonic cycle in the red blood corpuscles (erythrocytes) in the vertebrate host, indefinitely repeated or ending in production of gametocytes. It has now become evident, however, that the cycle is not so simple.

When sporozoites are injected by a mosquito they do not enter erythrocytes at once to start their development. In various species of bird malaria it has been demonstrated that the sporozoites, within a few minutes after injection, leave the blood stream and enter tissue

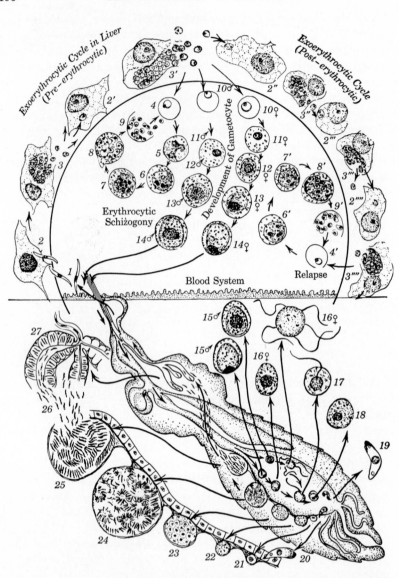

Fig. 49. Life cycle of *Plasmodium vivax*. *1*, sporozoites injected; *2*, sporozoites entering liver cell; *3*, exoerythrocytic schizogony; *4–9*, erythrocytic schizogony, repeated indefinitely; *10–14*, development of ♂ and ♀ gametocytes; *4'–9'*, reinvasion of blood by exoerythrocytic merozoites, causing relapse; *15*, ♂ and ♀ gametocytes in stomach of Anopheles; *16* ♀, female gamete; *16* ♂, formation of male gametes by exflagellation; *17*, fertilization; *18*, zygote; *19*, oökinete; *20*, same, penetrating stomach wall; *21–25*, development of oöcyst; *23* shows sporoblasts, *24* and *25* development of sporozoites; *26*, sporozoites liberated into body cavity when oöcyst bursts; *27*, sporozoites collecting in salivary gland cells and ducts.

cells where they go through at least two schizogonic cycles before invading the blood. The first generation of these pre-erythrocytic tissue parasites are called by Huff " cryptozoites "; the following ones he calls " metacryptozoites." After two or more of these exoerythrocytic cycles the parasites invade the blood stream and enter erythrocytes, but in some species, at least, the exoerythrocytic forms may continue to multiply indefinitely. In some species in favorable hosts, when erythrocytic parasites are injected instead of sporozoites, some of these may penetrate the tissues and become exoerythrocytic. To distinguish these from the pre-erythrocytic forms Huff and Coulston (1946) use the term " phanerozoites," but obviously, except at the beginning of an infection, there would be no way of distinguishing exoerythrocytic forms derived from sporozoites from blood forms that had reverted to an exoerythrocytic life. The exoerythrocytic forms do not have pigment granules in them.

The morphology of the exoerythrocytic forms and host cells selected by them differ in different species of Plasmodium in birds. Huff and his colleagues recognize a *gallinaceum* type in which development occurs in lymphoid and macrophage cells, and an *elongatum* type in which development occurs in all the blood and blood-forming cells. Sometimes, for example in *P. gallinaceum* in chicks, overwhelmingly heavy exoerythrocytic infections may occur; they may be so abundant in the walls of brain capillaries that they cause death by clogging the vessels. Pure exoerythrocytic infections have been produced in chicks after inoculation with parasites from tissue cultures and chick embryos.

In monkeys and man the exoerythrocytic stages long escaped detection, though it was certain that they existed, since the sporozoites disappear from the blood stream 30 minutes after inoculation and continue to hide out until 6 days later in *vivax* infections and 8 days in *falciparum* infections. Shortt *et al.*, however, in 1948 succeeded in finding the schizonts in the parenchyma cells of the liver of a rhesus monkey after very heavy inoculation with sporozoites of *P. cynomolgi* and subsequently found them in the liver of a human volunteer after similar heavy inoculation (Fig. 50).

The later history of *falciparum* infections suggests that in this species all the parasites are expelled into the blood within a few weeks; when the blood infection is destroyed by drugs no relapse occurs. In *vivax* and *malariae* infections, on the other hand, the exoerythrocytic forms seem to persist, causing relapses when a falling off in immunity or drug treatment makes it possible for them to reinvade the blood stream. Apparently, however, the erythrocytic forms do *not* revert to exoerythrocytic life as they do in *gallinaceum* infections in birds, for in *vivax* infections induced by blood inoculation no relapses occur once the blood parasites are destroyed.

Erythrocytic Stages. About a week or ten days after mosquito infection the parasites invade erythrocytes and begin a process of schizogony. The earliest form of the parasites seen in the corpuscles is the "ring stage" (Fig. 47, *1*); it appears like a little signet ring caused by the presence of a transparent or vacuolated area in the

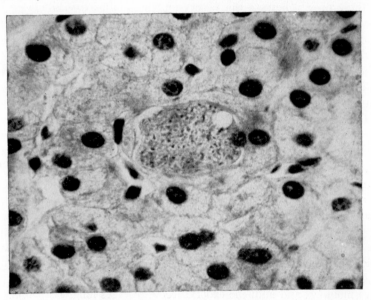

FIG. 50.   Pre-erythrocytic form of *Plasmodium vivax* in human liver, 7th day after massive sporozoite infection.   (Photo supplied by Dr. H. E. Shortt.)

center of the parasite surrounded by a delicate ring of cytoplasm and a tiny nucleus at one side, like the setting in a ring. With the usual blood stains (Giemsa or Wright) the cytoplasmic ring stains blue and the nucleus ruby-red. The rings of *vivax, malariae,* and *ovale* are about one-third the diameter of the blood cells and are indistinguishable, but those of *falciparum* are only about half this size, have hairlike rings, and tend to be perched on the periphery of the corpuscles; corpuscles containing two or more rings are common.

As the parasite grows larger it becomes rounded or irregular in shape. In *Plasmodium falciparum* the infected corpuscles at this stage become viscid and clump together in internal organs and are not seen in the peripheral circulation, but those of the other species continue to circulate in the peripheral blood in all stages. As noted in the table on

p. 188, *vivax* infections are distinguishable in all stages beyond the rings by the enlarged, pale corpuscles which they occupy, studded with red-staining granules called "Schüffner's dots." Similar dots appear in *ovale* infections, but the infected corpuscles are oval and not enlarged. No such dots appear in *malariae* infections, and the infected cells fail to enlarge or grow pale. In *falciparum* infections the infected cells (located in internal organs) may have large, irregular reddish clefts called "Maurer's dots"; they have a darker "brassy" color and may also have a bluish stippling.

As the parasites grow, the nucleus divides into two, then four, and eventually more parts. As maturity approaches the nuclei tend to take up peripheral positions in the schizont, and a small portion of the cytoplasm concentrates around each. These *segmenters* eventually break free from the corpuscles in which they have developed, and the individual *merozoites* thus liberated attack new corpuscles and repeat the process. The numbers of merozoites in the different species is shown in the table.

The merozoites of *vivax* attack almost exclusively the young immature corpuscles (reticulocytes) and those of *malariae* the older ones, but *falciparum* indiscriminately enters any that are handy. The result is that *vivax* parasites are seldom found in even 1 per cent of the corpuscles and *malariae* in seldom more than 1 in 500, whereas *falciparum* may infect 10 per cent or more, with dire results.

The pigment and other waste products left behind when the parasite breaks up are released into the blood stream where they are carried to all parts of the body and deposited in the spleen or other organs, or under the skin, causing the sallow color so characteristic of malarial patients. It is at the time of the bursting of corpuscles and release of waste products that the characteristic paroxysms of chills and fever are felt.

The species differ in the time they take to mature. *P. vivax, ovale,* and *falciparum* take about 48 hours in which to complete the shizogonic cycle, whereas *P. malariae* takes 72 hours, whence the names tertian and quartan. These are derived from the old Roman method of figuring, which counts the day on which something happens as the first day, the second day following being therefore the third (tertian) and the third following day the fourth (quartan). Although the schizogonic cycles of the human species are all 48 or 72 hours, the paroxysms, particularly in early stages of *vivax* and *falciparum* infections, commonly occur daily (quotidian), presumably because the exoerythrocytic forms enter the blood at various times and consequently different broods mature on different days. The liberation of merozoites does not take place at all hours, however, but is timed by some physiological condition in the host and is largely concentrated within a few hours on each day.   In *falciparum* infections the sporulation of all the parasites is less closely synchronized than in the other species, resulting in longer drawn out paroxysms of chills and fever.

After a few generations of schizonts have been produced in the blood some of the merozoites have a different destiny.   They grow more slowly, produce more pigment, and develop into large single-nucleated organisms.   These are the gametocytes, which continue to circulate in the blood for àt least a number of weeks, but undergo no further development within the human body.   The gametocytes of *falciparum* are crescent shaped, whereas those of the other species are rounded. Distinguishing characters of the gametocytes of the different species and of the males (microgametocytes) and females (macrogametocytes) are shown in the table.

Mosquito Cycle.   When removed from the warm blood by being sucked up by a mosquito, or even if placed on a microscope slide, the microgametocytes undergo a striking development.   The nucleus quickly divides, and within 10 or 15 minutes from 6 to 8 long flagella-like structures are extruded; the parasite is then known as a "flagellated body."   This process of exflagellation is in reality the formation of microgametes.   These slender structures break free and swim actively among the corpuscles ingested by the mosquito in search of a macrogamete.   The macrogametes meanwhile undergo little change except that the *falciparum* crescents become rounded (Fig. 49, *15*, *16*).

The result of the union of the filament from the flagellated body with the inactive female gamete is a "zygote," which corresponds to a fertilized egg of a higher animal.   This new individual, the beginning of a new generation, grows, elongates, and becomes quite like a little worm (Fig. 49, *19*, *20*) ; it is 18 to 24 μ in length and 3 to 5 μ in width, and is called a vermicule or oökinete.   It now penetrates the stomach wall of the mosquito, lodging itself under the outer limiting membrane. Here rapid growth takes place and a cyst wall develops, formed partly by the parasite, and partly by the elastic membrane lining the mosquito's stomach.   The oöcyst thus formed protrudes like a little wart on the outer surface of the stomach wall (Fig. 51) and grows until it has a diameter of 50 to 60 μ.

Meanwhile its contents undergo important changes.   The nucleus divides repeatedly, and a number of faintly outlined cells called sporoblasts are formed, varying in size and number (Fig. 49, *23*).   As further nuclear division occurs, dots of refractile chromatin arrange themselves around the periphery of each sporoblast.   Granular streaks appear in the protoplasm, and slender spindle-shaped sporozoites develop, each with a chromatin dot as a nucleus. The sporoblasts, meanwhile, enlarge and coalesce, vacuoles form in them, and a sponge-like mesh is produced (Fig. 49, *24*). Eventually the sporozoites, each about 15 μ in length, break loose from their moorings and form a tangled mass in the oöcyst, which is crammed with them to the bursting point (Fig. 49, *25*). Such an oöcyst may contain more than 10,000 sporozoites, and there may be as many as 50 oöcysts on one mosquito's stomach. In about 10 days to 3 weeks, according to temperature, after the mosquito has sucked

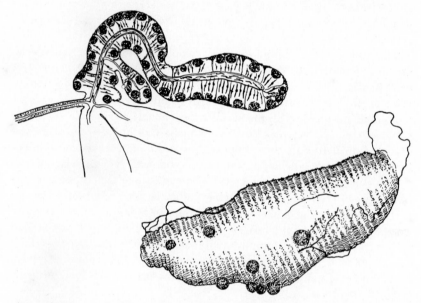

Fig. 51. *Upper:* One lobe of 3-lobed salivary gland of an infected mosquito, showing sporozoites in cells and lumen. *Lower:* stomach of *Anopheles quadrimaculatus*, showing oöcysts of *Plasmodium vivax*.

blood containing gametocytes, the oöcyst becomes mature and bursts, releasing the sporozoites into the body cavity of the mosquito. From here they make their way to the three-lobed salivary gland lying in the fore part of the thorax and connecting with the proboscis. They assemble in the cells lining the salivary glands (Fig. 50); there may be up to 200,000 in one mosquito. The sporozoites now invade the lumen of the ducts and are discharged with the saliva when the mosquito bites. Many more may be discharged at one bite than at another, but it takes 20 bites or more to discharge them all.

James in 1926 reported one remarkable mosquito which was caught on August 5 and was finally dissected on November 16 of the same year, with active sporozoites still in its salivary glands. In the meantime it had spent a hectic life in incubators, refrigerators, hospitals, railway trains, etc., and had successfully infected more than 40 general paralysis patients as a means of treatment. Humidity does not affect the cycle of development in the mosquito if the mosquito itself can survive.

Usually the number of oöcysts which develop on a mosquito's stomach is proportional to the number of gametocytes in the blood sucked, but only a small percentage actually develop. The number of sporozoites in the salivary glands may have little relation to the number of oöcysts; sometimes the development never goes beyond the oöcyst stage.

The differences in the mosquito development of the different species are only minor. According to Boyd and Kitchen (1937), infective gametocytes of *vivax* appear in the blood of a patient within 5 days after the first appearance of the parasites, and as few as 10 gametocytes per cubic millimeter of blood may be enough to infect *Anopheles quadrimaculatus*, whereas infective gametocytes of *falciparum* are not observed until 10 days after appearance of the parasites, and no infections of *A. quadrimaculatus* were successful with less than about 100 gametocytes per cubic millimeter. However, there is no close correlation between the number of gametocytes in the blood and infectiveness for mosquitoes; the gametocytes in some patients seem to be quite worthless, although the reason is unknown. Sometimes when bird malaria is inoculated into unfavorable hosts the gametocytes lack sexual potency although normal in appearance. The effect of drugs on viability of gametocytes is considered in the section on treatment, p. 207.

Temperature affects the time required for development in mosquitoes. At 85° to 90° F. both *falciparum* and *vivax* may produce sporozoites in 7 or 8 days, although the mosquito mortality is high. At 65° to 75° F., *vivax* requires 15 to 17 days and *falciparum* about 19 days; below 65° *falciparum* gives up the struggle, but *vivax* still develops slowly down to about 60° F. Although cold weather entirely inhibits the cycle of development, the parasites may remain alive and resume development when warm weather comes. According to Grassi the minimum temperature at which microgametes are formed is 65°, so no mosquito infections could be expected below this point.

The Disease. Although the course of a typical initial case of malaria, with its recurring chills and fever, is very easy for any physician to diagnose, even if he never saw one before, the symptoms may be profoundly modified by treatment, immunity, etc., particularly in old or repeated infections.

In some cases the gastro-intestinal tract is affected and symptoms resembling cholera or dysentery develop, either due to the malarial infection alone or to the lighting up of a chronic dysentery infection. In some the symptoms are suggestive of influenza or bronchopneumonia; in others, of dengue; in others, of encephalitis or meningitis. Sometimes the only symptoms are jaundice, anemia, albuminuria, malaise, or digestive disturbances. Any individual who has lived in a malarial locality and shows symptoms of a chronic infection not otherwise diagnosed should be suspected of malaria and his blood should be examined for it. Such blood examinations should be as routine as Wassermann tests or urinalysis.

In typical cases the incubation period is usually about 10 to 18 days in primary *vivax* infections, somewhat shorter in *falciparum* infections, and a little longer in *malariae* infections; it is commonly longer in subsequent infections. When the parasites have reached a concentration in the blood of something like 200 per cubic millimeter, or about one billion in the entire body, the characteristic symptoms appear. Sometimes in *vivax* infections the symptoms at this time are so slight as to be overlooked and the case remains latent, with clinical symptoms first appearing from 6 to 7 months later with the first relapse.

The characteristic recurrent chills and fever of malaria are correlated with the liberation of successive broods of merozoites from disrupted blood corpuscles. As noted on p. 193, the intervals between sporulations of the parasites and consequent paroxysms is at first irregular, tending to be quotidian before it eventually assumes the typical 48- or 72-hour cycle. In relapses and in subsequent infections the appearance of the paroxysms on every second or third day may be apparent from the beginning.

Each attack begins with a shivering chill, sometimes accompanied by convulsions so severe that the teeth chatter, gooseflesh stands out, and the bed rattles. Yet the temperature will be found to be several degrees above normal and still going up. In the wake of the chill comes a burning and weakening fever, with violent headache and nausea and a temperature up to 106° or even higher. The fever stage in turn is followed by a period of sweating so profuse that the clothes or bedding may become wringing wet. The sweating gradually subsides, the temperature drops rapidly, often below normal, and after 6 to 10 hours the patient rests fairly easily until the next attack. The fact that the attacks most commonly occur between midnight and noon, instead of in the evening, is often useful in distinguishing malaria from other intermittent fevers.

In *P. vivax* infections the paroxysms of chills and fever continue every other day for from 8 to 10 days to 2 weeks or more. Then they become less pronounced, the parasites become sparse, and the patient feels well and remains free from fever for from 10 days to several weeks. He may then have what James calls a " recrudescence "; the intermittent chills and fever begin again, usually as severe as in the primary attack. These recrudescences may continue for many months but usually become more widely spaced. Sometimes the interval between attacks is much longer; James refers to attacks after an interval of 8 to 24 weeks as a relapse, whereas after still longer intervals of 30 or 40 weeks he calls them recurrences. The shorter recrudescences may be due to renewed activity of persisting blood parasites, but the relapses after longer intervals are undoubtedly due to reinvasion of the blood by exoerythrocytic forms, since the blood is negative in the intervals. In blood-induced infections relapses rarely, if ever, occur.

In *vivax* infections the relapse pattern varies with strains. In the " Saint Elizabeth " strain, for instance, there are no recrudescences after the primary attack, the first relapse occurring after 7 to 11 months. Some strains show a series of recrudescences and less tendency to later relapses. The " Chesson " strain from the Southwest Pacific continues to be reactivated throughout the period of infection, with no latent period. Some strains recur even after years, perhaps on the occasion of some physiological shock, such as a change of climate, exhaustion, an intercurrent infection, starvation, etc. In the long latent periods the blood usually shows no parasites even when transfused.

After repeated attacks the patient's vitality is lowered, he becomes anemic, his spleen enlarges, and he finally reaches a chronic run-down condition.

P. ovale infections are not prone to relapse and are more susceptible than any of the other species to drug treatment.

In *P. malariae* infections the paroxysms occur at 72-hour intervals, are milder and of shorter duration, recur more regularly, and the infections persists for a longer time. The milder nature of the disease often results in failure to seek treatment, and this, together with its long duration and tendency to relapse, is believed to explain the frequent kidney disease which is found in quartan cases. Lambers found nephritis in nearly 50 per cent of such cases in a hospital in Dutch

Guiana as compared with 4 or 5 per cent in *vivax* and *falciparum* infections; one-sixth of all the nephritis cases were due to quartan malaria.

In *falciparum* malaria we have to deal with a quite different disease In natives of hyperendemic localities primary infections are seldom seen except in very young children but are common in visitors. The paroxysms of chills and fever are less well defined, last from 12 or 14 to 36 hours, are severe in nature, and often occur daily, a fresh attack sometimes beginning before the previous one has entirely subsided. On days intervening between attacks the patient is sick and does not have a " well " day as in *vivax* infections. As already noted, the parasites frequently become excessively numerous and the spleen becomes very large. The temperature is likely to rise above 105° F., and is often accompanied by vomiting and delirium. The attacks usually last 8 or 10 days, and then the temperature slopes off. In just a few days, however, there is a second series of paroxysms, perhaps even more severe, and these recrudescenses then continue in declining severity every 10 or 12 days for about 6 or 8 weeks, after which they become more irregular, although the blood continues to be infective. In the absence of reinfections the disease usually dies out completely in 6 to 8 months. In malarial countries in the tropics, however, no such course is seen, since reinfection is more or less continuous. Under these circumstances the infected persons become " carriers " harboring a few parasites, possibly too few to be found in blood smears, and showing few symptoms or none at all. In subtropical regions, on the other hand, as in southern United States and Italy, the infections die out in cold weather and fresh outbreaks occur every year.

A number of pernicious conditions may develop, usually in *falciparum* malaria. The tendency of corpuscles infected with *P. falciparum* to cling together results in clogging capillaries and preventing the proper flow of blood in vital organs. In the brain this, as well as a direct toxic effect, leads to numerous symptoms, among them total loss of consciousness, or coma, and sometimes sudden death by a " stroke." This " cerebral malaria " causes a large fraction of malarial deaths. In some cases violent gastro-intestinal symptoms resembling cholera, typhoid, or dysentery develop, and in others, heart failure or pneumonia. *Falciparum* malaria is always an accompaniment of blackwater fever, but its exact relation to that disease is still uncertain (see p. 212).

Prenatal infection is not infrequent, especially in *falciparum* malaria. Gastro-intestinal and pulmonary forms of malaria are especially common in infants.

Immunity. The nature of the acquired resistance to an existing malaria infection and immunity to superinfections has been extensively studied. From the very beginning of an infection there is considerable destruction of the parasites. Knowles pointed out that a single parasite producing 20 merozoites at each successive multiplication, if unchecked, would have increased in 20 days to the point where there would be about four parasites to every blood corpuscle, and the patient would die.

Much information, most of it probably applicable to human malaria, has been obtained about the development of immunity in malaria of birds and monkeys. Huff and his colleagues showed that in bird malaria immunity to blood forms does not protect against exoerythrocytic forms, and they think it possible that two different antibodies may be involved. In human malaria where the exoerythrocytic forms are far less abundant than in some bird species, it is doubtful that complete immunity to exoerythrocytic forms ever develops. Garcia in 1948 reported that injection of tetanus toxoid inhibits malarial relapses, presumably by stimulating the immune mechanisms of the body against exoerythrocytic forms.

The mechanism on which the blood immunity depends has been demonstrated by Taliaferro and his colleagues to be mainly phagocytosis by cells of the reticulo-endothelial system, particularly in the spleen, liver, and bone marrow. The phagocytosis begins probably at once, and consists of the engulfing and destruction of the entire parasitized blood corpuscles and not merely the free merozoites. This destruction of invaded corpuscles is believed to be an important factor in malarial anemia. As the disease progresses the activity of these voracious cells is gradually increased, and they begin multiplying in number until a climax is reached when the rate of destruction of parasites greatly exceeds their production. At this time the liver and spleen are enlarged and show great activity of the phagocytic cells in them. There is also a marked increase in lymphoid tissue to build a mesenchymal reserve for the rapid production and mobilization of more macrophages.

This condition gradually declines during the latent period, but rapid mobilization against fresh invaders of the same species may occur for years, especially if the infection has not entirely died out. Boyd and Mathews report one case in which a patient failed to become infected by injection of 180 million trophozoites 3½ years after a *vivax* infection, and who at the end of 3 years more suffered no clinical symptoms from a mosquito-inoculated infection, although a few parasites appeared in his blood. The immunity is, however, highly specific and not only fails to protect against attack by other species but sometimes even by other strains of the same species. Even an existing infection with one species does not suppress a superimposed infection with another species.

In nature the immunity to a particular species or strain persists as long as parasites continue to exist in the body, owing either to a suppressed latent infection or to repeated reinfection; this type of immunity is sometimes called "premunition." Presumably relapses occur when the blood immunity falls sufficiently to allow exoerythrocytic forms to reinvade the blood stream.

The persistence of *vivax* and *malariae* infections in the body over a period of several years, usually punctuated by relapses, leads to a higher ultimate degree of immunity in these than in *falciparum* infections. This leads to differences in the epidemiology of the diseases, as will be seen on pp. 203–204. Since immunity, at least to *falciparum* infections, is rapidly lost, it is actually dangerous, as Clark and Komp have shown, to create a nonmalarial oasis of treated cases in the midst of a highly endemic area.

Negroes have a higher degree of tolerance to malaria parasites than do whites. Many are refractory to infection even with exotic strains to which they could not have developed specific immunity. Watson and Rice in a study in the Tennessee Valley in 1946, found that although the parasitemia rate in Negroes was 5 times that in whites, the whites experienced about 10 times as many reported cases of malaria and over 15 times as many sick days. It is largely because of extensive immunity to the human species in malarial regions that the monkey species, *P. knowlesi*, is often used as a substitute in the treatment of general paralysis.

Epidemiology. As a result of the work of Ross and Grassi, which set such an important milestone in the progress of preventive medicine, malaria is now known to be transmitted naturally, except in some prenatal infections, only by the bites of certain species of mosquitoes, all belonging to the genus Anopheles.

The only important exception is in the case of heroin addicts, who frequently pass infections around by means of hypodermic needles. These infections, mostly *falciparum*, have a high fatality rate and have become an important problem in some cities. The drug addict's hypodermic outfit has been referred to as the Anopheles of New York City. It is apparently by this method that quartan malaria was introduced into the New Orleans area in about 1940; it has now become endemic there.

More than a hundred species of Anopheles have been described, but less than two dozen species are of any real importance in the transmission of malaria. This matter is discussed in the chapter on mosquitoes (p. 678). As shown there, some species are eliminated because they do not readily nurse the malaria parasites through their sporogonic cycle; some are eliminated because of their habits; and others are of no importance on account of their rarity. Local conditions may influence the importance of particular species of mosquitoes in transmitting malaria, and therefore local epidemiological surveys to determine the prevalent transmitters are important. Since the different species vary greatly in their breeding habits, control measures must depend on the habits of the particular species involved.

Malaria does not become endemic wherever suitable Anopheles mosquitoes occur; it requires a certain density of mosquitoes in order to insure the successful propagation of the disease. A small deviation above or below the critical point may mean the difference between ultimate extermination, which has occurred in northern United States, and permanent establishment. The actual number of Anopheles necessary for successful propagation depends on the species of Anopheles present, the number of human cases available, climatic conditions, and contacts between the human inhabitants and the mosquitoes, as influenced by screening, spray-guns, etc.

The habits of the local Anopheles play an important part in the epidemiology of malaria, and the species of malaria is also important. Different anophelines vary with respect to food preferences, tendency to enter houses, time of activity, and dispersion from a breeding or feeding place, and also in the extent to which they nurse the different species of malaria to the infective stage. The presence of abundant Anopheles in certain localities in Europe without accompanying malaria when neighboring localities with fewer Anopheles might be highly malarious was a mystery until it was found that the European *A. maculipennis* really consists of several distinct races, some of which are " zoöphilic " and only exceptionally bite man, whereas others show no discrimination against human blood (see pp. 678–679).

Other factors besides fondness for human blood may be involved. In the Punjab, for instance, abundant Anopheles may be present without causing much malaria when the atmospheric humidity is low, because infected mosquitoes do not live long enough for the sporogonic cycle to be completed, whereas with high humidity relatively few Anopheles may cause a severe outbreak. James found that in England in April and May less than 10 per cent of the infected *A. maculipennis* lived long enough to become infective, whereas in August and September 50 per cent did so, from which he deduced that a great abundance of the mosquitoes in spring is of less importance than a few in early fall. Furthermore, in the Netherlands and in England an abundance of Anopheles in summer has little effect because the number of mosquitoes in stables is some 200 times as great as in houses, and the chance of an infected mosquito re-entering a house or again biting a man is very small. But in autumn, after the egg-laying season, the mosquitoes remain in the houses after feeding. One race of *A. maculipennis* which does not hibernate but feeds intermittently through the winter is therefore in an excellent position to spread the infection within the household.

The species or strains of malaria parasites are also important. Some mosquitoes become infected much more easily with some species or strains of parasites than others. An infected *A. quadrimaculatus*, for instance, usually transmit *P. falciparum* by a single bite, whereas it often requires several bites to transmit *vivax*. *A. quadrimaculatus* seems to be susceptible to most if not all strains of both *vivax* and *falciparum*, including those from the South Pacific, but *A. albimanus* from Cuba or Panama, though highly susceptible to malaria strains from its own region, is refractory to Florida strains. A similar partiality was observed by James, Nicol, and Shute, who were able to infect English *A. maculipennis* with strains of *falciparum* from Italy, but not with strains from India. Huff, working with Culex vectors of bird malaria, found that refractoriness of mosquitoes to malarial infection is hereditarily transmitted.

Another epidemiological factor is the tendency for many infections, especially in northern Europe, to give rise to very mild attacks, or none at all, after infection in the fall, and then to produce clinical attacks 6 or 9 months later. The result is an outbreak of malaria (nearly all *vivax*) in early summer when the Anopheles density is near its lowest point. In the tropics it is common for *vivax* infections to reach a peak in late summer, with a milder peak in spring due to relapses. *Falciparum* infections, on the other hand, usually reach a peak in autumn.

Epidemics of *vivax* malaria rarely occur since the disease often continues to exist in the host for several years, keeping up immunity by occasional relapses. Only if a new strain of *P. vivax* were introduced from foreign parts could an epidemic occur. In tropical regions there are no *falciparum* epidemics either, the reason being constant reinfection. In a hyperendemic locality in India Christophers found that children under 2 years of age suffered from continuous malarial fever, and averaged over 10,000 parasites per cubic millimeter of blood; between the ages of 2 and 5 the infection was still 100 per cent, but the parasites were only 1200 per cubic millimeter, and fever attacks nearly a month apart; between 6 and 10 the infection was still 100 per cent, but the parasites were less than 100 per cubic millimeter, and there was no fever; in adults infection was 50 per cent, but there were few parasites and full tolerance to the infection.

Adults in such localities have practically complete immunity to the effects of the disease, and this never lapses as long as there are constant reinfections. When exposure to infection is limited to 8 months a year instead of 12, adults as well as children have enlarged spleens and suffer from febrile attacks. In general, in less infected areas, the lighter the malarial incidence the later will be the age of maximum number of infections.

In subtropical areas where climatic conditions are such as to cause marked seasonal reduction in anopheline density, true epidemics of *falciparum*, and to a less extent of the other species, may occur; their violence is largely dependent upon the interval between seasons of highly favorable conditions for infection. Under these conditions the average tolerance of the community to the disease suffers an annual diminution and may constantly decrease for a number of years. When the immunity as a whole becomes quite low and there is a sudden increase in the probability of infection by a great increase in number of mosquitoes or in imported human cases, an epidemic may occur of such extraordinary severity as to involve almost the entire population and to cause a mortality of several hundreds per thousand. Such devastating epidemics, nearly always of the *falciparum* type, have been termed " fulminant malaria "; they have been especially severe in parts of India, in Ceylon, and in Italy.

Local epidemics may also arise from the bringing in of a new strain of parasite, from the introduction of a new species of Anopheles, e.g., *A. gambiae* into Brazil and during World War II into Egypt, or from the development of more favorable conditions for the breeding of dangerous species of Anopheles. In Holland as the water in reclaimed areas becomes sweet, zoophilic strains of *A. maculipennis* replace the malaria-transmitting strains. In parts of Europe inhabited by zoophilic strains of *maculipennis*, malaria disappears as animal husbandry develops. In Java improvement and reconstruction of houses for protection against plague has led to a serious increase in malaria; this is apparently due to a combination of several factors, such as tile roofs, borrow pits for building material, and importation of new parasite strains with laborers.

Diagnosis. In acute cases of malaria the clinical symptoms are usually sufficient for a diagnosis. In more chronic cases a combination of anemia and enlarged spleen, where kala-azar and certain less common conditions can be ruled out, almost unmistakably advertises malaria infection. Nevertheless all diagnoses should be confirmed by blood examination whenever possible. If not possible, failure of a test course of an antimalarial drug to relieve the symptoms indicates that the fever is not due to malaria.

Accurate diagnosis is made by examinations of blood smears stained by a Romanowsky stain, preferably Giemsa's. In thin smears, made by spreading a film on a slide by drawing a drop across it in the acute angle behind the line of contact of the film slide and the spreading slide, the infected corpuscles are spread in a single layer, and the parasites are stained in their natural positions in the corpuscles. Characters which differentiate the species and stages are easily recognizable in such films. Thick smears, however, are far more valuable for detection of cases in which the parasites are sparse, though the identification is more difficult. These smears are made by thoroughly drying thick drops, dehemoglobinizing before or during staining, and then examining for the more concentrated parasites free from the corpuscles. An injection of adrenalin a few minutes before taking the blood for a smear is helpful in finding parasites when they are sparse.

The degree of malariousness of a district can be determined fairly accurately by finding the percentage of children between about 2 and 10 years of age who have enlarged spleens. The " spleen rate " in adults is of little value in highly malarial places because of a reduction in spleen enlargement with continued immunity; it is of use only as an indication of the number of active cases. Any spleen that can be felt below the last rib when a child is lying down may be classed as enlarged and is usually indicative of malaria; in extreme cases the spleen may reach the pubis.

Serological tests for malaria have been recommended but are not generally considered reliable enough to replace examination for parasites. Complement fixation tests may be helpful in chronic cases if the antigen, prepared from dried monkey blood with *Plasmodium knowlesi* infection, is made commercially available.

Treatment. About three centuries ago, in 1640, a countess returning to Europe from Peru brought with her some bark from a cinchona tree, an infusion of which had been used by the native Indians to cure an attack of malaria from which she suffered. The value of the drug was established at once, and for nearly three hundred years the essential principles of cinchona bark — quinine and allied alkaloids — were practically without competition as remedies for malaria.

Cinchona bark contains a number of alkaloids that act against malaria, though they vary in effectiveness and toxicity. Quinine is the preferred one, but a mixture of the alkaloids called cinchona febrifuge, or, when in standardized form, totaquine, is much less expensive and almost as effective but can be given only by mouth, whereas in critical cases intravenous injection may be required.

The quinine dosage recommended for adults is 15 grains 3 times a day for 2 days, followed by 10 grains 3 times a day for the next 5 days. This, as well as all other antimalarial drugs, is given by mouth except in critical cases, when intravenous or intramuscular injections of suitable preparations are indicated.

Although quinine is a highly effective drug against the schizonts of malaria parasites, it has several disadvantages: (1) it is not well tolerated by many people, in whom it causes unpleasant ringing in the ears, dizziness, vomiting, and sometimes more alarming symptoms; (2) it cannot be used in cases of blackwater fever (see p. 212), since it aggravates the condition; (3) it is entirely ineffective against the gametocytes of *P. falciparum* and relatively ineffective against those of other species; and (4) it is ineffective against exoerythrocytic parasites, therefore failing to prevent relapses in *vivax* and quartan malaria, and also failing to prevent clinical attacks by these species after prophylactic treatment is stopped (see p. 208). Quinine, therefore, though curative in *falciparum* malaria and an excellent suppressive against *vivax* and quartan malaria, is neither a permanent cure nor a true causal prophylactic for those infections.

The search for better drugs for use against the erythrocytic schizonts, which are the sole cause of clinical malaria, has been more successful than the search for a good drug for use against exoerythrocytic forms and gametocytes. During World War II more intensive research was directed toward finding better antimalarial drugs than toward any other project except the atomic bomb. Under the sponsorship of the U. S. Government over 15,000 compounds have been tested in birds for curative and prophylactic action, and the more promising ones then tried on human malaria. In 1948 Terzian found that mosquitoes could be used for testing drugs against sporozoites, thus greatly speeding up the testing process. Although an ideal antimalarial drug has not yet been found, some definite advances have been made. It now seems unlikely that any single drug will be found that is effective against both erythrocytic schizonts on the one hand and exoerythrocytic forms and gametocytes on the other. Moreover, it is unsafe to rely completely on any single drug since the parasites may develop a high degree of tolerance which is persistently retained even through sexual cycles. Some strains of *Plasmodium vivax* have become so tolerant to paludrine (see below) that they are unaffected by doses that are rapidly fatal to the hosts.

The first step toward better schizonticides was made in 1933 when atebrin (quinacrine or mepacrine) was introduced. Although apparently as effective as quinine, it is a yellow dye that tints the skin a bilious saffron color, and since it seemed to have no great advantages over quinine at the outbreak of World War II it was still not well known either to physicians or to the public. When, however, the quinine supply was cut off by the Japanese at a time when it was needed more than ever before, of necessity we turned to atebrin. It soon became evident that atebrin was not only as good as quinine for most malarial conditions but was actually the drug of preference except in critical cases where a large concentration of drug was needed in the blood stream at once. It also proved to be more effective and as a rule better tolerated than quinine as a suppressive or prophylactic, and it could be used safely in cases of blackwater fever. The recommended dosage of atebrin is 0.2 gram every 6 hours for 5 doses on the first day, followed by 0.1 gram 3 times a day for the next 6 days. Cases of intolerance to atebrin are rare, but exceptionally, especially after long use of small daily doses as a suppressive, the drug may cause skin lesions, psychoses, blood changes, and eye injuries (Findlay, 1947). One shudders to think what havoc malaria might have wrought during World War II had atebrin not been available.

As the result of wartime research, two drugs, chloroquine and paludrine, have been discovered which are superior to atebrin as schizonticides. Chloroquine, developed in America, is more effective and less toxic than either atebrin or quinine and does not tint the skin. It is an effective suppressive when taken in a small, well-tolerated dose only once a week, and it abruptly terminates clinical *vivax* infections and cures *falciparum* infections in only 1 to 3 days, as compared with 7 days for atebrin. Paludrine, developed in England, is a nontoxic drug that brings about clinical cure and disappearance of blood schizonts at about the same speed as quinine or atebrin; a single dose will effectively control an attack of *vivax* malaria, and a few doses completely cure *falciparum* infections. Shute and Maryon in 1948 found that the drug greatly decreases the number of gametocytes in the blood after a period of 9 days, and beginning after 24 hours successful development of oöcysts in mosquitoes is almost completely inhibited. The drug appears to act on the gametocytes very slowly, perhaps particularly at the time of nuclear division. Paludrine is absorbed rapidly and is excreted in the urine.

The search for drugs effective against exoerythrocytic forms and gametocytes has also met with some success. The first step in this direction was the discovery of plasmochin (pamaquin) in 1926. It was used as a complement to quinine to kill gametocytes, since it had little if any effect on the schizonts. Subsequently it was found to be destructive to exoerythrocytic forms also. Its use in combination with a schizonticide would be ideal if it were not that plasmochin is a very toxic drug in the doses required, often causing acute hemolytic anemia and other dangerous symptoms.

Search for less toxic drugs of the same chemical type (8-amino-quinolines) resulted in the discovery of pentaquine and in 1948 iso-pentaquine. The former has over twice the margin of safety that plasmochin has, and isopentaquine has over four times, but the latter has not yet been tested on a large scale. The evidence thus far indicates that 60 mg. of these drugs given with 2 grams of quinine daily for 14 days, in divided doses every 4 hours, will radically cure (i.e., prevent relapses) in a high percentage of *vivax* cases; 30 mg. daily will usually suffice in cases where partial immunity has developed. With isopentaquine 60 mg. so far seems to be a safe dosage. These drugs also prevent development of clinical malaria in experimental cases if given for 8 days, beginning the day before infection. When relapses are not entirely prevented, they are spaced farther apart and are less severe.

For suppression or prophylaxis atebrin at the rate of 0.1 gram every day was adopted by the U. S. military forces; when conscientiously taken no clinical malaria appeared until it was discontinued, but many uncooperative men avoided taking their daily doses by sleight-of-hand or tongue tricks. Now, however, a single pill of 0.15 gram of chloroquine once a week appears to do the job just as well.

Prevention. Sir Leonard Rogers remarked that the simplicity in theory of prophylaxis against malaria is equaled only by its difficulty in practice. After Ross's discovery of the transmission of malaria, optimists got the impression that malaria control required merely the simple application of well-known principles. Only gradually has it become apparent that in almost every area the control of malaria is a separate problem, and one that requires ingenuity, perseverance, cooperation, and money. As Hackett (1937) put it, malaria control is like a game of chess, played with a few pieces, but capable of an infinite variety of situations.

It requires community rather than individual effort. Ross said: " It [malaria] is essentially a political disease — one which affects the welfare of whole countries; and the prevention of it should therefore be an important branch of public administration. For the state as for the individual health is the first postulate of prosperity. And prosperity should be the first object of scientific government." But governments are notoriously slow in making large investments in public health, even if assured of ultimate large returns. Many of the most brilliant examples of malaria control have been executed by private industrial organizations and business concerns, which have been quick to see the importance of protecting the health of their employees solely as a business proposition.

A brilliant example of malaria control was the elimination of the disease in northeastern Brazil by the complete eradication of *Anopheles gambiae,* made possible by a cooperative project financed by the Brazilian government and the Rockefeller Foundation. Introduced from Africa to Natal, Brazil, in 1930, *A. gambiae* spread hundreds of miles to northeastern Brazil and created a malaria epidemic that has probably never been equaled in intensity. In the first 6 months of 1938 it killed at least 14,000 people, and by the end of 1939 had caused some 300,000 cases, according to some estimates affecting 90 per cent of the population. The Malaria Service of the Northeast began work in 1939 and completed it in 1940. The need for constant guard against reintroduction of this species is evident, however, from the fact that in 1943 living specimens were found several times in planes arriving from Africa and once in homes near the Natal airport.

During World War II introduction of *A. gambiae* to Egypt from Sudan started a devastating epidemic comparable with the earlier Brazilian one, but in 1945 it, too, was eradicated. Another notable accomplishment was the complete eradication of malaria and its vector, *A. pseudopunctipennis,* from Chile in 1945 after a 10-year campaign by Noé.

The means that can be employed for control of malaria are (1) chemotherapy and chemoprophylaxis to prevent clinical cases and mosquito infection, (2) protection against adult mosquitoes, (3) destruction of mosquito larvae, (4) permanent elimination of breeding places and care to avoid creating them, and (5) exploitation of natural enemies. Various combinations of these methods are usually necessary. Improvements in these various means of control have, however, been so great since the outbreak of World War II that, as already stated, the total elimination of malaria from the United States is possible before 1960, and according to Soper it is a conservative statement that 90 per cent of malaria in the world can be wiped out by that time.

Treatment of all clinical cases and all cases showing parasites in the blood is unquestionably a valuable aid while mosquito control is under way and in areas where there is no immediate prospect of adequate mosquito control.   Clark, Komp, and Jobbins (1941), who attempted to control malaria in an area in Panama by drug administration alone over a period of 10 years, concluded that it is not possible to eradicate malaria by this means or to greatly lessen its transmission.   They did, however, *almost* eliminate severe clinical malaria and thought a drug control program economically justifiable because of increased labor efficiency.

The protection of human beings against adult mosquitoes has proved of great value, particularly since the development during World War II of two new tools for destruction of mosquitoes and other insects — aerosols and residual DDT spraying — both of which are discussed in the chapter on mosquitoes (p. 700).   Even in the days of the Panama Canal construction, when adult mosquitoes in houses were killed by swatting or trapping, LePrince saw the value of this procedure.   Before World War II malaria was successfully controlled in a number of places in the tropics by periodic spraying of native huts with pyrethrum in kerosene.   But the aerosol bombs used during the war were as far ahead of old-fashioned spray guns in efficacy and ease of use as electric fans are over hand-operated palm leaves.

The greatest development during the war was residual spraying with DDT (see p. 493).   Surfaces sprayed with DDT emulsions remain toxic for several months to mosquitoes resting on them.   Since many species of Anopheles usually rest on walls, etc., for considerable periods before and after feeding, it is obvious that a high percentage of those which bite malaria patients in or around houses that have been sprayed will die before they can transmit the disease.   Hinman and Cutkomp in 1947 found that much better results were obtained at only little more expense by spraying all important resting places on premises instead of only houses and privies.   In the Tennessee Valley one spraying early in June would provide protection for a whole season.   Residual spraying is less effective for species like *aquasalis* and *albimanus*, which do not habitually rest in houses in the daytime.

Screens are a valuable protection, especially if sprayed with DDT and if kept in good repair, but screened houses are not extensively available in the tropics except in American zones.   Under these conditions bed nets are of great value.   Some protection can be obtained from repellents (see p. 495), but in military operations they are likely not to be used as they should be.   A surplus of 12 million bottles had accumulated in the South Pacific by the end of 1944!

The control of mosquitoes by the use of larvicides or natural enemies in breeding places, as well as the elimination of favorable breeding places, is considered in Chapter 27.   Malaria can seldom if ever be permanently controlled except by fighting malarial mosquitoes in their larval stage. The methods which are effective in doing this vary widely from place to place, depending upon the habits of the particular Anopheles involved and the local conditions.

The control of malaria by antimosquito methods is not a problem of general mosquito control, or even Anopheles control, but *species* control directed against one or two important local vectors in the particular locality. It is of paramount importance to identify the principal malaria carriers of a region, to study their habits, and then to institute measures directed specifically against these. There are less than two dozen dangerous malaria-carrying species of Anopheles in the whole world, but sometimes the habits of individual species vary from place to place, so local studies of them are required.

A malarial survey is *always* required before intelligent control measures can be instituted in any locality. This consists in mapping the locality to show distribution of population, malaria cases, Anopheles breeding places, etc.; collection and breeding out of Anopheles larvae, and collection and dissection of adults; determination of the spleen rate; and determination of both incidence of parasite carriers and average numbers of parasites per cubic millimeter of blood. The results of the survey will not only indicate the local facts of epidemiology but will also furnish a standard of measurement of improvements brought about by the control measures used.

It is important not only that existing mosquito breeding places be controlled but also that care be taken to prevent the establishment of new ones. LePrince (1916) called attention to the surprising number of mosquitoes brought into existence by engineers who leave borrow pits, dam up streams, etc., out of pure carelessness, when it would cost little if any more to provide for proper drainage. An amazing amount of malaria is man-made, not only by carelessness but also by irrigation, flooding, impounding, etc. Even Trinidad's malaria is man-made; the shade trees that harbor the bromeliads in which *A. bellator* breeds were planted there to protect cocoa groves. During military operations bomb craters, shell holes, foxholes, ditches, vehicle ruts, etc., made many an Anopheles happy, for under natural conditions even mosquitoes are often troubled by what corresponds to a housing shortage. Man is an occasionally rational being who in the past has probably done as much to help malaria as he has done to eradicate it.

The cost of malaria control measures often seems prohibitive and the prospects of success discouraging, but it has been found over and over again that malaria control always returns large dividends in the course of time, often far beyond what could possibly have been anticipated, and it has also been found that some feasible means of control is available if the problem is adequately studied. Many of the failures have been due to haphazard application of methods which do not fit the local situation, to lack of cooperation among health officers, engineers, and government officials, and to impatience in the accomplishment of results. Russell pointed out in 1945 that success in malaria control depends on men trained and organized, and backed by administrative authority; the day of the amateur malariologist has passed.

Failure also results from a lack of educated and effective public opinion against malaria. One may question the wisdom of a school program that has a child report on the social achievements of an ancient civilization from lips blanched by malarial anemia, about which he learns only from folklore and patent medicine advertisements. Conservation of health is a major social function; it should not be neglected in schools.

In the meantime there is, as Meleney has emphasized, no reason, at least in our own country, why malarial *deaths* could not be largely done away with. This could be accomplished by educating people to the inadequacy and dangerousness of home treatment of the disease, by curbing the largely valueless " chill tonics " advertised on so many barns and outhouses, and by using intravenous injections for critically ill patients.

Brown (1940) secured information about 101 persons who were reported to have died of malaria in Georgia. Of these, 50 per cent of the whites and 75 per cent of the Negroes were ill a week before calling a physician, and 13 and 16 per cent, respectively, for a month, and 38 per cent were so ill that they died within two days. Even more disturbing is the fact that so many died in spite of early diagnosis and treatment. About 40 per cent failed to receive adequate treatment, and in only half the cases was a blood smear examined. Even fewer blood examinations are reported in Tennessee and Mississippi. Moreover, the fact that only one-half of the positive smears were diagnosed as having *falciparum* infections, which is the only form of malaria commonly causing death, suggests error in diagnosis. Failure to use adequate therapy along with inaccurate or no blood examination is a reflection on medical education and calls attention to the neglect of parasitology in medical schools.

Blackwater Fever

In many parts of the world where severe malignant tertian malaria is present, but not in all, a disease occurs which is known as blackwater fever, about the real nature of which there has been more argument and less definite knowledge than of almost any other human disease. It is a veritable scourge in many parts of Africa and in some parts of India, Malaya, and the East Indies, and it occurs in parts of southeastern Europe and in the southeastern United States. The disease is characterized by a fever accompanied by an intense jaundice and a tremendous destruction of red blood corpuscles and excretion of hemoglobin in the urine. In severe cases 60 to 80 per cent of the red blood corpuscles may be destroyed within 24 hours. The disease is usually accompanied by a contraction of the spleen. Severe attacks are usually fatal; cases that recover are prone to subsequent attacks if they remain in an endemic area. Often a blackwater fever attack wipes out the malarial infection.

There have been various theories about the true nature of blackwater fever; one is that it is caused by a specific spirochete or virus, another that it is due to a combination of malaria and quinine poisoning, since it is often precipitated by administration of quinine. Whatever causes it is not in the cells, for even introduced normal cells are affected. Another theory is that in some individuals parasitized cells stimulate production of antibodies which then react against normal as well as parasitized cells, possibly because of antigenic similarity to the Rh factor or to other agglutinogens in the blood corpuscles. For a review of these theories, see Maegraith (1946). The evidence seems overwhelming, however, that it is a manifestation of *falciparum* malaria, though its much greater frequency in some localities than in others has not been adequately explained. Debility, attacks of malaria in adults who have developed no immunity, malnutrition, exhaustion, and exposure to cold seem to be predisposing factors.

Treatment with quinine, plasmochin, or the pentaquines is contraindicated, but atebrin or chloroquine can be given safely. Patients should stay in bed, keep the skin warm and carefully protected from drafts, and drink plenty of warm, salty, alkaline fluids. About half the deaths are due to kidney failure. Complete quiet, diuretics, and a milk diet are recommended, with intravenous saline or glucose injections in some cases, as well as blood transfusions. Enough alkali should be given to make the urine alkaline. Some authors have found injections of liver extract to be of great benefit if given along with atebrin.

REFERENCES

Malaria

ABERLE, S. D., Primate Malaria, *Natl. Research Council Monogr.*, 171 pp. (1945).
AMER. ASSOC. ADVANCEMENT SCIENCE, A Symposium on Human Malaria, edited by F. R. Moulton, *Pub. 16*, 1, 1941 (43 papers by 42 authors).

BISPHAM, W. N., *Malaria, Its Diagnosis, Treatment and Prophylaxis,* Baltimore, 1944.

BOYD, M. F., On Strains or Races of the Malaria Parasites, *Am. J. Trop. Med.,* **20,** 69 (1940).

An Historical Sketch of the Prevalence of Malaria in North America, *Am. J. Trop. Med.,* **21,** 223 (1941).

A Review of Studies on Immunity to Vivax Malaria, *J. Natl. Mal. Soc.,* **6,** 12–31 (1947).

BOYD, M. F., and KITCHEN, S. F., Series of Papers on Induced Malaria, *Am. J. Trop. Med.,* **15–23** (1935–1943).

BROWN, H. W., The Problem of Malaria Mortality, *Am. J. Publ. Health,* **30,** 1199 (1940).

CLARK, H. C., KOMP, W. H. W., and JOBBINS, D. M., A Tenth Year's Observations on Malaria in Panama, with Reference to the Occurrence of Variations in the Parasite Index, during Continued Treatment with Atabrine and Plasmochine, *Am. J. Trop. Med.,* **21,** 191–216 (1941).

COATNEY, G. R., Chemotherapy of Malaria, *Bull. Pan-Amer. Sanit. Bur.,* **28,** 27–37 (1949).

COGGESHALL, L. T., Malaria as a World Menace, *J. Am. Med. Assoc.,* **122,** 8 (1943).

Immunity in Malaria, *Medicine,* **22,** 87 (1943).

FAIRLEY, N. H., Chemotherapeutic Suppression and Prophylaxis in Malaria; Experimental Investigations Undertaken by Medical Research Teams in Australia, *Trans. Roy. Soc. Trop. Med.. Hyg.,* **38,** 311–365 (1945).

Sidelights on Malaria in Man Obtained by Subinoculation Experiments, *Trans. Roy. Soc. Trop. Med. Hyg.,* **40,** 621–676 (1947).

FOURTH INTERN. CONGR. TROP. MED. AND MALARIA, *Proceedings,* Sect. V, 601–945, 1948.

FAUST, E. C., Clinical and Public Health Aspects of Malaria in the United States from an Historical Perspective, *Am. J. Trop. Med.,* **25,** 185–201 (1945).

FAUST, E. C., and HEMPHILL, F. M., Malaria Mortality and Morbidity in the United States for the Year 1946, *J. Natl. Mal. Soc.,* **7,** 285–292 (1948).

FINDLAY, G. M., The Toxicity of Mepacrine in Man, *Trop. Diseases Bull.,* **44,** 763–779 (1947).

HACKETT, L. W., Biological Factors in Malaria Control, *Am. J. Trop. Med.,* **16,** 341 (1936).

Malaria in Europe, London, 1937.

HUFF, C. G., and COULSTON, F., The Development of *Plasmodium gallinaceum* from Sporozoite to Erythrocyte Trophozoite, *J. Infectious Diseases,* **75,** 231–249 (1944).

The Relation of Natural and Acquired Immunity of Various Avian Hosts to the Cryptozoites and Metacryptozoites of *Plasmodium gallinaceum* and *Plasmodium relictum, J. Infectious Diseases,* **78,** 99–117 (1946).

HUFF, C. G., COULSTON, F., LAIRD, R. L., and PORTER, R. J., Pre-erythrocytic Development of *Plasmodium lophurae* in Various Hosts, *J. Infectious Diseases,* **81,** 7–13 (1947).

Malaria and Other Insect-Borne Diseases in the South Pacific Campaign, 1942–1945 (four papers by various authors), *Am. J. Trop. Med.,* **27,** (3), Suppl., 1–128 (1947).

MELENEY, H. E., The Problem of Malaria Mortality in the United States, *Am. J. Trop. Med.,* **17,** 15 (1937).

MILAM, D. F., and KUSCH, E., Observations on *P. knowlesi* Malaria in General Paresis, *Southern Med. J.*, **31**, 947 (1938).

RUSSELL, P. F., WEST, L. S., and MANWELL, R. D., *Practical Malariology*, Philadelphia and London, 1946.

SAPERO, J. J., New Concept in the Treatment of Relapsing Malaria, *Am. J. Trop. Med.*, **27**, 271–283 (1947).

SHANNON, R. C., Brief History of *Anopheles gambiae* in Brazil, *Caribbean Med. J.*, **4**, 123, 1942.

SHORTT, H. E., GARNHAM, C. C., COVELL, G., and SHUTE, P. G., The Pre-erythrocytic Stage of Human Malaria, *Plasmodium vivax*, *Brit. Med. J.*, 4550, 547 (1948).

SIMMONS, J. S., *et al.*, Malaria in Panama. *Amer. J. Hyg., Monogr. Ser.*, **13**, 326 pp. 1939.

SWELLENGREBEL, N. H., and DE BUCK, A., *Malaria in the Netherlands*, Amsterdam, 1938.

TALIAFERRO, W. H., and CANNON, P. R., The Cellular Reactions During Primary Infections and Superinfections of *P. brasilianum* in Panamanian Monkeys, *J. Infectious Diseases*, **59**, 72 (1936).

WILCOX, A., Manual for the Microscopical Diagnosis of Malaria in Man, *Natl. Inst. Health Bull.*, 180, 1943.

YOUNG, M. D., *et al.*, Studies on Imported Malarias, 1–5, *J. Natl. Mal. Soc.*, **4**, 127–131, 307–320 (1945); *Am. J. Hyg.*, **43**, 326–341 (1946); *Am. J. Trop. Med.*, **26**, 477–482 (1946).

Blackwater Fever

FOY, H., and KONDI, A., Researches on Blackwater Fever in Greece, I–IV, *Ann. Trop. Med. Parasitol.*, **29**, 383, 395, 497 (1935); **30**, 423 (1936).

MAEGRAITH, B. G., Blackwater Fever — Modern Theories. A Critical Review, *Trop. Diseases Bull.*, **43**, 801–809 (1946).

ROSS, G. R., Researches on Blackwater Fever in Southern Rhodesia, *Memoirs Lond. Sch. Trop. Med.*, No. 6, 1932.

YORKE, W., Recent Work on the Pathology of Blackwater Fever, A Critical Review, *Trop. Diseases Bull.*, **19**, 631 (1922).

CHAPTER 10

Other Sporozoa, and Arthropod-Borne Micro-Organisms Other than Protozoa

Other Haemosporidia

Haemoproteus and Leucocytozoön. As noted on p. 183, the genera Haemoproteus, found in birds and reptiles, and Leucocytozoön, found in birds only, are very closely related to Plasmodium, differing principally in that schizogony is *confined* to tissue cells and only gametocytes appear in the blood. In consequence these parasites cannot be transmitted by blood inoculations. Development in insects closely parallels that of Plasmodium but, at least in some cases, is more rapid; sporozoites of *Leucocytozoön smithi* of turkeys appear in the salivary glands of Simulium in from 72 to 120 hours.

In Haemoproteus long branched schizonts appear in capillaries, containing large numbers of minute merozoites. Descriptions of schizogony stages in Leucocytozoön have varied greatly, and even their existence has been denied, but Huff (1942) found relatively small schizonts in liver cells and extremely large ones, 60 to 105 μ long, containing thousands of merozoites, in heart, liver, spleen, and intestine. The gametocytes of Haemoproteus (Fig. 52, *1*), called halteridia, are halter shaped; they curve around the nucleus in red blood cells and contain pigment granules. Those of Leucocytozoön (Fig. 52, *2*), occur in round or distorted spindle-shaped cells of uncertain origin, probably cells of the reticulo-endothelial system, and contain no pigment.

The life cycle of only two species of Haemoproteus have been worked out and in both cases pupiparous flies of the family Hippoboscidae (see p. 656) serve as intermediate hosts. The common pigeon parasite, *H. columbae*, develops in *Pseudolynchia canariensis*. According to Rivero fertilization occurs in the intermediate host, and the oökinetes are inoculated into pigeons; no oöcysts are formed. Oökinetes also develop in Triatoma nymphs; pigeons could be infected by the stomach content of bugs after 24 to 72 hours. The intermediate hosts of Leucocytozoön are black flies, and from epidemiological evidence Huff (1942) suspects that these flies may also transmit some species of Haemoproteus. Two species of Leucocytozoön cause serious losses —

L. simondi (= *anatis*) of ducklings and *L. smithi* of turkeys.   None of the malarial drugs affect Leucocytozoön infections.

Babesiidae.   Two genera, Babesia (formerly Piroplasma) and Theileria, cause important diseases in domestic animals, characterized by destruction of red blood corpuscles and elimination of hemoglobin with the urine. They produce fever, anemia, jaundice, and injury to the liver and kidneys. *B. bigemina* (Fig. 52, 7) is the cause of Texas fever or red-water fever in cattle, of world-wide distribution. The disease is transmitted by ticks of the genus Boöphilus (see p. 534) in which the parasites, after fertilization in the hind-gut, invade the reproductive organs. They become enclosed with the eggs and subsequently undergo extensive multiplication and migration to all the tissues of the developing tick embryo. Some of the parasites enter the salivary glands and can then be transmitted by the seed ticks when they feed (Dennis, 1932). The adult ticks do not transmit the infection. The developmental cycle of Babesia in the vertebrate host is not fully known; the only forms known are small oval or pear-shaped bodies which bud to produce clusters of two, or in some species four, parasites (Fig. 52, 7 *a, b,* and *c*).

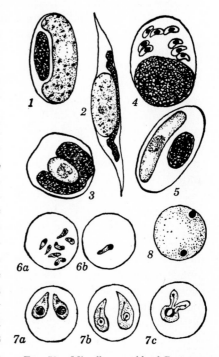

Fig. 52.   Miscellaneous blood Protozoa. *1, Haemoproteus columbae* (after Roudabush and Coatney); *2, Leucocytozoön simondi* (after O'Roke); *3, Hepatozoön muris,* in mononuclear leucocyte of rat (after Wenyon); *4, Toxoplasma gondii,* in leucocyte of a rodent (after Nicolle); *5,* Haemogregarina from turtle; *6a* and *6b, Theileria parva* from cattle (after Nuttall); *7a, Babesia bigemina* from cattle, Giemsa stain; *7b* and *7c,* same, iron hematoxylin stain (after Dennis); *8, Anaplasma marginale,* from cattle.

By quarantine and anti-tick methods this one-time scourge of cattle has been completely eliminated in the United States. *Rhipicephalus sanguineus* transmits a similar serious disease of dogs. Babesia infections also occur in horses, sheep, and various other mammals, particularly in the Old World.

The Theileriae, which undergo schizogony in endothelial cells and finally invade red cells as gametocytes but do not multiply in them, are parasites of ruminants.   They do not cause anemia, jaundice, and hemoglobinuria as do the Babesiae, but they do cause fever.   *T. parva* (Fig. 52, *6*) is the cause of the deadly East Coast fever of cattle in Africa.   The Theileriae are not transmitted hereditarily in ticks as are the Babesiae, but by later stages of a tick infected as a larva or nymph.   The life cycle was not fully known until worked out for *T. dispar* by Sergent *et al.* in 1936.

Another organism sometimes classed with the Babesiidae, though of very uncertain affinities, is Anaplasma (Fig. 52, *8*).   It appears in the red corpuscles as minute, round, deep-staining dots, one species habitually on the margins, another in the center of the corpuscles. Anaplasma may be transmitted by instruments in dehorning, etc., and by interrupted feeding of tabanids, but it is probably usually transmitted in nature by ticks, and frequently accompanies Babesia.   Seventeen different species of ticks have been incriminated in the United States.   Cattle often die from the infection, which entails high fever and intense anemia.   Animals that recover may remain carriers for years.   Infections in which as many as 50 per cent of the corpuscles show these bodies can be produced by inoculation, and immunity results, which argues in favor of their being real parasites.   However, their resemblance to the red granules called " Jolly bodies," which are found in the red corpuscles of young and anemic animals and are believed to be remnants of nuclei, throws suspicion on them.   Wenyon suggests that there is possibly an invisible virus producing anemia in cattle, one of the features of which is the production of numerous Jolly bodies.

Hepatozoön and Hemogregarines

These parasites, although classified in the order Coccidia, resemble the Haemosporidia in requiring an intermediate host.   The forms found in cold-blooded animals may belong to either of two genera: (1) Haemogregarina, in which the schizogonic cycle and the gametocytes (Fig. 52, *5*) may both occur in blood corpuscles, and oöcysts containing free sporozoites develop in leeches; or (2) Karyolysus, in which schizogony occurs in endothelial cells, producing merozoites which enter red corpuscles and become gametocytes, the sporogonic cycle occurring in mites.   The hemogregarines of birds and mammals are placed in the genus Hepatozoön; schizogony occurs in the reticulo-endothelial cells of liver, spleen, or bone marrow, and the gametocytes (Fig. 52, *3*) develop in circulating mononuclear leucocytes.   The sporogonic cycle of *Hepatozoön muris* of rats occurs in dermanyssid mites (see p. 511) of the genus Laelaps, whereas that of *H. canis* of dogs occurs in Ixodid ticks. In these intermediate hosts there develop large coccidium-like oöcysts containing numerous sporocysts, each with about 16 sporozoites. The resemblance to coccidians is further indicated by the fact that the sporocysts cause infection only via the alimentary canal, when swallowed with the mites or ticks in which they develop. *H. canis* causes a serious and sometimes fatal illness in dogs in India and Africa.

The gametocytes of hemogregarines in red cells are distinguishable from those of Haemoproteus by the lack of pigment.

Toxoplasma

This organism, as Manwell *et al.* (1945) pointed out, is still one of the least understood of human parasites. Its affinities, its frequency in man or animals, and the source or route of infection are all in doubt, and no reliable methods of diagnosis, treatment, or prevention are known. It is even uncertain whether it is a protozoan or a fungus, although it is much more probably the former. It is found free, or inside cells of many different types, particularly cells of the reticulo-endothelial system, white blood cells, and epithelial cells; it is found chiefly in the brain, liver, spleen, lung, and subcutaneous tissues.

The parasites (Fig. 52, 4) are crescent-shaped or oval, 6 to 12 μ long, with a discrete central nucleus; they usually occur in pairs or groups of pairs and apparently multiply by binary fission. In chronic symptomless cases they occur in large intracellular "pseudocysts" containing 50 or more organisms, apparently in an inactive resting state, since they cause no inflammatory reaction as do the free forms.

The organism is found naturally in mammals and can be inoculated into birds as well; mice and canaries both suffer rapidly fatal infections. Many birds in nature are found harboring organisms which have been regarded as Toxoplasma, but, since these are not inoculable into other animals and appear to differ in other fundamental characters, Manwell *et al.* (1945) believe they are probably of coccidian nature. It is probable that all forms of true mammalian Toxoplasma belong to a single species, *T. gondii,* which has a cosmopolitan distribution.

Nothing is known of the natural mode of transmission; the infection can be acquired by eating flesh containing the parasites, by prenatal infection, and by ingestion of feces, but ordinarily it is not acquired by cage mates. Rats, which have chronic and often symptomless infections, may be an important natural reservoir. Perrin, Brigham, and Pickens (1943) filed another indictment against these unwelcome companions of man when they demonstrated toxoplasmosis in the brains of 14 of 160 wild rats in Georgia — nearly 8 per cent.

Toxoplasmosis was first recognized as a human disease in 1939, but it is becoming evident that it is far commoner than is realized. Diagnosis depends on finding the parasites or inoculating animals, and is difficult in chronic cases. Serum containing antibodies mixed with Toxoplasma prevents necrosis of the skin of rabbits which is otherwise produced by inoculation of these parasites. The majority of recognized cases have been acute, fatal brain infections in infants, apparently prenatally infected from mothers who showed no evidence of infection. The symptoms involve the central nervous system and include impairment of vision, convulsions, delirium, jaundice, respiratory symptoms, and vomiting. Since World War II a number of adult cases with a fever and rash suggestive of typhus have been recognized. In these adult cases pseudocysts occur commonly in the muscles and have been confused with Sarcosporidia. Sulfapyridine has been reported to be effective in treatment of experimental infections in animals. Summers (1947) found that 0.15 per cent sodium sulfathiazole in the diet would protect young mice from fatal doses of Toxoplasma.

Coccidia

General Account. Although negligible as human parasites, Coccidia cause a greater economic loss among domestic and game animals in temperate climates than any other group of Protozoa. They are of major importance to poultry raisers and produce serious disease in rabbits and cattle. Horses, sheep, goats, pigs, dogs, cats, guinea pigs, ducks, geese, pigeons, and even canaries frequently suffer from their attacks.

The Coccidia are most commonly parasites of the epithelial cells of some part of the intestine, although some species attack the liver and other organs. The species which cause important infections in domestic animals belong to two genera, Eimeria and Isospora, which differ from each other mainly in details of development within the oöcysts. The life cycle is graphically shown in Fig. 53. After one, two, or more schizogonic cycles the merozoites develop into gametocytes, usually in the same type of cells in which the schizogony occurred. The microgametocytes produce a swarm of minute two-flagellated microgametes which fertilize the macrogametes, usually after the latter have escaped from the cells which mothered them. The macrogametes are provided with cyst walls but have a small opening called a micropyle at one end through which the microgametes are able to enter. The resulting zygote is a young oöcyst, ready for escape from the host in which it was developed, and prepared to withstand conditions in the outside world until opportunity to enter another host is afforded.

In most species the oöcysts (Fig. 55*A*) are undeveloped when they leave the host with the feces and require from 30 hours to 2 weeks to develop, depending upon the species and the temperature. Development takes place in two steps, (1) a division of the nucleus and cyto-

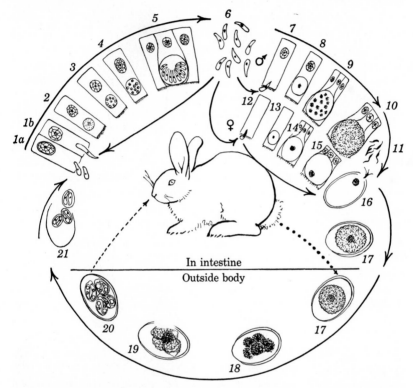

FIG. 53. Life history of *Eimeria perforans* of rabbit. *1a*, sporozoite entering intestinal cell; *1b*, merozoite entering intestinal cell; *2*, developing schizont; *3–5*, multiplication of nuclei and formation of merozoites; *6*, liberated merozoites, reinfecting other intestinal cells; *7–10*, development of ♂ gametocyte; *11*, microgametes; *12–15*, development of ♀ gametocyte; *16*, fertilization of macrogamete; *17*, undeveloped oöcyst ready to leave body of rabbit, and after escape with feces; *18–19*, formation of sporoblasts; *20*, development of sporocysts and sporozoites (ripe oöcyst); *21*, escape of sporozoites after ingestion of ripe oöcyst. (Adapted from figures by Becker and by Wetzel.)

plasm into a number of parts called sporoblasts, often leaving a residual mass of cytoplasm which may subsequently disappear, and (2) the further development of these sporoblasts into sporocysts with resistant cyst walls, and the division of their contents into a number of sporozoites; sometimes each sporocyst has a residual mass of cytoplasm of its own. The sporocysts are cysts within cysts, and in some species may be liberated from the parent oöcysts before re-entering a host. In

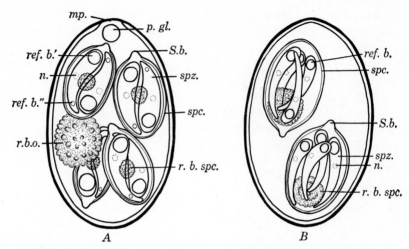

Fig. 54. Diagrammatic representation of oöcysts of Eimeria (*A*) and Isospora (*B*); *mp.*, micropyle; *n.*, nucleus of sporozoite; *p. gl.*, polar globule; *r.b.o.*, residual body of oöcyst; *ref. b.*, refractile bodies of sporozoites; *r. b. spc.*, residual body of sporocyst; *S.b.*, Stieda body or "plug" of sporocyst; *spc.*, sporocyst; *spz.*, sporozoite. (Adapted from Boughton and Volk.)

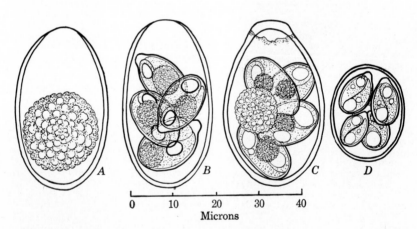

Fig. 55. Various types of oöcysts of Eimeria; *A*, unsporulated oöcyst of *E. stiedae* of liver of rabbit; *B*, ripe oöcyst of *E. stiedae*, with residual bodies in sporocysts but not in oöcyst; *C*, ripe oöcyst of *E. magna* of intestine of rabbit, with residual bodies in both oöcyst and sporocysts; *D*, *E. tenella* of cecum of chickens, with no residual bodies. (*A* to *C* after Kessel and Jankiewicz; *D* original.)

the genus Eimeria each oöcyst produces 4 sporocysts each with 2 sporozoites (Fig. 54*A*), whereas in the genus Isospora each oöcyst produces 2 sporocysts each with 4 sporozoites (Fig. 54*B*).

The oöcysts are easily destroyed by a temperature of about 50° C., by desiccation, and by extreme cold, but are highly resistant to chemicals. They can be cultured in the laboratory in a 2 to 5 per cent dichromate or a 1 per cent chromic acid solution. It is startling to find them undergoing development in fixed and stained slides!

The sporozoites liberated from ingested oöcysts penetrate cells in their chosen sites of development, grow into schizonts, and then divide into a cluster of spindle-shaped merozoites, usually about 16 to 30, but in the deadly *E. tenella* of chicks about 900, and in *E. bovis* of cattle over 100,000. In most coccidians two or more generations of schizonts are produced before the sexual forms are developed, but in most if not all species the number of schizogonic generations is limited, and therefore continuation of the disease depends on repeated reinfections.

Eimeria bovis of cattle differs from typical Eimerias in producing a single generation of huge schizonts, 250 to 400 μ in diameter, easily visible to the naked eye, and containing over 100,000 merozoites. The sporozoites begin their development in endothelial instead of epithelial cells; the schizonts mature in 14 to 18 days and then occupy the outer portion of the interior of badly bulged villi. Obviously, with such prolific schizonts, one generation of them is enough. Although the schizonts of this species occur in the small intestine, the gametocytes and oöcysts develop in the cecum and colon; the pathological effects and symptoms are associated only with the latter.

The true nature of these huge schizonts has only recently been determined (Hammond *et al.*, 1946). Similar organisms occur in horses, sheep, and camels and were formerly recognized under the names Globidium or Gastrocystis. When the life cycles of more of these are determined it may be desirable to separate them from the genus Eimeria.

Species. The Coccidia comprise numerous species, most of which show marked host specificity; Isospora shows more laxity in its choice of hosts than Eimeria. Not only do most species inhabit only a single kind of animal or a few closely related ones, but also a single animal may harbor several different species of Coccidia. Members of the genus Eimeria have made themselves at home in almost every kind of vertebrate, especially herbivorous ones, and in some invertebrates. In cold-blooded animals the oöcysts mature before leaving the host; in warm-blooded ones they mature afterwards. Intestinal forms are very common in rodents, pigs, ruminants, and poultry, and one species is common in the liver of rabbits. Isospora is common in small birds (Fig. 56C); Boughton reported references to its occurrences in 173 species, mostly passerines, but whether these represent one or many species is unknown. English sparrows show a very high incidence of infection, especially in the southern states. Canaries suffer from the infection but chickens do not; the latter are afflicted only by Eimeria. Among mammals species of Isospora are especially frequent in carnivores but are also reported from man, pig, and hedgehog.

Chickens harbor at least 8 species of Eimeria, cattle 6, rabbits 6, and pigeons 1; dogs harbor 3 species of Isospora, all of which are shared by cats and foxes. It is probable that only one coccidian, an Isospora, is a true human parasite.

The various species of Coccidia vary in the site and developmental details of their schizogonic cycle but are nearly always identifiable by the oöcysts alone, which is fortunate since these are the only forms commonly seen. The principal characters used in distinguishing the oöcysts of different species are size and shape of entire oöcysts, size and shape of sporocysts, the distinctness of the micropyle, the presence or absence of residual bodies in the oöcyst and in the sporocysts, and the thickness of the oöcyst wall.

Ingestion of oöcysts of " foreign " coccidians, passing through the alimentary canal intact, may lead to errors of interpretation. Species which are parasitic in the liver of herrings and in the testes of sardines, for example, have been mistakenly described as human parasites, and it is possible that some of the reported Eimeria infections in man may have been pseudo-infections from eating rabbit livers infected with *E. stiedae* (Fig. 55). Passage of the oöcysts through insusceptible animals may serve as a means of distribution.

Human Infections. About 300 cases of infection of the human intestine with Isospora are known, most of them from the eastern Mediterranean area, southwest Pacific, and Japan. Barksdale and Routh (1948) encountered 50 cases among Americans in the southwest Pacific during World War II, 44 of them in the Philippines, and Liebow et al. (1948) reported 3 cases in 387 examinations in Okinawa. Magath (1935) thought that all the human cases are referable to a single species, *Isospora hominis*, and that this species might be identical with one of the forms found in cats and dogs. The rarity of the human infection suggests that there is a reservoir host from which man is only occasionally infected.

The oöcysts of *I. hominis* (Fig. 56A) vary considerably in size, but average around 25 to 30 μ in length by about half this width. They contain a single mass of granular protoplasm when passed, but com-

plete their development with production of 2 sporocysts and 8 sporozoites in 24 to 48 hours under favorable conditions. Young oöcysts
also contain a large residual mass which is gradually reduced to a few
granules. Nothing is known of the asexual cycle of this species, but it
is probably like that of Isospora in cats, in which 8, or rarely 16,
merozoites are produced in each schizogonic cycle. Mild diarrhea
with light-colored, fatty stools, abdominal distress, and eosinophilia
are commonly described in connection with human infections, but some
infections seem to be without symptoms. In experimental infections
diarrhea and fever appear in about a week. The infections appear to
be self-limited and last only a few weeks.

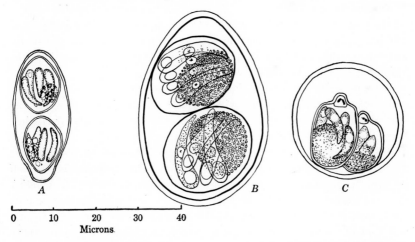

FIG. 56. Oöcysts of three species of Isospora. *A, I. hominis* of man (after Haugh-
wout); *B, I. felis* of cats (after Wenyon); *C, I. lacazii* of sparrows (after Becker).

Infections in Animals. In animals the pathogenic effect varies considerably with different species and with the severity of the infection.
In light cases there are often no symptoms, but in severe attacks by
pathogenic species there is extensive destruction of the epithelium in the
chosen sites, with sloughing of the walls and severe hemorrhage. The
symptoms are loss of appetite, emaciation, weakness, pallor, diarrhea,
bloody feces, and sometimes fever. Animals develop immunity from
repeated sublethal infections, but much more quickly and permanently
against some species than against others. The immunity is local in
nature, with no relation to antibodies in the blood.

Chickens harbor 8 species of Eimeria; fortunately most of them are
mildly pathogenic, but *E. tenella* and *E. necatrix* are very harmful, the
former causing severe injury to the ceca in young chicks, with often
fatal bloody diarrhea, the latter a more chronic intestinal disease in

older birds, characterized by leg weakness, pallor, and general unthriftiness. In cattle several species are pathogenic, including *E. zurnii*, *E. bovis*, and *E. alabamensis*. *E. bovis* has a cycle of development in the host of 20 days and produces huge schizonts visible to the naked eye with merozoite families numbering over 100,000 (see p. 223); *E. alabamensis* has a cycle of 8 to 12 days and produces modest merozoite families of 16 or less. Almost all calves in the southern states are infected; if heavily infected they suffer red or watery diarrhea, weakness, and emaciation, which is often fatal. Other species of coccidia harmful to domestic animals are *E. debliecki* in pigs, *E. truncata* in geese, and *E. solipedum* and *E. ungulata* in horses.

Treatment and Prevention. A number of drugs are capable of preventing infection if given with food or water prior to establishment of the infection, e.g., sulfur, certain organic sulfur compounds, and many sulfa drugs (sulfonamides), especially sulfaguanidine. The last has therapeutic effect against *E. bovis* in cattle but not against *E. alabamensis*, presumably because the abundant merozoites of the former are more exposed while making their way to the large intestine where the sexual stages develop, while the few merozoites of *E. alabamensis* immediately enter neighboring cells (Boughton, 1943).

Sulfa drugs with a pyrimidine nucleus (sulfadiazine, sulfamethazine, and sulfamerazine especially) have been found to have curative as well as preventive action against cecal coccidiosis in chickens (*E. tenella*) if given as soon as symptoms appear, or before. However, since symptoms do not usually appear until the fifth day after infection, and 90 per cent of the mortality occurs by the end of the seventh day, there is not time for much procrastination. These drugs, added to the food at the rate of 0.5 to 2 per cent for 3 days beginning within 4 days after infection, greatly reduce mortality in chicks (Swales, 1946). Addition of 2 grams of sodium sulfamerazine per quart of drinking water for 3 days is also effective and perhaps better, since infected chicks lose their appetites but not their desire for water. Sulfaquinoxaline at the rate of 0.05 per cent of the food, given intermittently, or ¼ that dose continuously, effectively controls *Eimeria tenella* and *E. necatrix* infections in chicks, reducing deaths from over 17 per cent to 1 or 2 per cent. It prevents development of later stages if given up to the fourth day after infection.

About all a harassed poultryman or animal raiser can do to hold in check the ravages of coccidiosis is to try by sanitary means to limit the ingestion of oöcysts to a number that will lead to immunity rather than death, and to utilize the sulfa drugs in food or water as soon as evidence of infection appears. Methyl bromide applied at the rate

of 0.15 to 0.3 cc. per square foot of litter or soil inactivates oöcysts. It
can also be used as a space fumigant in brooder houses; 2 lb. per
1000 cu. ft. prevents infection.

Arthropod-Borne Organisms Other than Protozoa

In this section we shall briefly discuss the organisms or disease agents
other than spirochetes and Protozoa that are commonly transmitted
biologically by arthropods, in order to give a more comprehensive view
of them and a better understanding of their relations to each other and
to their arthropod hosts than could be obtained from discussions of
them in the chapters dealing with the various vectors. Three groups
will be considered: the rickettsias and related forms; the filtrable
viruses; and the bacteria, among which only the genus Pasteurella is
biologically transmitted. As far as is known at present no fungus
infections are habitually transmitted by arthropods.

Rickettsia and Related Organisms

General Characters. Rickettsias, which are minute organisms believed to be related to bacteria, are strictly intracellular parasites and,
like filtrable viruses, have not yet been cultivated except in the presence
of living cells in tissue cultures or chick embryos. This is evidently
because, again like filtrable viruses, they are degenerate parasites
which have become dependent on host cells for essential enzymes.
They vary in form, being coccus-like, rod-shaped, or filamentous, and
they do not stain readily with aniline dyes as do bacteria, but respond
well to Giemsa's stain as do Protozoa. Their primary habitat is in the
tissues of arthropods, where some have become necessary commensals;
in the hosts to which they are well adapted they cause no apparent
disturbance and may be transovarially transmitted generation after
generation, e.g., in ticks, but in hosts to which they are poorly adapted
they may cause fatal infections, e.g., the rickettsia of epidemic typhus
in lice.

Vertebrate infections are undoubtedly a secondary development,
resulting when rickettsias in a blood-sucking arthropod are inoculated
into a vertebrate and are able to multiply there. Sometimes the infections may then be passed to other individuals without the arthropods
being further concerned, as in Q fever infections. In vertebrate hosts
the organisms multiply principally in endothelial cells of blood and
lymph vessels and in cells lining serous cavities.

Some authors have divided the rickettsias into several genera or subgenera, e.g., those of the spotted fever group which invade nuclei as well
as the cytoplasm of host cells have been named Dermacentroxenus, and

those of Q fever which have a filtrable stage and give no positive Weil-Felix reactions (see following paragraph) have been named Coxiella. For a review of the nomenclature of rickettsias see Philip (1943).

Typhus and Typhus-like Diseases. The typical rickettsias cause typhus or typhus-like diseases which are transmitted by ticks, mites, fleas, or lice. The diseases of this group all have similar general pathology and clinical character and show various degrees of cross-immunity. In all of them the serum of an immunized animal causes agglutination of certain strains of bacilli of the genus Proteus, although these bacteria are in no way related to the rickettsias; this is called a Weil-Felix reaction. In the tick-borne, flea-borne, and louse-borne types of typhus, as well as rickettsialpox, strains called OX19 and OX2 are agglutinated in various titers; in the mite-borne scrub typhus, strain OXK is agglutinated but the others are not.

Characteristic features of the typhus group of diseases are fever, an eruptive rash or purplish spotting of the skin a few days after onset, nervous and often gastro-intestinal symptoms, microscopic nodules around arterioles, and a marked reduction in leucocytes (leucopenia). In some, e.g., scrub typhus and boutonneuse fever, an ulcer develops at the site of the infective bite.

The various forms of tick-typhus (see p. 541) caused by the Dermacentroxenus group are certainly closely related, although the New World spotted fever group and the Old World boutonneuse fever group are sufficiently distinct, clinically and immunologically, to be separated. There is likewise a close relationship between flea-borne endemic or murine typhus (see p. 602) and louse-borne epidemic typhus (see p. 579); they differ principally in their effects on laboratory animals. There is some evidence that either one of these types may revert to the other. The flea-borne type is undoubtedly the primitive one, from which the louse-borne type developed when lice originally acquired the rickettsias from humans who were accidentally infected by rat fleas, for lice invariably die from typhus infections, whereas fleas do not appear to be inconvenienced. However, transovarial transmission does not occur even in fleas, so one may speculate that possibly a tick- or mite-borne type was the parent of the flea-borne type and the grandparent of the louse-borne type.

Scrub typhus (see p. 511), transmitted by larval trombiculid mites (redbugs) and called by various names in different parts of the Orient, is immunologically a distinct type, though clinically it resembles other typhus diseases. In 1946 a rickettsia resembling that of scrub typhus, and thought to be transmitted by *Trombicula microti*, was found infecting numerous meadow mice (Microtus) on an island in the St.

Lawrence near Quebec. No human infections have been observed. Rickettsialpox (see p. 513) is another mite-borne type, but its vectors are mites of an entirely different kind and it is immunologically closer to the spotted fever group.

Treatment and Prophylaxis. Specific drug treatment was not successful until 1948, when two antibiotics, aureomycin and chloromycetin, were found to be effective against all forms of rickettsial diseases. p-Aminobenzoic acid, one of the B vitamins, inhibits the multiplication of the organisms and has marked protective action against these infections. Prophylactic vaccinations are very effective; the vaccines used in the United States are prepared from rickettsias grown in the yolk sacs of chick embryos, but in some countries vaccines are prepared from massive infections in the lungs of mice or rats, or even rabbits and dogs, resulting from intranasal inoculations.

Other Rickettsial Diseases. The rickettsia of Q fever (see p. 546), as noted above, is distinct from the typhus group, being placed in the subgenus Coxiella. It is originally tick-borne or mite-borne but is secondarily transmitted by contact with cattle or their feces, with milk, or with inhaled dust or droplets. This rickettsia is not transovarially transmitted in ticks, and in the disease pneumonic symptoms are prominent and there is no rash.

In addition to these forms, rickettsias or rickettsia-like organisms have been described from Bullis fever (see p. 546) and trench fever (see p. 580) in man and from African East Coast fever of animals. A number of elementary bodies of filtrable viruses (see p. 231) have also been interpreted by some workers as rickettsias. Actually, the borderline between rickettsias and filtrable viruses with visible elementary bodies is becoming increasingly obscure, as Philip (1943) pointed out.

A list of the true and questionable rickettsial diseases of man and the principal ones of animals is given in the table on p. 230. All the arthropod-borne rickettsial diseases are discussed further under their respective vectors.

Bartonella. The organisms assigned to the genus Bartonella resemble rickettsias in morphology and staining. They are found both in reticulo-endothelial cells and in red blood corpuscles in the body, but unlike rickettsias they can be grown in cultures without living cells.

One member of this genus, *B. bacilliformis*, is the cause of Oroya fever or verruga peruviana in Andean valleys (see p. 623), and is transmitted by sandflies.

A Bartonella infection transmitted by lice occurs in rats and mice, but it is demonstrable only when the spleen is removed, when it causes a profound anemia.

DISEASE	SPECIES OF RICKETTSIA, AND WEIL-FELIX TYPE, IF ANY	TRANSMITTERS
Spotted fever group		
Spotted fever	*R. rickettsi* (OX19, OX2)	Ticks
Boutonneuse fever	*R. conori* (OX19, OX2)	Ticks
South African tick-bite fever	*R. pijperi* (OX19, OX2)	Ticks
Typhus group		
Endemic typhus	*R. typhi* (= *mooseri*)(OX19)	Fleas
Epidemic typhus	*R. prowazeki* (OX19)	Lice
Scrub typhus	*R. orientalis* (OXK)	Trombiculid mites
Quebec rodent typhus	Not named	Trombiculid mites (?)
Rickettsialpox	*R. akari* (OX19)	Mouse and rat mites
Q fever	*R. burneti* (None)	Ticks (originally) and mites
Questionable forms		
Bullis fever	Not named	Ticks (?)
Trench fever	*R. quintana*	Lice
African East Coast fever	*R. ruminantium*	Ticks

Filtrable Viruses

A considerable number of important human diseases have causative agents so small that they are beyond the range of visibility and will pass through filters which will hold back any microscopically visible organisms. These filtrable viruses are probably not primitive forms of life but highly degenerate forms that have become more and more dependent on the cells in which they live to provide them with enzymes and materials that free-living organisms provide for themselves. The intracellular rickettsias and some of the largest viruses, e.g., vaccinia, are only a little less complex than bacteria, but the process of loss and of concomitant decrease in size continues until in the smallest and simplest viruses, like those of tobacco mosaic and poliomyelitis, little or nothing is left but naked nucleoprotein molecules which have inherent in them the power of reproduction. The host cells provide all the necessary enzymes and materials. In many ways the simplest viruses are comparable with genes both in size and properties, differing mainly in the ability to move from cell to cell. Like genes they are subject to mutation.

Although not a natural group, all viruses have certain features in common. They are more resistant to antiseptics than bacteria. They all tend to stimulate the cells in which they grow to increased multiplication, followed by death of the cells, but the necrosis may occur too rapidly for the growth stimulus to be apparent, and this is the only observed effect in nerve cells, which cannot multiply. Many produce "inclusion bodies" which are in reality masses of the elementary filtrable bodies. As noted on p. 229, some of the larger of these elementary bodies are not unlike rickettsias, and those of trachoma, psittacosis, and lymphogranuloma have been so interpreted. Sometimes the masses of elementary bodies are surrounded by a mantle of amorphous material produced by cellular reaction, suggesting Protozoa, for which a special class "Chlamydozoa" (mantled animals) was once proposed. All viruses stimulate formation of neutralizing antibodies which inactivate them and thereby provide the most commonly used method for identifying them.

The viruses that are primarily arthropod-borne consist of two principal groups. One, including yellow fever, dengue, sandfly fever, and Colorado tick fever, causes fevers, sometimes a rash, and a marked decrease in leucocytes (leucopenia). Of these only yellow fever enters the central nervous system and develops "neurotropic" strains. The other group, including various forms of encephalomyelitis and encephalitis, causes fever but affects primarily the central nervous system. In addition to these, a number of other viruses are transmitted by arthropods but are not primarily dependent on them; such are fowlpox of birds and swamp fever of horses.

It is still uncertain what role arthropods play in transmission of poliomyelitis, but the epidemiology strongly suggests their implication. The disease is prevalent in summer, is more frequent in small towns and edges of cities than in the centers of them, and does not spread in crowds. Flies harbor the virus, which they acquire from human feces, and monkeys eating food contaminated by infected flies show evidence of infection by developing neutralizing antibodies, as do a large percentage of humans when an outbreak occurs, but there is no paralysis. Furthermore, fly-controlled areas in south Texas had as high an incidence of polio cases as did uncontrolled areas. Might it not be possible that infection via the digestive system by small doses of virus deposited on food by flies may lead to immunity without paralysis? The absence of the virus from the blood argues against arthropods acquiring it by sucking blood, although they might possibly inoculate it if infected in some other way. The writer wonders whether mosquitoes like Culex might not acquire the virus from sewage-polluted water as larvae, and subsequently inoculate it after becoming adults.

Of the first group of primarily arthropod-borne virus diseases mentioned above, yellow fever is the most severe and is the only one causing mortality. It is transmitted by mosquitoes, although an instance of its transmission to a monkey by a mite has been reported (see p. 512). The disease is discussed in more detail on p. 686. The virus is present in the blood of patients for only 3 days and requires about 10 days for a mosquito to become infective, after which it persists for life, although it is not transovarially transmitted. Dengue fever (see p. 693), of which there are at least three distinct antigenic types, is also transmitted only by mosquitoes, but the evidence is conflicting as to how long it takes for mosquitoes to become infective and whether transovarial transmission can occur (see p. 694). Sandfly fever is very similar to dengue but is transmitted only by *Phlebotomus papatasi*, in which it is transovarially transmitted; at least two antigenic types exist. Colorado tick fever (see p. 549) is also very similar to dengue but is transmitted by ticks; transovarial infection occurs.

Of the group of arthropod-borne viruses causing encephalomyelitis or encephalitis, sometimes erroneously called sleeping sickness, there are many mosquito-transmitted strains (see p. 697). Three strains are common in the United States and Canada — eastern and western equine and St. Louis encephalomyelitis; two in South America, Venezuelan and Argentinian; two in the Far East, Japanese B and Russian spring-summer encephalitis; and no less than eight, distinct from all the others, have been found in Africa. All appear to be primarily mosquito- or mite-borne and are discussed further on pp. 512 and 697, except the Russian spring-summer disease, which is transmitted by ticks and is discussed on p. 549. As Warren pointed out in 1946, there is a very close relationship between the virus of this disease and that of louping ill in sheep; the former commonly attacks man in Siberia, and the latter is a disease of sheep in Russia and northern Britain.

In addition to the arthropod-borne viruses, at least two viruses are commonly transmitted by helminths; one, causing salmon poisoning in dogs, is transmitted by a fluke (see p. 305), and one, causing swine influenza, is carried by a lungworm (see p. 418). Another, lymphocytic choriomeningitis, has been shown to be transmissible by Trichinella larvae. One cannot help speculating on the possibility that poliomyelitis might be similarily transmitted, perhaps by Enterobius.

Arthropod-Borne Bacteria. Although a few bacteria are able to cause disease in arthropods, the latter, particularly some of the blood suckers, are remarkably resistant to the establishment and multiplication of most bacteria other than the atypical spirochetes and rickettsias. In many species, e.g., bedbugs, lice, and some ticks, the intestine contains potent bactericidal properties and may be completely sterile, whereas the intestines of others are packed with particular kinds of bacteria (see Steinhaus, 1946). In many insects, e.g., flies, roaches, and ticks, the intestine may harbor various bacteria (such as those of anthrax and the intestinal group causing typhoid, dysentery, and food poisoning) long enough for them to pass through and be voided in the feces, sometimes perhaps with a little multiplication en route; however, such infections do not persist. In the case of ticks such infections are often transmitted while the tick is biting. Ornithodorus and fleas have been found to harbor *Salmonella enteritidis* and to transmit it to experimental animals; ticks, bedbugs, and fleas may be vectors of brucellosis (see p. 548). The tick *Dermacentor albopictus* has been shown to harbor a bacterium, *Klebsiella paralytica,* that causes a disease of moose (see p. 537).

The only typical bacteria which establish themselves, multiply, and persist in arthropods, so that the arthropods act as true biological transmitters, are two species of the genus Pasteurella: *P. pestis,* the cause of plague, and *P. tularensis,* the cause of tularemia. These are small, nonmotile, nonspore-forming bacilli which stain deeply at the ends (bipolar staining). *P. pestis,* when ingested by fleas with the blood of an infected animal, multiplies so prodigiously in the esophagus, proventriculus, and stomach that it frequently blocks the alimentary canal, but it does not invade other parts of the body and does not multiply in any other insects. *P. tularensis,* on the other hand, can be transmitted by a variety of arthropods, including ticks, deerflies, lice, bedbugs, and fleas. However, there is little doubt that ticks are the primary arthropod hosts. Unlike *P. pestis* in fleas, *P. tularensis* invades the hemocele in ticks and is transovarially transmitted. Plague is discussed further on pp. 597–602, and tularemia on p. 547.

REFERENCES

ALCOCK, A., *Bartonella muris-ratti* and the Infectious Anemia of Rats, *Trop. Diseases Bull.,* **26,** 519 (1929).

AM. ASSOC. ADVANCEMENT SCI., A Symposium on the Rickettsial Diseases of Man, 1948.

BARKSDALE, W. L., and ROUTH, C. F., *Isospora hominis* Infections among American Personnel in the Southwest Pacific, *Am. J. Trop. Med.,* **28,** 639–644 (1948).

BECKER, E. R., *Coccidia and Coccidiosis,* Ames, Iowa, 1934.

BOUGHTON, D. C., Sulfaguanidine Therapy in Experimental Bovine Coccidiosis, *Am. J. Vet. Research,* **4** (10), 66–72 (1943).

BOYTON, W. H., and WOODS, G. M., Some Information on Anaplasmosis for the Veterinarian, *Mich. State Coll. Vet. Sci.,* **25** (1944).

BRUMPT, E., and BRUMPT, L.-CH., Étude épidémiologique concernant l'apparition de la verruga du Pérou en Colombie, *Ann. parasitol. humaine et comparée,* **19,** 1–50 (1942).

BURNET, F. M., DERRICK, E. H. SMITH, D. J. W., *et al.,* Studies in the Epidemiology of Q Fever, *Australian J. Exptl. Biol. Med. Sci.,* **18,** 99, 103, 193, 409 (1940); **20,** 105, 213 (1942).

CALLAHAN, W. P., JR., RUSSELL, W. D., and SMITH, M. C., Human Toxoplasmosis, Medicine, **25,** 343–397 (1946).

CASTAÑEDA, M. R., Bivalent Typhus Vaccine of High Immunizing Value, *Science,* **96,** 304 (1942).

CHANDLER, A. C., and RICE, L., Observations on the Etiology of Dengue, *Am. J. Trop. Med.,* **3,** 233 (1923).

COWEN, D., WOLF, A., and PAIGE, B. H., Toxoplasmic Encephalomyelitis, VI, Clinical Diagnosis of Infantile or Congenital Toxoplasmosis; Survival beyond Infancy, *Arch. Neurol. Psychiat.,* **48,** 689 (1942).

COX, H. R., Cultivation of the Rocky Mountain Spotted Fever, Typhus, and Q Fever Groups in the Embryonic Tissues of Developing Chick, *Science,* **94,** 399 (1941).

DENNIS, E. W., The Life Cycle of *Babesia bigemina* (Smith and Kilbourne) of Texas Cattle-fever in the Tick, *Margaropus annulatus* (Say), *Univ. Calif. Pub. Zool.,* **36,** 263 (1932).

FLORIO, L., and MILLER, M. S., Epidemiology of Colorado Tick Fever, *Am. J. Publ. Health,* **38,** 211–213 (1948).

FRANCIS, E., Arthropods in the Transmission of Tularemia, *Trans. 4th Intern. Congr. Ent.,* **2,** 929 (1929).

HAMMON, W. McD., The Arthropod-Borne Virus Encephalitides, *Am. J. Trop. Med.,* **28,** 515–525 (1948).

HAMMOND, D. M., BOWMAN, G. W., DAVIS, L. R., and SIMMS, B. T., The Endogenous Phase of the Life Cycle of *Eimeria bovis, J. Parasitol.,* **32,** 409–427 (1946)

HARVARD SCHOOL OF PUBLIC HEALTH, *Virus and Rickettsial Diseases,* Symposium Volume, 1940.

HERMAN, C. M., The Blood Protozoa of North American Birds, *Bird-Banding,* **15,** 90–112 (1944).

HERTIG, M., Phlebotomus and Carrion's Disease, *Am. J. Trop. Med.,* **22,** No. 5, Suppl. (1942).

HORNBY, H. E., Piroplasms of Domestic Animals, *12th Intern. Vet. Congr., 1934,* **3,** 314 (1935).

HUFF, C. G., Schizogony and Gametocyte Development in *Leucocytozoön simondi,* and Comparisons with Plasmodium and Haemoproteus, *J. Infectious Diseases,* **71,** 18 (1942).

JOHNSON, E. P., Further Observations on a Blood Protozoan of Turkeys transmitted by *Simulium nigroparvum* (Twinn), *Am. J. Vet. Research,* **3,** 214 (1942).

KIRK, R., Some Observations on the Study and Control of Yellow Fever in Africa, with Particular Reference to the Anglo-Egyptian Sudan, *Trans. Roy. Soc. Trop. Med. Hyg.,* **37,** 125 (1943).

LIEBOW, A. A., MILLIKEN, N. T., and HANNUM, C. A., Isopora Infections in Man, *Am. J. Trop. Med.,* **28,** 261–273 (1948).

LIVESAY, H. R., and POLLARD, M., Laboratory Report on a Clinical Syndrome Referred to as " Bullis Fever," *Am. J. Trop. Med.,* **23,** 475 (1943).

MAGATH, T. B., The Coccidia of Man, *Am. J. Trop. Med.,* **15,** 91 (1935).

MANWELL, R. D., COULSON, F., BINCKLEY, E. C., and JONES, V. P., Mammalian and Avian Toxoplasma, *J. Infectious Diseases,* **76,** 1–14 (1945).

MEYER, K. F., The Known and the Unknown in Plague, *Am. J. Trop. Med.,* **22,** 9–37 (1942).

O'ROKE, E. C., A Malaria-like Disease of Ducks Caused by *Leucocytozoön anatis* Wickware, *Univ. Mich. Sch. Forestry and Conserv. Bull.,* **4** (1934).

PARKER, R. R., Rocky Mountain Spotted Fever, *J. Am. Med. Assoc.*, **110**, 1185, 1273 (1938).

PERRIN, T. L., BRIGHAM, G. D., and PICKENS, E. G., Toxoplasmosis in Wild Rats, *J. Infectious Diseases*, **72**, 91 (1943).

PHILIP, C. B., Nomenclature of the Pathogenic Rickettsiae, *Am. J. Hyg.*, **37**, 301–309 (1943).

PINKERTON, H., WEINMAN, D., and HERTIG, M., Carrion's Disease (Oroya Fever and Verruga peruviana) I–V, *Proc. Soc. Exptl. Biol. Med.*, **37**, 587 (1937).

RICKETTSIALPOX — A Newly Recognized Rickettsial Disease, I–VI (Various authors); I, *Publ. Health Rept.*, **61**, 1605 (1946); II, *J. Am. Med. Assoc.*, **133**, 901–906 (1947); III, *Am. J. Publ. Health*, **37**, 860–868 (1947); IV, *Publ. Health Rept.*, **61**, 1677–1682 (1946); V, *ibid.*, **62**, 777–780 (1947).

SAWYER, W. A., La fiebre amarilla en las Americas, English Summary, *Bol. oficina sanit. panamer.*, **21**, 320 (1942).

SERGENT, E., DONATIEN, A., PARROT, L., and LESTOQUARD, F., Cycle évolutif de *Theileria dispar* du boeuf chez la tique, *Hyalomma mauritanicum*, *Arch. inst Past. Algérie*, **14**, 259 (1936).

SIMMONS, J. S., ST. JOHN, J. H., and REYNOLDS, F. H. K., Experimental Studies of Dengue, Monogr. 29, Bur. Science, Manila, 1931.

SOPER, F. L., Present Day Methods for the Study and Control of Yellow Fever *Am. J. Trop. Med.*, **17**, 655 (1937).

The Newer Epidemiology of Yellow Fever, *Am. J. Publ. Health*, **27**, 1 (1937).

SOPER, F. L., DAVIS, W. A., MARKHAM, F. S., and RIEHL, L. A., Typhus Fever in Italy, 1943–1945, and Its Control with Louse Powder, *Am. J. Hyg.*, **45**, 305–334 (1947).

STEINHAUS, E. A., *Insect Microbiology*, Ithaca, N. Y., 1946.

STRONG, R. P., *Trench Fever Report*, Med. Research Comm. Am. Red Cross, Oxford Univ. Press, 1918.

SWALES, W. E., On the Chemotherapy of Cecal Coccidiosis (*Eimeria tenella*) in Chickens, I, *Can. J. Research, D*, **22**, 131–140 (1944); II, *Can. J. Comp. Med. Vet. Sci.*, 3–13, January, 1946.

TOPPING, N. H., CULLYFORD, J. S., and DAVIS, G. E., Colorado Tick Fever, *Publ. Health Rept.*, **55**, 2224 (1940).

TYZZER, E. C., THEILER, H., and JONES, E. E., Coccidiosis in Gallinaceous Birds, II, *Am. J. Hyg.*, **15**, 319 (1932).

VAN ROOYEN, C. E., and RHODES, A. J., *Virus Diseases of Man*, 2nd ed., New York, 1948.

WEINMAN, D., Bartonellosis: A Public Health Problem in South America, *J. Trop. Med. Hyg.*, **44**, 62 (1941).

Chronic Toxoplasmosis, *J. Infectious Diseases*, **73**, 75 (1943).

PART II — HELMINTHOLOGY

CHAPTER 11
Introduction to the "Worms"

Classification. The name "worm" is an indefinite though suggestive term popularly applied to any elongated creeping thing that is not obviously something else. There is hardly a branch or phylum of the animal kingdom that does not contain members to which the term worm has been applied, not excepting even the Chordata. In fact some animals, such as many insects, are "worms" during one phase of their life history and something quite different during another.

In a more restricted sense the name worm, or preferably helminth, is applied to a few phyla of animals, all of which superficially resemble one another in being unquestionably "wormlike," though in life and structure they are widely different. To these animals, together with some other heterogeneous forms, the collective name "Vermes" was applied by the early workers on zoological classification. Upon more detailed study it became obvious that different types of the Vermes differed from one another very extensively. Some zoologists split the Vermes into seven or eight distinct phyla or branches of the animal kingdom, but some of the groups concerned contain comparatively few forms and are of minor importance, and so are often grouped with other forms with which they seem to have the most in common.

The great majority of the worms with which we have to deal fall into two of these phyla: the Platyhelminthes or flatworms, including the flukes and tapeworms; and the Nemathelminthes or threadworms, including the nematodes. In addition, we shall deal briefly with the Acanthocephala or spiny-headed worms. These were formerly thrown in with the Nemathelminthes in order not to be bothered with too many phyla, but they probably represent an offshoot from the Platyhelminthes. We shall also very briefly consider the leeches, which belong to an entirely distinct phylum, the Annelida, from which the arthropods undoubtedly arose in the course of evolution.

236

The relative importance of the major groups of helminths may be roughly judged by Stoll's 1947 estimate that there exist in the world today, among some 2200 million people, 72 million cestode, 148 million trematode, and over 2000 million nematode infections. Of course, like money and brains, these are not evenly distributed among the individuals!

Platyhelminthes. This phylum contains the helminths of lowest organization. The great majority of them are flattened from the dorsal to the ventral side, hence the common name flatworm. Unlike nearly

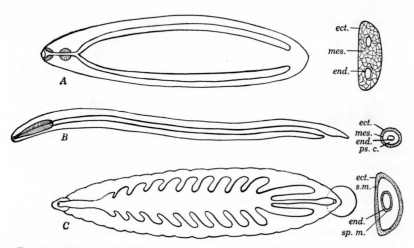

Fig. 57.   Diagrams of digestive tracts and cross-sections of bodies of representatives of Platyhelminthes (*A*), Nemathelminthes (*B*), and Annelida (*C*). *A*, fluke; gut branched into two ceca, no anus, and no body cavity. *B*, nematode; gut a simple tube with only pharynx differentiated, anus present, body cavity a pseudocelome not lined by splanchnic mesoderm internally. *C*, leech; gut with ceca for surplus food, anus present, body cavity a true celome lined by splanchnic mesoderm internally and somatic mesoderm externally. Abbrev.: *ect.*, ectoderm; *end.*, endoderm; *mes.*, mesoderm; *ps. c.*, pseudocelome; *s.m.*, somatic mesoderm; *sp. m.*, splanchnic mesoderm.

all other many-celled animals they have no body cavity, the organs being embedded in a sort of spongy " packing " tissue. The digestive tract in its simplest form, and as it occurs in the larval generation of flukes known as rediae, consists of a blind sac with only a single opening, serving both as a mouth and as a vent, but in most adult forms this sac is variously branched and in a few flukes even has an anus; on the other hand the tapeworms have dispensed with the digestive tract entirely, food being absorbed through the outer surface of the body, some from the contents of the lumen of the intestine in which they live, some from the mucous membrane with which they are in contact. The nervous system is very simple, and the primitive ganglia which serve as a brain are located in the anterior portion of the worm. Performing the function of kidneys is a system of tubes, the terminal branches of which are closed by " flame cells," so called from the flame-like flickering of a brush of cilia which keeps up a flow of fluid toward the larger branches of the system and ultimately to the excretory pore, thus conducting the waste products out of the body.

The most highly developed systems of organs, occupying a large portion of the body, are those concerned with reproduction. Usually the Platyhelminthes are hermaphroditic, containing complete male and female systems in each individual; in tapeworms both systems are usually complete in each segment and there may even be double sets in each segment. In addition to the ordinary sexual reproduction of the adults, the continued production of new segments in the neck region of a tapeworm, thus forming chains of what are in most respects separate individuals, may be considered an asexual method of reproduction in the adult stage. Still other methods of reproduction are resorted to by most flukes and some tapeworms. Many flukes multiply asexually before reaching the adult stage, producing in the course of their development a series of generations of dissimilar individuals, comparable with the alternation of hydroids and medusae in some coelenterates. A few tapeworms multiply in the larval stage by a process of multiple budding.

The flatworms are usually divided into three classes, the Turbellaria, the Trematoda, and the Cestoidea, but some zoologists include also the Nemertea, a group of band-shaped marine worms of uncertain relationships, none of which are of interest in connection with human parasitology.

The Turbellaria are ciliated and for the most part free-living animals; they include the " planarians " which can be found creeping on the underside of stones in ponds. The Trematoda include the flukes, all of which are parasitic, some externally on aquatic animals, others internally on aquatic or land animals. They are soft-bodied, usually flattened animals, commonly oval or leaf-shaped, and furnished with suckers for adhering to their hosts. The flukes that live as external parasites of aquatic animals have a comparatively simple life history, whereas those that are internal parasites have a complex life history, including two or three asexual generations, in the course of which they pass through two or three different hosts.

The third class, the Cestoidea or tapeworms, with the exception of one primitive family living in the body cavity of ganoid fishes, and the members of one genus which are able to complete their development precociously in annelid worms, are (in the adult stage) invariably parasites of the digestive tracts of vertebrate animals and are pro-

foundly modified for this kind of an existence.   Except for a few evolutionarily precocious forms in the genus Hymenolepis (see p. 346), all
tapeworms begin their development in an alternative host, which may
be either a vertebrate or an invertebrate.   In some forms two or even
three intermediate hosts are involved in the life cycle. Although in
some forms a number of adults may develop from one larva as the
result of a budding process, there is never an alternation of generations
such as occurs in most trematodes.   In one subclass, the Cestodaria,
the adult worms are single individuals, like flukes; they differ from
flukes most strikingly in the absence of a digestive tract.   In the other
subclass, Cestoda, all but the members of a single degenerate family
consist of chains of segments.

Nemathelminthes.   Of somewhat higher organization than the flatworms is the phylum Nemathelminthes, a term meaning " threadworms."   With rare exceptions they are elongated and cylindrical
instead of flattened, they possess a body cavity, and they lack flame
cells.   The majority of the included forms are true nematodes, belonging to the class Nematoda, but the Gordiacea, or horsehair worms, are
also included.

The true nematodes are cylindrical worms covered by a very resistant
cuticle; they have a simple digestive tract with mouth and anus, a fluid-
filled body cavity which is not lined by epithelium as in other animals,
and usually separate sexes, with the sex glands continuous with their
ducts in the form of slender tubules.   There is an excretory system consisting of a glandular apparatus opening through an anteriorly situated
excretory pore, in some forms connected with longitudinal lateral
canals.   The development is always direct and simple but sometimes
requires two hosts for its completion.

The Gordiacea are widely different from nematodes in structure and
development, in spite of their superficial resemblance to them.   The
popular name " horsehair snake " comes from a popular idea, not yet
dead, that they develop out of horsehairs that fall into water.   They
are very long and slender hairlike worms that live as parasites in
insects until almost mature, when they emerge from the insects and
reproduce in water or soil.   Occasionally they are accidentally swallowed with drinking water and are usually promptly vomited, much to
the surprise and horror of the temporarily infested person.

Acanthocephala.   Though long included in the Nemathelminthes,
the Acanthocephala have little in common with the nematodes in either
structure or development; they constitute a very aberrant and sharply
defined group of parasites of vertebrate animals.   They are characterized by having a large body cavity, complete lack of a digestive

tract, a spiny proboscis retractile into a sac, and separate sexes with reproductive systems of unique character (see Chapter 14). The development, which involves an arthropod intermediate host, more nearly resembles that of flatworms than that of nematodes. For the present it seems best to recognize Acanthocephala as a distinct class with affinities closer to the cestodes than to nematodes, without definitely placing them in the Platyhelminthes. Van Cleave (1948) considers them as constituting a distinct phylum.

Annelids. The most highly organized group of worms is the phylum Annelida, including the segmented worms or annelids. In three important respects these worms are the first animals in the scale of evolution to develop the type of structure characteristic of the vertebrate animals, namely, a division of the body into segments, the presence of a blood system, and the presence of " nephridia " — primitive excretory organs of the same fundamental type as the kidneys of

Fig. 58.   Japanese land leech, *Haemadipsa japonica*, extended.   × 2.
(After Whitman.)

higher animals.   In addition the digestive system is highly developed and there is a well-developed nervous system with a primitive brain in the head.   In some annelids the sexes are separate, though in others both reproductive systems occur in the same individual.

Three classes of Annelida are usually recognized, of which one, the Hirudinea, or leeches, are of interest as bloodsuckers.   These differ from other annelids in lacking setae, in the possession of suckers for adhering, and in the fact that the external annulation of the body does not correspond exactly to the true internal segmentation.   These animals superficially resemble flukes, so much so that liver flukes are often referred to as liver leeches, but they can be distinguished externally by the segmentation of the body and internally by their totally different anatomy.   Both sexes are represented in the same individual.

Every boy who has experienced the delights of hanging his clothes on a hickory limb and immersing his naked body in a muddy-bottomed river or pond is familiar with leeches.   These are related to the medicinal leeches that were an important stock in trade of medieval physicians.   Still more familiar with them is any tourist who has journeyed on foot through the jungles of Ceylon or Sumatra, or through the warm moist valleys of the Himalayas or Andes, for hordes of bloodthirsty land leeches infest these places. Furthermore, thirsty horses, and occasionally men, gulping water from pools or streams in Palestine, North Africa, and China, may suffer severe or even fatal loss of blood from the settling of "horse leeches" of the genera Limnatis or Haemopis in the pharynx or nasal passages or sometimes in urinary passages, where they may hang on for days or months (Masterson, 1908). Leeches lodged in the nasopharynx let go when 5 per cent cocaine is sprayed into the nostrils.

Although land leeches are nasty pests in some places, they are not known to be vectors of any human infection. Aquatic leeches serve as intermediate hosts for trypanosomes of fish and amphibia. Some large species in northern United States feed voraciously on large snails and thereby seem to have rendered some lakes free of swimmer's itch (see p. 277). These species do not suck blood from vertebrates.

Parasitic Habitats. Hardly any organ or tissue is exempt from attack by worms of one kind or another. There are flukes parasitic in man which habitually infest the intestine, liver, lungs, and blood vessels, and one species occasionally wanders to the muscles, spleen, brain, and many other organs. In other animals there are species with even more specialized habitats; some inhabit the Eustachian tubes of frogs, the frontal sinuses of polecats, the eye sockets of birds, cysts in the skin of birds, etc. All the adult tapeworms of man are resident in the small intestine, but there are species in sheep and goats and one in rats which habitually live in the bile duct; larval tapeworms are found in a great variety of locations — in the liver, spleen, muscles, subcutaneous tissues, eye, brain, etc.

The majority of the parasitic nematodes of man are resident in the intestine, but the filariae and their relatives inhabit various tissues and internal organs, such as the lymph sinuses and subcutaneous connective tissue. Nematode parasites of other animals, many of which are occasional or accidental in the human body, may occur in all parts of the alimentary canal and in its walls, and in liver, lungs, kidneys, bladder, heart, blood vessels, trachea, peritoneum, skin, eye, and sinuses. None however, live as adults in the central nervous system. The surface of the body and cavities of the nose and throat of man are not the habitat of any helminth parasites except leeches and the tongueworms; the latter are really arthropods (see p. 518), although they have much more in common with the helminths.

Physiology. Parasitic worms vary in their diet. Tapeworms, having no alimentary canal are thought to absorb carbohydrates from the intestinal fluid in which they are bathed but to obtain nitrogenous and probably other substances from the mucous membranes with which they are in contact (Chandler, 1942). Flukes feed in part on blood and lymph, in part on cells and tissue debris. Some nematodes, e.g., hookworms, feed mainly on blood, but others subsist principally on tissues, either ingesting them and digesting them in the intestine or first liquefying them by the products of esophageal glands. Ability to dissolve tissues is also shared by some flukes. As we have seen on p. 23, the tissues seem to be capable of developing resistance to digestion by the worms; this is a reversal of the anti-enzyme armament of the parasites which keeps them from being digested by the host. In hosts immunized by repeated or long-standing infections, intestinal nematodes, unable to feed in the midst of plenty, fail to grow and are soon eliminated.

Although parasites located in the tissues have oxygen available, those in the intestinal tract do not. Hookworms overcome this difficulty by keeping a constant stream of blood passing through their bodies, but nonbloodsucking worms such as Ascaris seem to be capable of a true anaerobic existence, obtaining their energy by the breakdown of glycogen into carbon dioxide and fatty acids.

Although helminths are very poorly equipped with sensory organs they show amazing ability to react when the necessity arises. With no evident specialized sense organs of any kind whatever a single male Trichinella finds a single female in the relatively vast expanses of a rat's intestine; Clonorchis larvae almost unerringly discover the minute opening to the bile duct; and miracidia, the larvae of flukes, are attracted by their proper snail hosts as are filings by a magnet.

Life History and Modes of Infection. The life history and modes of infection of worms vary with the habitat in the body. Every parasitic worm must have some method of gaining access to the body of its host and must have some means for the escape of its offspring, either eggs or larvae, from the host's body in order to continue the existence of its race. Many species utilize intermediate hosts as a means of transfer from one host to another; others have a direct life history, i.e., they either develop inside the escaped egg and depend on such agencies as food and water to be transferred to a new host, or they develop into free-living larvae which are swallowed by or burrow into a new host.

Methods of Entry and Exit. Most of the intestinal parasites enter their host by way of the mouth, and the eggs escape with the feces. Many species enter as larvae in the tissues of an intermediate host which is eaten by the final host, e.g., most of the tapeworms, many flukes, and some nematodes (spiruroids). Some nematodes of the intestine, such as the pinworm and whipworm, make their entry as fully developed embryos in the eggs. Others, like the schistosomes, hookworms, and Strongyloides, usually reach their destination in an indirect way by burrowing through the skin. All the intestinal worms except Trichinella produce eggs or larvae that escape from the body with the feces. In Trichinella the larvae encyst in the muscles, and their salvation depends on their host's being eaten by another animal.

Many of the helminths of other organs of the body also enter by way of the mouth and digestive tract, though they have various means of exit for the eggs or larvae. The liver flukes enter and escape from the body as do ordinary intestinal parasites; the schistosomes enter by burrowing through the skin, and the eggs escape with either feces or urine; the filariae enter and leave the body by the aid of bloodsucking insects; the guinea worm enters by the mouth, and the larvae leave through the skin. The larval tapeworms which infest man enter either by the mouth or by accidental invasion of the stomach from an adult in the intestine. Like Trichinella they are usually permanently sidetracked in man, except among cannibals, since they can escape only by being eaten with the tissues in which they are imbedded.

Adjustments in Life Cycles. It is obvious that parasitic worms have a tremendous problem to solve in insuring the safe arrival of their offspring in the bodies of other hosts, on which the survival of the race depends, for sooner or later the body which is affording food and shelter will die, and however immortal the soul may be, the parasites can derive little comfort from it. The problem is difficult enough for worms like Ascaris, Trichuris, and hookworms, whose offspring merely have to spend a relatively short time in the great outdoors before being ready to return, either as stowaways in food or water or by their own burrowing, to another host of the same species. But flukes and tapeworms are so hampered by heritage and tradition that they have to undergo a preliminary development in some entirely different but often very particular kind of animal, and sometimes must even spend an apprenticeship in a third kind, before they are ready for their ultimate life of ease and comfort in the definitive host. When one considers the experiences through which a lung fluke, for example, must go in order to live and reproduce its kind, first as a minute free-swimming protozoan-like organism, then as an asexually reproducing parasite of certain species of snails, then as a tissue-invading parasite of crabs, and finally as a human invader that must find its way from the stomach to the lungs, he would be incredulous if he were not confronted with the fact that the lung fluke not only succeeds in accomplishing this, but succeeds so well that in some places it constitutes a serious menace to the health of whole communities.

Since the vicissitudes of life for the offspring of parasitic worms are so great, it is obvious that there must be a tremendous waste of offspring which do not succeed in the struggle, and therefore a sufficiently large number of eggs or young must be produced so that the chances of survival are a little greater than the chances of destruction. The numbers necessary to accomplish this are amazing. The hookworm, *Ancylostoma duodenale,* lays in the neighborhood of 20,000 eggs a day, and it may do this for at least 5 years; the total offspring of such a worm would number over 36,000,000. If the number of hookworms in a community remains about constant, as it usually does, and the percentage of males and females is equal, the chances against a male and female hookworm gaining access to a host, and living for the full period of 5 years, is then 18,000,000 to 1. The hookworm, however has a comparatively simple time of it. Flukes and tapeworms have an even more difficult problem to face. According to estimates of Penfold *et al.* (1937), a beef tapeworm produces over 2500 million eggs in 10 years, yet this worm is rare enough so that most practitioners keep specimens in bottles on their shelves!

Flukes and tapeworms owe such success as they have to two special devices in their life cycles. In the first place, they have to a large extent substituted self-fertilization for cross-fertilization; they combine male and female organs of reproduction in a single individual and do not take chances on other individuals of the opposite sex being present to render the eggs viable. In the second place, efficient egg-making machines as they are, they have found the production of sufficient eggs by one body inadequate. A tapeworm overcomes the difficulty by constantly reproducing, sometimes for years, more egg-producing segments, in essence new individuals, by a process of budding; some, such as Multiceps and Echinococcus, go even further and produce several or even many thousands of buds while in the larval stage, each of which is capable of developing into a new individual when, if ever, it reaches its final host.

Flukes attain the same end in a different way. Instead of producing a sufficient number of eggs to overcome the chances of destruction through the whole cycle of development, they distribute the risk. They produce enough eggs to overcome the chances against their reaching the mollusk which serves as the first intermediate host; then, in order to overcome the odds against them in the subsequent part of the life cycle, the successful individuals reproduce asexually. A single schistosome embryo, after successfully reaching the liver of a snail may give birth, by asexual reproduction, to over 100,000 progeny. Without this advantage a schistosome would have to produce thousands of times as many eggs as it does.

Significance of Intermediate Hosts. One might reasonably ask why some worms adhere to the life cycles which they have, when so much simpler ways of reaching their hosts would seem to be available. A fluke which lives as a parasite in the intestine of a bat, for example, would seem to be very ill-advised to select a snail, on which bats do not feed, as an intermediate host, when an insect would serve so much better. Nature is in this respect strangely inconsistent — she is a peculiar mixture of progressiveness and conservatism. In many instances, as we have seen, she has evolved the most intricate specializations both in life cycle and in structure; there are innumerable instances in the animal kingdom of short cuts and detours in life cycles, devised to meet newly developing conditions. On the other hand, there are some short cuts that Nature is too conservative to take. It is one of the fundamental precepts of embryology that ontogeny, i.e., the development of the individual, recapitulates phylogeny, which is evolutionary development of the race. Many unnecessary phases are, however, slurred over or greatly altered, and sometimes entirely new phases are interposed to meet the exigencies of the situation, as, for example, the pupae of insects (see p. 485).

Now intermediate hosts, in which partial development occurs, are unquestionably in many instances ancestral hosts. Mollusks are probably to be regarded as the hosts of the redia-like or cercaria-like ancestors of flukes. In the course of evolution these developed further until they reached the condition of modern flukes. Nature, however, has been too conservative to produce flukes in which the mollusk phase of the phylogeny is omitted in the ontogeny; this is apparently too radical a short cut. The result is that all flukes with the exception of one unorthodox species, *Cercaria loossi*, that develops in annelids, regardless of their final destiny, must first be molluscan parasites, just as a chicken must have gill slits like a fish before it can have lungs like its parents. Therefore, we have the irrational condition of flukes becoming first parasites of snails, then of insects, and only after sojourns in these animals, parasites of bats or birds. Undoubtedly the earliest method of transfer of flukes to their final hosts was by the eating of the infected mollusks, a method still adhered to by many flukes of mollusk-eating animals. In more highly specialized flukes, however, the cercariae leave the mollusk to encyst on vegetation if the host is a vegetarian, in fishes or other animals if it is carnivorous, or, in the case of the schistosomes, to take an active instead of a passive attitude and burrow directly into their final hosts.

Effects of Parasitism. The effects produced by parasitic worms depend in part on the organs or tissues occupied, in part on the habits of the worms, and in part on the poisonous qualities of their secretions or excretions. The effects of some kinds of worms is a much-disputed point. Some investigators tend to minimize the damage done by helminths, especially intestinal ones, whereas others undoubtedly overestimate it. Improved facilities for discovering infection have demonstrated the presence of intestinal parasites in so many unsuspected cases that we are likely to incriminate them in nearly every morbid condition for which we cannot, with equal readiness, discover another cause. It cannot be doubted, however, that many of the morbid conditions really are, in part at least, produced by intestinal worms.

The difference of opinion regarding the effects of worm infestations is due in part to the variable susceptibility of different races and individuals; in part to overlooking the difference in effect on normal, otherwise healthy, individuals and those handicapped by malnutrition, overwork, or chronic infections such as malaria and tuberculosis; and in large part to failure to take into consideration the *degree* of the infestation. Worm infections differ radically from bacterial or protozoan infections in that the worms do not multiply in the body of the host, and thus the infections are quantitative in nature; the severity of the infection, therefore, is not controlled almost entirely by the resistance of the host, which varies from time to time, but depends very largely on the actual number of worms acquired. The bite of a single lightly infected mosquito may produce as severe a case of malaria as numerous bites by heavily infected mosquitoes, but the acquisition of a few hookworms, liver flukes, or filariae produces in a given individual a very different effect from the oft-repeated acquisition of large numbers of these worms. The term " infestation " instead of " infection " is frequently used to distinguish nonmultiplying invaders from multiplying ones.

In some instances even single worms may cause a serious disturbance. Thus a single *Dibothriocephalus latus* may cause severe anemia; a single gnathostome may cause a fatal perforation of the stomach wall; a single Ascaris may block the bile or pancreatic duct; and a single guinea worm creeping under the skin may lead to an infection causing loss of a limb. In the majority of cases, however, the pathogenicity of worms is proportional to the number present.

The principal ways in which helminths harm their hosts are by mechanical damage, by devouring tissues, and by toxic effects. Some large worms, such as the larger tapeworms, may rob the host of enough food to have an effect at least in young growing children, but usually this is negligible.

Mechanical Injury. The mechanical injuries are almost as numerous as the kinds of worms. Some, such as the hookworms, bite the intestinal wall and cause hemorrhages, which are intensified by a secretion which prevents the blood from coagulating; some, such as the lung flukes and guinea worms, cause tissue damage and inflammation by burrowing; some, such as schistosomes and numerous Spirurata (Gnathostoma, Gongylonema, Onchocerca, Spirocerca, etc.), cause the formation of tumors, and in some cases — either by irritation or toxic action — of true cancerous growth; some, such as Ascaris, may block ducts or even cause intestinal obstruction; some, such as gnathostomes and occasionally Ascaris, may cause perforation of the walls of the digestive tract and consequent peritonitis; some, such as the liver flukes, may choke up the bile passages of the liver; some, such as Bancroft's filaria, may interfere with the normal flow of lymph and divert it into abnormal channels; some, such as hydatid cysts, may interfere with the proper functioning of neighboring organs by pressure; some, such as the schistosomes, may produce profound irritation of the tissues by extruding their spined eggs into them; and some, such as hookworms and spiny-headed worms, open up portals of entry for bacteria. We have awakened to the importance of a " whole skin " and the danger which accompanies the piercing of it by the unclean proboscides of biting flies, bugs, or other insects. We have not yet fully awakened to the importance of an uninjured mucous membrane. As has been pointed out by Shipley, the intestinal worms play a part within our bodies similar to that played by bloodsucking arthropods on our skins, except that they are *more* dangerous since, after all, only a relatively small number of biting insects have their proboscides soiled by organisms pathogenic to man, whereas the intestinal worms are constantly accompanied by bacteria that are capable of becoming pathogenic if they gain access to the deeper tissues. Weinberg found that, whereas he was unable to infect unparasitized apes with typhoid bacilli, apes infested with tapeworms or whipworms readily contracted typhoid fever, the bacteria presumably gaining entrance through wounds in the mucous membrane made by the worms.

Toxic Effects. The most consistently serious injury from intestinal worms is undoubtedly the toxic or allergic effects of their secretions and excretions. We know that the diseases caused by most bacteria and protozoans are the result, not of the actual damage done by the parasites in devouring tissues, but of poisonous waste products and secretions given off by them, or of allergic sensitization to them. Until recently little was known about the toxic effects of worms, but that toxins were produced by them was evident from symptoms disproportionate to the mechanical injury the parasites could do, and from effects which could in no way be the direct result of mechanical injury.

Toxic substances that have an irritating action on mucous membranes, that have blood-destroying properties, or that poison the nervous system have been demonstrated in such worms as Dibothriocephalus, Ascaris, and some others. The general distribution of these toxic substances in the body sometimes produces profound anemia, more or less severe nervous symptoms, and a marked loss of general vitality, as shown by reduced energy, endurance, and resistance to disease. In the case of Dibothriocephalus the effect seems to be one of precipitating a pernicious primary anemia to which there is a pre-existing tendency, but from which the host may escape entirely in the absence of a Dibothriocephalus infection. This is in contrast to the secondary anemia of hookworm which is caused by blood loss and not by a toxic effect. The anemia may, however, be the result of absorption by the worms of vitamins necessary for production of blood corpuscles, as suggested by Chandler in 1942.

Toxic effects with marked allergic symptoms may be produced by the larval phases of worm infections. Another symptom of worm infection is a change in number and kinds of leucocytes or white blood corpuscles. An almost universal symptom, though one which is occasionally absent even in the infections in which it is most characteristic, is an increase in the number of eosinophiles, white blood corpuscles containing granules which stain red with eosin. These cells are supposed to be for the purpose of destroying toxins in the blood. The mere presence of an increased number of them seems, therefore, sufficient reason for assuming the presence of toxins for them to destroy. The normal number of eosinophiles varies from 1 to 4 per cent of the total number of leucocytes, whereas in infections with such parasites as Trichinella, schistosomes, and Echinococcus cysts the number nearly always rises to 5 per cent or higher and sometimes reaches over 75 per cent.

Diagnosis. The diagnosis of infection with various species of worms depends principally on the identification of their eggs or larvae as found in the feces or other excretions by microscopic examination. Nearly every species of parasite has recognizably distinct characteristics of the eggs, the chief variations being in size, shape, color, thickness of shell, stage in development, appearance of the embryo if present, and presence or absence of an operculum or lid.

In many instances whole groups of worms have egg characteristics in common; for example, the eggs of flukes, except schistosomes, have an operculum at one end; those of schistosomes have spines; those of Dibothriocephalus also have an operculum, but the other tapeworms have eggs containing six-hooked embryos, and those of the family

Taeniidae have thick, striated inner shells; the eggs of ascarids are thick shelled, bile stained, and with surface markings; those of whipworms and their allies are brown with an opercular plug at each end; those of oxyurids are colorless and flattened on one side; and those of the hookworms and all their allies of the same order have thin-shelled, unstained eggs without either opercula or surface markings. Some of the commoner worm eggs are shown in a comparative way in Fig. 59.

Most worm infections of the digestive system can be diagnosed by finding eggs or larvae in the feces, but this cannot be relied on in some kinds of infections. Tapeworms, other than Dibothriocephalus and its allies, have no natural exit for the eggs from the segments, but in most species the eggs are easily released from ruptures of the uterus at the ends of the detached ripe segments. Hymenolepis eggs are probably always released inside the body and become mixed with the feces. *Taenia saginata* eggs are more frequently found on the skin near the anus, since the detached segments often squirm out of the rectum. However, infections with the larger tapeworms are best discovered by examining the surface of freshly passed stools for the segments, which squirm actively like flukes (for which they are sometimes mistaken). Pinworms (Enterobius) do not ordinarily deposit the eggs in the feces at all; the females crawl out of the anus and deposit the eggs on the perianal skin, where they can be picked up by special devices described on p. 431. Trichinella, since its embryos do not normally leave the body at all, cannot often be diagnosed by fecal examination, though sometimes some of the adult worms can be expelled by violent purges or anthelmintics.

Other intestinal worm infections can usually be diagnosed by finding eggs or larvae, though the number present may vary considerably from day to day. In heavy infections microscopic examination of a simple smear in water, thin enough to read newspaper print through, is sufficient, but many light infections escape detection by this method and concentration methods are necessary.

Flotation methods in heavy salt or sugar solutions are valuable for eggs of most kinds of nematodes and some tapeworms but fail to float the eggs of schistosomes, the operculated eggs of flukes or Dibothriocephalus, the porous eggs of tapeworms of the family Taeniidae, the eggs of Acanthocephala, or the unfertilized eggs of Ascaris. The best method for these, according to Jahnes and Hodges, is first to comminute and strain through gauze and then to centrifuge or sediment in 10 per cent ethyl alcohol, which they consider better than the 0.5 per cent glycerine usually recommended. Sedimenting three times, for 60, 45, and 30 minutes, respectively, is advised, samples of the top and

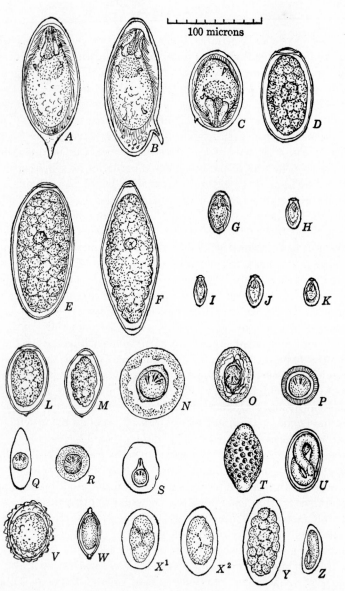

FIG. 59. Eggs of parasitic worms, drawn to scale; *A* to *K*, flukes; *L* to *S*, tapeworms; *T* to *Z*, nematodes.

FLUKES	TAPEWORMS	NEMATODES
A. *Schistosoma haematobium*	L. *Dibothriocephalus latus*	T. *Dioctophyma renale*
B. *Schistosoma mansoni*	M. *Spirometra mansonoides*	U. *Gongylonema sp.*
C. *Schistosoma japonicum*	N. *Hymenolepis diminuta*	V. *Ascaris lumbricoides*
D. *Paragonimus westermanni*	O. *Hymenolepis nana*	W. *Trichuris trichiura*
E. *Fasciolopsis buski*	P. *Taenia or Echinococcus*	X^1. *Ancylostoma duodenale*
F. *Gastrodiscoides hominis*	Q. *Raillietina madagascariensis*	X^2. *Necator americanus*
G. *Dicrocoelium dendriticum*	R. *Dipylidium caninum*	Y. *Trichostrongylus sp.*
H. *Clonorchis sinensis*	S. *Bertiella studeri*	Z. *Enterobius vermicularis*
I. *Opisthorchis felineus*		
J. *Heterophyes heterophyes*		
K. *Metagonimus yokogawai*		

bottom of the residual sediment then being examined. This method is also good for protozoan cysts. For schistosome eggs and unfertilized Ascaris eggs the AEX method (see below) is effective.

For flotation saturated NaCl (sp. gr. 1.200), or $ZnSO_4$ (sp. gr. 1.180), which also brings up protozoan cysts, is most frequently used, though a sugar solution is preferred by some. The simplest flotation method is that of Willis (1921), in which a tin 1-oz. or 2-oz. container for collecting fecal samples is left one-sixth to one-tenth full of feces, which is then stirred gradually with salt solution until brimful. A 2 by 3 in. glass slide is then placed over it in contact with the fluid; in 10 minutes the slide is carefully lifted by a straight upward pull, inverted, and examined.

Lane (1928) devised a method of direct centrifugal flotation (DCF). About 1 cc. of stool is thoroughly mixed with water in a centrifuge tube with a ground top, centrifuged, and the supernatant poured off. The residue is then mixed with saturated NaCl or $ZnSO_4$ (sp. gr. 1.180), the tube filled to the top, covered with a No. 2 cover glass, and placed in centrifuge buckets provided with four projecting horns to prevent the coverglass from sliding off during the centrifuging (Fig. 60). After centrifuging for 1 minute at 1000 rpm, the cover is removed and the adhering fluid examined as a hanging drop or by dropping the cover on a slide. The special apparatus is unnecessary if the last few drops of solution to fill the tube are added after centrifuging, and the surface film is removed by touching a cover to it or by means of a 4-mm. bacteriological loop. The DCF method demonstrates a high percentage of the eggs present, and in a small area.

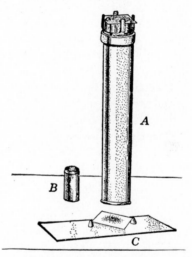

Fig. 60. Apparatus for Lane's DCF method. *A*, special horned bucket containing tube with ground top and with cover; *B*, cylinder for measurement and comminution; *C*, slide ready for examination, the cover mounted on plasticine cones. (After Lane, from Chandler's *Hookworm Disease*.)

Loughlin and Stoll (1946) described an " AEX " method which they found even better for hookworm, Ascaris, and Trichuris eggs, and effective for infertile Ascaris and schistosome eggs. A sample of stool suspension is centrifuged in acid (20 per cent HCl), ether, and xylol; a drop of 0.1 N NaOH is added to the sediment after decanting, and the entire suspension is examined.

Egg Counts. About 1920 Darling called attention to the importance of quantitative diagnosis of worm infections. The earlier laborious and impractical method of worm counts after treatment has been supplanted by egg counts. Stoll in 1923 devised a satisfactory method of estimating eggs per gram of feces by diluting a measured quantity of feces in a measured volume of 0.1 N NaOH, counting the eggs in a measured fraction, and multiplying by the proper factor. Stoll and Hausheer in 1926 recommended the use of a special narrow-necked flask filled to a 56-cc. mark with 0.1 N NaOH, and then to a 60-cc. mark with feces, thus diluting 4 cc. fifteen times. After thorough shaking, the eggs in a 0.075-cc. drop of this are counted under a 25-mm. square cover glass. The eggs counted, multiplied by 200, represent the eggs per gram. The method will not do for very light infections and is unreliable in individual counts, but Stoll showed enough correlation between the eggs per gram and number of worms harbored, when averaged even for small groups, to make the method useful in estimating the worm burden of a community, and in determining the number of light, medium, and heavy infections. Another effective egg-count method was devised by the Caldwells in 1926 in which the sample is disintegrated in antiformin and the eggs then floated in a sugar solution.

Treatment. Treatment of the various worm infections is considered under the head of the different kinds of worms, but a few general principles should be noted here.

Drugs which are used for expelling worms are known as anthelmintics. An ideal anthelmintic is one which effectively kills or expels the particular worms for which it is used, is not injurious to the host in the dose required, is easily administered, and is cheap. The search for new, safe, and effective anthelmintics has been very active, with the result that many of the older standard anthelmintics, such as thymol, beta-naphthol, chenopodium, santonin, carbon tetrachloride, and "lêche de higuerón," have been largely discarded in favor of newer ones such as tetrachlorethylene, hexylresorcinol, butyl chloride, emetin, Acranil, atebrin, gentian violet, hexachlorethane, and phenothiazine for intestinal worms; hetrazan for filariasis and some intestinal worms; and new antimony compounds for schistosomiasis. Drugs are usually tested first *in vitro* on worms that are easily obtained, then tested on laboratory animals and their pharmacological and physiological effects studied, and finally tried out on man or domestic animals.

REFERENCES

BAYLIS, H. A., *A Manual of Helminthology,* Medical and Veterinary, London, 1929.
BAYLIS, H. A., and DAUBNEY, R. A., *Synopsis of the Families and Genera of Nematodes,* London, 1926.

BROWN, H. W., Recent Developments in the Chemotherapy of Helminthic Diseases, *Proc. 4th Intern. Congr. Trop. Med. and Malaria*, **2**, Sect. VI, 966–974 (1948).

CAMERON, T. W. M., *The Internal Parasites of Domestic Animals*, London, 1934.

CHANDLER, A. C., Studies on the Nature of Immunity to Intestinal Helminths, I–VI, *Am. J. Hyg.*, **22**, 157, 242 (1935); **23**, 46; **26**, 292, 309 (1937); **28**, 51 (1938).

The Nature and Mechanism of Immunity in Various Intestinal Infections, *Am. J. Trop. Med.*, **19**, 309 (1939).

CHITWOOD, B. G., and CHITWOOD, M. B., An Introduction to Nematology, Sect. I, Pts. I–III and Sect. II, Pts. I and II so far published. Washington and Babylon, N. Y., 1937–1942.

CHOPRA, R. N., and CHANDLER, A. C., *Anthelmintics and Their Uses in Human and Veterinary Medicine*, Baltimore, 1928.

DAVEY, D. G., and INNES, J. R. M., The Present Position of Phenothiazine as an Anthelmintic, *Vet. Bull.*, **12**, R7–R14 (1942).

FAUST, E. C., *Human Helminthology*, 3rd ed., Philadelphia, 1949.

KUKENTHAL, W. (Editor), *Handbuch der Zoologie*, Bd. II, 1 u. 2, Vermes, Berlin, 1928–1933.

LAPAGE, G., *Nematodes Parasitic in Animals*, London, 1937.

LOUGHLIN, H., and STOLL, N. R., An Efficient Concentration Method (AEX) for Detecting Helminthic Ova in Feces (Modification of the Telemann Technic), *Am. J. Trop. Med.*, **26**, 517–527 (1946).

McCOY, O. R., The Physiology of the Helminth Parasites, *Physiol. Revs.*, **15**, 221 (1935).

MÖNNIG, H. O., *Veterinary Helminthology and Entomology*, London, 1934.

MORGAN, B. B., and HAWKINS, P. A., *Veterinary Helminthology*, Minneapolis, 1949.

NEVEU-LEMAIRE, M., *Traité d'helminthologie médicale et vétérinaire*, Paris, 1936.

PENFOLD, W. J., PENFOLD, H. B., and PHILLIPS, M., *Taenia saginata;* Its Growth and Propagation, *J. Helminthol.*, **15**, 41 (1937).

STOLL, N. R., This Wormy World, *J. Parasitol.*, **33**, 1–18 (1947).

STUNKARD, H. W., The Physiology, Life Cycles, and Phylogeny of the Parasitic Flatworms, *Am. Mus. Novitates*, No. 908 (1937).

SWALES, W. E., The Use of Phenothiazine in Veterinary Parasitology, *Canad. J. Comp. Med. Vet. Sci.*, December, 1940.

VAN CLEAVE, H. J., Expanding Horizons in the Recognition of a Phylum, *J. Parasitol.*, **34**, 1–20 (1948).

WHITLOCK, J. H., *Illustrated Laboratory Outline of Veterinary Entomology and Helminthology*, Minneapolis, 1947.

YORKE, W., and MAPLESTONE, P. A., *The Nematode Parasites of Vertebrates*, London, 1926.

Leeches

MASTERSON, E. W. G., Hirudinea as Human Parasites in Palestine, *Parasitology*, **1**, 182 (1908).

NEVEU-LEMAIRE, M., Hirudinea, in Traité d'entomologie médicale et vétérinaire, 1938.

WHITMAN, C. O., Leeches of Japan, *Quart. J. Microscop. Sci.*, **26**, 317 (1886).

CHAPTER 12

The Trematodes or Flukes

General Account. The trematodes are animals of a very low order of development in some respects and of very high specialization in others; all of them are parasitic. There are two principal groups: the monogenetic flukes with no asexual generations, which are primarily external or semiexternal parasites of aquatic animals; and the digenetic flukes with two or more asexual generations and an alternation of hosts, which are internal parasites of all kinds of vertebrates. Since only the digenetic flukes are of interest as parasites of man and domestic animals, the following account refers to this group except when otherwise specified.

In shape the flukes are usually flat and often leaflike, with the mouth at the bottom of a sucker, usually at the anterior end; in most groups there is a second sucker, for adhesion, on the ventral surface. The monogenetic flukes have highly specialized compound suckers at the posterior end, usually supplemented with hooks.

The development of the nervous system is of low grade; a small ganglion at the forward end of the body gives off a few longitudinal nerves. Sense organs are almost lacking. There is no blood or blood system, the result being that the digestive tract and excretory system are branched, often to a surprising extent, in order to carry food to all parts of the body and to carry waste products out from all parts. The digestive system (Fig. 62) usually has a muscular *pharynx* near the mouth, and then branches into two blind pouches, the *intestinal ceca;* in some of the larger flukes, e.g., *Fasciola hepatica,* these ceca have numerous branches and subbranches, while in the schistosomes the ceca reunite posteriorly to form a single stem. Only in a few aberrant species do the ceca open posteriorly.

The excretory system consists of a complicated arrangement of branched tubules. At the ends of ultimate fine branches are flame cells which keep up a flow of fluid towards the excretory pore. The finer branches unite in a definite manner, varying in different groups, until finally there are only two collecting tubules which open into an excretory bladder, posteriorly placed. This in turn opens to the exterior by an excretory pore (Fig. 61). The type of branching of the

254

excretory system is of value in classification but is difficult to determine in the adults; group differences are more readily determined in the living cercariae, and are even present in the ciliated embryos or miracidia.

Few animals have more intricate and highly specialized reproductive systems, and their life histories are so marvelously complex as to tax our credulity. A butterfly's life history is simple by comparison. Many flukes, especially those living as internal parasites in land animals, pass through four and sometimes even five distinct phases of existence, during some of which they are free-living, and during others may parasitize successively two, three, or even four different hosts.

In all flukes except those of the family Schistosomatidae both male and female reproductive systems occur in the same individual and occupy a large portion of the body of the animal.

In the female system there are separate glands for the production of the ova proper, the yolk and shell material, and the fluid in which the eggs are carried. In a typical fluke the organs are arranged as diagrammatically shown in Fig. 62, although there are many variations. The *ovary* has a short duct, the *oviduct*, which is joined by a *yolk* or *vitelline duct*, a short duct from a *seminal receptacle* if one is present, and by a duct which leads to a pore on the dorsal surface of the fluke, called *Laurer's canal*. Close to where these various ducts meet there is a slight bulblike enlargement called an *oötype*, surrounded by a cluster of unicellular glands called *Mehlis' gland* and formerly thought to be a shell gland; it is now known that the shell material comes from granules in the yolk cells.

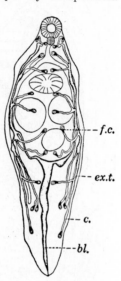

Fig. 61. Excretory system of an adult fluke (Dicrocoelium); *bl.*, bladder; *c.*, collecting tubule; *ex. t.*, excretory tube; *f.c.*, flame cell. (From *Human Helminthology* by Ernest Carroll Faust, Ph.D., Lea and Febiger, Publishers, Philadelphia.)

The oötype is an assembly plant for the production of finished eggs; in some flukes the daily output is estimated at 25,000! The yolk and shell material are provided by clusters of little *vitelline glands* usually situated in the lateral parts of the fluke but occasionally posteriorly or anteriorly. These clusters of glands are connected by ducts to one main transverse duct from either side; these right and left ducts come together to form a common duct shortly before entering the oötype, often with a small *vitelline reservoir* at their junction. Sometimes there is no separate seminal receptacle; instead the sperms are stored in the region of the oötype or lower part of the uterus. Laurer's canal, sometimes connected with the seminal receptacle or its duct instead of directly to the oviduct, is believed to be a vestigial vagina, but in many species it fails to reach the dorsal surface; like the human appendix, it is a useless heirloom. In most flukes it is probable that the sperms make their way down through the uterus before this becomes jammed with eggs.

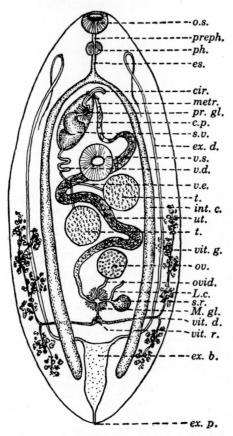

FIG. 62. Diagrammatic fluke to illustrate principal morphological characteristics. Abbrev.: *cir.*, cirrus; *c.p.*, cirrus pouch; *es.*, esophagus; *ex. b.*, excretory bladder; *ex. d.*, excretory duct; *int. c.*, intestinal cecum; *L.c.*, Laurer's canal; *metr.*, metraterm; *M. gl.*, Mehlis' gland (surrounding oötype); *o.s.*, oral sucker; *ov.*, ovary; *ovid.*, oviduct; *ph.*, pharynx; *preph.*, prepharynx; *pr. gl.*, prostate glands; *s.r.*, seminal receptacle; *s.v.*, seminal vesicle; *t.*, testis; *ut.*, uterus; *v.d.*, vas deferens; *v.e.*, vas efferens; *vit. d.*, vitelline duct; *vit. g.*, vitelline glands; *vit. r.*, vitelline reservoir; *v.s.*, ventral sucker.

When the eggs are fertilized, supplied with yolk cells to provide nourishment, and surrounded by shell material which gradually hardens and darkens, they enter the *uterus*. This, usually much coiled and convoluted, leads to the *genital pore*, where it opens in common with the male reproductive system. The terminal part of the uterus is often provided with special muscular walls and is called the *metraterm*.

The male system consists of two or more *testes* for the production of the sperms; two sperm ducts which meet to form a *vas deferens*, usually with an enlargement, the *seminal vesicle*, for the storage of sperms; a cluster of *prostate glands;* and a retractile muscular organ or *cirrus* which serves as a copulatory organ. The seminal vesicle, prostate glands, and cirrus are usually enclosed in a *cirrus sac*. All these complex sex organs in a single animal which may be no larger than the head of a pin!

Important variations that are of taxonomic value occur in (1) the absolute and relative positions of the ovary and testes; (2) the position of the uterus; (3) the position and arrangement of yolk glands; (4) the presence or absence of a seminal receptacle; (5) the position of the genital pore; (6) the presence or absence of a cirrus sac and the nature of the cirrus; and (7) the presence of a seminal vesicle inside or outside the cirrus sac. The Schistosomatidae, as already noted, are set off from all the other flukes by having the male and female systems in separate individuals.

Life Cycle. The more primitive monogenetic flukes, belonging to the orders Monogenea and Aspidogastrea, have a direct development involving a simple metamorphosis but no interpolated nonsexual generations. The Monogenea are parasitic externally or in the excretory bladder or on the gills of aquatic vertebrates, whereas the Aspidogastrea are parasitic on or in the soft parts of mollusks or in the intestines of aquatic vertebrates. Some Aspidogastrea develop to maturity in a single molluscan host, whereas others have achieved an alternation of hosts without an alternation of generations. Flukes of the order Digenea, on the other hand, have very complicated life cycles involving several nonsexual generations as well as an alternation of hosts.

Miracidia. Digenetic flukes produce eggs, often by tens of thousands, which escape from the host's body with the feces, urine, or sputum, according to the habitat of the adults. Either before or after the eggs have escaped from the host ciliated embryos develop within them; these hatch either in water or in the intestines of mollusks which serve as intermediate hosts. The embryos, called miracidia, are free-swimming animals suggestive of ciliated protozoans. They are covered by a ciliated epithelium of relatively few large flat cells (Fig. 63B) and have a short saclike gut, one or more pairs of penetration glands, one or more pairs of flame cells and excretory tubules, and a cluster of germ cells which are destined to give rise to a new generation of organisms (Fig. 63). Many miracidia have eye spots, but some are blind. The miracidia do not feed, and they die in a few hours if unsuccessful in finding a proper molluscan host.

Free miracidia swim in a characteristic spirally rotating manner, in quest of a mollusk of the particular species which is to serve as an intermediate host. When they come near such a mollusk they become greatly excited and make a headlong dash for it, although they ignore other kinds of mollusks. They attach themselves to the soft part of the mollusk by the secretion of their glands and proceed to bore or digest their way into the tissues. Some miracidia, e.g., those of Clonorchis and Dicrocoelium, hatch only after the eggs have been eaten by

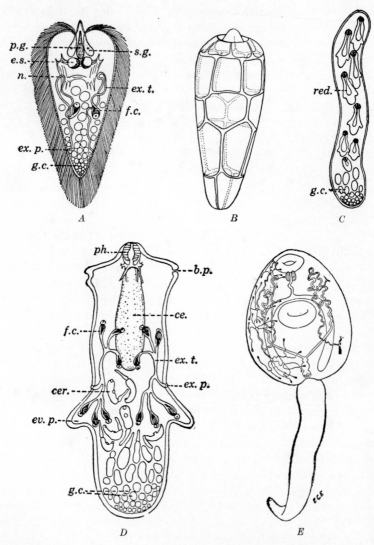

Fig. 63. Stages in life cycle of a fluke. A, miracidium, showing internal structure and cilia; *ex. p.*, excretory pore; *e.s.*, eye spot; *ex. t.*, excretory tube; *f.c.*, flame cell; *g.c.*, germ cells; *n.*, nervous system; *p.g.*, primitive gut; *s.g.*, secretory glands. B, miracidium of *Fasciola hepatica*, showing ectodermal cells; in this species there are 5 rows with 6, 6, 3, 4, and 2 cells, respectively. C, sporocyst; *g.c.*, germ cells; *red.*, developing rediae. D, redia; *b.p.*, birth pore; *ce.*, cecum; *cer.*, developing cercariae; *ev. p.*, evaginate appendages; *ex. p.*, excretory pore; *ex. t.*, excretory tube; *f.c.*, flame cell; *g.c.*, germ cells; *ph.*, pharynx. E, cercaria, showing digestive and excretory systems, but not glands; note oral and ventral suckers, pharynx, and intestinal ceca, and excretory system more complex than in redia, with posterior bladder and pore. (All but B from *Human Helminthology* by Ernest Carroll Faust, Ph.D., Lea and Febiger, Publishers, Philadelphia; B adapted from Dawes.)

the proper snails. It is obvious that only a very small percentage of the embryos are likely to survive the double risk of not reaching water and, if safely in water, of not reaching a suitable mollusk in which to develop.

Development in Mollusks. Once safely within the tissues of the mollusk the miracidium enters upon the second phase of its existence, during which it reproduces to make up for the enormous mortality encountered by its sisters during the adventurous journey from vertebrate host to mollusk, and to insure the survival of at least a few individuals on the equally perilous journey from snail to vertebrate, which has subsequently to be undertaken.

Having arrived in the tissues of its particular kind of mollusk, the miracidium bores its way to the lymph spaces in the liver which in snails is at the apical end, and there proceeds with its development. It changes in form to an irregular-shaped saclike or filamentous body called a sporocyst (Fig. 63C). This absorbs nourishment and excretes waste products through its body wall and devotes all its energies to the development of its progeny from the germ cells, the body cavity serving as a brood chamber. It is now a mature individual which reproduces by a process which has been variously interpreted as asexual, parthenogenetic, or bisexual. The evidence is now conclusive that in the majority of flukes, at least, the reproduction results from asexual multiplication of cells of the germinal line (polyembryony), complicated in some groups by a secondary polyembryony resulting in formation of "germ masses," which may continue to produce offspring throughout the life of the sporocysts or rediae containing them (see Cort, 1944).

In the schistosomes and others of the suborder Strigeata, the offspring of the sporocysts develop into a second generation of sporocysts, but in most flukes they grow into organisms of a new type, the rediae, constituting the second asexual generation. The redia (Fig. 63D) possesses a pharynx and simple saclike gut, an excretory system of flame cells and tubules, and, in the posterior part of its body, more germinal cells for the production of another generation of offspring. Most rediae have a birth pore for the escape of their offspring when they develop, and many have a pair of blunt appendages on the sides of the body. When the rediae are nearly mature they burst free from the mother sporocyst and begin an independent life in the snail's liver.

In many kinds of flukes the progeny of these rediae are a second generation of rediae, which in many cases are morphologically distinguishable from their mothers. Sometimes there is even a third generation of them.

Cercariae. Eventually the rediae, either the daughters or the grand-daughters of the sporocysts, produce progeny of a different type, the cercariae. These do not undergo further reproduction in the mollusk host, but remain larvae. In order to complete their development, they must reach, directly or indirectly, the final vertebrate host in which the sexually mature form is developed. The cercariae (Fig. 63*E*) have a structure more like that of the adults. The digestive system has a pharynx and a pair of intestinal ceca; there is a more complicated excretory system and the body is provided with suckers and a tail, except in a few species which develop in land snails. Nearly all cercariae have a number of pairs of single-celled cephalic glands which open near the oral sucker and which secrete a tissue-dissolving substance enabling them to penetrate the tissues of the final host, e.g., schistosomes, or of a second intermediate host. In some flukes such as Fasciola and Fasciolopsis these glands apparently do not function. Most cercariae except those of schistosomes also have laterally placed glands which produce a viscous substance that " sets " as a cyst wall around the cercaria after it has lost its tail. This encysted, tailless organism is called a metacercaria.

The cercariae may encyst on vegetation after leaving the snail, e.g., Fasciolopsis and amphistomes, or they may encyst after penetrating a second intermediate host, e.g., Clonorchis and Paragonimus, or, if the snail is eaten by the final host, they may encyst in the snail or even in the body of their mother redia. Thus the two types of secretory glands (cephalic and cystogenous) serve either separately or in cooperation to terminate the free life of the cercaria.

Examination of Mollusks for Asexual Generations and Cercariae. When mollusks are collected and brought to the laboratory for examination for immature stages of flukes, those producing cercariae can readily be determined by placing them, first in groups and later individually, in half-pint bottles and leaving them for 12 to 24 hours. The emerged cercariae will then be seen swimming in the water or, in a few instances, crawling on the bottom. The output of cercariae is often very large; Cort has observed the escape of 5000 in a single day. In many species there is a marked daily periodicity. The number of cercariae and the duration of the shedding season undoubtedly vary not only with the degree of infection in the mollusk but also with the species, but it usually extends over at least several weeks. In some species the total output of an infected snail amounts to tens or even hundreds of thousands.

Sporocysts and rediae are found by crushing the mollusks or picking away the shell until the body can be dragged out intact. In most cases they will be found in the brown digestive gland of the mollusk; their presence can often be detected with the naked eye as yellowish mottlings. These must then be dissected out carefully. Cercariae obtained after crushing a mollusk are frequently immature and unlike those escaping naturally. The cercariae, sporocysts, and rediae should be studied in the living state as much as possible, with the help of such

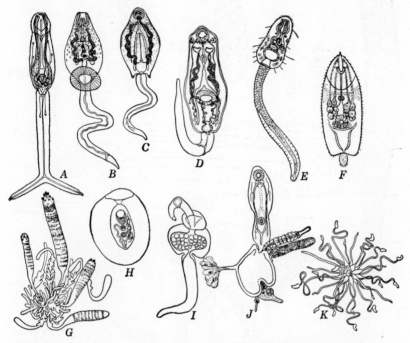

FIG. 64. Some types of cercariae. *A*, furcocercous (*Schistosoma japonicum*); *B*, amphistome (*C. inhabilis*); *C*, monostome (*C. urbanensis*); *D*, echinostome (*Echinostoma revolutum*); *E*, pleurolophocercous (*Opisthorchis felineus*); *F*, stylet, microcercous (*Paragonimus westermanni*); *G*, colored sporocysts of *Leucochloridium paradoxum*, which grow out from tentacles of land snail; *H*, metacercaria from a sporocyst of *Leucochloridium migranum*, enclosed in jellylike cyst capsule; *I*, cystocercous (gorgoderine) (*C. macrocerca*); *J*, cystophorous (hemiurid), showing cercarial body and various appendages evaginated from tail cyst; *K*, cluster of "rattenkönig" cercariae (*C. gorgonocephala*). (Adapted from various authors.)

intra-vitam strains as neutral red (1:1000) or nile blue sulfate. Subsequent studies can be made on material fixed and stained by various standard tissue methods.

Types of Cercariae. The cercariae of various groups of flukes differ widely in form and structure; up to the present time only a relatively small number of cercariae have been correlated with the flukes to which they give rise. Various classifications of cercariae have been devised, but a natural classification is not possible until the entire life cycle is known; some of the most striking peculiarities, particularly of the tail, are adaptive and of no phylogenetic significance, while sometimes phylogenetic features that would be expected may be absent, e.g., the

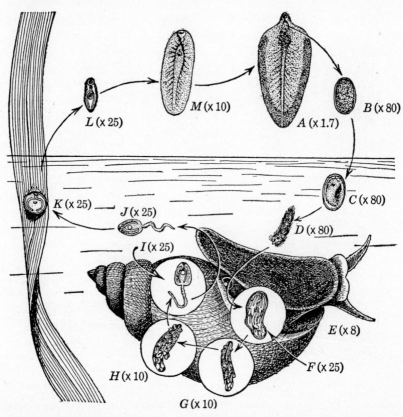

FIG. 65. Life history of liver fluke, *Fasciola hepatica; A*, adult in liver of sheep; *B*, freshly passed egg; *C*, egg with developed embryo, ready to hatch in water; *D*, ciliated embryo in water, about to enter pulmonary chamber of snail (*E*); *F*, sporocyst containing rediae; *G*, redia containing daughter rediae; *H*, redia of second generation containing cercariae; *I*, cercaria; *J*, same, having emerged from snail into water; *K*, cercaria encysted on blade of grass; *L*, cercaria liberated from cyst after ingestion by sheep; *M*, young fluke developing in liver of sheep.

ventral sucker of some species where this is present in the adult. On the other hand, cercariae frequently, have characters which clearly relate them to adult groups, e.g., the crown of spines of echinostomes (Fig. 64*D*) and the posterior sucker of the amphistomes (Fig. 64*B*). Cercariae of gasterostomes have the tail in two forks with no elongated stem (Fig. 66), whereas those of strigeids, schistosomes, and a few presumably related forms have forked tails with stems (Fig. 64A). The cercariae of distomes vary tremendously in the different families; one large group is provided with a stylet in the oral sucker (Fig. 64F) to aid in boring into arthropod larvae; the group of flukes with stylet cercariae are sometimes placed in a distinct superfamily Plagiorchioidea. Tailless cercariae occur in a number of unrelated flukes which develop in land snails. Figure 64 gives some idea of nature's uninhibited ideas as to what a cercaria should look like.

Transfer to Final Host. The manner in which the cercariae accomplish the transfer from snail to final host varies greatly. The cercariae of schistosomes are self-reliant and actively seek the final host and bore into it when found, but most cercariae depend on the host to pick them up. The simplest method of transfer is encystment directly in the primary snail host, as happens in some echinostomes. Leucochloridium has the cercariae encysted in large colored sporocysts that grow out of the tentacles of snails and resemble tempting worms for birds to peck at (Fig. 64G, H). In flukes like the Fasciolidae and amphistomes, which reach maturity in herbivorous animals, the cercariae encyst on vegetation in the water and patiently wait to be eaten by the final host. In flukes which mature in carnivorous hosts, the cercariae penetrate into the tissues of fish, crabs, etc., where they encyst and await salvation by the second intermediate host being eaten by the final one. It is for this reason that many human fluke infections are prevalent only in the Orient, where fish or crabs are eaten without thorough cooking. Occasionally metacercariae are progenetic, i.e., they become sexually mature before reaching the final host.

The skin-penetrating cercariae of schistosomes are carried to their final destination in the mesenteric blood vessels by the blood stream, but encysted metacercariae always enter by way of the mouth. Their cyst walls are digested away in the stomach, and the young liberated flukes migrate by various routes to the parts of the body in which they are to mature.

The commoner types of life cycles of flukes are seen in graphic form in the chart below, copied from Leiper.

Host	Transition	Intermediate Host		Transition	Host
Egg	Miracidium (or ciliated embryo)	Sporocyst Sporocyst.........Daughter sporocysts Sporocyst.........Rediae Sporocyst.........Rediae, daughter rediae	Cercariae	Encysted 　in mollusk 　in crustacean 　in insect 　in fish 　on vegetation Free-swimming	Adult

Classification. The classification of flukes is still in a very uncertain state, as Stunkard (1946) pointed out. The earliest classification was based on the number, position, and character of the suckers, as the names "polystome," "distome," and "monostome" suggest. Later more attention was paid to the details of the internal organs, such as the location and features of the reproductive organs and details of the excretory system, but, though these were extensively employed as criteria for families and genera, the old arrangement of orders and suborders based on suckers was retained. With the development of knowledge of the life cycles of flukes it has become apparent, as LaRue pointed out in 1928, that a taxonomic system which really indicates relationship must be based on comparative anatomy of all the stages in the life cycle and especially of the miracidia and cercariae. However, we must not lose sight of the fact that many characters of cercariae, as well as those of adults, may be adaptive and not phylogenetic. Of internal structures the arrangement of the excretory system is usually most dependable in showing relationship, but even this sometimes fails.

Life-cycle studies have brought some astonishing revelations, showing unimpeachable evidence of close relationship of forms which show little or no resemblance to one another in the adult stage. For example, not only have the apparently totally unlike schistosomes and strigeids been shown to be sisters under the skin, but a bird fluke, Clinostomum, and a family of flukes of mammals and birds (Brachylaemidae), most of which have tailless cercariae that develop in land snails, show evidence of similar close relationship, although nobody would ever have suspected it from the appearance of the adults. On the other hand, in 1932 three families were listed under the superfamily Heterophyoidea, but on the basis of life-cycle studies two have had to be rejected, and meanwhile the families Heterophyidae and Opisthorchiidae had to be united into the same superfamily, in spite of the fact that they do not look like even distant cousins.

So many of these unexpected skeletons in family closets have appeared that some parasitologists are losing faith entirely in the present system of classification. Stunkard (1946), for instance, thinks that in the present state of uncertainty the only groups higher than families in the entire class Trematoda to which one can pin any faith is the division into the two subclasses, Monogenea and Digenea; he thinks the gasterostomes and Strigeata merge into each other, and the Strigeata into some of the Distomata; and he thinks the separation of Distomata, Monostomata, and Amphistomata is obsolete. The small family Aspidogastridae, parasitic in mollusks, fish, and turtles, is recognized by Faust as a third subclass but is believed by Stunkard to belong with the Digenea, in spite of the fact that it has no asexual reproduction; some species do have an alternation of hosts.

Dawes (1946) agrees with Stunkard in many particulars but does not decimate the long-accepted classification quite so drastically. He divides the Trematoda into three orders, Monogenea, Aspidogastrea, and Digenea, and divides the Digenea into two suborders, Gasterostomata and Prosostomata. This seems a reasonable arrangement for the present and is adopted here. Families containing human parasites are listed; their characters are given elsewhere in the chapter.

Order Monogenea. External or semiexternal parasites of aquatic animals; direct development with no asexual multiplication; large posteroventral disc or haptor (Fig. 67), usually armed with hooks or spines and often with pairs of muscular suckers; excretory pores two, anteriorly situated.

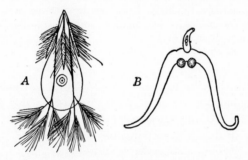

Fig. 66. Gasterostome miracidium (*A*) and cercaria (*B*). (*A* adapted from Woodhead, *B* from Lühe.)

Order Aspidogastrea. External or internal parasites of mollusks, fish, or turtles; no asexual multiplication in life cycle but may have alternation of hosts. Rows of sucking alveoli on ventral surface, usually on a large ventral disc. Intestine a single blind sac; excretory pore single, posterior.

Order Digenea. Internal parasites; asexual generations interposed in life cycle, nearly always in mollusks; one or two suckers for adhesion; excretory pore single, posterior.

Suborder Gasterostomata. Mouth on midventral surface; intestine a simple sac; genital opening posterior; miracidia with cilia restricted to comb-plates and protruding bars (Fig. 66*A*); sporocysts branched; cercaria with long forks without elongated stem (Fig. 66*B*). Parasites of fishes; asexual generations harmful to oysters and mussels.

Suborder Prosostomata. Mouth at or near anterior end, in oral sucker; ceca bifurcated in adult; genital opening usually anterior; miracidia usually covered with cilia; cercariae with various type tails or none, but with tail stem if forked.

    1. Strigeidae (p. 309) (holostomes or strigeids). Numerous pathogenic species in intestines of birds and mammals. *Prohemistomum vivax* accidental in man.

2. Schistosomatidae (p. 268). Blood parasites of various vertebrates. Three spp. in man, highly pathogenic. Several spp. in domestic animals.
3. Clinostomatidae (p. 290). Usually in water birds, accidental in man.
4. Paramphistomatidae (p. 298). Amphistomes. Common in digestive tract of herbivorous animals; *Watsonius watsoni* rare in man.
5. Gastrodiscidae (p. 298). Amphistomes. Gastrodiscoides in intestine of man and pigs; Gastrodiscus in domestic animals.
6. Fasciolidae (pp. 287 and 300). Fasciola in liver and Fasciolopsis in intestine of man; Fasciola and Fascioloides important in liver of ruminants.
7. Echinostomatidae (p. 306). Echinostomes. A number of species in intestine of man; important in water birds.
8. Dicrocoeliidae (p. 290). Important parasites of liver and pancreas of birds and mammals; occasional in man.
9. Opisthorchiidae (p. 292). Liver parasites of fish-eating mammals; several genera and species in man.
10. Heterophyidae (p. 302). Intestinal parasites of fish-eating mammals and birds. Several genera and species in man.
11. Troglotrematidae (p. 282). In various locations in birds and mammals. Paragonimus in lung of man and fish-eating mammals; Troglotrema carries salmon-poisoning in dogs.
12. Isoparorchiidae (p. 290). In swim bladder of fishes, one species accidental in man.

The flukes which infect man may be divided for convenience into four groups, (1) the blood flukes or schistosomes, (2) the lung flukes, (3) the liver flukes, and (4) the intestinal flukes. Over 40 different species have been recorded as human parasites, but only 10 of these are common enough to be more than medical curiosities.

Control. In most cases the most feasible method of control of fluke diseases is destruction of the snails which serve as intermediate hosts. The methods employed depend upon the species of snails involved and on local conditions. The long-cherished notion that they could be destroyed by desiccation seems not to be true. Barlow in 1937 showed that clearance of vegetation from canals in Egypt led to an enormous reduction in snails in the following year. Ducks are destructive to snails in some types of pools and streams; small fish, especially certain guppies, feed voraciously on snail eggs. In some Minnesota lakes large leeches have destroyed enough snails to eliminate swimmer's itch.

Destruction of snails by the use of chemical substances is often feasible and offers valuable possibilities. Liver flukes of cattle and sheep do not occur in salty pastures, and a liberal use of salt can under very special conditions be of advantage. The writer (Chandler, 1920) found that all species of snails are destroyed by very high dilutions of copper salts. Since then copper sulfate and copper carbonate have been more extensively employed for destruction of both aquatic and amphibious snails than any other chemicals. Although lime has been advocated for some snails, McMullen and Graham found it of no value against the snail host of *Schistosoma japonicum* in the Philippines, but they found calcium cyanamide a good substitute for copper salts against this snail. It has been reported that a dust

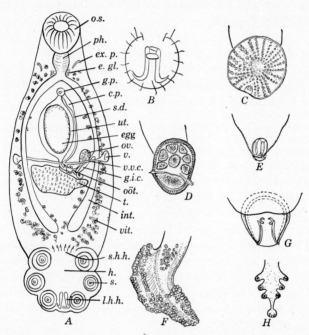

FIG. 67. Monogenea. *A, Polystomoidella oblongum* (Polystomatidae) (after Cable). *B–H*, various types of haptors of Monogenea; *B*, Gyrodactylidae (after Mueller); *C*, Acanthocotylidae (after Price); *D*, Monocotylidae (after Price); *E*, Microbothriidae (after Price); *F*, Microcotylidae (after Yamaguti); *G*, Capsalidae (after Little); *H*, Discocotylidae (after Lebour). Abbrev.: *c.p.*, cirrus pouch; *e. gl.*, esophageal glands; *ex. p.*, excretory pore; *g.p.*, genital pore; *g.i.c.*, genito-intestinal canal; *h.*, haptor; *int.*, intestine; *l.h.h.*, large haptorial hooks; *oöt.*, oötype; *o.s.*, oral sucker; *ov.*, ovary; *ph.*, pharynx; *s.*, sucker; *s.d.*, sperm duct; *s.h.h.*, small haptorial hooks; *t.*, testis; *ut.*, uterus; *v.*, vagina; *vit.*, vitellaria; *v.v.c.*, vitello-vaginal canal.

containing 5 to 6 ppm. of the γ isomer of benzene hexachloride controlled Planorbis and Bulinus within 24 hours in laboratory and field tests in Egypt.

Methods of protection against cercariae or metacercariae will be considered in the sections on particular fluke infections.

Monogenea

The majority of the monogenetic flukes are parasites of the gills, skin, and cloaca of fishes, but some have established themselves in the urinary bladder of amphibians and in the urinary bladder or mouth cavity of turtles, and one genus is found in the eyes of hippopotamuses. Some of the species attacking the gills and fins of fishes cause serious losses in fish hatcheries, where they are of much more importance than their endoparasitic relatives. In nature they seldom cause much trouble since there is less opportunity for heavy infections early in life, and a protective immunity develops. Most Monogenea produce large eggs that hatch into larvae which at once attack their definitive hosts, but those of one family, Gyrodactylidae, give birth to larvae of large size, one at a time. Polystomum develops either on the gills of tadpoles or in the urinary bladder of adult toads or frogs. Most Monogenea are fairly specific with respect to hosts.

Schistosomes or Blood Flukes (Schistosomatidae)

Importance. The most important flukes parasitic in man are three species of Schistosoma (formerly Bilharzia) which live in the mesenteric blood vessels. In some countries schistosomiasis causes more sickness and death than any other single disease. In Egypt, for instance, which is scourged by two species, 60 to 85 per cent of the entire population is affected over the greater part of the country; in some localities 10 per cent of the deaths are directly due to the disease, and nobody can say how many indirectly. Christopherson said in 1919, " Bilharzia (Schistosoma) probably is accountable more than anything else for the indolence of spirit, want of character, and the backward condition of development of the Egyptian peasant," a class constituting 90 per cent of the population.

Over vast areas in the Orient, also, schistosomiasis is one of the most important human diseases. Stoll (1947) estimated that there are 114,000,000 people infected with schistosomes in the world, 46,000,000 of them with *S. japonicum* in the Orient. Yet few Americans, even physicians, ever heard of schistosomiasis until the infection of thousands of American soldiers during the invasion of the Philippines brought it into the limelight and the possibility of its transplantation into this country had to be considered. Stunkard (1946) tested 72 species of North American snails as possible intermediate hosts of human schistosomes with negative results; the only species so far incriminated are a planorbid in the south, *Tropicorbis havanensis*, which is a rather poor host for *S. mansoni*, and *Pomatiopsis lapidaria* (see p. 284), in which *S. japonicum* can develop.

The Parasites. The schistosomes and their allies, constituting the family Schistosomatidae, differ quite widely from most other flukes in a number of respects, both in structure and in life cycle. Their most striking peculiarity is the development of separate males and females. The relation of the sexes is peculiar. The mature male worm (Fig. 68), usually about 8 to 16 mm. in length and 0.5 mm. in width, has a cylindrical appearance due to the fact that the sides of the flat body are folded over to form a ventral groove or " gynecophoric canal." In this groove, projecting free at each end but enclosed in the middle, is

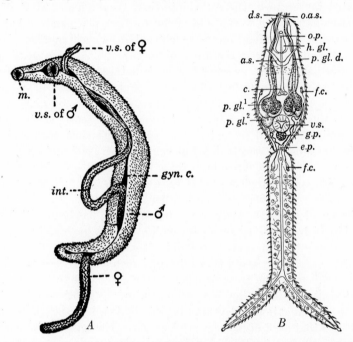

Fig. 68. *A*, blood fluke, *Schistosoma haematobium*, male (♂) carrying female (♀) in gynecophoric canal (*gyn. c.*); *int.*, intestine of ♀; *m.*, mouth of ♂; *v.s.*, ventral sucker. × 8. (After Looss.) *B*, cercaria of *S. japonicum;* *a.s.*, anterior sucker; *c.*, cecum; *d.s.*, duct spines; *e.p.*, excretory pore; *f.c.*, flame cells; *g.p.*, genital primordium; *h. gl.*, head gland; *o.a.s.*, orifice of anterior sucker; *o.p.*, oral pore; *p. gl.*[1], 2 acidophilic penetration glands; *p. gl.*[2], 3 basophilic penetration glands; *p. gl. d.*, penetration gland ducts; *v.s.*, ventral sucker. × 275. (Adapted from Faust and Meleney.)

the longer and slenderer female, safe in the arms of her spouse. While young the sexes live apart, but when sexual maturity is attained or approached they couple together. In most schistosomes they seem to remain permanently wedded and monogamous, the uncoupled females remaining spinsters, but in *Schistosoma mansoni* the union is of more companionate nature; Faust, Jones, and Hoffman (1934) believe the coupling to be a temporary phenomenon in that species, and found the majority of the worms living singly.

Both male and female worms are provided with oral and ventral suckers; in the male the ventral sucker is large and powerful. The digestive tract has no pharynx, and the esophagus forks, as usual, just anterior to the ventral sucker, but the forks reunite in the middle portion of the body to be continued as a single tube (Fig. 71). The male worm has several testes just behind the ventral sucker, and it is here that the genital pore opens. The female has an elongated ovary situated in the fork where the intestinal ceca rejoin. Most of the posterior half of the worm is occupied by the yolk glands. Anterior to the ovary is a straight uterus which contains a small number of eggs, from 1 to 50 or more in the different species.

Unlike most flukes, the schistosomes do not develop great numbers of eggs all at once, but instead develop them gradually and have only a few in the oviduct at any one time. Schistosomes live for many years.

Life Cycle. The human schistosomes and most of the other species live in small mesenteric or pelvic veins, but one species in cattle, *Schistosoma nasale,* lives in veins in the nasal and pharyngeal mucosa. The female forces her slender body into as small blood vessels as possible, and there deposits her eggs, one at a time. The eggs (Fig. 70) usually retain their position by their spines and by the contraction of the vessels after the body of the parent worm has been withdrawn; aided by histolytic secretions of the embryo inside, they gradually work their way out of the vessels and into the tissues of the walls of the intestine or bladder, and finally into the lumen of these organs, whence they escape with the feces or urine. Some of the eggs, however, are accidentally carried to the liver or lungs where, as in other organs, they set up inflammations. Eventually the irritated tissues become so thickened that most of the eggs are trapped. The eggs of *S. japonicum* take 9 or 10 days to develop mature miracidia while passing through the tissues, and will live for 10 or 12 days longer if not expelled, but many die in the tissues, becoming blackened and calcified.

Cross-fertilization between different species is possible. The sex of the future adult worms is already determined in the miracidium; of the thousands of cercariae developing from a single miracidium all produce worms of one sex. Oddly enough, female worms do not mature in hosts in which no male worms are present.

Dilution of the feces or urine in water causes the eggs to hatch within a few minutes to 16 hours or more; in undiluted feces or urine the eggs die in a few days, but in water in cold weather they may survive for several months. The miracidia (Fig. 69A) live for 24 hours or less, and therefore must find a snail of a suitable species within this time. The snails that will serve as intermediate hosts are different for each species of schistosome. When the miracidia come close to a suitable snail they become excited and make a dash for it, burrowing into the tentacles or other parts, much to the irritation of the snail. Many miracidia become mired in the tough tissues of the foot or head; those attacking the soft parts succeed in embedding themselves within a half hour after the attack begins. During penetration the ciliated outer coverings are shed and the miracidia elongate and become tubular sporocysts. These make their way through the viscera to the digestive gland at the innermost extremity of the snail.

In *S. mansoni* the sporocysts reach a length of 1 mm. in about two weeks, and begin to produce a limited number of daughter sporocysts (20 to 25) which burst free from the mother sporocyst. These in turn, reaching a length of 1.5 mm. by 0.09 mm., produce forked-tailed cer-

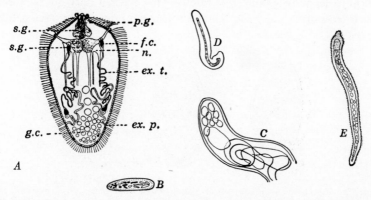

FIG. 69. Stages in life cycle of schistosomes. *A*, miracidium of *S. haematobium*; abbrev. as in Fig. 63*A*; × 300. (From *Human Helminthology* by Ernest Carroll Faust, Ph.D., Lea and Febiger, Publishers, Philadelphia.) *B*, primary sporocyst 8 days after infection. *C*, mature primary sporocyst (19 days). *D*, young daughter sporocyst (19 days). *E*, mature daughter sporocyst. (*B*, *C*, *D*, and *E* × 35; after Faust and Hoffman.)

cariae from germ-masses at their posterior ends. The mature cercariae (Fig. 68*B*) begin emerging from a birth pore situated near the anterior end of the sporocyst, which continues to produce more and more of them for several months. *S. haematobium* and *S. mansoni* are said to begin shedding cercariae about 4 to 6 weeks after infection under optimum conditions, but in Leyte *S. japonicum* was found to require 11 weeks. A snail infected by a single miracidium of *S. mansoni* was observed by Faust and Hoffman (1934) to discharge an average of 3500 cercariae a day for a long time; in one instance the total progeny of a single miracidium exceeded 200,000.

The cercariae of *haematobium* and *mansoni* have a body about 200 μ long with a tail stem slightly longer and forks about 75 μ long; those of *japonicum* are slightly smaller. They escape from the snail into the water in " puffs," a number at a time. The cercariae alternately swim and rest in the water for two or three days; if they fail to reach a final host in this time they die. If successful they burrow through the skin, using the histolytic secretions of their cephalic glands just as the miracidia do. The natives of some parts of Africa where *S. haematobium* occurs realize that infection may result from bathing, but from the nature of the disease they believe that infection takes place by way of the urinary passages, and therefore employ various mechanical devices to prevent infection in this manner. Ruminants, because of the neutral or alkaline nature of parts of the stomach, can become infected with schistosomes by drinking cercaria-infected water, but other animals cannot.

Skin penetration requires 15 minutes and may or may not be accompanied by a prickling sensation and subsequent dermatitis (see p. 277).

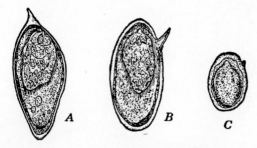

Fig. 70. Eggs of Schistosoma; *A, S. haematobium*, from urine; *B, S. mansoni*, from feces; *C, S. japonicum*, from feces. Note developed embryos in all. × about 200. (*A* and *B* after Looss, *C* after Leiper.)

If ingested with water the cercariae attach themselves to the mucous membranes of the mouth or throat and similarly bore in. They leave their tails behind them, and can be found in the skin for about 18 hours, but eventually they find their way into the blood system and are carried via the heart to the lungs. Young *S. mansoni* accumulate in the lungs on the second and third days; by the sixth day they appear in numbers in the liver, where they are well established by the fifteenth day. Apparently these larvae feed only on the portal blood, but once in the liver they grow rapidly. Migration of this species to the mesenteric veins begins about the twenty-third day, and mating and egg production about the fortieth day.

Species in Man. Three species of the genus Schistosoma — *S. haematobium, S. mansoni,* and *S. japonicum* — habitually live in man, but these species also develop in other animals, and there are rare instances of other species maturing in man. *S. bovis* of cattle, for instance, is an accidental human parasite, and eggs of a pig schistosome, *S. incognitum*, have been found in human feces.

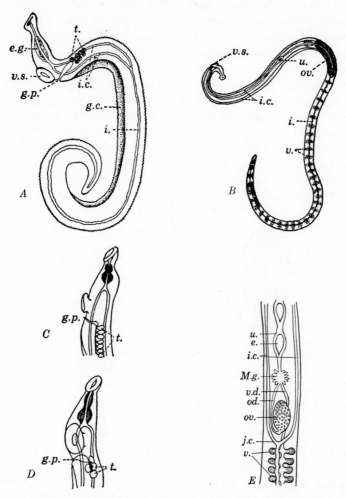

Fig. 71. Anatomy of schistosomes. *A*, ♂ *S. mansoni*; *B*, ♀ *S. mansoni*; *C*, anterior end of ♂ *S. japonicum*; *D*, anterior end of ♂ *S. haematobium*; *E*, ovarial region of *S. haematobium*; *e*, egg; *e.g.*, esophageal glands; *g.p.*, genital pore; *g.c.*, gynecophoric canal; *i.*, intestine; *i.c.*, intestinal ceca; *j.c.*, junction of ceca; *M.g.*, Mehlis' gland; *od.*, oviduct; *ov.*, ovary; *t.*, testes; *u.*, uterus; *v.*, vitellaria; *v.d.*, vitelline duct; *v.s.*, ventral sucker. (Adapted from various authors.)

The adult schistosomes differ in details of their anatomy and are easily identifiable by their eggs (Fig. 70). Those of *S. haematobium* and *S. mansoni* are very large (115 to 170 μ by 45 to 65 μ), the former with a well-developed terminal spine, the latter with a conspicuous lateral spine. Those of *S. japonicum* are less elongate (70 to 100 μ by 50 to 65 μ) and have a rudimentary lateral spine, often difficult to see. *S. bovis* has spindle-shaped eggs with a spine at one end, whereas the eggs of *S. incognitum* are slightly flattened on the spine side, the spine being subterminal. The cercariae of the different species are distinguishable with certainty only by the number and type of the cephalic glands.

The principal differential characters of the adults are as follows: in *S. haematobium* the male has a tuberculated body and 4 to 5 large testes, while the female has the ovary slightly behind the middle of the body, and a long uterus with 20 to 30 eggs in it; in *S. mansoni* the male also has a tuberculated body but has 8 or 9 small testes in a zigzag row, and the female has the ovary anterior to the middle, with the vitellaria occupying about three-fifths of the body, and the uterus with usually only one egg in it. In *S. japonicum* the size is larger, the male has most of the body smooth and has 7 testes in a regular column, and the female has the ovary behind the middle of the body and a long uterus with 50 or more eggs in it.

The three species differ in their distribution. *S. haematobium* has a very wide distribution in Africa and in some localities in Palestine, Iraq, and Portugal. *S. mansoni* occurs along with *haematobium* in many parts of Africa and is also widely distributed in the West Indies and northern South America, from Venezuela to Brazil; it seems highly probable that it was imported from West Africa in the slave days. The third species, *S. japonicum*, is an Oriental one, found in Japan, Formosa, China, some of the Philippine Islands, and Celebes.

Schistosoma mansoni. This fluke is an important parasite in many parts of Africa and tropical America. In some irrigated districts in Venezuela, Scott estimated up to 90 per cent of the males over 10 years of age to be infected.

The eggs of this species (Fig. 70*B*) are large, with lateral spines, and are normally voided with the feces. This species also infects monkeys, and many rodents can be experimentally infected, though ordinarily viable eggs do not appear in the feces. Stunkard (1946), however, developed rodent strains in which eggs *did* appear in the feces. Although dogs are usually refractory, puppies become infected in South America.

An extensive study of this species was made by Faust *et al.* (1933, 1934) in Puerto Rico. The adults have a special predilection for the veins draining the bowel near the ileocecal junction; a few can usually be found in the liver. Although usually only a single developed egg is found in the uterus, the female probably produces from 100 to several hundred eggs per day.

The intermediate hosts are certain species of snails of the family Planorbidae. In Africa the intermediate hosts are mainly species of Planorbis, subgenus Biomphalaria — principally *P. boissyi* in Egypt, *P. ruppellii* in Central Africa, and *P. pfeifferi* in South Africa and Madagascar. In South America *Australorbis glabratus* (Fig. 72*B*) and *Tropicorbis centimetralis,* and in the West Indies *A. glabratus* and *A. antiguensis,* serve as hosts. It is interesting that miracidia from the American strain of *S. mansoni* fail to infect *P. boissyi,* even though this parasite was undoubtedly originally introduced from Africa. Stunkard (1946) thinks that, once the larva of a fluke has become

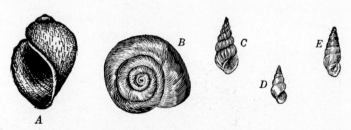

FIG. 72. Intermediate hosts of schistosomes, drawn to scale. *A, Bulinus truncatus,* principal host of *S. haematobium* in Egypt; *B, Australorbis glabratus,* host of *S. mansoni* in tropical America; *C, D,* and *E, Oncomelania hupensis, quadrasi* and *nosophora,* hosts of *S. japonicum* in China, Philippines, and Japan, respectively. All × 2. (*A,* after Leiper; others original.)

adapted to a new host, it may develop in it better than in the original host. Thus snails like *Tropicorbis havanensis* in this country might develop into very hospitable hosts.

Schistosoma haematobium. This species is a scourge in many parts of Africa, Madagascar, and southwestern Asia. A few cases have been reported in India, but it does not thrive there because of absence of a good intermediate host. Egypt suffers especially severely, for although *S. mansoni* is confined to the delta north of Cairo, *S. haematobium* occurs throughout the country, affecting 60 per cent or more of the population wherever perennial canal irrigation is practiced. It also infects monkeys but not other animals.

The adult worms live in pairs in the pelvic branches of the portal system, and the females normally deposit their eggs in vessels on the surface of the bladder, through the wall of which they work their way to be excreted with the urine. Late in the infection, however, the eggs fail to get through the thickened wall. Campbell-Begg in 1942 found eggs in the urine of only 3 per cent of cases positively diagnosed by cystoscopy. Eggs in urine hatch within a few minutes after dilution with water.

The intermediate hosts are nearly always snails of the genus Bulinus

(Fig. 72) and the closely related Physopsis, which inhabit slow-flowing canals and rivers and quiet ponds and lagoons. In Egypt and neighboring regions the principal species involved is *Bulinus truncatus*, in South Africa *Physopsis africana*, and in west and central Africa the closely related *P. globosa*. In Portugal, however, a species of Planorbis, *P. dufourii*, and in South Africa a Lymnaea, *L. natalensis*, have been incriminated.

Schistosoma japonicum. This Oriental species is not confined to man, but infects cats, dogs, cattle, horses, and pigs among domestic

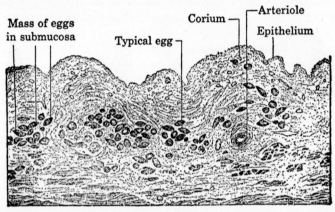

Fig. 73. Section of wall of urinary bladder showing eggs of *Schistosoma haematobium*. (After Brumpt.)

animals, and also field mice; many laboratory animals are susceptible. Cattle and water buffaloes are important reservoir hosts. Intensive studies of this worm have been made since the outbreak in American troops in the Philippines.

The adult worms live in the mesenteric veins; the eggs are deposited in vessels near the lumen of the intestine and easily penetrate into it. Later when the intestinal wall becomes thickened more difficulty is encountered, and many eggs are swept back to the liver, many of them going on to the lungs. Eggs are commonly embedded in the appendix also, often leading to appendicitis.

The intermediate hosts of *S. japonicum* are small operculated snails of the family Amnicolidae and belong to a small group which some writers place in three closely related genera, Oncomelania, Katayama, and Schistosomophora, while others consider all these as subgenera of Oncomelania. In Japan the host is *O. (Katayama) nosophora*, a smooth-shelled form; in China it is the rib-shelled *O. (Oncomelania) hupensis* and perhaps one or two related species, and in the Philippines it is *O.* (*Schistosomophora*) *quadrasi,* with a smooth, pointed shell (see Fig. 72). The nearest relative in the United States is Pomatiopsis, which is a host for Paragonimus (see p. 284) ; Stunkard got partial but not complete development in these snails, but subsequently workers at the National Institutes of Health succeeded in producing cercariae in this snail.

The snails of this group are only 7 to 10 mm. long with high-spired shells. The young snails live in water but when mature they are amphibious and live in damp places at the edges of water and are commonly found climbing on vegetation in rice fields and along irrigation ditches and edges of ponds and streams, especially where the water or soil is enriched with humus or night soil, for they feed on filth. They are frequently submerged with rising or disturbed water and are carried from dirty village ditches to rice fields, where they thrive. While submerged they are attacked by the miracidia, which habitually swim near the surface of the water.

Other Species. The writer (1926) found a small schistosome egg with subterminal spine in India in feces thought to be human but possibly from pigs, and named it *Schistosoma incognitum.* This has since been found to be common in pigs in various parts of India, and occasional in dogs. A considerable number of species of schistosomes attack birds and mammals. Cattle, sheep, and goats are severely affected by several species, the most important of which are *S. bovis,* widely distributed in Africa and southwestern Asia, and *S. spindale* in India and the East Indies. *S. bovis* has been reported as a human parasite, but the evidence is not convincing; its eggs resemble those of *S. haematobium,* but it affects the intestine. The eggs of *S. spindale* are spindle shaped. *S. bovis* develops in the same snails as *S. haematobium,* while *S. spindale* develops in a planorbid (*Indoplanorbis exustus*). *S. nasale* has been shown to cause a " snoring disease " of cattle by its localization in the nose, where it produces cauliflower-like growths on the nasal septum. The cercariae penetrate into the nose while the animals are drinking. This fluke affects 80 per cent of cattle in some parts of India. *S. indicum* is a common parasite of Indian ungulates, particularly horses, in which it is very harmful.

Schistosome Dermatitis. The penetration of the skin by the cercariae of human schistosomes usually causes a prickling sensation and may or may not cause an itching rash or papules; these skin effects are undoubtedly conditioned by the extent of prior invasion and sensitization or immunity.

As Cort demonstrated in 1928, certain species of " foreign " cercariae, incapable of infecting man, cause a severe dermatitis or " swimmer's itch " when they penetrate the skin of bathers or waders who have become sensitized by repeated exposure. This condition is common in the north central states and in southern Canada, as well as in a few other parts of the United States, Europe, and India. In the northern United States and Canada at least nine species of cercariae are capable of causing dermatitis, but some develop in snails that thrive principally in marshes where only hunters or parasitologists are likely to suffer. Others develop in snails that frequent sandy beaches and thereby ruin otherwise good summer resorts.

In Michigan *Cercaria stagnicolae* is the most important since its host, *Stagnicola emarginata,* inhabits sunny bathing beaches and sheds the cercariae during the bathing season; the cercariae, like the bathers, swarm near the surface in shallow water on warm sunny days. Other species, especially *C. physellae* and *C. elvae,* may make a nuisance of themselves locally; a species close to *C. elvae* has been found to cause swimmer's itch in Portland, Oregon. McMullen and Beaver (1945) worked out the life cycles of the three species mentioned above; the adults are all species of Trichobilharzia, parasitic in water birds. These authors believe that in the north central states the snails acquire their infections mainly from migrating ducks in the fall, and that protection of bathing beaches from flocks of ducks during the fall migration might greatly reduce schistosome dermatitis. Swimmer's itch can be avoided by swimming in deep water. Since the cercariae penetrate principally when the water is drying on the skin, the annoyance can be greatly reduced by wiping the skin dry immediately after leaving the water. Children getting alternately wet and dry in shallow water are affected worst. The dermatitis begins with a prickly sensation followed by the development of extremely itchy papules, which sometimes become pustular and may be accompanied by considerable swelling. Some individuals are much more severely affected than others and may lose much sleep and even be prostrated. It usually takes about a week for the condition to subside.

After penetration the only possible treatment is by soothing applications. The dermatitis can be effectively controlled in small bodies of water by the use of copper salts to kill the snails. McMullen and Brackett recommend copper sulfate for shallow water, and a 2 to 1 mixture of copper sulfate and copper carbonate for water over 2 ft. in depth, at the rate of 3 lb. of the mixture per 10,000 sq. ft. of bottom. In larger lakes attention to water currents is necessary.

Pathology of Schistosomiasis. The diseases produced by various schistosomes are similar in many respects but differ in details. Much information on the early symptoms and course of the disease was obtained from the outbreak of *S. japonicum* infection in American troops in Leyte. The severity of the disease, depending principally on degree of exposure in cercaria-infested water, varies from symptomless cases to death within a few weeks. From one to several days after heavy exposure there is an irritating bronchial cough lasting a few days, followed two or three weeks later by an urticaria. During the period of migration and growth of the worms general toxic symptoms appear, including headache, general malaise, loss of appetite, aches, abdominal pains, anemia, and fever, and, in reinfections, urticaria and difficult breathing, probably due to allergy. During this stage of the infection there is marked leucocytosis and a high degree of eosinophilia, the latter gradually becoming less prominent later in the disease. About a month after infection, nausea, diarrhea, and sometimes dysentery develop.

The second or acute stage is that in which the eggs of the worms begin filtering through the tissues; it lasts for several months before going into the early chronic stage. In the intestinal species this period is marked by abdominal pain, dysentery with bloody, mucous stools, and enlarged and tender liver. These symptoms are brought on mainly by the inflammation caused by the eggs. In *S. japonicum* infections a stiff neck, pain and stiffness in the muscles, and chilly sensations with hot skin are also frequently present, and in the upper rectum small yellow nodules, really nests of eggs, may be seen. In *S. haematobium* infections the general symptoms are similar, but the gastro-intestinal symptoms are replaced by bladder pains and bloody urine. In mild cases the latter may be the only obvious symptom for years, but eventually a scalding or intensely painful sensation appears.

After a number of months the disease progresses to a chronic stage in which the affected tissues become gradually thickened and fibrosed owing to the irritation and inflammation caused by the passage of the eggs through them, and this is rendered worse by the increasing number of eggs which become permanently embedded. In the intestine there is loss of tone and interference with digestive function leading to dyspepsia, constipation with occasional bouts of diarrhea, appendicitis, and formation of papillomas and ulcerations, not infrequently ending in cancerous growths. Gradually, also, the deposition of eggs in the liver, especially in *japonicum* infections, leads to a fibrosis and shrinking of that organ, which may be studded with pseudotubercles around the embedded eggs. As the liver shrinks the spleen enlarges from engorgement and the abdomen becomes enlarged and bloated, while the rest of the body becomes pitifully emaciated.

The lungs may also be seriously affected by deposited eggs, and a few even manage somehow to get through into the general circulation, eventually being deposited in the brain or skin. Sometimes the lung lesions cause interference with the pulmonary circulation and the right ventricle of the heart is affected. These lung and heart lesions are common in Egypt. There is some evidence that " Egyptian spleno-megaly " or Banti's disease, characterized by huge spleen enlargement, edema, and anemia, may also be a manifestation of schistosomiasis.

In *S. haematobium* infections thickening and inflammation of the bladder and urethra lead to irregularity and painfulness of urination, blockage of ducts, formation of stones, fistulas, and even malignant tumors. Often the penis is badly affected also. Meanwhile, as in intestinal schistosomiasis, the victim becomes extremely weak and emaciated.

Lesions in other parts of the body (ectoptic lesions) result from aggregates of tubercles forming around eggs which have escaped and have been carried to distant parts of the body; they vary in size from pinhead lesions in the conjunctiva to lesions the size of an orange in the brain. In *S. japonicum* infections a significant proportion occur in the brain, probably because, according to Faust, the vertebral veins provide a natural channel from the portal and caval veins.

Diagnosis. In early or acute cases, after the worms begin oviposit-ing, diagnosis of urinary schistosomiasis can usually be made by finding the eggs in sedimented urine or diluting the urine and watching for hatched miracidia within an hour. In later cases the eggs are often not found, but cystoscopy is often helpful in conjunction with clinical symptoms. Complement fixation tests and skin tests, using alcoholic extracts of infected snails as antigen, are very helpful in diagnosis in old chronic cases in which eggs cannot be found, especially in intestinal schistosomiasis. The formol gel test (see p. 148) is positive, as it is in leishmaniasis.

In intestinal infections, eggs can usually be found in simple smears during the acute stage, especially after a purge, though several films should be examined because of irregular distribution. Examination of scrapings from the upper rectum are even more reliable. In light or chronic cases concentration methods are needed; of these the AEX method (see p. 251) is best, though repeated sedimentation of fecal suspensions in 0.5 per cent glycerin or 10 per cent alcohol is also recommended.

Treatment. Tartar emetic (sodium antimony tartrate) and other trivalent antimony compounds, particularly potassium antimony tar-trate, anthiomaline, and fuadin, have specific effects in schistosomiasis. These drugs cause degenerative changes in the adult worms, especially

affecting the reproductive organs.   The injured worms lose their hold
and are swept into the liver.   It has been thought that the drugs also
directly affect the eggs, since soon after treatment is started only dead,
blackened eggs are found, but Bang and Hairston (1946) doubt that the
eggs are affected.   When egg production is stopped, the percentage of
dead eggs in the tissues would increase until no living ones were present
after about 3 weeks.

The greatest difficulty with treatment, especially of large groups of
people, has been the time required — injections every other day for
about 4 weeks.   Alves and Blair (1945), however, claimed success with
a 2-day treatment, and Alves in 1946 reported no eggs in the feces of
131 patients 4 weeks after a 1-day treatment of 3 or 4 slow intravenous
injections of sodium antimony tartrate of 2 grains each.   Such treatment would not, however, be safe where there is serious liver damage.

In advanced cases where the rectum or urinary organs have been
severely damaged, and in all cases of splenomegaly, surgical treatment
is necessary.

Prevention and Control.   Some protection against schistosome infection can be obtained by carefully wiping the skin after immersion in
water containing cercariae, but better results are obtained by impreg-
nating the clothing with dimethyl phthalate, dibutyl phthalate, benzyl
benzoate, or a mixture of 45 per cent of each of the last two with 10
per cent " Tween 80 " emulsifier.   According to experiments by Ferguson et al. in 1946 these repellents are effective for at least 3 hours,
but some experiments at the National Institute of Health (1947)
showed that clothing impregnated with dibutyl phthalate would protect against cercarial penetration even after 96 hours of rinsing, or
several soap and water washings.

Cercariae can be killed in water to be used for drinking by impounding for 48 hours, or by sufficient chlorination to give a residual of about
1 ppm. at 10 minutes, or as little as 0.1 ppm. at 30 minutes.   Sand
filtration and alum treatment are ineffective.

In most places the control of the disease resolves itself into control
of the snails involved.   In Egypt the disease is associated with the
modern perennial irrigation system from high-level canals; only light
infection exists under the old method of annually flooding basins when
the Nile is in flood.   The use of alternate canals, with periods of drying,
has not done much good, but annual canal clearance is helpful (see
p. 266).   Copper sulfate or copper carbonate treatment of water to
kill snails has been used with success in various places in north Africa
and Rhodesia and might be useful in some places in tropical America.
There the disease is mostly associated with irrigation and is a disease

of the rural laboring class. Application of slaked lime every 3 months to irrigation ditches to give a 0.1 per cent solution has been advocated in Venezuela but is ineffective against the African intermediate hosts. Benzene hexachloride dust has been reported to be effective against Bulinus and Planorbis in Egypt (see p. 267).

In Oriental schistosomiasis the problem is altogether different; in China and Japan it is largely associated with rice growing. In the Philippines, however, it is associated more with marshes and uncultivated areas. All the hosts of *S. japonicum* are amphibious and are often found in damp places far from water, on plants above the water line, so clearing or treatment of water with copper salts is not feasible. McMullen *et al.* (1947) found that destruction of *Oncomelania quadrasi* was best effected in the dry season, by applying copper sulfate or calcium cyanamide dust. Even where there was dense vegetation, application of 12 lb. of either of these per 1000 sq. ft. was completely effective.

Protection of snail habitats from schistosome eggs by removing villages from irrigation canals, fencing, and providing wells for water for domestic use has resulted in substantial reduction in schistosomiasis in some parts of Sudan. Such efforts would be in vain against Oriental schistosomiasis. It would be helpful in China and Japan if some practicable method of destroying schistosome eggs in night soil could be found.

Lung Flukes (*Paragonimus*)

The lungs of various mammals, including man, carnivores, rats, pigs, and opossums, may be infected with flukes of the genus Paragonimus, belonging to the family Troglotrematidae. The members of this family are rather small egg-shaped flukes with a spiny cuticle and with the large testes situated side by side behind the ovary (Fig. 74A). Besides Paragonimus the family includes *Troglotrema salmincola*, the salmon-poisoning fluke (see p. 305), and a fluke that lives in cutaneous cysts in birds, *Collyriclum faba*.

Species. Opinion is divided as to the number of species of lung flukes. In the adults differences occur principally in the body spines and in the size of the eggs, but these are both variable characters. The first form described was *Paragonimus westermanni* from Bengal tigers, whereas the first human specimen, from Formosa, was named *P. ringeri.* A North American form, found in carnivores and shown by Ameel to be normally a parasite of mink, has been named *P. kellicotti.* Investigations of the life cycles have demonstrated differences in both the morphology and behavior of the different developmental stages not only between Korean and American forms but also between Korean and Chinese forms. Chen found a form in rats near Canton which would not experimentally infect carnivores, pigs, guinea pigs, or monkeys.

A final settlement of the species in this genus is not yet possible. The North American form has proved to be a rather common parasite of

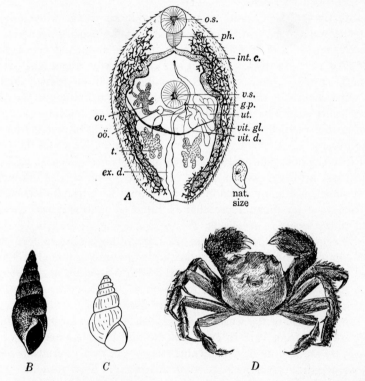

FIG. 74. Lung fluke, *Paragonimus westermanni*, and first and second intermediate hosts. *A*, adult fluke; *g.p.*, genital pore; *oö.*, oötype; other abbrev. as in Fig. 62. *B*, *Melania libertina*, snail host in Japan and Korea. *C*, *Pomatiopsis lapidaria*, host of *P. kellicotti* in United States. *D*, *Eriocheir japonicus*, a common second intermediate host in Japan. (*A* adapted from Leuckart; *B* from Faust; *C* from Walker, in Ward and Whipple; *D*, from Yoshida.)

mink in Michigan, and infected crayfish have been found over a large part of the United States. Byrd and Reiber in 1942 reported one infection from an opossum in Tennessee. Since infection is caused by eating raw crabs or crayfish, which serve as second intermediate hosts, human infection is sporadic in most places but is endemic in many parts of the Orient, especially among Japanese. Sporadic human infections have been reported from New Guinea, Dutch East Indies, India,

Africa, and both North and South America. There are some districts in Korea, Japan, and Formosa where 40 to 50 per cent of the population are infected.

The adult flukes are reddish brown, thick, and egg-shaped, about 8 to 12 mm. long and 4 to 6 mm. in diameter. The cuticle is clothed with minute simple or toothed spines. The arrangement of the organs can be seen from Fig. 74A.

Life Cycle. The adults live normally in the lungs where, shortly after they have arrived, the host forms cystlike pockets around them, which rupture and liberate the eggs into the bronchial tubes, to be excreted with sputum. These cysts are usually about the size of filberts or larger, and contain commonly two but sometimes as many as six worms, together with infiltrated cells and numerous eggs in a rust-brown semifluid mass. Many of the eggs escape into the tissue, giving it a reddish, peppered appearance and causing small tubercle-like abscesses. In some cases the worms apparently get on the wrong track in the body and end up in such places as the spleen, liver, brain, intestinal wall, eye, or muscles. Musgrave found in the Philippines that sometimes many parts of the body may be infested at once, and in one case he found more than a hundred mature parasites in a muscular abscess.

The eggs of the lung fluke (Fig. 59D) are yellowish brown, from 80 to 118 μ in length by 48 to 60 μ in diameter; they are commonly found in the feces as the result of being swallowed. Miracidia develop in the eggs slowly after they leave the body, requiring at least 3 weeks, during which time the eggs must be kept moist.

The life cycle of the worm was established in part by several Japanese workers from 1918 to 1921, but the first complete account of the life cycle and of the developmental stages was that of Ameel (1934), who studied the American form in Michigan. The miracidia (Fig. 75, 1) live only a few hours after hatching, and if successful in finding a suitable snail in this short span of life they burrow into it and continue their development. In the Orient the snail hosts are species of the genus Melania, particularly *Melania libertina* (Fig. 74B), or related forms; these are operculated aquatic snails living attached to stones, etc., in ponds and streams. In Michigan, Ameel found the snail host to be a related operculated form, *Pomatiopsis lapidaria* (Fig. 74C), which is amphibious and nocturnal in habit.

In the snails the miracidia change into irregular-shaped saclike sporocysts (Fig. 75, 2) which produce about 12 first-generation rediae (Fig. 75, 3), which in turn produce a similar number of second-generation rediae (Fig. 75, *5*). The latter produce 20 or 30 fully developed cercariae.

The cercariae (Fig. 75, *6*) are 175 to 240 μ long, have a small knoblike tail, spiny cuticle, a stylet, and 14 penetration glands; these cercariae appear 78 days or more after infection of the snail. The cercariae

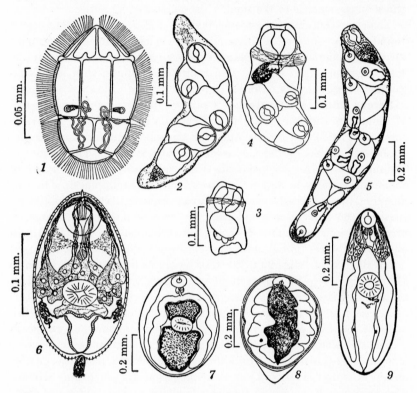

FIG. 75. Stages in the life cycle of *Paragonimus kellicotti*. *1*, miracidium, showing ciliated epidermal plates and flame cells; *2*, mature sporocysts containing first-generation rediae; *3*, young first-generation redia; *4*, mature first-generation redia containing second-generation rediae; *5*, mature second-generation redia containing cercariae; *6*, cercaria; *7*, young encysted metacercaria, five weeks old; *8*, mature encysted metacercaria; *9*, excysted metacercaria, showing excystation glands and beginnings of genital organs. (After Ameel.)

do not swim, but creep in a leechlike manner or float with the current. Those of the American species pierce the cuticle of the crayfish, which is the next host in the series, at vulnerable points and make their way invariably to the heart and pericardium where they become encysted and gradually develop into mature infective metacercariae, a process which takes 6 weeks or more. In China and Japan various species of fresh-water crabs serve as second intermediate hosts, and in Korea a crayfish is involved. The Japanese form does not choose the cardiac region but encysts principally in the muscles and viscera of the cephalo-thorax in crayfish and in the gills and leg muscles in crabs. Chen found those near Canton to encyst principally in the liver of crabs and some-times on the surface of the shell.

The cysts containing the metacercariae (Fig. 75, 7 and 8) are nearly round, 0.5 mm. or less in diameter. The enclosed spiny metacercariae lie straight, unlike most encysted forms, and are characterized by the large excretory vesicle filled with refractile granules, with large con-voluted intestinal ceca on either side.

Second Intermediate Hosts. Crabs of the genera Eriocheir and Potamon are commonly infected in Japan. Eriocheir (Fig. 74D) in-habits rice fields near the sea and small streams inland for 40 or 50 miles in Japan and Korea and is extensively used as food. The species of Potamon are coarse-shelled crabs which abound in shallow water of mountain streams in Japan, Formosa, and the Philippines. The raw juices of the frequently infected Korean crayfish, *Astacus similis*, are used by the natives as a medicine for fever and diarrhea. Another frequently infected crab is Sesarma, but this is not an edible form. In the United States probably all the species of Cambarus serve as hosts; small sluggish streams, 20 to 30 ft. or less in width, have been found to contain the greatest numbers of infected crayfish, whereas large streams contain few if any.

Infection usually results from eating the infected crabs or crayfish without cooking. In parts of China and the Philippines, as well as in Japan and Korea, crabs are eaten raw with salt or dunked in wine or vinegar. Possibly water containing cysts liberated from the gills of dead crabs may also be a source of infection, for such cysts live for some weeks. Ameel found that cats, which do not willingly eat cray-fish, become infected by eating animals containing young flukes that have not yet entered the lungs.

Development in Final Host. When the young flukes (Fig. 75, 9) are freed from their cysts in the duodenum of their final hosts, they bore through the walls of the intestine, wander about in the abdominal cavity for some time, then go through the diaphragm to the pleural cavity, into the lungs, and finally to the bronchioles, where they remain and grow to maturity in the cysts formed by the host's lung tissue. In a normal host they may reach the pleural cavity in about 4 days and enter the lungs after about 2 weeks, but Ameel found that in white rats they may still be loitering in the abdominal cavity, bereft of ambition or purpose in life, after more than 8 months. Man is probably not the normal host of this worm; the frequency with which the worms get lost and find themselves in abnormal localities may be correlated with this fact (see p. 26).

Once the worms have reached their final destination in the lungs and have been imprisoned in cysts by the host, they are very long-lived, persisting for at least several years. A German who had become infected in America while enjoying the delicacies provided by a Chinese cook claimed to have had symptoms of lung infection for 10 years before his trouble was diagnosed, and it was not until 13 years later that his symptoms finally disappeared.

The effects produced by Paragonimus infection are usually not serious, although they are suggestive of tuberculosis; a differentiation can be made only by finding the eggs of the worm instead of tubercle bacilli in the sputum. The only constant symptoms are a cough, which is usually intermittent, and blood-stained sputum. Sometimes there are vague sensations of discomfort in the chest, and occasionally considerable hemorrhage. Rarely, however, are the patients incapacitated for work. When the parasites localize in other parts of the body the symptoms depend on their position; brain infections are marked by epileptic fits and other symptoms characteristic of brain tumors, and usually in time cause death.

Treatment and Prevention. No reliable treatment is known, but injections of antimony compounds or emetin or emetin and prontosil, at least relieve symptoms temporarily. Faust (1929) recommended removal of patients from endemic areas when possible; recovery follows in 5 or 6 years, even though the worms may survive longer.

Prevention of infection consists either in the destruction of the snails which act as the first intermediate host by the use of copper sulfate (see p. 266), or by abstinence from the use of raw crabs or crayfish as food, and in avoidance of water for drinking which may possibly contain detached cysts.

In Korea the infection has been greatly reduced by health officers by collecting and destroying edible crabs, by forbidding their sale, and by educational propaganda.

Liver Flukes

Fasciolidae

The liver and bile ducts of man and domestic animals are inhabited by flukes of the families Fasciolidae, Dicrocoeliidae, and Opisthorchiidae.

The Fasciolidae include several species of the genera Fasciola and

Fascioloides which are very important liver parasites of cattle, sheep, and goats, one of which, *Fasciola hepatica*, is not infrequently parasitic in man. This family also includes *Fasciolopsis buski* (see p. 300), an important intestinal fluke of man and pigs. The Fasciolidae are large leaflike flukes with branched reproductive organs and usually branched ceca also, with a small coiled uterus lying entirely in front of the sex glands. The eggs are very large; the cercariae (Fig. 65*J*), which have long simple tails, encyst on water vegetation.

Fasciola hepatica is 25 to 30 mm. long, with a small anterior cone, as in other members of this genus, giving it a shouldered appearance. The general arrangement of the organs can be seen from Fig. 76. It is found in cattle, sheep, and goats in nearly all parts of the world and may parasitize many other herbivorous animals, particularly rabbits, kangaroos, and man. Olsen in 1948 called attention to the importance of rabbits as reservoirs of infection. In many parts of Africa and the Orient, including Hawaii, *F. hepatica* is replaced by a similar but even larger species, *F. gigantica*. Another related form, *Fascioloides magna*, which lacks the anterior cone, is primarily a parasite of deer in North America but also frequently infects cattle; in cattle it commonly becomes encapsulated in the liver tissue, whence its eggs fail to escape from the host. Sheep may be severely affected by this species (Swales, 1935).

In cattle, sheep, and goats these liver flukes cause very considerable damage, especially in young animals, which become unthrifty and emaciated and under adverse conditions die. Olsen estimates that on the Gulf Coast alone there is an annual loss of 44 tons of condemned livers (23 per cent) and 58 tons of meat, to say nothing of mortality, particularly among calves, reduction in milk production, and curtailed breeding. In India, according to Bhalerao, *F. gigantica* causes more damage to cattle than any bacterial or virus disease.

Human cases are comparatively rare, but this is probably due to infrequent exposure to the metacercariae rather than to failure of the infecting metacercariae to develop in man. Watercress is one of the commonest means of infection, but home-grown watercress is seldom exposed to Fasciola cercariae. In Cuba Kourí (1948) reported human fascioliasis to be quite common, particularly in certain provinces, in some years actually reaching epidemic proportions. Serious symptoms appear, involving the liver, gall bladder, alimentary canal, and nervous system. During the period of invasion there is a syndrome of fever and eosinophilia.

In the Near East Fasciola has been considered the cause in man of a " parasitic laryngo-pharyngitis," or " halzoun," an acute irritation

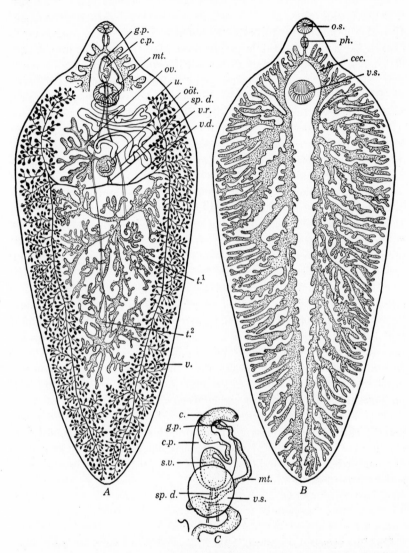

FIG. 76. *Fasciola hepatica.* *A*, showing reproductive systems only; *B*, showing digestive system only; *C*, cirrus pouch region. Abbrev.: *c.*, cirrus; *cec.*, cecum; *c.p.*, cirrus pouch; *g.p.*, genital pore; *mt.*, metraterm; *oöt.*, oötype; *o.s.*, oral sucker; *ov.*, ovary; *ph.*, pharynx; *sp. d.*, sperm duct; *s.v.*, seminal vesicle; *t.*[1], anterior testes; *t.*[2], posterior testis; *u.*, uterus; *v.d.*, vitelline duct; *v.r.*, vitelline reservoir; *v.s.*, ventral sucker. (Adapted from Leuckart.)

of the throat from temporary attachment of worms eaten with raw food; it is said to come from eating raw livers of sacrificial animals. Witenberg, however, thinks it is usually due to eating improperly cooked fish containing the large metacercariae of Clinostomum. Similar attacks are common in Japan. Clinostomum is normally parasitic in water birds; in this country the metacercariae in fish are called " yellow grubs "; their presence ruins vast numbers of fresh-water fish, especially perch, for food. Incidentally, another temporary fluke infection was found by the writer to be quite common in the state of Manipur in Assam, caused by eating raw swim bladders of catfish infected with a large flat fluke, *Isoparorchis hypselobagri*, superficially resembling Fasciolopsis.

Eggs of Fasciola develop after leaving the host and hatch in about 2 weeks. The miracidia develop in snails of the genus Lymnaea (Fig. 65) or closely related genera (Stagnicola, Fossaria, Galba) and go through a sporocyst and two redia stages before the cercariae are produced. The latter leave the snail in 5 to 6 weeks or more and encyst on water vegetation, where they remain until eaten by the final host. The cercariae are not infective until about 12 hours after encysting. The cysts withstand short periods of drying. The young flukes normally reach the liver by burrowing through into the abdominal cavity and entering from the surface, but occasionally they get into the circulation and may be distributed to abnormal locations. According to Schumacher (1939), they bore into the liver parenchyma on the second to sixth day after infection but do not enter the bile passages until the seventh or eighth week.

Olsen in 1943 confirmed the usefulness of hexachloroethane for treatment of cattle; he administered it in a drench with bentonite and water; at the rate of 10 grams of the drug per 100 lb. of weight he got 90 per cent cures with no ill effects. Kourí recommends emetin as a specific treatment in man.

Dicrocoeliidae

The Dicrocoeliidae are small flat flukes, with the testes in front of the ovary and the uterus looped far posteriorly. They have small eggs and long-tailed stylet cercariae which are expelled from land snails in slime, most species probably using insects as second intermediate hosts.

Dicrocoelium dendriticum (*lanceolatum*) is a common liver parasite of sheep and other ruminants as well as other herbivorous animals in many parts of the world, but particularly in Europe and Asia. Human cases are not infrequent, though often the presence of eggs in human feces is not due to infection but to ingestion of liver of infected animals. The effects are similar to those produced by Fasciola, but less severe. This fluke is 5 to 15 mm. long by 1.5 to 2.5 mm. broad (Fig. 77A). The thick-shelled brown eggs, measuring 40 to 45 μ by 22 to 30 μ, usually contain miracidia when laid. When eaten by certain species of land snails the eggs hatch in the tissues of the snail. Development is slow; after several months second-generation sporocysts are developed, containing the stylet cercariae previously known as *Cercaria vitrina*.

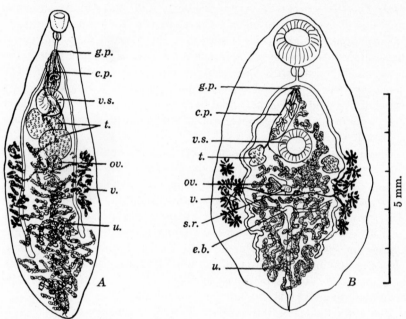

Fig. 77. *A*, *Dicrocoelium dendriticum; B*, *Eurytrema pancreaticum; e.b.*, excretory bladder; *u.*, uterus; *v.*, vitellaria; other abbrev. as in Figs. 62 and 74*A*. (Adapted from Travassos.)

Cameron in 1931 found that when sheep eat infected snails they acquire Dicrocoelium infections. Neuhaus in 1938, however, found that the developed cercariae invade the respiratory chamber of the snail, where several hundreds may be enclosed in a slimy cyst. Several such cysts may be rolled together into a "slime ball." The slime balls are dropped by the snail on moist vegetation. After ingestion by a suitable host the cercariae reach the liver via the portal blood system and are unusual in not losing their tails or stylets until they have reached their final destination.

Another fluke of the same family, *Eurytrema pancreaticum* (Fig. 77*B*), lives in the pancreatic ducts of pigs and in the biliary ducts of cattle, water buffaloes, and camels in China. Its thicker body and large oral sucker suffice to distinguish it from Dicrocoelium. A few human cases have been recorded from South China.

Opisthorchiidae

The flat, elongate, semitransparent flukes of this family occur in fish-eating animals, particularly in Europe and Asia, but one species, *Metorchis conjunctus,* is very common in Canada, and *Amphimerus pseudofelineus* occurs in cats in the United States. The general arrangement of the organs can be seen from Figs. 78 and 80. The eggs of these flukes are very small and contain miracidia when laid, but the latter do not ordinarily hatch until eaten by a suitable snail. The cercariae have long fluted tails and no stylets; they encyst in freshwater fishes, and reach their final hosts when these are eaten. Characters distinguishing the cysts from others found in the Far East are shown in Fig. 79.

Clonorchis sinensis. This, the most important human parasite in the family, is widely distributed in the Far East from Korea and Japan through China to Indo-China and India. It is common in cats and dogs throughout its range, but human infection is limited to localities where raw fish is esteemed as food. Heavy human infections are common in local areas in Japan, in the vicinity of Canton and Swatow in China, and in the Red River delta in French Indo-China. In some places in Japan the majority of the inhabitants are infected, whereas in Canton the human incidence is about 12 per cent. Stoll (1947) estimated about 19,000,000 human cases in all.

The adult flukes vary from 10 to 25 mm. in length and are from 3 to 5 mm. wide, with an arrangement of organs as shown in Fig. 78*A*. The deeply branched testes distinguish this genus from the related Opisthorchis, in which the testes are round or lobed. The adults live both in the small biliary ducts of the liver and also in the larger bile ducts leading to the gall bladder, often in hundreds or even thousands.

Life Cycle. The small yellow-brown eggs, averaging 27 by 16 μ in size, are shaped like an old-fashioned carbon-filament light bulb, the operculum fitting into a thickened rim of the shell like the lid on a sugar bowl (Fig. 78*B*). The miracidia hatch when eaten by small, conical, operculate snails of the subfamily Bythiniinae, which belong to the same family as the intermediate hosts of *Schistosoma japonicum.* The most important species is *Parafossalurus striatulus* (Fig. 78*D*), which is widely distributed in canals and ponds throughout the area where human infections occur.

According to Faust and Khaw (1927), the miracidia, which have asymmetrical internal organs (Fig. 78B), develop into rounded sporocysts which produce rediae. The rediae give birth to cercariae with long tails provided with fluted lateral fins (Fig. 78C). These attack fresh-water fishes and encyst in the flesh. According to Hsü *et al.* (1936–1938) the metacercariae (Fig. 79E and F) are found in oval cysts averaging 138 by 115 μ in size, with thin walls. They are eye-

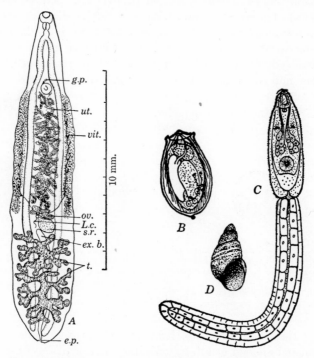

Fig. 78. *Clonorchis sinensis.* A, adult fluke (abbrev. as in Fig. 62); B, miracidium; C, cercaria × 120; D, intermediate host, *Parafossalurus striatulus*, × 2. (A, original; B, C, and D adapted from Faust and Khaw.)

less and have a large excretory bladder, not Y-shaped, filled with coarse granules. The cuticle is covered with fine spines, and both cephalic and skin glands are present.

Numerous species of fresh-water fish, most of them of the minnow and carp family (Cyprinidae), serve as second intermediate hosts. According to Hsü the metacercariae normally encyst in the flesh and only exceptionally under the scales or in the gills. When infected fish are eaten raw the metacercariae are liberated and enter the bile duct within a few hours after being eaten.

Migration to the liver via the bile duct by the Opisthorchiidae is in contrast to the route taken by Dierocoelium via the portal veins or by Fasciola through the intestinal wall and abdominal cavity. It takes about 3 weeks for the flukes to reach maturity and to begin shedding eggs.

Epidemiology. Observations by Faust and Khaw in infected localities show how Clonorchis infections thrive. In the mulberry-growing areas near Canton, latrines are placed over fish ponds, feces falling directly into the water or onto night-soil rafts. Suitable snails occur in the ponds and feed on the fecal material, the fish are later attacked by the cercariae, and the people become infected when they eat the raw fish sliced with radishes or turnips and highly seasoned. The fish are often not eaten entirely raw, but are laid on top of a dish of

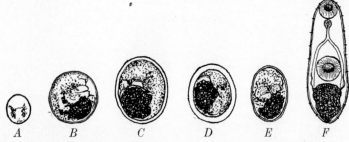

FIG. 79. Comparison of metacercarial cysts found in Japanese fishes. All × 100. *A, Echinochasmus perfoliatus.* Length 70 μ; excretory system with lateral stems filled with large concretions. *B, Metagonimus yokogawai.* Length 130 μ; flattened, discoidal; excretory bladder Y-shaped; cyst wall thin. *C, Heterophyes heterophyes.* Length 180–220 μ; cyst wall 5 to 10 μ thick. *D, Metorchis orientalis.* Length 150 μ; cyst wall 20 μ thick. *E, Clonorchis sinensis.* Length 120–150 μ; cyst wall thin (3 μ). *F, Clonorchis sinensis.* Liberated metacercaria. (Fig. *C* original; others adapted from Hsü and Khaw.)

steaming rice where they are heated sufficiently to remove the raw taste, but not enough to kill cysts in the interior of the flesh. Others merely dip the fish into hot " congee " with similar results. The cysts are unaffected by vinegar or sauces.

Clonorchis infections have been found in Orientals in all parts of the world, but two factors are necessary for it to become endemically established, (1) the presence of a suitable snail to serve as an intermediate host, and (2) the habit of eating raw fish. No suitable snail hosts are known to occur in the United States, and, even if they did, the failure of Americans to appreciate the gastronomic virtues of raw fish would prevent its spread as a human parasite beyond a few colonies of Orientals.

The Disease and Its Treatment and Prevention. The flukes injure the epithelium of the biliary ducts, and if numerous they may seriously

clog them.   The walls of the ducts become thickened, and neighboring
portions of the liver tissue may be involved, in severe cases leading to
a general cirrhosis.   Light infections may show no symptoms at all;
more severe infections are accompanied by diarrhea, often with blood,
edema, enlarged liver, and abdominal discomfort.

Treatment is uncertain.   Some workers have obtained good results
with injections of antimony compounds, but complete cures are not
usually obtained.   Faust and Khaw found that complete cures could be
effected in early cases by gentian violet and related dyes given in the
form of coated pills, and that even in cases of long standing a proportion of the worms could be reached by a sufficient concentration of
the dye to kill them.

Prevention would be possible by storing night soil undiluted or
adding 10 per cent of ammonium sulfate to kill the eggs before snails
got access to them.   Susceptibility of the fish to copper sulfate pro-
hibits its use for snail destruction.   The best preventive measure is to
prohibit the sale of raw fish in public eating places and to educate
people to the dangers of eating raw fish.   However, it is never easy to
suppress well-established tastes in food, and, besides, the cost of fuel
for cooking is in some places a real economic factor.

Opisthorchis spp.   The genus Opisthorchis, differing from Clonorchis in having round or lobed testes (Fig. 80A), contains several
species of flukes that are parasitic in cats and dogs and related animals,
and sometimes in man.   One very widespread and common species is
O. felineus, found from central and eastern Europe to Japan; in some
parts of its range it is a common human parasite.   It is about 7 to 12
mm. long and 2 to 3 mm. broad, with habits similar to Clonorchis.
Vogel (1934) found the snail host in East Prussia to be Bythinia leachi
(Fig. 81, 8), and the principal fish host the tench.   The eggs (Fig. 81, 1)
are more slender than those of Clonorchis, averaging about 30 by 14 μ.
According to Vogel, the miracidia hatch in the gut of Bythinia leachi
and grow into slender sporocysts (Fig. 81, 2), which produce numerous
rediae over a period of several months; these in turn produce the cercariae.   The latter (Fig. 81, 4) are born in an undeveloped state and
finished their development in the tissues of the snails, eventually leaving the snail after several months.

After penetrating certain fish hosts, for which they show distinct
preferences, the cercariae burrow into the tissues and secrete a cyst wall
within 24 hours, but it appears to require about 6 weeks of ripening
before the metacercariae are infective.   During this time they grow to
three or four times their original size.   Ripe cysts (Fig. 81, 6) measure
about 300 by 200 μ, with a cyst wall about 20 μ thick.   As with other

members of the family the liberated metacercariae (Fig. 81, 7) reach the liver via the bile duct.

Human infections are common in certain districts where the fish are eaten uncooked, as in East Prussia and in parts of Siberia. Two other species, *O. viverrini* and *O. noverca,* in southeastern Asia and in India,

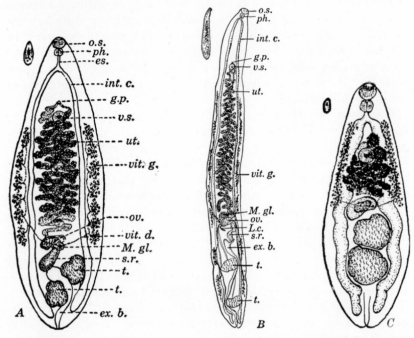

Fig. 80. *A,* Opisthorchis felineus, × 5; *B,* Amphimerus pseudofelineus, × 5; *C,* Metorchis conjunctus, × 20; abbrev. as in Figs. 62 and 74*A.* (*A* and *C* original; *B* after Barker.)

respectively, have similar habits and have also been recorded from man. *O. viverrini* occurs in about 25 per cent of the natives of the Lao country of northern Thailand, according to stool examinations.

Other Opisthorchiidae. The genus Amphimerus, distinguished from Opisthorchis by having a postovarian division of the yolk glands, contains a species, *A. pseudofelineus* (Fig. 80*B*), found in cats and coyotes in central United States. The genus Metorchis contains flukes that are shorter and broader than Opisthorchis, with a rosette-shaped uterus (Fig. 80*C*). Cameron (1939, 1944) reported the common occurrence of *M. conjunctus* over a wide area in Canada east of the Rockies. It is a small fluke, 1 to 6.6 mm. long; it has been found naturally in dogs, foxes, cats, mink, and raccoons, and occasionally in man, and is injurious to fur-bearing animals. According to Cameron (1944) the snail host is *Amnicola limosa porata,* and the metacercariae encyst in the flesh of the common sucker, *Catostomus commersonii,* sometimes in great numbers.

The pathogenic effects, treatment, and epidemiology of these infections do not differ in any way, so far as known, from those of Clonorchis.

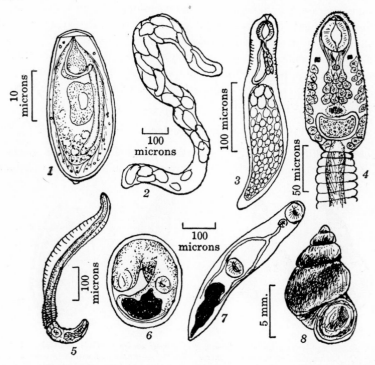

FIG. 81. Stages in life cycle of *Opisthorchis felineus. 1,* Egg containing miracidium (note single long gland); *2,* sporocyst with developing rediae; *3,* young redia with germ balls; *4,* anterior end of cercaria, showing large oral sucker, developing ventral sucker, large excretory bladder, penetration and cystogenous glands, and eye spots; *5,* cercaria, showing characteristic " tobacco pipe " posture and large fluted tail; *6,* mature cyst showing suckers and excretory bladder (black); *7,* excysted metacercaria; *8, Bythinia leachi,* with operculum covering opening. (Adapted from Vogel.)

Intestinal Flukes

The great majority of flukes inhabit the intestine of their hosts, yet there are no flukes that can be considered *primarily* parasites of the human intestine. A few species are very commonly found in man in some localities, though primarily parasitic in other animals, but the majority that have been reported from man are rather rare or accidental infections. On account of the omnivorous and variable food habits of the human being, he is subject to a wide range of such accidental parasites, including species properly belonging to both carnivorous and herbivorous hosts; probably no animal except the pig can compete with man in this respect.

We shall consider the following groups or species of intestinal flukes: (1) amphistomes (families Gastrodiscidae and Paramphistomatidae), normally parasitic in herbivores; (2) Fasciolopsis (family Fasciolidae), normally in pigs; (3) Heterophyidae, normally in fish-eating birds and mammals; (4) echinostomes (family Echinostomatidae), commonly parasitic in aquatic birds and mammals; and (5) a few other families which contain important intestinal parasites of lower animals, and sometimes rarely of man — the Strigeidae, Clinostomatidae, Troglo-trematidae, and Plagiorchidae.

Amphistomes

Long considered a distinct suborder, Amphistomata, this group of flukes is characterized by having the ventral sucker near the posterior

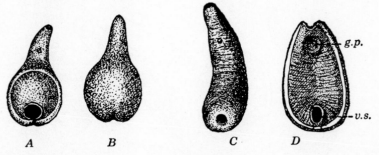

FIG. 82. Amphistome flukes. *A* and *B*, *Gastrodiscoides hominis*, ventral and dorsal views; *C*, *Paramphistomum cervi*, ventral view; *D*, *Watsonius watsoni*, ventral view. × about 4. (*A*, *B*, and *C* original; *D* after Stiles and Goldberger.)

end. A few are found in cold-blooded vertebrates and birds, but most of them live in the stomach or intestine of herbivorous mammals; some-times they literally carpet considerable areas of the stomach or intes-tine. Most of those in mammals belong to the families Gastrodiscidae, which have a large ventral disc (Fig. 82*A*), and Paramphistomatidae (Fig. 82*C* and *D*), which are superficially maggot-like in appear-ance.

Gastrodiscoides hominis, in the Gastrodiscidae, is the only amphi-stome found at all frequently in man; it is a common parasite of pigs in India. Buckley (1939) found it in over 40 per cent of 221 people examined in three villages in Assam, where it is probably widely dis-seminated. By means of soap-water enemas he obtained nearly 1000 worms from an 8-year-old boy.   Although it is present in 50 per cent of pigs in some places in Bengal and Assam, pigs were rare in the locality visited by Buckley and could hardly have served as a reservoir. Human infections have also been reported from Cochin China.

The worm inhabits the cecum and large intestine of its host, where it causes some inflammation and diarrhea.   The adults (Fig. 82*A* and *B*), 5 to 7 mm. in length when preserved, have an orange-red appearance when living, caused by a fine network of bright red capillary-like structures in the cuticle, against a flesh-colored background.   The body is divided into two parts — a very active, slender, conical or finger-like anterior portion which has the genital pore on its ventral side, and an almost hemispherical posterior portion, scooped out ventrally in a disc-like manner, with a sucker near its posterior border and a notch at the posterior end.   Several closely related species in the genus Gastrodiscus occur in the intestines of horses and pigs in Africa.

The eggs (Fig. 59*F*) are very large, as are those of other amphistomes, and rather rhomboidal in shape, tapering rapidly towards each end.   The miracidia develop after the eggs have escaped from their host, but nothing is known of the life cycle beyond this

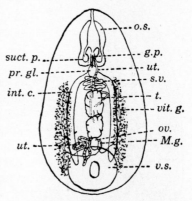

Fig. 83.   Internal anatomy of *Watsonius watsoni; suct. p.,* suctorial pouch; *g.p.,* genital pore; other abbrev. as in Fig. 62.   × 6.   (After Stiles and Goldberger.)

point.   By analogy with other amphistomes, there is little doubt that the cercariae encyst on water vegetation, and that the life cycle is essentially similar to that of the Fasciolidae.   Gastrodiscoides is not easily removed by anthelmintics but sometimes responds to soap-water enemas.

Watsonius watsoni, the only other amphistome thus far, which is found in man, has been recorded but once, from the small intestine of an emaciated Negro who died from severe dysentery in Nigeria; its normal hosts appear to be monkeys, in which the parasite has been found in Africa, Malaya, and Japan.   The worm when living is reddish yellow; it is a thick, pear-shaped animal, about 8 to 10 mm. long, slightly concave ventrally, with a translucent gelatinous appearance. It belongs to the family Paramphistomatidae, which contains many species parasitic in the fourth stomach (rumen) of ruminants.   *Paramphistomum cervi* is widespread in the Old World, but *Cotylophoron*

cotylophoron is the common species in southern United States. Its life cycle was found by Bennett (1936) to be very similar to that of Fasciola. Bhalerao (1947) states that immature amphistomes cause swelling of the lower jaw and fatal diarrhea in heavy infections, whereas the adults appear to be harmless.

Fasciolopsis

Another parasite which man shares with pigs is *Fasciolopsis buski*, a member of the family Fasciolidae (see p. 287). This is a large flat

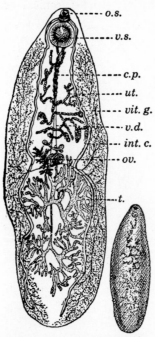

o.s.
v.s.
c.p.
ut.
vit. g.
v.d.
int. c.
ov.
t.

nat. size

Fig. 84. *Fasciolopsis buski;* abbrev. as in Fig. 62. × 2½. (Adapted from Odhner.)

fluke (Fig. 84), creamy pink in color, which reaches a length of 2 to 7.5 cm. When preserved it contracts and thickens, but fresh, relaxed specimens are very large and rather thin and flabby. In general arrangement of organs it resembles Fasciola, but it has no thickened cone at the anterior end, and has unbranched intestinal ceca. It is widely distributed in pigs in southeast Asia from central China to Bengal and in many of the East Indian Islands. Stoll (1947) estimated a total of 10 million human infections, most of them in China, though there are a few endemic localities in Assam and Bengal. In some villages near Shaohsing, China, according to Barlow, 100 per cent of the people examined were found to be infected. The eggs (Fig. 85A) are large and very variable in size but average about 138 by 83 μ. The miracidia require several weeks to develop after they are passed by the host. The intermediate hosts are members of the family Planorbidae, principally small, flatly coiled, aquatic snails of the genus Segmentina (Fig. 85J).

In the snails the miracidia change into sporocysts, which are peculiar in possessing a saclike gut like a redia, but no pharynx. Two generations of rediae are produced, the second generation of which produce large heavy-tailed cercariae (Fig. 85G), measuring, with the tail, nearly 0.7 mm. in length. These begin leaving the snail after about a month. The free-swimming life is brief, occupying only time enough for the cercaria to get to the plant on which the snail is feeding. In from 1 to

3 hours the cercaria has lost its tail and has encysted.   The cysts are white and about 200 μ in diameter.   The whole development from infection of snails to encystment takes from 5 to 7 weeks.

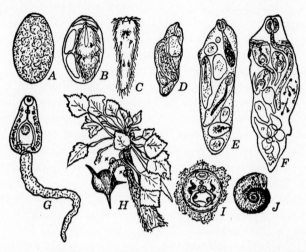

Fig. 85.   Stages in life cycle of *Fasciolopsis buski*.   *A*, egg as passed in feces, showing yolk balls; *B*, egg containing developed miracidium, with " mucoid plug " at anterior end and oil globules at one side;   *C*, miracidium, showing eye spots;   *D*, sporocyst containing developing mother rediae;   *E*, mother redia containing developing daughter rediae;   *F*, daughter redia containing developing cercariae;   *G*, cercaria;   *H*, Chinese caltrop or water ling (*Trapa natans*) with snails at points marked " X ";   *I*, encysted cercaria;   *J. Segmentina schmackeri*, intermediate host.   *A–D*, $\times$ 140;   *E*, $\times$ 50;   *F*, $\times$ 40;   *G* and *I*, $\times$ 70;   *H*, $\times \frac{1}{5}$;   *J*, $\times$ 1¼.   (Sketched from figures by Barlow.)

Mode of Human Infection.   In China, human infection has been traced mainly to the eating of the nuts of a water plant known as the red caltrop or red ling (*Trapa natans*) (Fig. 85*H*), on the pods of which the cercariae encyst.   These plants are extensively cultivated in ponds in the endemic areas and are fertilized by fresh night soil thrown into the water.   The little snails abound in these warm stagnant pools; the plants are fairly alive with snails creeping over their stems and leaves. The nuts are eaten both fresh and dried.   When fresh they are kept moist and are peeled with the teeth, during which process the cysts gain access to the mouth and are swallowed.   Barlow examined nuts from typical ponds, and found from a few to over 200 cysts on each nut. The writer (1928) traced some cases of infection in eastern Bengal to the eating of a water nut, *T. bicornis*, closely related to the Chinese nut. Another plant carrying infection is the so-called water chestnut, *Eliocharis tuberosa*, which has tubers like gladiolus bulbs.

Pathology.   *Fasciolopsis buski* usually lives in the small intestine, where it causes local inflammation, with bleeding and formation of ulcers. Symptoms develop about 3 months after infection. There is first a period of latency during which there is some asthenia and mild anemia. This is followed by diarrhea, a marked anemia, and usually some abdominal pain. The combination of chronic diarrhea and anemia, together with a distended abdomen, edema of the legs and face, and stunted development, is characteristic of a long-standing infection. In heavy infections the continued diarrhea and edema lead to severe prostration and sometimes death.

According to Barlow *F. buski* is easily gotten rid of by a number of different drugs, among which he includes oil of chenopodium, beta-naphthol, thymol, and carbon tetrachloride, but some of these drugs would be too toxic for many persons weakened by this infection. Hexylresorcinol crystoids given as for Ascaris infections (see pp. 426–427) give excellent results. Probably tetrachloroethylene, given as for hookworm infections, would also be effective.

Prevention consists in educating the people of endemic areas to the danger of eating fresh-water ling, water chestnuts, or other water vegetables unless they are cooked or at least dipped in boiling water. Sterilization of night soil would also be effective, but that presents a vastly more difficult problem.

Heterophyidae

The flukes of this family are extremely small, sometimes only 0.5 mm. in length, and egg-shaped; they are normally parasitic in fish-eating animals. They have the cuticle covered with minute scale-like spines. The genital pore opens into a retractile suckerlike structure which is either incorporated in the ventral sucker or lies to one side of it; Witenberg called this structure a " gonotyl." The arrangement of organs can be seen from Figs. 86A and 87. The life cycle is practically the same as that of the Opisthorchiidae, and a closely related group of snails serve as intermediate hosts.

The eggs (Fig. 86B) are very small, being in most species about 20 to 35 μ in length by 10 to 20 μ in diameter. They resemble the eggs of Clonorchis, but the enclosed miracidia have the internal organs symmetrically arranged (compare Figs. 81, *1*, and 86B). Hatching occurs when the eggs are eaten by the proper species of snails. As far as known these are species of Melania (Fig. 74B) or related genera. In the snails two generations of rediae are produced.

The cercariae have eye spots and large tails with fluted lateral fins; they are strikingly like those of the Opisthorchiidae but have a special arrangement of spines around the mouth. After leaving the snail host the cercariae usually encyst in fishes, mullets being especially favored, but one species has been found to encyst in frogs as well. Development in the final host is very rapid, maturity being reached in 7 to 10 days.

Host-Parasite Relations. Numerous species of Heterophyidae have been described. They all seem remarkably versatile with respect to the hosts in which they can mature, but their behavior in abnormal hosts suggests that they feel uncomfortably out of place — in the right pew but in the wrong church, as it were. Faust and Nishigori (1926) found that certain heterophyids of night herons, when experimentally

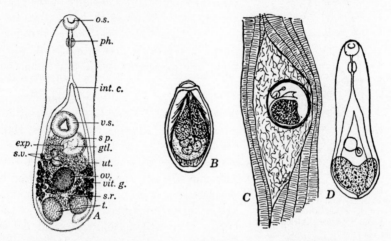

FIG. 86. *Heterophyes heterophyes. A,* adult fluke, × 40; *gtl.,* gonotyl; *sp.,* spines of gonotyl; other abbrev. as in Fig. 62. *B,* egg, × 900 (note symmetrical arrangement of internal organs of miracidium; compare with Fig. 78*B*). *C,* metacercaria encysted in muscles of mullet, × 60. *D,* metacercaria freed from cyst, × 50. (*A* original, *B* after Nishigori, *C* and *D* after Witenberg.)

fed to mammals, gradually shifted their position farther and farther back in the gut until finally expelled. Another and more important reaction was observed by Africa, Garcia, and de Leon in 1935. They noted the tendency of various species in the Philippines, when infecting dogs and man, to become buried deep in the mucous membranes. The eggs, instead of escaping normally in the feces, are taken up by the lymphatics or blood vessels and distributed over the body. Often the worms die imprisoned in the tissues. In an American species, *Cryptocotyle lingua,* studied by Stunkard (1941), no actual invasion of the tissues was noted, although there was much tissue damage, especially in abnormal hosts.

Stunkard's experiments showed that, in hosts which survive an initial infection, immunity develops which results in expulsion of worms (self-cure) and resistance to further infection.

Injury to Heart and other Viscera. Africa *et al.* showed that eggs of "foreign" species of Heterophyidae distributed over the body may cause serious injury. The most frequent damage is in the heart, where the eggs are deposited in large numbers. A dropsical condition and acute dilatation of the heart may result, producing symptoms similar to cardiac beri-beri and often fatal. Thirty-four of 297 autopsies in Manila were positive for intestinal heterophyid infection; nearly half of these had visceral complications, usually of the heart, and 13 were believed to have died from heart failure. The eggs have also been found in the brain and spinal cord, where they are associated with grave nervous symptoms.

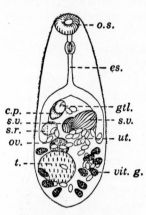

FIG. 87. A species of Haplorchis, × about 100; *gtl.*, gonotyl; other abbrev. as in Fig. 62. (After Africa and Garcia.)

The species of Heterophyidae causing these conditions belong to a number of different genera, including Heterophyes, Haplorchis (Fig. 87), and Diorchitrema. *Haplorchis yokogawai*, measuring about 0.7 by 0.28 mm., is the species most frequently causing trouble in man in the Philippines. According to experiments by Africa *et. al.* (1936) it lives a normal intestinal life in cats but not in dogs or man. It is possible that man may be susceptible to infection with any of the species of Heterophyidae, but that the small species may be most likely to invade the mucosa.

Normal Intestinal Heterophyids of Man. Two species, *Metagonimus yokogawai* and *Heterophyes heterophyes*, may be regarded as normal parasites of man and other mammals, since they appear to lead an orthodox life in the lumen of the intestine and are very common human parasites in certain localities.

M. yokogawai is a common parasite of dogs and cats in Japan, Korea, China, Palestine, and the Balkans. Human infection is frequent in Japan and in eastern Siberia. Like other members of the family, this tiny fluke is not very particular about its final host, for it infects not only carnivores, pigs, and man, but also pelicans and, experimentally, mice.

The adult worms live in the duodenum, sometimes by thousands. They are only 1 to 2.5 mm. in length and about 0.5 mm. broad. A characteristic feature is the displacement of the ventral sucker to the right side of the body, with the genital opening in a pit at the anterior border of it. The eggs are about 28 to 30 μ by 16 to 17 μ. The snails which serve as intermediate hosts are species of Melania (Fig. 74B, left). The cercariae (Fig. 64) attack fresh-water fishes, particularly a species of trout, *Plecoglossus altivelis,* and infection of the final host occurs when the uncooked fish are eaten. The cysts (Fig. 79B) are discoidal and found principally in pockets under the scales.

H. *heterophyes* (Fig. 86A) is also a very small fluke; relaxed specimens in dogs measure up to 2.7 mm. by 0.9 mm., but in cats they are only about 1.3 by 0.3 mm. They have the ventral sucker on the median line, with a separate genital sucker to the right of it. These flukes live in cats, dogs, and allied animals in Egypt, Palestine, India, and the Far East. According to Witenberg they are the commonest parasites of these animals in Jerusalem. Human infections are common both in the Far East and in Egypt and Palestine.

Khalil in 1933 found a common marine and brackish water snail, *Pirenella conica,* to be the snail host in Egypt. The cercariae encyst under the scales and in the flesh of mullets, especially *Mugil cephalus,* and rarely in other fish; in one mullet from the fish market in Jerusalem, Witenberg found over 1000 cysts per gram of flesh. The round cysts (Fig. 86C) lie in spindle-shaped masses of fat globules and measure from 0.13 to 0.26 mm. in diameter. The metacercariae, lying folded inside, have the anterior part of the body flattened.

Pathology. In infections with the normal human species the symptoms are usually negligible, though in heavy infections there may be mild digestive disturbances and diarrhea.

Like other intestinal flukes, these species are susceptible to the group of anthelmintics used for nematodes, but their small size and ability to hide away between the villi make treatment unsatisfactory unless the intestine is thoroughly cleaned of contents and mucus beforehand. Prevention consists in eschewing raw infected fish.

Troglotrema salmincola

These small flukes (Fig. 88), 1 mm. or less in length, belong to the same family as Paragonimus, Troglotrematidae. They are common parasites of fish-eating mammals in northwestern United States, the metacercariae encysting in salmon. The snail host in Oregon, according to Donham, Simms, and Shaw (1932), is *Goniobasis plicifera,* a common species in running water. The cercariae resemble those of Paragonimus. Human infection has been reported from eastern Siberia.

This parasite is of particular interest because it is associated with a highly fatal disease of dogs called " salmon poisoning." Simms *et al.*

(1932) obtained evidence that the disease is caused by a virus for which the fluke serves as a vector. After an incubation period of a week or more there is loss of appetite, fever, and sensory depression, followed by edema, violent vomiting, and dysentery. If diagnosed within 3 hours of onset, 2 to 6 mg. of apomorphine by mouth is protective. Animals that recover become immune. As yet this disease has not been observed in man.

FIG. 88. *Troglotrema salmincola.* × 50. (After Witenberg.)

Echinostomes

The family Echinostomatidae includes numerous species of flukes parasitic in many kinds of vertebrates, particularly aquatic birds. Most species are characterized by a spiny body and spines near the anterior end. Most of them, like the Heterophyidae, are remarkably promiscuous as to their final hosts, and many are not very particular about their snail hosts, either.

The eggs are large, usually over 100 μ long, and contain partly developed embryos when laid; the miracidia have a median eye spot and develop in water. In their snail hosts, usually planorbids, Johnston in 1920 believed the miracidia to develop directly into rediae, omitting the sporocyst stage, but actually, at least in some species, a single mother redia develops in the miracidium and gives rise to daughter rediae. The cercariae (Fig. 64D) have well-developed tails and usually bear a collar of spines similar to that of the adults. Some species encyst directly in their snail hosts, sometimes in the body of their parent redia; others leave the snail that spawned them and encyst in other snails or in bivalves, insects, frogs, fishes, or on vegetation. The metacercarial cysts are oval or round, and only from about 70 to 150 μ in diameter (Fig. 79A and 89); the contained metacercariae are folded and show two branches of the excretory bladder filled with coarse granules; the collar of spines can be seen on careful examination.

A number of species of echinostomes have been recorded from man, but most are rare and purely accidental parasites.

Echinostoma ilocanum (Fig. 89B) is common in the Ilocanos of the Philippines and was found by Sandground in Java. It is 2.5 to 10 mm. long and 0.5 to 1.5 broad, with 51 collar spines. It is primarily a parasite of field rats, but Chen in 1934 found it common in dogs in Canton. The cercariae of this species, after leaving the small planorbid snail, *Gyraulus prashadi,* in which they develop, commonly encyst

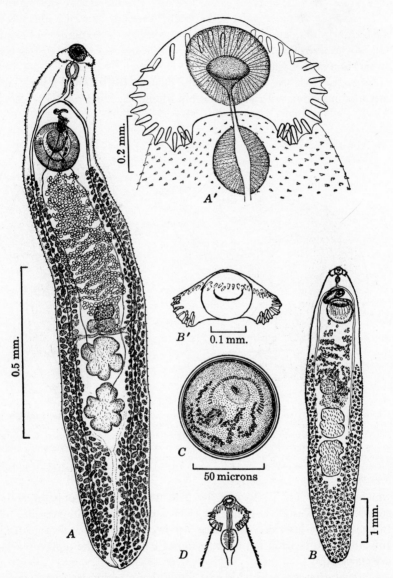

FIG. 89. Echinostomes. *A, Echinostoma lindoense; A'*, head of same (after Sandground); *B, E. ilocanum; B'*, head of same; *C*, encysted metacercaria of same (after
Tubangui and Pasco); *D*, head of *Echinochasmus perfoliatus*, × 30. (After Tanabe.)

in a large snail, *Pila luzonica*, which the Ilocanos enjoy eating raw.

E. malayanum, a broader fluke (5 to 10 mm. by 2 to 3.5 mm.) with 43 collar spines, another Far Eastern species, is common in certain tribes who live on the Sino-Tibetan frontier and has also been reported from Malaya and Sumatra.

In central Celebes, Sandground and Bonne (1940) found a high incidence of infection with another echinostome, *E. lindoense* (Fig. 89*A*),

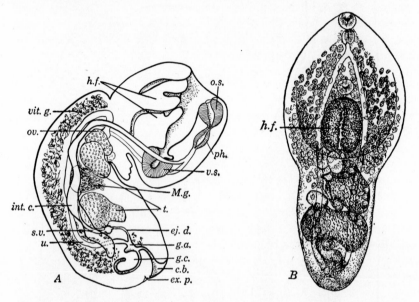

FIG. 90. Two types of strigeids. *A*, *Cotylurus flabelliformis* of ducks, example of Strigeidae; *B*, *Fibricola texensis* of racoons, example of Diplostomatidae. Note pouch-like character of forebody in *A*, and holdfast organ (*h.f.*) in form of anterior and posterior transverse lips, whereas in *B* the forebody is spatulate and the holdfast organ oval; *c.b.*, copulatory bursa; *ej. d.*, ejaculatory duct; *g.a.*, genital atrium; *g.c.*, genital cone; *h.f.*, holdfast organ; other abbrev. as in Fig. 62. (*A*, adapted from Van Haitsma; *B*, from Chandler.)

which is larger (13 to 16 mm. by 2 to 2.5 mm.) with only 37 collar spines. This was at first thought to be a primary human parasite, but Bonne and Lie later reported it as a parasite of ducks and other fowl. Infection results from eating lake mussels in which the metacercariae are encysted.

E. revolutum, a world-wide parasite of ducks and geese, is a sporadic human parasite. It is a small species with 37 collar spines. In Formosa it is said to affect 3 to 6 per cent of the people, a penalty for eating raw fresh-water mussels. Five cases have been reported from Mexico and a few from Java.

Other species of Echinostoma which occasionally crop up in man are: *E. melio* (= *E. jassyense*), with 27 spines, normally found in Mustelidae in North America, Europe, and Asia; *E. recurvatum, macrorchis,* and *cinetorchis* of rats, etc., in Japan; and *E. paraulum* of pigeons, reported once in a Russian. The genus Echinochasmus, differing in having a dorsal break in the spiny collar, contains two species, *E. perfoliatus* (Fig. 89D) in Europe and India and *E. japonicus* in Japan, which are common in cats and dogs and occasional in man. Their metacercariae encyst in many species of fish. Other echinostomes reported from man are *Paryphostomum sufrartyfex* of pigs in India, and *Himasthla muehlensi,* probably of a marine bird.

Strigeids

The strigeids, belonging to the families Strigeidae, Diplostomatidae, and several related families, are characterized by having a special "hold-fast organ" (Fig. 90, *h.f.*) on the ventral side, provided with histolytic glands; the body is usually divided more or less distinctly into a mobile forebody, and a hindbody containing the reproductive organs (Fig. 90). They are common parasites of aquatic birds or fish- or frog-eating mammals. In life cycle they closely parallel the schistosomes, having miracidia with two pairs of flame cells, daughter sporocysts instead of rediae, and forked-tailed cercariae. The cercariae, however, are usually distinguishable from those of schistosomes by having a pharynx and by burrowing into a second intermediate host, usually fish, tadpoles, frogs, or water snakes. The metacercariae are often very harmful to fish, since some species encyst in the lens or chambers of the eye, in the spinal cord, or around the heart; some

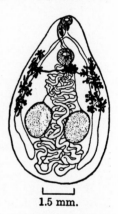

1.5 mm.

Fig. 91. Oviduct fluke of poultry, *Prosthogonimus macrorchis.* (After Macy.)

encyst in the skin or muscles, causing "black spot." A typical life cycle has been graphically illustrated by the Hunters (1935).

These parasites when numerous may be very injurious in the intestines of their final hosts. Fortunately man is rarely parasitized by them, but Nasr (1941) called attention to human infection with an Egyptian species, *Prohemistomum vivax,* properly a parasite of kites, but also extremely common in dogs and cats which eat, or are fed, raw Nile fishes or tadpoles. One man with 2000 specimens complained of dysenteric symptoms.

Plagiorchiidae

This and a number of closely related families include numerous parasites of various insect-eating vertebrates, especially cold-blooded vertebrates. All have stylet cercariae which encyst in arthropods or vertebrates. An unidentified species of Plagiorchis was once recovered from an Ilocano in the Philippines.

The only important species in domestic animals are members of the genus Prosthogonimus, which inhabit the oviduct and bursa fabricii of birds. Several species, including *P. macrorchis* (Fig. 91) in north central United States, are important parasites of poultry, causing a marked falling off in egg production and sometimes fatal disease. The cercariae of these flukes, after developing in snails (Amnicola), encyst in dragonfly nymphs. Birds become infected by eating either nymphs or adults of dragonflies.

REFERENCES
Flukes in General

BHALERAO, G. D., Applied Helminthology, Its Past and Future in India, *Proc. 34th Indian Sci. Congr.* (1947).

CHANDLER, A. C., Control of Fluke Diseases by Destruction of the Intermediate Host, *J. Agr. Research*, **20**, 193 (1920).

CORT, W. W., The Germ Cell Cycle in the Digenetic Trematodes, *Quart. Rev. Biol.*, **19**, 275–284 (1944).

DAWES, B., *The Trematoda*, Cambridge, England, 1946.

FAUST, E. C., *Human Helminthology*, 3rd ed., Philadelphia, 1949.

FUHRMANN, O., Trematoda, In *Handbuch der Zoologie* (ed. by Kukenthal, W.), Bd. II, Hälfte 1, Vermes Amera, 1928.

LaRUE, G. R., Life History Studies and Their Relation to Problems in Taxonomy of Digenetic Trematodes, *J. Parasitol.*, **24**, 1 (1928).

POCHE, F., *Das System der Platodaria*, Berlin, 1926.

STILES, C. W., and HASSALL, A., Index Catalogue of Medical and Veterinary Zoology: Trematoda and Trematode Diseases, *Hyg. Lab. Bull.*, **37** (1908).

STOLL, N. R., This Wormy World, *J. Parasitol.*, **33**, 1–18 (1947).

STUNKARD, H. W., Interrelationships and Taxonomy of the Digenetic Trematodes, *Biol. Reviews, Cambridge Phil. Soc.*, **21**, 148–158 (1946).

Monogenea

MIZELLE, J. D., Comparative Studies on Trematodes (Gyrodactyloidea) from the Gills of North American Freshwater Fishes, *Univ. Illinois Bull.*, **36**, No. 8 (1938).

MUELLER, J. F., The Gyrodactyloidea of North American Freshwater Fishes, *Fish Culture* (N. Y. Conserv. Dept.) (1937).

PAUL, A. A., Life History Studies on North American Freshwater Polystomes, *J. Parasitol.*, **24**, 489–510 (1938).

Schistosomiasis

ALVES, W., and BLAIR, D. M., Schistosomiasis; Intensive Treatment with Antimony, *Lancet,* Jan. 5, 1946, pp. 9–12.

AMBERSON, J. M., Schistosomiasis and Its Control In Egypt, *U. S. Naval Med. Bull.,* **46,** 977–1010 (1946).

BANG, F. B., HAIRSTON, N. G., GRAHAM, O. H., and FERGUSON, M. S., Studies on Schistosomiasis Japonica, I–V, *Am. J. Hyg.,* **44,** 313–378 (1946).

BHALERAO, G. D., Blood Fluke Problem in India, *Proc. 35th Indian Sci. Congr.* (1948).

BRACKETT, S., Studies on Schistosome Dermatitis, V–VIII, *Am. J. Hyg.,* **31,** D, 49, 64; **32,** D, 33, 85 (1940).

BRUMPT, E., Observations biologiques diverses concernant *Planorbis (Australorbis) glabratus,* hôte intermédiaire de *Schistosoma mansoni, Ann. parasitol. humaine et comparée,* **18,** 9 (1941).

CORT, W. W., and TALBOT, S. B., Studies on Schistosome Dermatitis, I–IV, *Am. J. Hyg.,* **23,** 349, 385; **24,** 318 (1936).

FAUST, E. C., *et al.,* Studies on Schistosomiasis mansoni in Puerto Rico, I–III, *Puerto Rico J. Pub. Health Trop. Med.,* **9,** 154, 228; **10,** 1 (1934).

FAUST, E. C., and MELENEY, H. E., Studies on Schistosomiasis Japonica, *Am. J. Hyg., Monogr. Ser.,* **3** (1924).

FAUST, E. C., WRIGHT, W. H., McMULLEN, D. B., and HUNTER, G. W., III; The Diagnosis of *Schistosomiasis japonica;* I. *Am. J. Trop. Med.,* **26,** 87–112; II (FAUST, E. C.), *ibid.,* 113–123; III (FAUST, E. C., and INGALLS, J. W.), *ibid.,* 559–584 (1946).

McMULLEN, D. B., and BEAVER, P. C., Studies on Schistosome Dermatitis, IX, *Am. J. Hyg.,* **42,** 128–154 (1945).

McMULLEN, D. B., *et al.,* The Control of Schistosomiasis Japonica, I–IV, *Am. J. Hyg.,* **45,** 259–298 (1947).

NATIONAL INSTITUTE OF HEALTH (various authors), Studies on Schistosomiasis, *Natl. Inst. Health Bull.,* **189,** 212 pp. (1947).

PONS, G. A., Studies on Schistosomiasis Mansoni in Puerto Rico, V, Clinical Aspects, *Puerto Rico J. Pub. Health Trop. Med.,* **13,** 171 (1937).

SCOTT, J. A., The Incidence and Distribution of Human Schistosomes in Egypt, *Am. J. Hyg.,* **25,** 566 (1937).

The Epidemiology of Schistosomiasis in Venezuela, *Am. J. Hyg.,* **35,** 337 (1942).

STUNKARD, H. W., Possible Snail Hosts of Human Schistosomiasis in the United States, *J. Parasitol.,* **32,** 539–552 (1946).

WELLER, T. H., and DAMMIN, G., The Incidence and Distribution of *Schistosoma mansoni* and other Helminths in Puerto Rico, *Puerto Rico J. Pub. Health Trop. Med.,* **21,** 125 (1945).

Paragonimus

AMEEL, D. J., Paragonimus, Its Life History and Distribution in North America and Its Taxonomy, *Am. J. Hyg.,* **19,** 279 (1934).

BERCOVITZ, Z., Clinical Studies on Human Lung Fluke Disease, *Am. J. Trop. Med.,* **17,** 101 (1937).

KOBAYASHI, S., On the Development of the *Paragonimus westermanii* and its Prevention, *Japan Med. World,* **1,** 14 (1921); *Trans. Far Eastern Assoc. Trop. Med.,* 6th Bienn. Congress, **1,** 413 (1925).

LaRue, G. R., and Ameel, D. J., The Distribution of Paragonimus, *J. Parasitol.*, **23**, 382 (1937).

Tubangui, M. A., Preliminary Notes on the Crustacean Vector of the Mammalian Lung Fluke (Paragonimus) in the Philippines, *J. Parasitol.*, **32**, 150–151 (1946).

Vogel, H., Wu, K., and Watt, J. Y. C., Preliminary Report on the Life History of Paragonimus in China, *Trans. Far Eastern Assoc. Trop. Med.*, 9th Bienn. Congress, **1**, 509 (1935).

Wu, K., The Epidemiology of Paragonimiasis in China, *Far Eastern Assoc. Trop. Med., C. r. dix congrés*, Hanoi (1938).

Fasciola and Fascioloides

Kourí, P., Diagnostico, Epidemiologia y profilaxis de la fascioliasis hepatica humana en Cuba, I, *Bol. ofic. del. col. med. vet. nat.*, Nos. 3 and 4; II and III, *Revista Kuba de med. trop. parasitol.*, **4**, Nos. 3, 4, and 5 (1948).

Mehl, S., Die Lebensbedingungen der Leberegelschnecke, *Arb. Bayer. Landesanst. Pflanzenbau Pflanzenschutz*, München, **10**, 1932.

Olsen, O. W., Hexachlorethane-Bentonite Suspension for Controlling the Common Liver Fluke, *Fasciola hepatica*, in Cattle in the Gulf Coast Region of Texas, *Am. J. Vet. Research*, **8**, 353–366 (1947).

Shaw, J. W., and Simms, B. T., Studies in Fascioliasis in Oregon Sheep and Goats, *Oregon State Agr. Expt. Sta. Bull.*, **226**, 1930.

Schumacher, W., Untersuchungen über den Wanderungsweg und die Entwicklung von *Fasciola hepatica* in Endwirt, *Z. Parasitenk.*, **10**, 608 (1938).

Swales, W. E., The Life Cycle of *Fascioloides magna*, *Can. J. Research*, **12**, 177 (1935).

Dicrocoelium

Neuhaus, W., Der Invasionsweg der Lanzettegelcercariae bei der Infektion des Endwirtes und ihre Entwicklung zum *Dicrocoelium lanceatum*, *Z. Parasitenk.*, **10**, 479 (1938).

Opisthorchiidae

Cameron, T. W. M., The Morphology, Taxonomy, and Life History of *Metorchis conjunctus* (Cobbold, 1860), *Can. J. Research*, D, **22**, 6–16 (1944).

Faust, E. C., and Khaw, O. K., Studies on *Clonorchis sinensis* (Cobbold), *Am. J. Hyg., Monogr. Ser.*, **8** (1927).

Hsü, H. F., *et al.*, Studies on Certain Problems of *Clonorchis sinensis*, I–IV, *Chinese Med. J.*, **50**, 1609 (1936); **51**, 341 (1937); *Suppl.* II, 385 (1938), III, 234 (1940); *Festsch. Nocht*, 216 (1937).

Vogel, H., Der Entwicklungszyklus von *Opisthorchis felineus* (Riv.) nebst Bemerkungen über die Systematik und Epidemiologie, *Zoologica*, **33**, 86 (1934).

Amphistomes

Bennett, H. J., The Life History of *Cotylophoron cotylophoron*, a Trematode from Ruminants, *Illinois Biol. Monogr.* (*n.s.*) **14**, No. 4 (1936).

Buckley, J. J. C., Observations on *Gastrodiscoides hominis* and Fasciolopsis in Assam, *J. Helminthol.*, **17**, 1 (1939).

Leiper, R. T., Observations on Certain Helminths of Man, *Trans. Roy. Soc. Trop. Med. Hyg.*, **6**, 265 (1913).

Stiles, C. W., and Goldberger, J., A Study of the Anatomy of *Watsonius* (n.g.) *watsoni* of Man, *Hyg. Lab. Bull.*, **60** (1910).

Fasciolopsis

Barlow, C. H., The Life Cycle of the Human Intestinal Fluke, *Fasciolopsis buski* (Lankester), *Am. J. Hyg., Monogr. Ser.*, **4** (1925).
McCoy, O. R., and Chu, T. C., *Fasciolopsis buski* Infection among School Children in Shaohsing, and Treatment with Hexylresorcinol, *Chinese Med. J.*, **51**, 937 (1937).
Vogel, H., Beobachtungen über Fasciolopsis Infektion, *Arch. Schiffs- u. Tropen-Hyg.*, **40**, 181 (1936).
Wu, K., Deux nouvelles plantes pouvant transmettre le *Fasciolopsis buski*. Revue generale, *Ann. parasitol. humaine et comparée*, **15**, 458 (1937).

Heterophyidae

Africa, C. M., and Garcia, E. Y., Heterophyid Trematodes of Man and Dog in the Philippines, with Descriptions of Three New Species, *Philippine J. Sci.*, **57**, 253 (1935).
Africa, C. M., de Leon, W., and Garcia, E. Y., Visceral Complications in Intestinal Heterophydiasis of Man, *Acta Med. Philippina, Monogr. Ser.*, **1** (1940)
Chen, H. T., A Study of the Haplorchinae, *Parasitology*, **28**, 40 (1936).
Faust, E. C., and Nishigori, M., Life Cycle of Two New Species of Heterophyidae, Parasitic in Mammals and Birds, *J. Parasitol.*, **13**, 91 (1926).
Stunkard, H. W., Pathology and Immunity to Infection with Heterophyid Trematodes, *Collecting Net*, **16**, No. 4 (1941).

Troglotrema salmincola

Simms, B. T., Donham, C. R., and Shaw, J. N., Salmon Poisoning, *Am. J. Hyg.*, **13**, 363 (1931).
Simms, B. T., McCapes, A. M., and Muth, O. H., Salmon Poisoning: Transmission and Immunization Experiments, *J. Am. Vet. Med. Assoc.*, **81**, 26 (1932).
Witenberg, G., On the Anatomy and Systematic Position of the Causative Agent of So-called Salmon Poisoning, *J. Parasitol.*, **18**, 258 (1932).

Echinostomes

Beaver, P. C., Experimental Studies on *Echinostoma revolutum* (Froelich), a Fluke from Birds and Mammals, *Illinois Biol. Monogr.*, **15** (1937).
Sandground, J. H., and Bonne, C., *Echinostoma lindoensis* n. sp., a New Parasite of Man in the Celebes with an Account of its Life History and Epidemiology, *Am. J. Trop. Med.*, **20**, 511 (1940).
Tubangui, M. A., and Pasco, A. M., The Life History of the Human Intestinal Fluke *Euparyphium ilocanum* (Garrison, 1908), *Philippine J. Sci.*, **51**, 581 (1933).

Strigeids

Dubois, G., Monographie des Strigeida (Trematoda). *Mém. soc. neuchateloise sci. nat.*, **6**, 535 pp. (1938).

HUNTER, G. W., III, and W. S., Further Studies on Fish and Bird Parasites, Suppl., 24th Ann. Rept., N. Y. State Conserv. Dept., 1934, No. IX, Rept. of Biol. Surv. Mohawk-Hudson Watershed (1935).

NASR, M., The occurrence of *Prohemistomum vivax*-Infection in Man, with a Redescription of the Parasite, *Lab. and Med. Progress,* **2,** 135 (1941).

Prosthogonimus

MACY, R. W. (Studies on *Prosthogonimus macrorchis*), *Univ. Minnesota Agr. Expt. Sta., Tech. Bull.,* **98** (1934).

CHAPTER 13

The Cestoidea or Tapeworms

General Structure. Except in a few primitive species a mature tapeworm is not an individual, but a whole family, consisting sometimes of many hundreds of individuals one behind the other like links of a chain (Fig. 92). The most striking feature is the complete lack of a digestive tract in all stages of development. Larval forms obviously absorb food from the host's tissues through their exposed surfaces, but it has usually been assumed that adult tapeworms in the intestine subsist by absorbing digested but unassimilated foods from the fluid intestinal contents in which they live. The writer (Chandler, 1943), however,

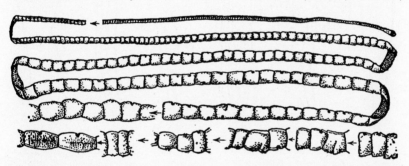

FIG. 92. Beef tapeworm, *Taenia saginata*, × ⅔. Note small head, gradual change in size of proglottids, and irregular alternation of sides of genital apertures. (After Stiles.)

showed that, though this may be true for carbohydrates, other food essentials are apparently absorbed from the host's mucous membranes with which the worms lie in contact. When many worms are present, crowding limits their contact and interferes with their nutrition, stunting their growth.

In the subclass Cestodaria no chain of segments is formed, and there is only one set of reproductive organs; this is true also of one family, Caryophyllaeidae, in the order Pseudophyllidea, but all other tapeworms consist of chains of segments with a " head " or scolex for attachment at one end. Just behind the scolex is a narrow region or " neck " which continually grows and, as it does so, forms partitions, thus constantly budding off new segments. The segments, however, remain connected internally by the musculature and also by nerve

315

trunks and excretory tubes.　As the newly formed segments push ahead the segments previously formed, there is produced a chain of segments called a strobila, each segment being known as a proglottid.　The proglottids just behind the neck are the youngest; they are at first indistinct and have no differentiation of internal organs.　As they are pushed farther and farther from the scolex, the organs progressively develop, so that it is possible in a single tapeworm to find a complete developmental series of proglottids from infancy to old age; the young undifferentiated segments just behind the neck gradually attain sexual maturity in the middle portions of the worm, and then the segments

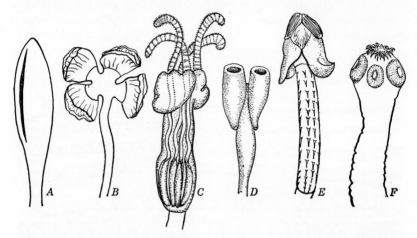

FIG. 93.　Types of scolices of tapeworms.　*A*, order Pseudophillidea (*Dibothriocephalus latus*); *B*, order Tetraphyllidea (*Phyllobothrium* sp.); *C*, order Trypanorhyncha (*Otobothrium* sp.); *D*, order Pseudophyllidea (*Bothridium* sp.); *E*, order Diphyllidea (*Echinobothrium* sp.); *F*, order Cyclophyllidea (*Taenia solium*).

either continue to produce and shed eggs throughout the rest of the strobila (in Pseudophyllidea) or there follows a gradual decadence of the reproductive glands (in Cyclophyllidea) as the segments " go to seed " and become filled by the pregnant uterus with its hordes of eggs. The whole process can be likened to the development of an undifferentiated bud into a perfect flower and then a seed pod.

Anatomy.　The scolex of a tapeworm serves primarily as an organ of attachment, though it also contains what little brain a tapeworm has. Considering the entire subclass Cestoda, the variety of holdfast organs developed by the scolex is remarkable (Fig. 93), consisting of groove-like, in-cupped, or earlike suckers, and in addition, in some species, crowns of powerful hooks or rows of spines on a fleshy anterior protuberance called a rostellum, in some forms retractile into a pouch.

In one order (Trypanorhyncha) there are long, protrusible, spiny proboscides retractile into canals in the neck (Fig. 93*C*). The scolices of the tapeworms infesting mammals, however, are comparatively monotonous in form.

The nervous system consists of a few ganglia and commissures in the scolex from which longitudinal nerve cords run through the length of the worm, the largest ones being a pair near the lateral borders. Coordination of movement is very limited, although the whole worm can contract at once, as when dropped into cold water. Individual ripe segments, when detached, show considerable sensitiveness and are often very active. The excretory system is fundamentally of the same type

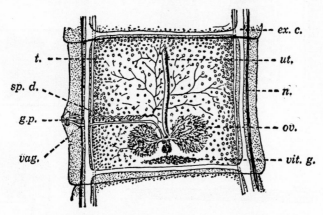

FIG. 94. Sexually mature proglottid of beef tapeworm, *Taenia saginata; ex. c.*, excretory canal; *n.*, nerve cord; *g.p.*, genital pore; *ov.*, ovary; *sp. d.*, sperm duct; *t.*, testes; *ut.*, uterus; *vag.*, vagina; *vit. g.*, vitelline gland. × 7. (Adapted from Leuckart.)

as in flukes and consist typically of two pairs of lateral longitudinal tubes, one larger than the other, connected by a prominent transverse tube near the posterior end of each proglottid and sometimes by a network of smaller tubes. From the main canals fine tubules ramify in the packing tissue or " parenchyma " of the worm and end in flame cells. The first-formed proglottid has a terminal bladder as in flukes, but this is lost when this proglottid is cast off, and subsequently the excretory tubes open separately at the end of the last segment still attached. The muscular system consists of longitudinal, transverse, and circular fibers, much better developed in the species which are thick and fleshy than in those which are thin and semi-transparent.

As of flukes, the main business of tapeworms is the production of myriads of eggs in order to safeguard the species against extermination in the perilous transfer from host to host. Each proglottid possesses complete reproductive systems of both sexes, fully as complete as in the flukes, if not more so (Fig. 94), and in some species each proglottid has a double set of organs.

The female system consists of an ovary, which may be single or in two more or less distinct lobes; yolk glands, either in a single or bilobed mass, or scattered through the segment; Mehlis' glands around an oötype, where the component parts of the egg are assembled; a vagina

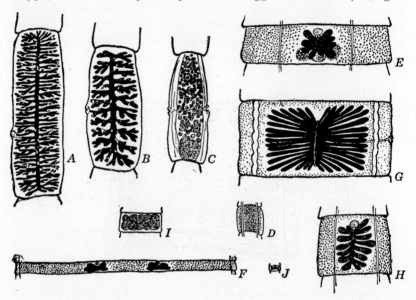

FIG. 95. Ripe proglottids of various tapeworms of man, drawn to scale. × 3. *A, Taenia saginata; B, T. solium; C, Dipylidium caninum; D, Raillietina madagascariensis; E, Dibothriocephalus latus; F, Pyramicocephalus arctocephalinus (= Diplogonoporus grandis); G, Taenia africana; H, Pyramicocephalus phocarus (= Diphyllobothrium cordatum); I, Hymenolepis diminuta; J, H. nana.*

for the entrance of the sperms, with an enlarged chamber, the seminal receptacle, for storage of sperms; and a uterus, which may or may not have an exit pore. In the tapeworms which have a pore (order Pseudophyllidea), the development and extrusion of eggs goes on continuously in many segments at once, but in the Cyclophyllidea there is no uterine opening. In these the uterus eventually becomes packed with eggs and may practically fill the segment, which is essentially a seed pod. Such " ripe " segments detach themselves from the end of the chain, subsequently liberating their eggs by disintegration, or by extrusion of the eggs through ruptures during the active contractions and expansions of the segments. The form of the ripe uterus varies in different genera and species, and is often useful in identification (Fig. 95).

The male system consists of a variable number of scattered testes connected by minute tubes with the sperm duct or vas deferens, which is usually convoluted and may have an enlargement, the seminal vesicle, for storage of sperms. The end of the vas deferens is modified into a muscular intromittent organ, the cirrus, which is retractile into a cirrus pouch or sac. In most tapeworms both cirrus and vagina open into a common cup-shaped genital atrium, with a pore on either the lateral border or the mid-ventral surface. Either self-fertilization of a single segment or cross-fertilization between different segments of the same or other worms can occur, but probably fertilization between segments is commonest. As a rule the male reproductive organs mature before the female.

Life Cycle. The life cycle is not quite so complicated as in flukes and does not involve asexual generations, although in some species the larval forms multiply by budding. The life cycle of many tapeworms, especially those of fishes, is still unknown; in fact, it was not until the middle of the last century that Küchenmeister proved that the bladderworms in pigs and cattle were in reality the larvae of the common large tapeworms of man; previous to that time they were classified in a separate order, Cystica.

The eggs of tapeworms develop within themselves little spherical embryos characterized by the presence of three pairs of clawlike hooks, whence they are known as oncospheres (Fig. 96A and B). One or two enclosing membranes inside the egg shell proper form about the developing embryo, the inner of which is called the embryophore.

In the order Pseudophyllidea the embryos, called coracidia (Fig. 100C), are covered by a ciliated embryophore. They have a brief free-swimming existence, like miracidia, in which they roll about by means of their cilia long enough to attract the attention of copepods which devour them. In these they shed their ciliated covering and change into elongated oval " procercoids " (Fig. 100E, F, G), comparable with sporocysts but solid and incapable of asexual reproduction. The six hooks are still present on a small caudal appendage. Further development into a " plerocercoid " (Fig. 99) occurs only when the infected copepod is eaten by a fish or other animal. The plerocercoids are solid wormlike larvae with a scolex invaginated at one end. When the animal containing them is eaten by the final host the scolex turns right side out and attaches itself to the intestinal wall, and the mature tapeworm develops.

In the order Cyclophyllidea, on the other hand, the oncosphere remains passively in the egg, surrounded by the nonciliated embryophore until eaten by the intermediate host. Here it transforms into a bladder-like structure, a part of the wall of which differentiates into one or more scolices turned inside out (invaginated) (Fig. 96C and D). Sometimes the whole embryo becomes hollow and grows into a large bladder, into the spacious cavity of which the relatively small scolex or scolices are invaginated; such a larva is called a *cysticercus* or bladder-worm if there is only one scolex, and a *coenurus* (Fig. 106) if there are a number of them. In one tapeworm, Echinococcus, the bladders add a further method of multiplication by budding off daughter and grand-daughter bladders, and the bladder walls, instead of directly producing scolices, first produce brood-capsules, each of which in turn produces on its wall a number of scolices, whereby one huge larval cyst, called a *hydatid,* may be the mother of many thousands of tapeworms (Fig.

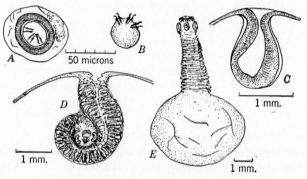

Fig. 96. Stages in life cycle of *Taenia solium.* *A*, egg containing embryophore; *B*, hatched oncosphere; *C*, invagination in cyst wall, at the bottom of which the scolex will form; *D*, cysticercus with head invaginated; *E*, same with head evaginated. (*A*, *B*, *C* and *E* after Blanchard from Brumpt; *D*, original.)

109). Sometimes the main portion of the body of the embryo remains solid and grows very little, while one end of it becomes hollowed out into a small bladder containing the invaginated scolex (Fig. 111). The undeveloped solid portion remains as a caudal appendage. Such a larva is called a *cysticercoid* and is characteristic of those tapeworms which use arthropods as intermediate hosts.

On being eaten by a final host only the scolices survive; these turn right side out (evaginate), attach themselves to the mucous membrane of the intestine, and grow each into a mature tapeworm. In one progressive genus, Hymenolepis, a few species have broken away from the traditional intermediate host idea and may complete their development in one host; the cysticercoids develop inside the intestinal villi and subsequently gain the lumen of the intestine where the mature phase is attained. For a long time parasitologists were very skeptical of the truth of such unorthodoxy on nature's part.

Classification. The classification of the Cestoidea is much more satisfactorily worked out than that of the Trematoda. There are two subclasses, Cestodaria and Cestoda. The Cestodaria do not form segments, having a single set of reproductive organs; the vagina and male genital opening are near the posterior end; and the embryos have 10 or 12 hooks. All are parasites of fishes. The Cestoda, which alone concern us here, produce a chain of segments with reduplicated reproductive organs except in one family (Caryophyllaeidae) of the order Pseudophyllidea. They have a well-developed scolex, genital openings anterior to the ovary, and embryos with only 6 hooks. Their classification, based mainly on the structure of the scolex, is as follows:

1. Order **Tetraphyllidea.** Head with four earlike or lappetlike outgrowths (Fig. 93*B*), or with four cuplike suckers; proglottids in various stages of development; vitelline glands scattered in two lateral rows or in broad dorsal and ventral layers; genital pores lateral. In elasmobranchs, except two families in higher cold-blooded vertebrates.
2. Order **Trypanorhyncha.** Head with two or four earlike " bothria " and four long evertible proboscides armed with hooks or spines, retractile into sheaths (Fig. 93*C*); otherwise similar to Tetraphyllidea. In elasmobranchs.
3. Order **Diphyllidea.** Head with dorsal and ventral bothria and a rostellum with rows of dorsal and ventral hooks (Fig. 93*E*); organs as in Tetraphyllidea, but genital pores sometimes mid-ventral. In elasmobranchs.
4. Order **Pseudophyllidea.** Head with two lateral or, rarely, one terminal, sucking grooves or " bothria " (Fig. 93*A* and *J* and 93*D*); majority of proglottids in similar stage of development, shedding eggs from a uterine pore; genital pores mid-ventral; vitelline glands scattered in dorsal and ventral sheets. In teleosts and land vertebrates.
5. Order **Cyclophyllidea.** Head with four in-cupped suckers (Fig. 93*F*); proglottids in all stages of development, ripe ones only near end of chain; no uterine pore; genital pores *usually* lateral. Majority in birds and mammals.

The Tetraphyllidea, of which the majority occur only in sharks and rays, are probably the most primitive. The family Proteocephalidae, found in higher fresh-water vertebrates and having cuplike suckers, bridges the gap between the Tetraphyllidea and the Cyclophyllidea. Another branch from the Tetraphyllidea probably gave rise to the Trypanorhyncha and the Pseudophyllidea, and another to the Diphyllidea.

Only the Pseudophyllidea and Cyclophyllidea contain species which attack man or domestic animals. Although 25 or 30 different species of tapeworms have been recorded in man, only 4 adult species and 3 larval species are at all common. The order Pseudophyllidea contains one in each group, *Dibothriocephalus latus* as an adult, and *Spirometra mansoni* as a larva; the order Cyclophyllidea includes as adults *Taenia solium, T. saginata,* and *Hymenolepis nana,* and as larvae *T. solium* and *Echinococcus granulosus. H. diminuta* and *Dipylidium caninum* are probably much less rare than the records indicate, but all the others, some of which are briefly described in the following pages, are rare.

Diagnosis. Tapeworms cannot invariably be diagnosed by examining feces for eggs. The pseudophyllidean tapeworms can be diagnosed in this way, since the operculated eggs are expelled through the uterine pores of many proglottids at a time and are therefore always present in the feces. Like the eggs of flukes, these eggs do not float in saturated salt solution; they can be concentrated by straining and sedimenting or centrifuging in water, or by the AEX method (see p. 251). Hymenolepis infections can also be diagnosed by fecal examination for eggs, even though no birthpore is present, since the segments broken off from the ends of the worms commonly rupture before leaving the body of the host. Hymenolepis eggs are easily found by flotation methods.

Taenia infections, on the other hand, as well as many of the rarer infections of man and many other common tapeworm infections of animals, cannot be reliably diagnosed in this manner, since the segments often escape from the body uninjured and still alive. Search must be made for the voided segments in the stools; the shape of the segment and form of the gravid uterus serves to identify the species. Taenia eggs are present in the feces whenever segments rupture, which they do rather frequently, and those of *T. saginata* can usually be found on the perianal skin, like those of Enterobius (see p. 431). The thick, striated embryophores are porous and therefore cannot be found by flotation.

The eggs of Dibothriocephalus (Fig. 59*L*) may be confused with those of flukes, but the shell is thinner and more transparent, and the operculum in fresh eggs is inconspicuous. They are different in size from any common human fluke eggs (60 to 70 μ), but they come nearest to those of Paragonimus. All other tapeworm eggs of man are recognizable as such by their six-hooked embryos. Taenia and Hymenolepis eggs (Figs. 59*N, O, P*) cannot be confused when one has once seen them, but many inexperienced physicians, unfamiliar with Hymenolepis, take all eggs with six-hooked embryos to be Taenia, sometimes with disconcerting results. A physician once complained to the writer that he was unable to expel even a few segments of a tapeworm by the use of male fern; it developed that he was hunting for expelled taenias when he had found only Hymenolepis eggs. In another case a physician found tapeworm eggs in the stool of a high-class Indian Brahmin and mortally offended him by telling him he had eaten insufficiently cooked beef or pork, when in reality the eggs were those of Hymenolepis.

Treatment. For the most part the drugs most useful in expelling tapeworms constitute a group distinct from those effective against nematodes, although carbon tetrachloride and hexylresorcinol are effective against both groups of worms. Brown (1948) quoted Hernandez-Morales as having freed 25 of 28 patients of their *Taenia saginata* when an adult dose of 1 gram of crystalline hexylresorcinol mixed with 2 grams acacia in 40 cc. of water was given by duodenal tube. The other tapeworm remedies consist of (1) a group of vegetable extracts (filix mas, cusso, and kamala), all of which are derivatives of a substance called phloroglucin; (2) pelletierin, an alkaloid derived from pomegranate bark; (3) arecolin and allied alkaloids from areca nuts; (4) atebrin and acranil, which had previously been found very useful against certain protozoan infections. Phenylmercuric compounds are effective against *Raillietina cesticillus* in poultry, but not against other poultry tapeworms.

Of these various remedies extract of filix-mas, or male fern, has been most extensively used in the past. Carbon tetrachloride, in doses not exceeding 3 cc. and in patients not deficient in calcium, is fairly effective, though the less toxic tetrachloroethylene, which can be substituted for carbon tetrachloride against hookworms, is ineffective. Present indications are that atebrin and acranil (0.8 gram divided into 2 portions) or hexylresorcinol by duodenal tube will largely replace the older classical tapeworm remedies. For *Hymenolepis nana* gentian violet, administered as for Strongyloides (see p. 439), has also been recommended.

Cleaning out of the intestine by a liquid diet for 24 hours before treatment, with a saline purge the night before and another 1½ to 2 hours after the drug, is believed to enhance the success of tapeworm treatments. Experiments by Addis in the writer's laboratory, however, suggest that starvation may be undesirable, since tapeworms are rapidly weakened by lack of carbohydrate in the diet and are more prone to break off and leave their heads behind them, in which case new strobilas are regenerated in a few weeks. This could be avoided by eating rock candy, honey, or well-sugared drinks.

Treatment should not be repeated until segments or eggs again appear in the feces.

Prevention. Prevention varies, of course, with the species of tapeworm and its intermediate host, but since infection with the common human species, with the exception of the species of Hymenolepis, results from eating raw or imperfectly cooked beef, pork, or fish in which the larvae have developed, the exclusive use of thoroughly cooked meat and fish is the best preventive measure. Pork and beef bladderworms are killed when heated to 55° C., but it is difficult to heat the center of a large piece of meat even to this point; a ham cooked by boiling for two hours may reach a temperature of only 46° C. in the center. When roasted, pork should always be cut into pieces weighing no more than three or four pounds to insure thorough penetration of heat. Beef which has lost its red or " rare " color is quite safe.

Since bladderworms are unable to survive the death of their host for more than a limited time, they are eventually destroyed by ordinary cold storage — the beef bladderworm within three weeks, the pork bladderworm not always so soon. Quick-freezing is destructive to cysticerci, as is thorough curing or salting of meat. The meat of sheep, goats, or chickens does not convey any parasites to man, even if uncooked.

Infected persons should be careful not to contaminate the food or water of domestic animals with their feces, bearing in mind that the eggs may be disseminated by streams, rain, insects, etc.

The dwarf tapeworm, *H. nana,* and those which develop in arthropods are subject to different means of prevention (see p. 347).

No effective method of protection of herbivores against anoplocephalid tapeworms, which utilize free-living mites as intermediate hosts, has yet been devised.

Order Pseudophyllidea

All the members of the Pseudophyllidea which live in man or domestic mammals are members of the family Diphyllobothriidae. These are large worms consisting of long chains of numerous segments and a head provided with a slitlike groove or bothrium on either side. The majority of the segments are mature and functional at one time and deposit eggs through the uterine pores as more are being developed. Eventually, as old age overtakes them, the proglottids cease to produce more eggs; they gradually empty their uteri and then, shrunken and twisted, are sloughed off in long chains. The general type of life cycle, involving a copepod as a first intermediate host and a vertebrate as a second, has already been described on p. 319.

There are about 75 species in the family, living in whales, porpoises, seals, sea lions, fish-eating land carnivores, fish-eating birds, and man. All of these, except a few bird tapeworms that have indistinct or no external demarkation of the segments (Ligula and Schistocephalus), have been commonly lumped together in the genus Diphyllobothrium. Since several well-defined groups occur, with quite well-marked characters, it has become desirable to break up this large group into several genera. Wardle, McLeod, and Stewart (1947) recognized seven genera, five of them parasitic in marine mammals. The species which commonly lives as an adult in man falls into the genus Dibothriocephalus, which was created for it before this and all the other species were merged into the genus Diphyllobothrium. The latter genus was first erected for a large species with a small oval head and no obvious neck, found in porpoises.

The genus Dibothriocephalus (not to be confused with Bothriocephalus, which has both its plerocercoid and adult stages in fishes) contains the human species, *D. latus,* and several others reported from fish-eating mammals and birds. They are large, slender, weakly muscular forms with an elongated, compressed scolex with slitlike grooves or " bothria " which are narrow and deep; a long slender neck; a rosette-

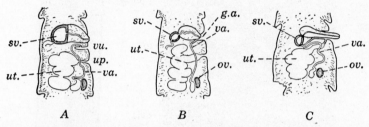

Fig. 97. Arrangement of organs of various genera in family Diphyllobothriidae as seen in sagittal sections. *A*, Spirometra, with separate openings for cirrus, vagina, and uterus; *B*, Dibothriocephalus, with common opening for cirrus and vagina; *C*, Pyramicocephalus, with common opening for cirrus, vagina, and uterus. Abbrev.: *g.a.*, genital atrium; *ov.* ovary; *sv.*, seminal vesicle; *up.*, uterine pore; *ut.*, uterus; *va.*, vagina; *vu.*, vulva. (After Mueller.)

shaped uterus; a common opening for cirrus and vagina (Fig. 97*B*); eggs rounded at the ends; and plerocercoids in fish. A closely related genus, Spirometra, contains smaller and weaker worms, found primarily in cats, which have broader and shallower bothria; a uterus with a spiral of close coils; separate openings for cirrus and vagina (Fig. 97*A*); eggs pointed at the ends; and plerocercoids usually in frogs, snakes, birds, or rodents. Some, possibly all, of this group can live in human flesh in the plerocercoid or " sparganum " stage, causing sparganosis. One species, *S. houghtoni,* has been recorded a few times as an adult from man in China.

A group of short, thick-bodied species with heart-shaped scolex and no neck, found in marine carnivores, was placed by Wardle *et al.* in the genus Cordicephalus, but according to Stunkard they should be called Pyramicocephalus. One species, *P. phocarus (Diphyllobothrium cordatum)*, has been reported from man and dog a few times, in Greenland, Japan, and Lake Baikal. The status of a species found in bears in Yellowstone Park, Wyoming, called *D. cordatum* by Scott in 1932, is uncertain.

Another large, thick worm with short, broad segments and a double set of reproductive organs (Fig. 95*F*) has been found in Japanese a few times. It has previously been known as *Diplogonoporus* (or *Krabbea*) *grandis*, but Wardle thinks it belongs in the same genus as *phocarus* and is identical with a species *Pyramicocephalus arctocephalinus* of sea lions. The subfamily Ligulinae contains worms with no external seg-

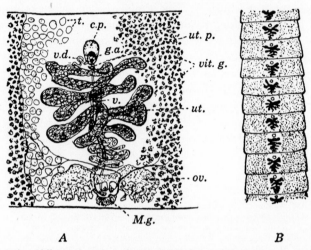

A   *B*

Fig. 98. *A*, middle portion of proglottid of *Dibothriocephalus latus*. Layer of vitelline glands partly peeled off on left side to expose testes; *c.p.*, cirrus pouch; *g.a.*, genital atrium; *M.g.*, Mehlis' gland; *ov.*, ovary; *t.*, testes; *ut. p.*, uterine pore; *ut.*, uterus; *v.*, vagina; *v.d.*, vas deferens; *vit. g.*, vitelline glands. × 10. *B*, portion of a chain of ripe segments, natural size.

mentation and poorly developed scolices, which almost reach maturity in fish before transfer to bird hosts. A few accidental human infections have been observed.

Morphology. The arrangement of the organs in mature proglottids of a Diphyllobothriid is shown in Figs. 98 and 102. The female system consists of a vagina opening on the mid-ventral surface in the anterior part of the segment and running almost straight posteriorly to an oötype surrounded by a Mehlis gland. The ovaries are paired in the posterior part of the segment. The yolk glands are scattered throughout the lateral fields. The uterus has an inner series of delicate coils as it leaves the oötype, followed by an outer series of large coarse ones. The uterine opening is on the ventral surface but is inconspicuous. The male system consists of a large number of testes scattered in the lateral fields, largely obscured by the vitelline glands which lie dorsal and ventral to them. The cirrus and cirrus pouch are anteriorly situated.

Dibothriocephalus latus. This worm, possibly constituting a group of nearly related species, is called the " broad " or " fish " tapeworm. It is the largest tapeworm found in man. It has long been known in many parts of central Europe and in the Baltic countries and more recently has been found widely distributed elsewhere. In some localities in Europe 80 to 100 per cent of the people are infected. In East Prussia nearly all the fisherfolk become infected from eating raw burbot liver spread on bread. Around Lake Baikal a small form thought by Russian scientists to be a separate species (*D. minor*) is common. Baltic lumberers are believed to have established *D. latus* in Minnesota, Michigan, and around lakes in the Canadian forests; it has recently been reported around Florida lakes also. However, the American worm possibly is a separate species, indigenous in native wild carnivores. In addition to man, the worm also develops in bears, cats, and other fish-eating mammals. Dogs also become infected, but they may not be important reservoir hosts since eggs passed by them are often not viable.

Wild Carnivora, especially bears, which Vergeer has found susceptible, undoubtedly help in the perpetuation of the parasite, for bears are fond of fish and commonly scoop them out of small streams in the spawning season.

D. latus is a veritable monster, reaching a length of 10 to more than 60 ft., with a width of 10 to 12 or even up to 20 mm., and with a total of 3000 to 4000 proglottids in large specimens. Tarassov tells of a Russian woman who harbored six worms aggregating over 290 ft., and of another who supported 143 worms. Fortunately in tapeworm infections the size of the worms usually is in inverse proportion to their number. The proglottids (Fig. 98) for the most part are much broader than long, although the terminal ones become approximately square.

Life Cycle. The broadly oval, operculated eggs, which average about 60 by 42 μ, contain abundant yolk cells (Fig. 59L). Ciliated embryos, or coracidia, develop slowly in the eggs, hatching after 8 or 10 days to several weeks, depending on temperature. The coracidia (Fig. 100C), 50 to 55 μ in diameter, swim by means of their cilia or creep on the bottom after slipping out of their ciliated coverings, but they must be eaten by certain species of copepods (Fig. 100D) in less than 24 hours if they are to continue their development and fulfil their destiny.

The worm is very fastidious about its first intermediate hosts, and in America develops only in certain species of the genus Diaptomus (distinguished by having very long first antennae), which live in the open water of lakes. Other species of Diaptomus, and most species of Cyclops (which have much shorter antennae), are not suitable hosts, although species of Cyclops are the preferred hosts of Spirometra.

Soon after the coracidium is ingested by a copepod it loses its ciliated covering, and the naked oncosphere, only 24 μ in diameter, bores through into the body cavity. In 12 to 15 days it develops into a solid, elongate creature. The embryonic hooks are at the posterior end, which is pinched off as an appendage that eventually shrinks; a cup-shaped depression, into which histolytic glands open, appears at the anterior end; some species also have spines at the anterior end. The worm is now, after 2 or 3 weeks, a procercoid, about 500 μ long (Fig. 100D, G).

Further development occurs in fish when the infected copepod is eaten. The passage through the intestine and body cavity of the fish is slow; it requires about 6 days for the larvae to reach the liver in young fish, and in older fish it may take 2 or 3 weeks. Finally the larvae reach the flesh of the fish and grow into elongated wormlike plerocercoid or " sparganum " larvae, from 4 or 5 mm. to several centimeters in length. They are not encysted and are found anywhere in the flesh and sometimes in other places. The smaller ones lie straight, but with growth they become increasingly bent and twisted (Fig. 99). The anterior end has a depression which is the withdrawn and inverted scolex; the remainder of the body is white, somewhat flattened, and marked by irregular wrinkles, but without segmentation. In uncooked fish their opaque white color shows clearly through the translucent flesh, but cysts of flukes or other tapeworms may be confused with them if they are not carefully examined. Cysts of tapeworms of the genus Proteocephalus are often present, but these have four or five cup-shaped suckers on the head; the elongate but cramped plerocercoids abundant in tullibee (Leuciscus) in some lakes in northern United States are readily distinguished by the tridents on the head; some of the other plerocercoids found in herring, perch, trout, etc., are more difficult to distinguish. Drum, gulf " trout," etc., from the Texas coast frequently contain the very elongate "spaghetti worm " plerocercoids of Trypanorhyncha, which mature in sharks and rays. None of these become human parasites.

The fish that serve as second intermediate hosts of *Dibothriocephalus latus* are carnivorous species, but they seem to differ in different localities. In northern United States and Canada pike and walleyes (Esox and Stizostedion) are far the most important hosts; in northern Europe, trout, perch, and burbot; in Lake Baikal, species of Coregonus

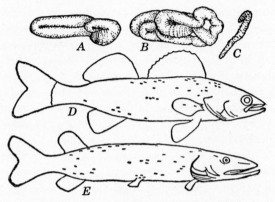

FIG. 99. A to C, plerocercoid larvae of D. latus as they appear in the flesh of fishes, × 3; D, outline of a wall-eyed pike (Stizostedon) showing distribution of 35 plerocercoids in the flesh; E, same of pickerel (Esox) with 37 plerocercoids. (After Vergeer.)

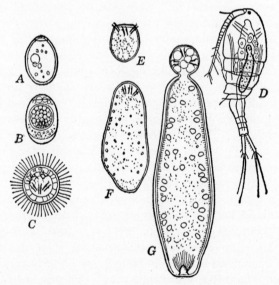

FIG. 100. Developmental stages of Dibothriocephalus latus. A, undeveloped egg; B, egg containing developed embryo; C, free embryo or coracidium; D, Cyclops strenuus containing procercoid; E, embryo after shedding ciliated envelope in Cyclops; F, growing procercoid; G, full-grown procercoid. (After Brumpt.)

and Thymallus; in the Far East, trout (Oncorhynchus and Salmo); and in Africa, the barbel (Barbus).

In some small lakes in northern United States and Canada 50 to 75 per cent of the pike and walleyes harbor larvae of this worm. These large carnivorous fish do not feed intentionally on copepods and probably ingest them in the stomachs of smaller fish on which they prey. It is a peculiarity of sparganum larvae that they are able to reinvade and become re-established in host after host until one is reached in which maturity can be attained in the intestine. Thus the spargana of *D. latus* can pass from fish to fish, and those of Spirometra may be passed about among frogs, reptiles, and mammals.

Infection of the final host comes from eating imperfectly cooked flesh or roe of infected fish or from conveying small plerocercoids to the mouth by the hands, to which they cling while fish is being cleaned. In 3 weeks they may have reached a length of 3 ft. and may begin producing eggs in that time. It has been estimated that one worm produces 36,000 eggs daily. In northern United States many towns pour their sewage directly into lakes, and the inhabitants fish for the prized pike, which harbor the plerocercoids, near the sewage outlets. Summer visitors in camps and hotels often partake of fish hastily prepared, content with a well-done exterior. Dogs and cats are usually given the raw refuse and help to keep the infection alive. Furthermore, millions of pounds of walleyes and pike are annually imported from infected Canadian lakes for the preparation of " gefüllte fish." Many cases develop among Jewish people, presumably as a result of tasting the fish during the preparation, before it is cooked.

Pathological Effects and Treatment. Common effects of *D. latus* infection are abdominal pain, loss of weight, and progressive weakness, similar to the symptoms of Taenia infections (see p. 338). This worm is, however, unique among tapeworms in sometimes causing a very severe anemia of the pernicious type, in which the corpuscles may be reduced to 1,000,000 per cubic millimeter or less. Fortunately, this severe anemia is the exception rather than the rule. In Finland, although the Finlanders are said to be more prone to Dibothriocephalus anemia than other races, the anemia rate is only one or two per 10,000 infections. There is strong evidence that the role of the worm is a sort of trigger mechanism, precipitating pernicious anemia in individuals who have a hereditary or racial tendency to it, but who may escape in the absence of a Dibothriocephalus infection. Chandler (1943) suggested that the anemia may possibly be due to absorption of too large amounts of the vitaminlike extrinsic antianemia factor. The tapeworm anemia responds readily to liver therapy even without removal of the worms.   Oleoresin of male fern is effective in expelling the worms.

Control.   Control of *D. latus* infection must depend mainly on more careful cooking of fish.   Housewives and cooks preparing " gefüllte fish " should refrain from tasting the raw fish to test their skill in flavoring.   Some reduction in the infection of fish could be obtained by education and regulation with respect to pollution of lakes, and the practice of feeding raw fish to dogs and cats should be discouraged.

" Sparganum " Infections.   The plerocercoid larvae of worms of the genus Spirometra, for which the name Sparganum was given before their adult forms were definitely known, normally developed in frogs, snakes, or amphibious mammals, but when opportunity is afforded can live in man.   The first intermediate hosts are Cyclops, which abound in shallow water.   Galliard and Ngu (1946) showed that *S. mansoni* in Indo-China apparently requires four hosts, the procercoids from Cyclops first infecting tadpoles, and later becoming fully

Fig. 101.   *Sparganum mansoni*, natural size.   (After Ijima and Murata.)

developed plerocercoids when these are eaten by frogs, reptiles, or mammals.   This recalls the use of minnows as an intermediate step between Diaptomus and carnivorous fish by *Dibothriocephalus latus*.

The larval worm as found in man, usually referred to as *Sparganum mansoni*, is a typical plerocercoid, much larger than that of *D. latus*, being from 3 to 14 in. in length (Fig. 101).   It is a whitish, elastic, wrinkled worm with an invaginated scolex at the broader end.   In man it is found in the muscles, subcutaneous connective tissue, or around the eye.   The largest number of cases have been recorded from Indo-China, China, and Japan, but scattered cases of this or closely related larvae are known from almost every part of the world.   In the Orient, human infection is acquired in a remarkable manner; split fresh frogs are commonly used by the natives as a poultice for sore eyes and wounds, and the spargana then transfer themselves to human flesh. Applied to the eye, they may settle in the lids or go to other parts of the face; they are easier to remove after being encapsulated.   As noted on p. 330, spargana are able, when eaten by a host which is not suitable for adult development, to reinvade and become encapsulated over again, ready for another try.   The range of hosts in which they can become re-established after development is much larger than that in which they can develop originally.

There is much confusion about the species of Spirometra, all of which are primarily cat and dog parasites when mature. Faust, Campbell, and Kellogg in 1929 described six species in China, but Iwata (1933) concluded that all the members of the group belong to a single species, *D. erinacei*, since he could find in the proglottids of a single worm all the types of structure described by Faust *et al.* in their different species. However, there appear to be biological differences between some of the species, and in some cases valid morphological differences also. Thus the sparganum of the European *D. erinacei* was found by Joyeux *et al.* to develop only in amphibians, although it could later establish itself,

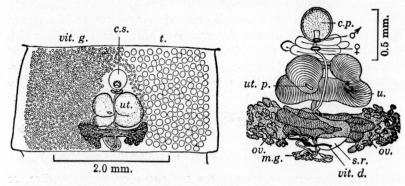

FIG. 102. *Spirometra mansonoides.* Left, young mature proglottid; *c.s.,* cirrus pouch; *t.,* testes; *ut.,* uterus; *vit. g.,* vitelline glands; right, reproductive organs; ♂ and ♀, genital openings; *c.p.,* cirrus pouch; *M.g.,* Mehlis' gland; *ov.,* ovary; *s.r.,* seminal receptacle; *u.,* uterus; *ut. p.,* uterine pore; *vit. d.,* vitelline duct. (After Mueller.)

when eaten, in anything from fish to mammals, except birds. The Chinese *D. mansoni*, on the other hand, develops more rapidly in mice than in frogs, and the American *mansonoides* fails to develop in frogs at all but develops readily in mice. Possibly *S. mansoni* in China is a composite of several closely related interbreeding species.

It is probable that any species of sparganum of the Spirometra group could establish itself in man if swallowed after development in frogs, reptiles, mice, or other intermediate hosts, but it is less probable that the swallowing of infected copepods would result in infection. A few cases of sparganum infection have been recorded in the United States, but there is no information as to the species to which they belong. *Spirometra mansonoides* (Fig. 102) has a wide distribution in wild and feral cats in eastern United States and uses wild species of mice for development of the spargana. Mueller and Goldstein have shown that when the young spargana of this species are experimentally implanted in human flesh they grow normally. Another sparganum of a species resembling *mansoni* has been found in water snakes (Natrix) in Florida.

A few cases have been recorded in which the spargana apparently multiply in the body. Thousands of worms, usually only 3 to 12 mm. in length but sometimes larger, may be present in acne-like nodules in the skin and elsewhere in the body. They apparently proliferate by formation of bud-like growths. This so-called *Sparganum proliferum* (Fig. 103) is now believed to be an abnormal growth in an unfavorable host; it has been found only in man. Mueller (1938), from a careful restudy of specimens of *S. proliferum,* concludes that they are abnormal, degenerate forms without scolices and without normal orientation of parts.

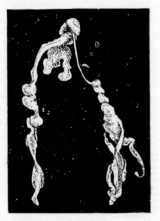

Fig. 103. *Sparganum prolif-erum,* from man in Florida.

Order Cyclophyllidea

The vast majority of the tapeworms of mammals and birds belong to the order Cyclophyllidea. These, as noted on p. 321, are distinguished by the presence of four in-cupped muscular suckers on the scolex and often a rostellum armed with hooks, by having the yolk glands concentrated into a single mass near the ovary, and by having no uterine pore. The embryos remain passively in the egg or embryophore until eaten by the host in which they are to develop; this may be either a vertebrate or an invertebrate. Reid in 1947 showed that they are provided with a pair of unicellular glands opening between the hooklets and probably helpful in penetration. The larva may be either a cysticercus, a coenurus, a hydatid, or a cysticercoid (see p. 320).

Six families contain species which are habitually or accidentally parasitic in man. These are:

Taeniidae. Medium-sized or large worms, except Echinococcus, which is very small. Scolex usually armed with a double row of large hooks but unarmed in *T. saginata;* ripe uterus with a central stem and lateral branches; genital pores lateral on alternating sides; ovaries and yolk gland in posterior part of segment; testes numerous; eggs with thick, striated inner shells. Important genera in man or domestic animals: Taenia, Multiceps, Echinococcus.

Hymenolepididae. Medium-sized or small worms, segments usually broader than long; scolex usually with a single row of hooks, but unarmed in *H. diminuta;* ripe uterus saclike, not breaking up into egg balls; genital pores lateral, usually all on one side; ovary and yolk gland near center of proglottid, and with 1 to 4 testes. Important genus: Hymenolepis.

Dipylidiidae (often considered a subfamily of Dilepididae, which is strikingly like Davaineidae except for the scolex). Medium-sized worms; scolex with a long rostellum retractable into a sac, armed with several rows of thorn-shaped hooks;

genital organs double, one set on each side of proglottid, near middle; testes numerous; uterus breaks up into egg balls. Important genus: Dipylidium.

Davaineidae. Medium-sized or small worms. Scolex with a double row of minute hammer-shaped hooks on rostellum and often with numerous minute hooklets on the margins of suckers; ovaries and yolk gland near center of segment; uterus breaks up into egg capsules; testes fairly numerous. Important genera: Davainea, Raillietina.

Anoplocephalidae. Medium-sized or large worms of herbivorous animals. Scolex unarmed; female genital organs single or double in each segment, situated laterally or near middle; testes numerous; uterus develops a transverse sac, later breaking up into compartments or breaking down entirely; eggs usually with pair of hornlike processes (pyriform apparatus) on one side of inner shell. Important genera: Moniezia, Anoplocephala, Bertiella, Inermicapsifer.

Mesocestoididae. Medium-sized or large worms of carnivorous birds and mammals. Scolex unarmed; genital pore on mid-ventral surface; ripe uterus with eggs collected in a para-uterine organ; ovaries and yolk glands posterior; testes numerous. One genus: Mesocestoides.

Taeniidae

The family Taeniidae includes for the most part relatively large worms parasitic in mammals. The form of the hooks in the armed

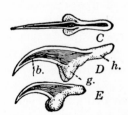

FIG. 104. *A*, unarmed scolex of *Taenia saginata; B*, armed scolex of *T. solium;* both × 10. *C–E*, hooks of *T. solium*, × 150; *C*, long hook, dorsal view; *D*, same, lateral view; *E*, short hook, lateral view; *b.*, blade; *g.*, guard; *h.*, handle or root.

species is shown in Fig. 104 and the arrangement of organs in the proglottids in Fig. 94. The eggs (Figs. 59*P* and 96*A*) have a very thin outer shell, sometimes provided with a pair of delicate filaments, which is ordinarily lost before the eggs are found in the feces. The inner embryophore has a thick, brown shell which on surface view looks honeycombed and in optical section looks striated. The larvae of most species are cysticerci, but in the genus Multiceps it is a coenurus and in Echinococcus a hydatid.

Taenia solium or Pork Tapeworm. This worm is common in parts of the world where pork is eaten without thorough cooking, especially in some localities in Europe, but it is rare in the United States. In Jewish and Mohammedan countries, where the eating of pork is a serious religious misdemeanor, this parasite has little chance of survival and is scandalous evidence of moral turpitude when it does occur, just as is the beef tapeworm in Hindus. It is a remarkable fact that in many parts of the world, e.g., North America, India, the Philippines, human infections with adult worms are so rare that many laboratories are unable to obtain specimens, yet bladderworm infections in pigs are of fairly frequent occurrence. Even human infections with the bladderworm of this species are commoner than infections with the adult. This is one of the unsolved mysteries of parasitology.

Morphology. The pork tapeworm usually attains a length of 6 to 10 ft.; records of specimens much longer than this are probably due to confusion of parts of more than one worm; there are 800 or 900 proglottids. The scolex (Fig. 104*B*) is hardly larger than the head of a pin, about 1 mm. in diameter, and has a rostellum armed with from 22 to 32 hooks, long ones (180 μ) and short ones (130 μ) alternating. Behind the head is a thin, unsegmented neck; the younger segments are broader than long, but in the middle part of the worm they become square, and the ripe ones are about twice as long as broad, shaped somewhat like pumpkin seeds and about 12 mm. long. The sexually mature proglottids closely resemble those of *T. saginata* (Fig. 94).

Soon after sexual maturity is reached and sperms for fertilizing the eggs have been received, the uterus begins to develop its lateral branches; in this species there are only from 7 to 10 main branches on each side, a fact which is of special value in distinguishing the ripe segments from those of *T. saginata*, which has about twice as many (cf. Figs. 95*A*, *B*). The fully ripe uterus usurps nearly the whole proglottid; most of the other reproductive organs degenerate.

Life Cycle. (Fig. 96.) A man infested with a pork tapeworm expels ripe segments, singly or in short chains, almost every day. Several hundred a month are cast off, each loaded with thousands of eggs; the embryophores are nearly spherical and measure 35 to 42 μ in diameter. The shed ripe proglottids, unlike those of *Taenia saginata*, according to Mönnig (1941), are flabby and inactive and are passed only in the feces, so pigs become infected as a result of coprophagous habits and are likely to have very heavy infections. Free eggs cannot consistently be found in the feces. The eggs probably survive for a considerable time in moist situations, as do those of *T. saginata*. The filthy way in which hogs are usually kept gives ample opportunity for their infection wherever there is human soil pollution or where privies are built in " open-back " style, or so that they leak. Young pigs are especially susceptible. The pig is not, however, the only intermediate host; the bladderworms can also develop in camels, dogs, monkeys, and man.

Upon ingestion by a suitable animal the oncospheres are liberated, bore through the intestinal wall, and make their way, via the blood or lymph channels, usually to the muscles or meat, but they may settle in almost any part of the body. They especially favor the tongue, neck, heart, elbow, and shoulder muscles, and certain muscles of the

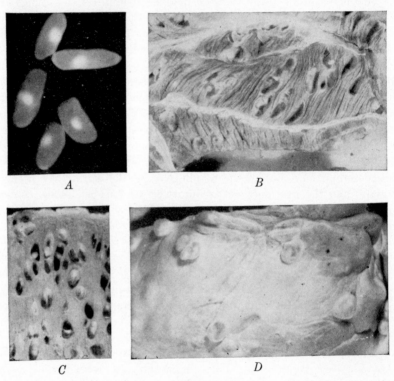

A   B

C   D

FIG. 105. *Cysticercus cellulosae.* A, freed cysticerci, (×1½); B, cut pieces of "measly" pork, heavily studded with cysticerci (× ½); C, cut piece of pig heart, loaded with cysticerci (× ½); D, same, surface view (slightly reduced).

hams. Having arrived at their destination they grow into bladder-worms or cysticerci, named *Cysticercus cellulosae.* The cysticerci are small, oval, whitish bodies with an opalescent transparency, 6 to 18 mm. long (Fig. 105), with a denser white spot on one side where the scolex is invaginated. Pork containing these larvae is called " measly " pork. Sometimes the cysticerci are so numerous as to occupy more than one half the total volume of a piece of flesh, numbering several thousands to a pound.

When cysticerci in pork are eaten by man all but the scolex is digested and it, turning right side out and anchoring itself to the wall of the small intestine, grows to maturity in about two or three months. Man is the only animal known to serve as a final host, though considerable growth takes place in dogs.

Pathogenicity. The adult worms in the intestine produce the same effects as *Taenia saginata* (see p. 338). This species, however, is particularly dangerous because the bladderworms as well as the adult can develop in man, causing cysticercosis. Self-infection with the eggs can result either from contaminated hands or from ripe proglottids being carried back to the stomach by reversed peristalsis, and the embryos being liberated there by action of the gastric juice. A century ago 2 per cent of the human autopsies in Berlin showed these cysticerci; they are less common now, but numerous cases were diagnosed in British soldiers serving in North Africa or India during World War II.

The effects depend on the location of the cysticerci in the body. A few in the muscles or subcutaneous tissues are nothing to worry about but, chiefly as the result of mechanical pressure, they may create unpleasant disturbances when they locate in the eye, heart, spinal cord, brain, or other delicate organs.

Eye infections require surgical removal. Brain infections lead to epileptic convulsions, violent headaches, giddiness, local paralysis, vomiting, and optic and psychic disturbances, often hysteria-like in nature. Probably many such cases are never correctly diagnosed. Presence of subcutaneous cysticerci should lead to suspicion. X-ray examination may show calcified cysticerci in old infections, appearing as ill-defined shadows the size of peas, but the majority of cases of cysticercosis of the brain cannot be diagnosed by this means. Cysts in the brain can sometimes be localized by the symptoms. Surgical removal may not be practicable if the cysts are numerous; no other treatment is known.

Treatment for expulsion of adult worms in the intestine is discussed on pp. 323–324.

Taenia saginata or Beef Tapeworm. This is the commonest *large* tapeworm of man and is cosmopolitan in distribution. In some localities, e.g., parts of Africa, Tibet, and Syria, where meat is broiled in large chunks over open fires, searing the surface but making the cysticerci in the interior only comfortably warm, it infects 25 to 75 per cent of the people old enough to eat meat. In the Hindu sections of India *T. saginata* is religiously ostracized, since only the lowest outcast will eat the meat of the sacred cow or even of water buffaloes.

Morphology. The beef tapeworm ordinarily reaches a length of 15 to 20 ft., but specimens up to 35 to 50 ft. have been recorded; the proglottids of an average worm number 1000 or more. The scolex (Fig.

104A) is 1.5 to 2 mm. in diameter and is without hooks.   Both mature
and ripe segments (Figs. 94 and 95A) are larger than those of *T. solium*.
The detached terminal segments are about 20 mm. long and 6 mm.
wide when relaxed.   When freshly passed, usually singly, they are firm
and very active, and crawl away like caterpillars; often they creep out
of the anus and deposit eggs from the ruptured ends of the uterus on
the perianal skin (see p. 322).   Several times active specimens from
the surface of a fresh stool have been sent to the writer as some new
kind of fluke!

   Life Cycle.   The life cycle is similar to that of *Taenia solium* except
that usually the intermediate hosts are cattle or allied animals.   However, giraffes, llamas, and pronghorn antelopes are occasionally infected
with cysticerci, and lambs and kids have been experimentally infected;
two valid human cases have been recorded.   In the tropics cattle and
buffaloes, habitually coprophagous, often have their flesh thoroughly
riddled by the cysticerci.   In India cattle, like pigs, frequently follow
human beings to the defecation sites in anticipation of a fecal meal.
Under favorable conditions the eggs remain viable in pastures for 6
months.   The cysticerci (named *Cysticercus bovis*) in measly beef are
7.5 to 10 mm. wide by 4 to 6 mm. long.   They are most frequently
present in the muscles of mastication and in the heart; these are the
portions of the carcass usually examined in meat inspections.   They
are, however, inconspicuous and can easily be overlooked in raw or rare
beef.

   Pathogenicity.   The damage done by adult Taeniae to their hosts is
often either under- or overrated.   There are some who believe that
the presence of a tapeworm is more or less of a joke, and as such to
be gotten out of the system but not to be taken seriously, while others
become unnecessarily disturbed over them.   They may cause mechanical injury by obstructing the intestinal canal and by injuring the
mucous membranes where they adhere, and they may absorb enough
nourishment to produce the proverbially ravenous " tapeworm appetite," although much more frequently they cause *loss* of appetite.

   Swartzwelder in 1939, in a series of 60 cases in New Orleans, found
abdominal pain, excessive appetite, weakness, and loss of weight to
be the commonest symptoms.   Other symptoms are nausea, difficult
breathing, digestive disturbances, dizziness, insomnia, restlessness, false
sensations, and occasionally convulsions and epileptic fits.   Many of
these symptoms might well be due to an induced vitamin deficiency in
hosts on a marginal or suboptimal supply, which is deplorably common
even in the relatively well-fed United States.   The writer (1943)
showed that tapeworms thrive even when there are no vitamins in the

diet of the host; the tapeworms therefore presumably absorb those they need from the intestinal wall, unless they can synthesize them. Anemia and eosinophilia are rare. The writer knew of a case in which tuberculosis was suspected; the patient was weak, easily exhausted, and emaciated, with sunken cheeks and staring eyes. A fortnight after two large Taeniae were expelled he was like a new man. In contrast, a colleague of the writer harbored a Taenia for years; in spite of a number of unsuccessful efforts to part company with it, " Horace," as he familiarly called his guest, stayed with him, yet there were never

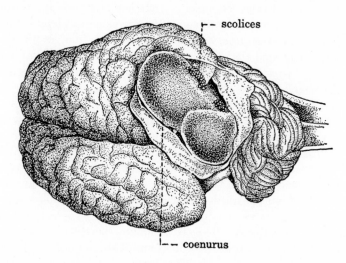

scolices

coenurus

FIG. 106. Left, brain of " giddy " sheep with coenurus showing masses of scolices. Right, section of cyst wall showing invaginated scolices. (After Neumann, from Hall.)

any symptoms other than segments in the stools, and the host continued in ruddy and robust health. The latter case is, perhaps, much more common than the former. For diagnosis see p. 322; for treatment and prevention, pp. 322–323.

Other Species of Taenia and Multiceps. The genus Taenia and the genus Multiceps, distinguishable only by the multiple heads produced in the larvae of Multiceps, include many species parasitic as adults in dogs and cats and as larvae in herbivores. Some of the commonest ones in dogs are *T. pisiformis* (= *serrata*), the larvae of which develop in the liver and mesenteries of rabbits; *T. ovis,* developing in the connective tissue in muscles of sheep; *T. hydatigena,* developing in the liver of sheep; *M. multiceps* (Fig. 106), developing as a coenurus in the brain of ruminants and causing gid; and *M. serialis,* developing in subcutaneous connective tissue of rabbits. *T. pisiformis* and *T. hydatigena*

occur also in cats, but the commonest form in these animals is
T. taeniaeformis, which develops in the livers of rats and mice.   One
human case is recorded.   The bladderworm of this species, *Cysticercus
fasciolaris,* contains a considerable chain of undeveloped segments and
is sometimes called a strobilocercus.   All these worms resemble *T. saginata* (Fig. 94) except in minor details; the scolices differ in the number
and size of the hooks.

About a dozen cases of coenurus infection in man have been recorded:
several brain infestations with *M. multiceps (Coenurus cerebralis),* one
of which caused epileptic symptoms; a number of muscular or subcutaneous infections, some identified as *M. serialis* and at least one of
the others as *M. glomeratus,* previously described from a gerbille.
Crusz in 1948 suggested that these are possibly all one species.   The
species of Multiceps are distinguished mainly by the number, size, and
shape of the rostellar hooks.

A few rare adult Taeniae have been found in man.   Four cases of
" *T. confusa* " have been reported in the United States and three from
eastern Africa, but Anderson (1934) believes this form to be only a
variant of *T. saginata.*   Probably *T. bremneri,* described from a
Nigerian, is the same thing.   Another species, of which two specimens
were obtained from an East African, is *T. africana.*   It has segments
broader than long, an unarmed scolex, and a uterus with unbranched
arms (Fig. 95*G*).

Echinococcus granulosus.   This is a minute species of tapeworm
living as an adult in the intestines of dogs and allied animals.   In contrast to its minute size as an adult it produces enormous larvae known
as hydatid cysts, which develop in many herbivorous animals and in
man.   Several related species occur in wild carnivores.

The worm is found in sheep- and cattle-raising countries, mostly
outside the tropics; it is especially common in North and South
Africa, Australia, New Zealand, and southern South America.   At the
end of the last century one-third to one-half of the people of Iceland
and the majority of its domestic animals had hydatids, although today
it is almost nonexistent there except in elderly people.   In some localities in Australia and New Zealand 50 per cent of the sheep and cattle
still have hydatids and one-fourth of the dogs harbor the adults.   In
Holland and other parts of Europe it is also a problem, a high percentage of stray dogs being infected.   In North America hydatids are
by no means rare in pigs, cattle, and sheep, although human cases are
few.

Morphology.   The adult (Fig. 107), though structurally much like a
Taenia, is very unlike one in size.   It is only 3 to 8 mm. in length, and

consists of a scolex and neck followed by only three or four successively larger segments, one immature, one or two mature, and usually one ripe or nearly ripe. The head has a protrusible rostellum armed with a double row of 28 to 50 hooks, usually 30 to 36. The worms occur by hundreds or even thousands in the intestines of dogs but are usually overlooked on account of their minute size. Each ripe segment contains 500 to 800 eggs. In spite of the small size of the adult worms, they require from 4 to 6 weeks to mature in a dog.

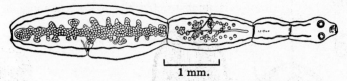

1 mm.

FIG. 107. *Echinococcus granulosus.* (After Ortlepp.)

Development of Hydatids. The development of the huge larvae has been studied especially by Dévé, Dew, and more recently Cameron. The eggs, about 30 by 38 μ, are indistinguishable from those of dog Taeniae. From the feces of dogs in pastures they gain access to their usual sheep or cattle hosts with contaminated forage or water. Most herbivorous animals, including pigs, horses, rabbits, and kangaroos, can harbor hydatid cysts. In Egypt over 30 per cent of camels are infected. Human infection usually results from contaminated water or from too intimate association with dogs; children are especially liable to infection by allowing dogs to " kiss " them or lick their faces with a tongue which, in view of the unclean habits of dogs, is an efficient means of transfer of tapeworm eggs. The most frequent site of development is the liver, and next to this, the lungs. Smaller numbers reach the kidneys, spleen, muscles, bone, heart, brain, and other organs.

Development of the cysts is slow. The young larva changes into a hollow bladder, around which the host adds an enveloping, fibrous cyst wall. At the end of a month these cysts measure only about 1 mm. in diameter; in 5 months they are about 10 mm. in diameter and the inner surface is beginning to produce hollow brood capsules. These ultimately remain attached only by slender stalks and often fall free into the fluid-filled cavity of the mother cyst. As the cyst grows larger more brood capsules form and the older brood capsules begin to differentiate, on their inner walls, a number of scolices, usually from 3 or 4 to 30 (Fig. 108). Sometimes the mother cyst, as the result of pressure, develops hernia-like buds which may detach themselves and continue their development independently as daughter cysts. The fluid of the cysts is nearly colorless; in older cysts there is a granular deposit consisting of liberated brood capsules and free scolices, called "hydatid sand." A cyst of 2 quarts capacity may produce more than 2 million scolices.

Eventually the cysts may reach the size of an orange or larger. After 10 to 20 years they may reach enormous size; one cyst removed from the abdomen of an Australian contained 50 quarts of fluid. When growth is unobstructed the cysts are more or less

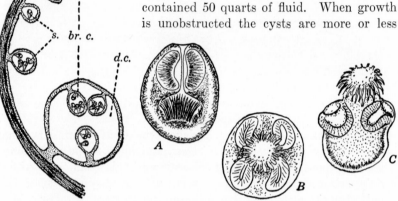

FIG. 108. *Left*, diagram of small hydatid cyst of Echinococcus, showing daughter cyst (*d.c.*), brood capsules (*br. c.*), and scolices (*s.*). Stippled inner wall of cyst is part of parasite; outer fibrous wall is capsule laid down by host. *Right*, scolices from cyst; *A*, invaginated; *B*, head-on view; *C*, evaginated.

spherical, but are often deformed by pressure. When developing in bones they fill the marrow cavities and may cause bone erosion. In

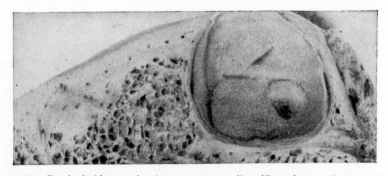

FIG. 109. Cut hydatid cyst showing numerous scolices like velvet on inner surface.

25 per cent of human cases more than one cyst is present, either due to original multiple infection or to development of detached daughter cysts.

Multilocular Cysts. Sometimes instead of forming single large vesicles, the development of the larva leads to the formation of a spongelike, constantly growing mass of small separate vesicles embedded in a fibrous tissue. It is not delimited by a capsule formed by the host, and the vesicles contain a gelatinous substance instead of fluid. Roots grow out into neighboring tissues. The central portions degenerate and die while growth continues on the outside, as in a true malignant tumor. Often portions of the growth become separated and continue to grow like the parent; such detached portions may be carried by the blood vessels to distant parts of the body. This type of hydatid known as a multilocular or alveolar cyst develops principally in the liver. It occurs especially in parts of Europe and Asia.

The fact that these dangerous growths are not known in Africa or Australia, where the ordinarily unilocular cysts are so common, and are the predominant type in some European localities has led to a belief by some parasitologists that they are caused by a different variety or species of Echinococcus, *E. multilocularis,* the adult of which may not be structurally distinguishable from *E. granulosus.* Others, however, think that the different effects are due to environmental conditions in the tissues of the host. In both types of cysts development is frequently imperfect and the parasite may fail in its life's work of producing scolices which can grow into adults. Sometimes no brood capsules are formed, and in other cases brood capsules but no scolices are produced; such cysts are " sterile."

Pathology. Hydatid cysts may cause serious disturbances by the pressure they exert on surrounding organs, with effects which vary, of course, according to the location of the cysts, but they resemble those of slow-growing tumors. The liver of an ox containing hydatids has been known to reach ten times its normal size. When Echinococcus embryos get lodged in the brain or eye, the results are likely to be disastrous.

The hydatid fluid contains toxic substances, but normally these are kept localized by the fibrous wall by which the host imprisons the parasite; this is evident from the presence of eosinophiles only in the immediate vicinity of the cyst. If, however, the cyst " leaks," the toxins are distributed and eosinophilia becomes general. When the cysts are ruptured by pressure or injury, not only is the toxic fluid liberated, sometimes with serious results, but liberated scolices and brood capsules or other parts of the germinative layer of the parasite are scattered and may become grafted on the peritoneal wall. Each may develop into a new cyst or, if the primary cyst happens to rupture into a blood vessel, they may be scattered all over the body and develop into cysts in very inconvenient places.

Diagnosis. Hydatid cysts are now usually diagnosed by serological methods; either hydatid fluid or an extract made from Taeniae can be used as an antigen. Precipitation and complement-fixation tests are possible, but the "Casoni reaction," in which the skin of an infected individual responds in a characteristic manner to injection of antigen, is easier and better. The older method of puncturing a cyst and withdrawing fluid in which scolices are sought is a dangerous one, because of risk of liberating hydatid fluid containing brood capsules, etc., which may produce allergic effects and also may result in the formation of secondary cysts. Presence of an unidentified abdominal mass together with eosinophilia is suggestive.

Treatment and Prevention. Treatment is purely surgical, but this parasite grows fast to the fibrous walls formed by the host and does not "shell out." It is dangerous to withdraw fluid directly, and it is customary to withdraw part of the fluid with a trocar and replace it at once, unless in the lung, with a formalin solution to kill the scolices, brood capsules, etc. Subsequently the fluid can be drained out. Multilocular cysts can seldom be operated on successfully, and generally lead to death in a few years.

Prevention, aside from avoiding too much intimacy with dogs and carefully washing dishes from which they have eaten, consists in avoidance of food or water which might have been contaminated by dogs and care that dogs are not fed, or do not get access to, the entrails or waste parts of slaughtered or dead animals from which they can become infected.

The practical elimination of the disease in Iceland was accomplished by licensing and annual treatment of dogs, and enforcing the burial or burning of infected material. Arecolin hydrobromide, 1/16 grain per 10 lb. wt., eliminates 95 per cent of Echinococcus from dogs; 3 doses usually eliminate all, and most Diphylidium and Taenia as well.

Hymenolepididae

This family contains a large number of species of tapeworms parasitic in birds and mammals, particularly in the former. Their characteristics are summarized on p. 333. Three species have been found in man. One, *Hymenolepis nana,* is a very common parasite of man and of rats and mice; another, *H. diminuta,* is abundant in rats and mice but relatively rare in man, though by no means a curiosity; the third, *H. lanceolata,* is a parasite of ducks and geese and has been recorded from man only once.

Hymenolepis nana. The dwarf tapeworm, *H. nana,* is the smallest adult tapeworm found in man, but it makes up for its diminutive size by the large numbers which are often present. It has a world-wide distribution, but it is far commoner in some localities than in others. It is the commonest tapeworm in southern United States, where about 1 to 2 per cent of the population, especially children, are infected. Sunkes and Sellers in 1937 collected data on 927,625 fecal examinations in the southern states and got records of 8085 tapeworm infections; all but 100 of these (98.6 per cent) were *H. nana.* In some parts of India as high as 18 to 28 per cent of the population were found by the writer to be infected.

The adult worm (Fig. 110, *1*) ranges from 7 to over 100 mm. in length. In general the length of the worms is inversely proportional to the num-

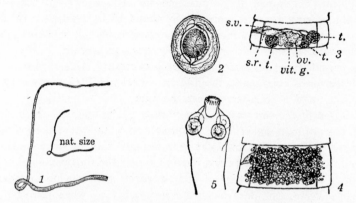

Fig. 110. Dwarf tapeworm, *Hymenolepis nana; 1*, adult worm, × 2, and natural size; *2*, egg, × 700; *3*, mature segment; *ov.*, ovary; *s.r.*, seminal receptacle; *s.v.*, seminal vesicle; *t.*, testes; *vit. g.*, vitelline gland; *4*, ripe segment; *5*, scolex.

ber present; in heavy infections it is commonly from 20 to 30 mm., with a maximum breadth of only 500 to 600 μ. The worm is so small and delicate that it resembles a strand of mucus in the feces, and therefore it is seldom found after treatment, even when diligently sought. The scolex (Fig. 110, *5*) has a well-developed retractile rostellum with a crown of 20 to 30 hooks. All the proglottids are considerably broader than long. The arrangement of the organs in mature proglottids can be seen in Fig. 110, *3*. The uterus develops as a sack with out-pocketings, and in ripe proglottids loses its form entirely, so that the whole segment between the longitudinal excretory vessels is solidly crammed with eggs.

The eggs have a very characteristic appearance (Figs. 59*O* and 110, *2*). The outer shell is oval, thin, and practically colorless; it commonly measures about 40 by 50 μ. The embryophore is lemon shaped, 16 to 20 μ long, with a little knob at either end from which arise a number of long, delicate, wavy filaments which lie in the space between the embryophore and the outer shell.

Life Cycle. *Hymenolepis nana* differs from almost all other tapeworms in being able to complete its entire life cycle in a single host. In this it is radically progressive, having broken away from the age-old tapeworm custom of utilizing intermediate hosts. It can, however, still revert to the habits of its ancestors and develop in fleas or grain beetles. When the eggs are ingested by man, rats, or mice, the oncospheres begin to claw actively inside their shells, and escape in the lumen of the intestine. They burrow into the interior of the villi and there develop into typical cysticercoids in about 4 days. On reaching maturity these escape into the lumen of the intestine, the scolices attach themselves, and the worms grow to maturity in about 15 to 20 days. In grain beetles, however, development of the cysticercoids takes 12 to 14 days.

As would be expected, since this worm is parenterally located in its cysticercoid stage, immunity to it develops readily (Hearin, 1941), and the infection is commonest in children. Larsh in 1942 showed that in mice immunity is transferred with the milk.

Relation of Human and Rodent Strains. The identity or otherwise of *H. nana* of man and *H. nana fraterna* of mice and rats has been much disputed. The human infection is relatively rare in some localities, especially northern Europe and Canada, where the rodent infections are common, and although eggs of human worms will develop in rodents, and vice versa, this does not occur as readily as when the eggs are ingested by the same hosts as those from which the eggs were derived. Shorb (1933) found similar differences between strains from rats and mice.

In India, however, the writer (1927) found an inverse correlation between the incidence of *H. nana* infections and that of Ascaris and Trichuris, which depend on human fecal contamination for transmission, but a direct correlation with prevalence of household rodents and conditions favoring their access to food, and with such rodent-borne infections as plague and *H. diminuta.* The fact that in our southern states *H. nana* infections are about equally common in cities with sewerage systems and in rural areas is also more suggestive of dissemination by rats and mice than by human contamination. The frequency of heavy infections is a further argument in favor of an important role of rodents in transmission, for though the accidental swallowing of a " mouse pill " with food could easily convey one or more whole segments of a worm with hundreds of eggs, such a wholesale contamination from human feces would be improbable.

The matter is an important one from the standpoint of prevention.

If, as the writer believes, human infection is commonly acquired from eggs derived from rodents, then the infection can be avoided by preventing access of rodents to human food which is to be eaten without further cooking, but if the infection is usually due to eggs derived from another infected human being, sanitary measures will be found necessary.

H. nana causes rather severe toxic symptoms, especially in children, including abdominal pain, diarrhea, convulsions, epilepsy, insomnia,

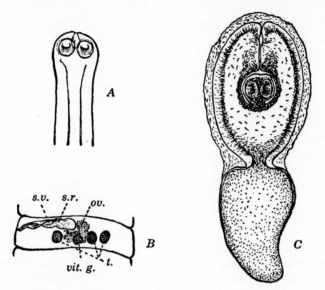

Fig. 111. *Hymenolepis diminuta*, *A*, unarmed scolex, × 35. *B*, sexually mature proglottid, × 8; *ov.*, ovary; *s.r.*, seminal receptacle; *s.v.*, seminal vesicle; *t.*, testes; *vit. g.*, vitelline gland. *C*, cysticercoid from beetle (Tenebrio), × 140.

and the like. Diagnosis is easily made by finding the eggs in the feces; like nematode eggs, they float in strong salt solutions. Treatment is considered on p. 323.

Other Species of Hymenolepis. *H. diminuta* (Fig. 111), very common in rats and mice in all parts of the world, is much less common in man. It is a much larger worm than *H. nana*, reaching a length of 1 to 3 ft., with a maximum diameter of 3.5 to 4 mm. The head, unlike that of nearly all other species of Hymenolepis, is unarmed, and the segments are much broader than long. The structure of mature and ripe segments is much like that of *H. nana*. The eggs (Fig. 59*N*) are larger (60 to 80 μ in diameter), yellow or yellow-brown, and usually spherical. The oncosphere lacks the knoblike thickenings at the poles, or at best they are rudimentary, and there are no filaments.

Like most kinds of Hymenolepis this worm requires an intermediate host for the development of its cysticercoids (Fig. 111, *right*). It is satisfied with any one of many grain-infesting insects, including larvae and adults of meal moths (*Pyralis farinalis*), nymphs and adults of earwigs (*Anisolobis annulipes*), adults of various grain beetles such as Tenebrio and Tribolium, dung beetles, the larvae of fleas, and even myriapods. Human infection results from eating such foods as dried fruits and precooked breakfast cereals in which the grain insects, infected from rat or mouse droppings, are present. Until about 1925 this infection was considered sufficiently rare in man so that every instance was published as an incident worthy of note, but the writer found 23 cases in about 10,000 fecal examinations in India and found no less than 3 in 50 examinations in one locality where the food habits and rat population were particularly favorable. As is usually true with human tapeworms which belong in another host, this worm is very easily expelled by anthelmintic treatment and is sometimes expelled spontaneously or after a cathartic.

The single record of human infection with *H. lanceolata* occurred in Germany. This is a short stumpy worm, 4 to 13 cm. long, which widens out to from 5 to 18 mm.; it is normally parasitic in ducks and related birds. The head has 8 hooks, and the proglottids are much broader than long. The intermediate hosts are water fleas or copepods.

Dipylidiidae

Dipylidium caninum. Although many species of Dipylidium have been described, Venard (1938) thinks nearly all of them are really one species, *D. caninum*, an extremely common parasite of flea-infested dogs and cats all over the world. Over 100 human cases, nearly all in children, are known. It is a delicately built tapeworm, commonly reaching a length of about a foot. The peculiar characteristics of the scolex and proglottids are mentioned on p. 333 and illustrated in Fig. 112. The uterus first develops as a honeycomb-like network and subsequently divides into numerous separate nests containing groups of eggs; each such " egg ball " contains from 5 to 15 eggs, and the eggs remain in the packets even when the segments disintegrate. The ripe proglottids are the size and shape of elongated pumpkin seeds and are often seen squirming actively in the freshly passed feces of infected animals.

The intermediate hosts are fleas (Ctenocephalides and Pulex) and dog lice (*Trichodectes canis*). Joyeux (1920) observed that the eggs could not be ingested by adult fleas but were devoured by the larvae when preying on bits of fecal debris or disintegrating segments. After ingestion by a flea larva the embryos hatch in the intestine and bore through into the body cavity, where they remain very little changed until the flea has transformed into an adult. The Dipylidium embryo then proceeds with its development into a cysticercoid, which infects the

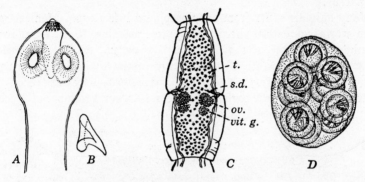

Fig. 112. *Dipylidium caninum.* *A*, scolex. *B*, single rostellar hook, much enlarged. *C*, mature proglottid, showing double reproductive systems; *ov.*, ovary; *s.d.*, sperm duct; *t.*, testes; *vit. g.*, vitelline gland. *D*, egg ball.

final host when the flea is nipped. Children are infected while playing with dogs, probably by accidentally swallowing lice or fleas, by crushing them and then putting infected fingers into the mouth, or by having their faces licked by a dog just after the dog has nipped a flea.

Anoplocephalidae

The Anoplocephalidae, the principal characters of which are mentioned on p. 334, are very common parasites of herbivorous animals, including cattle, sheep, goats, horses, camels, rabbits, rodents, and also apes and pigeons. They are often present in very young animals, and the incidence of infection may be very high.

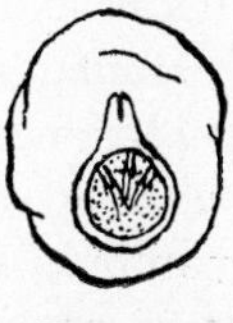

The life cycle of these worms was one of the outstanding mysteries of parasitology until Stunkard (1937) succeeded in developing the cysticercoids of Moniezia of cattle and sheep in mites of the superfamily Oribatoidea. The mites, living about the roots of grass, are seldom seen but may be very abundant and are undoubtedly often eaten by grazing animals. In a pasture at Beltsville, Md., there were estimated to be 6,000,000 oribatid mites (*Galumna virginiensis*) per acre, nearly 4 per cent of them harboring from 1 to 13 Moniezia cysticercoids — 400,000 potential tapeworms per acre! The cysticercoids of several other genera of Anoplocephalidae have been found to develop in oribatid mites, and it is quite

Fig. 113. Egg of *Bertiella studeri*, showing "pyriform apparatus." × 335. (Adapted from Blanchard.)

likely that they all do. The development in the mites is surprisingly slow, taking several weeks to several months. The embryophores of most anoplocephalids have processes called a " pyriform apparatus " (Fig. 113).

Many animals suffer from anoplocephalid infections. Moniezia are large worms of cattle, sheep, and goats, reaching 10 ft. or more in length, with double sets of reproductive organs in the proglottids. Sheep and goats in western United States commonly harbor the fringed tapeworm, *Thysanosoma actinioides,* characterized by fringes on the posterior borders of the segments. Horses harbor a number of species,

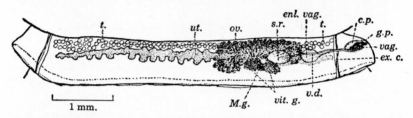

FIG. 114. Mature proglottid of *Bertiella studeri;* c.p., cirrus pouch, *enl. vag.,* enlargement of vagina; *ex. c.,* excretory canal; *g.p.,* genital pore; *M.g.,* Mehlis' gland; *ov.,* ovary; *s.r.,* seminal receptacle; *t.,* testes; *ut.,* uterus; *vag.,* vagina; *v.d.,* vas deferens; *vit. g.,* vitelline gland.

but the most important are two rather short, thick worms of the genus Anoplocephala: *A. magna,* about 10 in. long, in the small intestine, and *A. perfoliata,* only 1 to 2 in. long, in the cecum. Rabbits are commonly afflicted by members of the genus Cittotaenia. Young animals suffer digestive disturbances and retarded growth from these infections.

Human infection with members of this family is limited to *Bertiella studeri,* normally parasitic in apes and monkeys, and to *Inermicapsifer cubensis,* so far found only in Cuba. *B. studeri* has been reported from man only 11 times, mostly in children. It is a thick, opaque worm 25 to 30 cm. long and 10 to 15 mm. broad. The arrangement of organs is shown in Fig. 114. The ripe proglottids are very broad, but less than 1 mm. in length; they are shed in blocks of 20 or more. Most of the human cases have occurred around the Indian Ocean, but the infection appears also to have been established in the West Indies — an example of the danger of introducing foreign species of worms with captive animals. Stunkard (1940) developed minute cysticercoids (0.1 to 0.15 mm. in diameter) in oribatid mites but was unsuccessful in infecting man or monkeys with them.

Some worms (Fig. 115) found by Kourí in children in Cuba, of which 72 cases had been reported up to 1948, have been identified by

eminent helminthologists both as *Inermicapsifer cubensis*, an anoplocephalid, and as a species of Raillietina (see below), *R. kouridovali*.
Possibly two worms have been confused. They are 2 to 3 ft. long, the

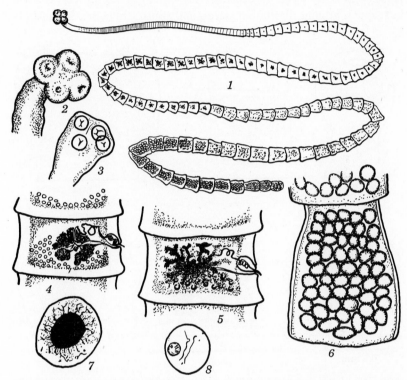

FIG. 115. *Raillietina kouridovali* from man in Cuba (confused with *Inermicapsifer
cubensis*). 1, Entire worm; 2, scolex with suckers everted; 3, scolex with suckers
retracted; 4, mature proglottid; 5, older proglottid with developing uterus; 6, ripe
proglottid with egg capsules; 7, egg capsule; 8, egg. (After Kourí.)

ripe segments 3 to 4 mm. long and 1 to 2 mm. wide. Kourí (1943)
reported similar worms from a wild ratlike rodent, *Capromys pilorides*.

Davaineidae

The majority of the tapeworms in this family are parasitic in birds,
and several are common and injurious parasites of poultry. The general
characteristics are given on p. 334. The cysticercoids of the chicken
parasites develop in various intermediate hosts: the minute but injurious *Davainea proglottina* in slugs; *Raillietina tetragona* in maggots of
the housefly; *R. echinobothrida*, another particularly pathogenic
species, in an ant; and *R. cesticillus* in various beetles. Phenylmer-

curic compounds in a dose of 50 mg. are effective against *R. cesticillus* but not against the others.

A number of cases of human infection with worms of the genus Raillietina have been recorded from various parts of the world — in seaports around the Indian Ocean and South China Sea from Mada-

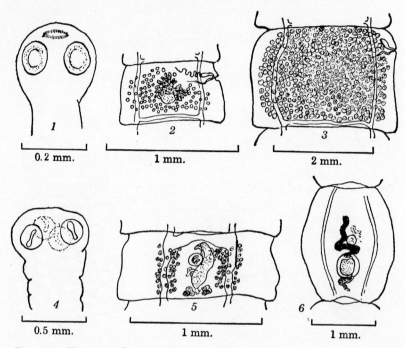

0.2 mm.   1 mm.   2 mm.

0.5 mm.   1 mm.   1 mm.

FIG. 116. Upper row, Davainea from man in Ecuador (*D. demerariensis?*); *1*, scolex, with double crown of about 150 small hooks, and minute spines on suckers; *2*, mature proglottid; *3*, ripe proglottid with about 200 to 300 egg capsules, each with about 7 to 10 eggs. (After drawings and description by Dollfus.) Lower row, *Mesocestoides variabilis* from child in Texas. *4*, Scolex, showing slitlike openings of suckers. *5*, mature proglottid, showing yolk glands and ovaries posteriorly; cirrus pouch near center; developing uterus; convoluted vagina; and testes on both sides of excretory canals. *3*, ripe proglottid, showing egg ball, remnants of uterus, and cirrus pouch. (After Chandler.)

gascar to Japan, in Cuba, and in Guiana and Ecuador in South America. The human cases undoubtedly represent accidental infections with species parasitizing local wild mammals; so far the species found in man have been found elsewhere only in rats. In South America the reservoir host has not yet been found.

For many years all the Old World human cases were referred to the species *R. madagascariensis*, but it appears evident from the work of Lopez-Neyra (1931) and Joyeux and Baer (1936) that a number of species are involved besides the original *madagascariensis*, e.g., *R. gar-*

risoni in the Philippines and *R. formosana* in Japan. In the New World a species named *R. demerariensis* was described from British Guiana many years ago; in 1935 Leon reported 16 cases in Ecuador, which Dollfus (1939–1940) thought represented five different species. Joyeux and Baer, on the other hand, not only think these are all one but also that they are the same as *R. demerariensis* (Fig. 116, *1–3*). The status of *R. kouridovali* in Cuba (see p. 351) is still uncertain.

One of the forms from Ecuador, which Dollfus named *R. quitensis*, found in 9 cases, is a tremendously long and slender worm, 32 to 39 ft. in length with a maximum width of only 3 mm., composed of about 5000 proglottids. All the other Raillietinae of man are slender worms 10 to 18 in. long and 1.5 to 3 mm. broad. So far as known all but one belong to the subgenus Raillietina, in which all the genital pores are on one side. The scolex has a double crown of small hooks (Fig. 115, *1*), and the suckers are armed with a number of rows of minute spines. The ripe proglottids are usually squarish or elongate and contain about 100 to 400 egg capsules each with several elongated eggs.

There is no question but that these worms utilize some arthropod as an intermediate host. Their frequent occurrence in wild rats, and especially water rats, in contrast to house rats, suggests some outdoor, possibly aquatic, vector. Probably many species are capable of infecting children if the vectors are swallowed.

Mesocestoididae

The members of this family, all in the genus Mesocestoides, have the peculiar characters listed on p. 334 and illustrated in Fig. 116, *4–6*. The number of species has been much disputed, since the worms show considerable variation and there are no good differential characters. The entire life cycle is unknown. Sparganum-like larvae called tetrathyridea occur free or encysted in reptiles, birds, and mammals, but these are probably second larval stages. The first human infection with a Mesocestoides was reported by the writer (Chandler, 1942) from a child in east Texas. The worms, estimated up to 40 cm. long and about 1.6 mm. wide, are probably *M. variabilis*, previously known from foxes, skunks, raccoons, and dogs in the United States. Subsequently another case was found in a Greenlander in Denmark.

REFERENCES
General

BROWN, H. W., Recent Developments in the Chemotherapy of Helminthic Diseases, *Proc. 4th Intern. Congr. Trop. Med. and Malaria,* **2,** Sect. VI, 966–974 (1948).

CHANDLER, A. C., The Effects of Number and Age of Worms on Development of Primary and Secondary Infections with *Hymenolepis diminuta* in Rats, and an Investigation into the True Nature of Premunition in Tapeworm Infections, *Am. J. Hyg.*, **29**, D, 105 (1939).

Studies on the Nutrition of Tapeworms, *Am. J. Hyg.*, **37**, 121 (1943).

FUHRMANN, O., Cestoidea, in *Handbuch der Zoologie* (ed. by Kukenthal, W.), Bd. II, Hälfte 1, Vermes Amera, 1931.

JOYEUX, C., and BAER, J. G., Les cestodes rares de l'homme, *Bull. soc. path. exotique*, **22**, 114 (1929).

MEGGITT, F. J., *The Cestodes of Mammals*, London, 1924.

SMYTH, J. D., The Physiology of Tapeworms, *Biol. Revs. Cambridge Phil. Soc.*, **22**, 214–238 (1947).

SUNKES, E. J., and SELERS, T. J., Tapeworm Infestations in Southern United States, *Am. J. Publ. Health*, **27**, 893–898 (1937).

Pseudophyllidea

BONNE, C., Researches on Sparganosis in the Netherlands East Indies, *Am. J. Trop. Med.*, **22**, 643 (1942).

FAUST, E. C., CAMPBELL, H. E., and KELLOGG, C. R., Morphological and Biological Studies on the Species of Diphyllobothrium in China, *Am. J. Hyg.*, **9**, 560 (1929).

GALLIARD, H., and NGU, D. V., Particularités du cycle évolutif de *Diphyllobothrium mansoni* au Tonkin, *Ann. parasitol. humaine et comparée*, **21**, 246–253 (1946).

IWATA, S., Experimental and Morphological Studies on the Post-embryonal Development of Manson's Tapeworm, *Diphyllobothrium erinacei, Japan. J. Zool.*, **5**, 209 (1933).

MUELLER, J. F., The Life History of *D. mansonoides* Mueller, 1935, and Some Considerations with Regard to Sparganosis in the United States, *Am. J. Trop. Med.*, **18**, 41 (1938).

THOMAS, L. J., The Life Cycle of *Diphyllobothrium oblongatum* Thomas, a Tapeworm of Gulls, *J. Parasitol.*, **33**, 107–117 (1947).

VOGEL, M., Studien zur Entwicklung von Diphyllobothrium, I, II, *Z. Parasitenk.*, **2**, 213, 629 (1929–1930).

WARD, H. B., The Introduction and Spread of the Fish Tapeworm (*D. latum*) in the United States, DeLamar Lectures, 1929–1930, Baltimore, 1930.

WARDLE, R. A., Fish Tapeworm, *Bull. Biol. Bd. Canada*, **45**, 1 (1935).

WARDLE, R. A., McLEOD, J. A., and STEWART, I. E., Lühe's " Diphyllobothrium " (Cestoda), *J. Parasitol.*, **33**, 319–330 (1947).

Taeniidae

ANDERSON, M., The Validity of *Taenia confusa* Ward, 1896, *J. Parasitol.*, **20**, 207 (1934).

BRAILSFORD, J. F., *Cysticercus cellulosae* — Its Radiographic Detection in the Musculature and the Central Nervous System, *Brit. J. Radiol.*, **14**, 79 (1941).

DEW, H. R., *Hydatid Disease*, Sydney, 1928.

DIXON, H. B. F., and SMITHERS, D. W., Epilepsy in Cysticercosis (*Taenia solium*), A Study of Seventy-one Cases, *Quart. J. Med.*, n. s., **3**, 603 (1934).

DUNGAL, N., Echinococcosis in Iceland, *Am. J. Med. Sci.*, **212**, 12–17 (1946).

HALL, M. C., The Adult Taenioid Cestodes of Dogs and Cats and of Related Carnivores in North America, *Proc. U. S. Natl. Museum*, **55**, No. 2258 (1919).

LOUCKS, H. H., Hydatid Cyst. A Review and a Report of Cases from North China, *Nat. Med. J. China*, **16**, 402 (1930).

MAGATH, T. B., Hydatid (Echinococcus) Disease in Canada and United States, *Am. J. Hyg.*, **25**, 107 (1937).

PENFOLD, W. J., PENFOLD, H. B., and PHILLIPS, M., *Taenia saginata;* Its Growth and Propagation, *J. Helminthol.*, **15**, 41 (1937).

SWARTZWELDER, J. C., Clinical Taenia Infection: An Analysis of Sixty Cases, *J. Trop. Med. Hyg.*, **42**, 226 (1939).

VILJOEN, N. J., Cysticercosis in Swine and Bovines, with Special Reference to South African Conditions, *Onderstepoort J. Vet. Sci. Animal Ind.*, **9**, 337 (1937).

Hymenolepididae

BERBERIAN, D. A., Treatment of *Hymenolepis nana* Infection with "Acranil," *Am. J. Trop. Med.*, **26**, 339–343 (1946).

CHANDLER, A. C., The Distribution of Hymenolepis Infections in India with a Discussion of its Epidemiological Significance, *Indian J. Med. Research*, **14**, 973 (1927).

HEARIN, J. T., Studies on the Acquired Immunity to the Dwarf Tapeworm, *Hymenolepis nana* var. *fraterna*, in the Mouse Host, *Am. J. Hyg.*, **33**, D, 71 (1941).

HUNNINEN, A. V., Studies on the Life History and Host-Parasite Relations of *Hymenolepis fraterna* (*H. nana* var. *fraterna* Stiles) in White Mice, *Am. J. Hyg.*, **22**, 414 (1935).

SHORB, D. A., Host Parasite Relations of *Hymenolepis fraterna* in the Rat and Mouse, *Am. J. Hyg.*, **18**, 74 (1933).

Anoplocephalidae

AFRICA, C. M., and GARCIA, E. V., The Occurrence of Bertiella in Man, Monkey, and Dog in the Philippines, *Philippine J. Sci.*, **56**, 1 (1935).

KOURÍ, P., and RAPPAPORT, I., A New Human Helminthic Infection in Cuba, *J. Parasitol.*, **26**, 179 (1940).

STUNKARD, H. W., The Development of *Moniezia expansa* in the Intermediate Host, *Parasitology*, **30**, 491 (1937).

The Morphology and Life History of the Cestode, *Bertiella studeri, Am. J Trop. Med.*, **20**, 305 (1940).

Dipylidiidae

JOYEUX, C., 1920 Cycle évolutif de quelques cestodes, *Bull. biol. France Belg.*, Suppl. 2 (1920).

VENARD, C. E., Morphology, Bionomics, and Taxonomy of the Cestode *Dipylidium caninum, Ann. N. Y. Acad. Sci.*, **37**, 273 (1938).

ZIMMERMAN, H. R., Life History Studies on Cestodes of the Genus Dipylidium from the Dog, *Z. Parasitenk.*, **9**, 717 (1937).

Davaineidae

DOLLFUS, R.-Ph., Cestodes du genre Raillietina trouvés chez l'homme en Amérique intertropicale, *Ann. parasitol. humaine et comparée*, **17**, 415, 542 (1939–1940).

JOYEUX, C., and BAER, J., Helminths des rats de Madagascar, Contribution à l'étude de *Davainea madagascariensis, Bull. soc. path. exotique,* **29,** 611 (1936).

LOPEZ-NEYRA, C. R., Relations du *Davainea madagascariensis* et des espèces parasites des mammifères, *Ann. parasitol. humaine et comparée,* **9,** 162 (1931).

Mesocestoididae

CHANDLER, A. C., First Record of a Case of Human Infection with Tapeworms of the Genus Mesocestoides, *Am. J. Trop. Med.,* **22,** 493 (1942).

CHAPTER 14

Acanthocephala (Spiny-Headed Worms)

As noted on p. 239, the Acanthocephala have usually in the past been attached as a rider to the Nemathelminthes for want of a better place to put them, but as Van Cleave (1941) pointed out, they have much more affinity to the Platyhelminthes, particularly the Cestoidea, both in structural characteristics and in life cycle. Although Van Cleave (1948) raised them to the rank of a phylum, we prefer to consider them a distinct class without definitely assigning them to any phylum. They are all intestinal parasites, found in all classes of vertebrates, though especially common in fishes and birds. They are remarkably uniform in general anatomy, life history, and habits.

Morphology. Like tapeworms, Acanthocephala are devoid of an alimentary canal throughout their lives. The body is divided into a posterior trunk and an anterior presoma, consisting of a spiny proboscis and unspined neck. In some the neck is a short transitional area; in others it may be long and conspicuous. The trunk and presoma are demarkated by an infolding of the cuticula and the derivation from the hypodermis of two elongate structures of unknown function called lemnisci (Fig. 117*A*) which lie in the body cavity. The proboscis, and often the neck also, is in most species retractile into a proboscis sac or receptacle by being turned inside out, and the whole presoma is also retractile, without inversion, into the fore part of the trunk by means of special retractor muscles inserted on the trunk wall (Fig. 117*A*, *r.m.*). The armature of the proboscis varies from a few to a great many hooks, which are usually in radial or spiral rows; in long proboscides they appear to be in longitudinal rows with quincunxial arrangement (Fig. 119).

The body is covered with a cuticle under which is a syncytial hypodermis or subcuticula. In more primitive forms this has a small number of large oval or ameboid nuclei; in some forms these break up into numerous nuclear fragments. The hypodermis also has a " lacunar " system of longitudinal and transverse vessels suggestive of, though not necessarily homologous with, the excretory system of cestodes. These structures are confined to the trunk.

One of the striking things about Acanthocephala is the small number of nuclei; after an acanthocephalan reaches its final host there is no further cell division except in germ cells, even though the body may grow to hundreds of times its original size.

The sexes are separate, and the males are nearly always smaller than the females. The reproductive organs in both sexes are located in the

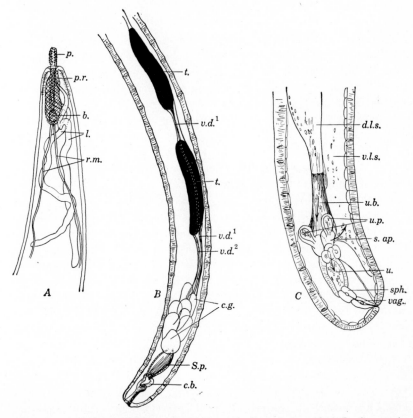

Fig. 117. *Moniliformis dubius.* *A*, anterior end; *B*, posterior end of ♂; *C*, posterior end of ♀; *b.*, brain; *c.b.*, copulatory bursa; *c.g.*, cement glands; *d.l.s.*, dorsal ligament sac; *l.*, lemnisci; *p.*, proboscis; *p.r.*, proboscis receptacle; *r.m.*, retractor muscles; *s. ap.*, sorting apparatus; *S.p.*, Saefftigen's pouch; *sph.*, sphincter; *t.*, testes; *u.*, uterus; *u.b.*, uterine bell; *u.p.*, uterine pouches; *vag.*, vagina; *v.d.*^{1}, and *v.d.*^{2}, vasa deferentia; *v.l.s.*, ventral ligament sac.

posterior part of the trunk, attached to a suspensory ligament. The males (Fig. 117*B*) have two testes, behind which are cement glands, usually 4 to 8 large unicellular glands but sometimes a syncytial mass. Behind the cement glands is a saclike structure sometimes called the ejaculatory duct but better "Saefftigen's pouch," through which, in most Acanthocephala, run the sperm ducts and ducts from the cement glands before they unite at its posterior end.   At the posterior end of the worm there is a muscular bursa which can be protruded or retracted into the body.

In females (Fig. 117C) an ovary is present only in early stages of development, later breaking up into masses of cells which continue to multiply and produce ova.   In some forms these are retained in liga-ment sacs; in others the sacs break down and the eggs are free in the entire body cavity.   Near the posterior end is a complicated structure called a uterine bell, into the wide-open anterior end of which the eggs are drawn.   It acts as a sorting device; the smaller immature eggs are returned to the body cavity through lateral openings, while the mature eggs are passed back through an oviduct to the posterior genital open-ing.   The eggs, when ripe, contain a mature embryo called an acanthor surrounded by three envelopes, the outer of which often has shapes or markings useful in identification.

Life Cycle.   The life cycle involves an intermediate host, which is usually an arthropod: small Crustacea for parasites of aquatic verte-brates; grubs, roaches, etc., for those of land animals.   When the embryonated eggs (Fig. 118A) are swallowed, the spindle-shaped acanthor (Fig. 118B) usually armed with rostellar hooks and small body spines, hatches and bores into the intestinal wall, eventually reaching the body cavity.   Meanwhile it grows and undergoes a gradual transformation; as development proceeds, the proboscis, proboscis sac, lemnisci, and rudiments of the sex organs are laid down. For this series of stages (Fig. 118C, D) leading up to the infective form Van Cleave applied the name " acanthella."   A number of workers have applied this name to the fully developed infective larva, and Moore (1946) applied the name " preacanthella " to the earlier pre-infective stages, but Van Cleave insists that his name acanthella should apply only to these pre-infective stages, and that the infective form should be called a " juvenile."   Since, however, " juvenile " is also applied to the re-encysted forms in secondary transport hosts, a new name is needed for the fully developed infective form.   For this the name " cystacanth " is here proposed.   The cystacanth (Fig. 118E) is enclosed in a delicate hyaline sheath produced by the larva.   The proboscis is fully formed but inverted, and the reproductive organs are sufficiently developed so that the sex is easily recognized.   In Monili-formis larvae the hypodermis is expanded into broad flanges.

Effects on Host.   Acanthocephala damage their hosts principally by local injury and inflammation at the point of attachment of the spiny proboscis.   When the worm moves and reattaches, the old sore may become infected by bacteria.   Occasionally the worms cause perforation of the gut wall and precipitate a fatal peritonitis. In heavy infections, loss of appetite and interference with digestion may lead to unthriftiness. Dogs and coyotes infected with Oncicola (see p. 363) are said sometimes to develop rabies-like symptoms, suggesting the possibility of transmission of a virus by the worms. Grassi and

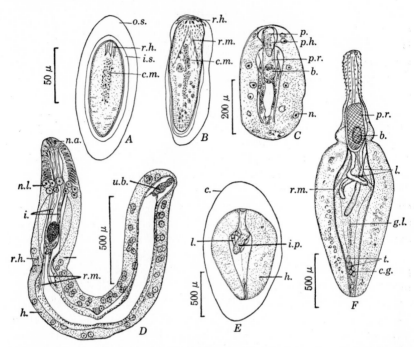

Fig. 118.   Life cycle of *Moniliformis dubius; A*, egg; *B*, acanthor in process of escaping from egg shell and membranes; *C*, median sagittal section of larva from body cavity of roach 29 days after infection; *D*, acanthella dissected from enveloping sheath, about 40 days after infection; *E*, cystacanth from body cavity of roach, with proboscis inverted, about 50 days after infection; *F*, cystacanth freed from cyst and proboscis evaginated. Abbrev.: *b.*, brain; *c.g.*, cement glands; *c.m.*, central nuclear mass; *g.l.*, genital ligament; *h.*, hypodermis; *i.*, inverter muscles; *i.p.*, inverted proboscis; *i.s.*, inner shell; *l.*, lemnisci; *n.*, subcuticular nucleus; *n.a.*, nuclei of apical ring; *n.l.*, nuclei of lemniscal ring; *o.s.*, outer shell; *p.*, proboscis; *p.h.*, developing proboscis hooks; *p.r.*, proboscis receptacle; *r.h.*, rostellar hooks; *r.m.*, retractor muscle; *t.*, testes; *u.b.*, uterine bell. (After Moore.)

Calandruccio in 1888 reported acute pain and violent ringing in the ears experienced by the junior author 19 days after infecting himself with Moniliformis larvae.

Burlingame and Chandler (1941) showed that, as with some adult tapeworms, no true immunity to Acanthocephala is developed, resistance to reinfection being primarily a matter of competition for food and for favorable locations in the intestine.

Classification. The Acanthocephala constitute a small group of about a dozen families and about 60 genera which are quite widely divergent from other groups of worms but which are remarkably uniform among themselves, both in morphology and life cycle. Once placed in a single genus, Echinorhynchus, they were later (1892) divided into several families, then (1931) into two orders, which were expanded to three in 1936 and finally elevated by Van Cleave (1948) into a phylum containing two classes and four orders: class Metacanthocephala with the orders Palaeacanthocephala and Archiacanthocephala, and the class Eoacanthocephala with the orders Gyracanthocephala and Neoacanthocephala.

To the writer the characters used by Van Cleave for differentiating these groups seem trivial. For example, in the table of characters given for distinguishing the orders, the only one in which the Gyracanthocephala and Neoacanthocephala differ is the presence or absence of trunk spines, and even this character is variable in one of the other orders. No good character is presented for differentiating the two classes. For the present, therefore, we prefer to consider the Acanthocephala as constituting a single class with three orders, as proposed by Van Cleave in 1936, though we consider even this rather extreme.

1. **Palaeacanthocephala.** Proboscis hooks usually in long rows; spines present on trunk; nuclei in hypodermis usually fragmented; chief lacunar vessels in hypodermis lateral; ligament sacs often break down; separate cement glands; eggs spindle-shaped, thin-shelled; mostly in fishes and aquatic birds and mammals, cystacanth in Crustacea.

2. **Eoacanthocephala.** Proboscis hooks usually in a few circles; trunk spines present or absent; nuclei in hypodermis few and large; chief lacunar vessels dorsal and ventral; distinct dorsal and ventral ligament sacs in ♀; syncytial cement glands; eggs ellipsoidal, thin-shelled; parasitic in fishes, except one in turtles, cystacanth in Crustacea.

3. **Archiacanthocephala.** Proboscis hooks either in long rows (e.g., Moniliformis) or in a few circles (e.g., Oncicola and Macracanthorhynchus); no spines on trunk; nuclei in hypodermis few and large; chief lacunar vessels dorsal and ventral; dorsal and ventral ligament sacs persist in ♀; separate cement glands; eggs usually oval, thick-shelled; protonephridia present in some; parasitic in terrestrial vertebrates, cystacanth in grubs, roaches, etc.

The only Acanthocephala found in man, *Moniliformis dubius* and *Macracanthorhynchus hirudinaceus*, belong to the Archiacanthocephala.

Moniliformis. The common spiny-headed worm of house rats, *Moniliformis dubius* (Figs. 117, 119*A*), has been found in man on a few occasions. Its body, 10 to 30 cm. long in females and 6 to 13 cm. in males, has annular rings which give it a tapewormlike appearance.

It has a nearly cylindrical proboscis with 12 to 15 rows of vicious thornlike hooks. It inhabits the small intestine of rats in many parts of the world, but in most places it is not common. In Houston, Texas, however, the writer found it in about 20 per cent of the roof rats (*Rattus alexandrinus*) but in a much smaller percentage of Norway rats. The eggs are over 100 μ in length. Cockroaches serve as intermediate hosts; the writer has found over 100 cystacanths in the body cavity of a *Periplaneta americana*. The eggs hatch in the mid-intestine of the roach, the liberated acanthors penetrating into the gut wall. By the tenth day they appear as minute specks on the outside of the intestinal wall, from which they eventually drop into the body cavity. The half-grown acanthella lies straight and has very broad ectodermal flanges (Fig. 118*C*), but with further development it bends V-shaped in its cyst (Fig. 118*D*), the body proper elongating and thickening until the flanges become inconspicuous. When fully developed, after 7 to 8 weeks, the cysts are about 1 to 1.2 mm. long and the cystacanths (Fig. 118*F*) 1.5 to 1.8 mm. long. In Europe a beetle (Blaps) has been involved as an intermediate host, but the form found in wild rodents in Europe is not identical with that found in rats in the United States and South America.

Sandground (1926) found numerous immature specimens in the intestines of toads and lizards, where they had evidently attached themselves after being eaten with the intermediate hosts. Considering the propensity of Acanthocephala for re-establishing themselves as larvae in abnormal hosts, human infection might be possible without postulating the eating of roaches or beetles.

Macracanthorhynchus. The only other spiny-headed worm which has been recorded from man is the relatively huge species, *Macracanthorhynchus hirudinaceus* (Fig. 119*B*), commonly parasitic in pigs. This large worm, of which the females are 25 to 60 cm. long, though the males are only 5 to 10 cm., is pinkish and has a transversely wrinkled body which tapers from a rather broad, rounded head end to a slender posterior end. The presoma is relatively very small, with a little knoblike proboscis armed by 5 or 6 rows of thorns. The eggs are 80 to 100 μ long with sculptured brown shells; they are very resistant to desiccation and cold and remain viable in soil up to 3½ years. White grubs, the larvae of " June bugs," serve as intermediate hosts. The cystacanth is cylindrical and quite different in appearance from that of Moniliformis.

Lindemann in 1865 recorded this worm as parasitic in man and stated it to be common among the peasants of the Volga Valley in southern Russia, where the white grubs of beetles are said to be eaten, but there are no subsequent confirmations of this. Lambl in 1859 found an immature acanthocephalan in a boy in Europe, which probably was this species.

Other Acanthocephala. Aside from Macracanthorhynchus in pigs, the only Acanthocephala of importance to domestic animals are two genera, Polymorphus and Filicollis, which are injurious to ducks and geese in Europe. In both cases the intermediate hosts are Crustacea; Polymorphus takes advantage of an amphipod, Gammarus, and Fili-

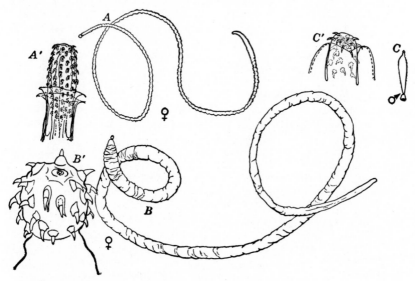

Fig. 119. Various Acanthocephala, adults drawn to same scale; *A, Moniliformis dubius* ♀; *A'*, proboscis of same; *B, Macracanthorhynchus hirudinaceus; B'*, proboscis of same; *C, Oncicola canis; C'*, proboscis of same. (Adapted from various authors.)

collis of an isopod, Asellus. Dogs in Texas are sometimes infected with *Oncicola canis* (Fig. 119C), the larvae of which are commonly found in armadillos and sometimes in the walls of the esophagus of turkeys. An arthropod undoubtedly serves as a first intermediate host; it is an open question whether the second intermediate host is obligatory or merely convenient.

Treatment. Almost nothing is known about anthelmintics for Acanthocephala. Sodium fluoride given pigs to eliminate Ascaris does not affect Macracanthorhynchus. Lal performed some experiments on Acanthocephala of fishes *in vitro* and found that CCl_4, $CuSO_4$, and thymol killed at 0.05 per cent, but santonin did not at 1 per cent. Extract of male fern removed Moniliformis in an experimental human infection.

REFERENCES

BURLINGAME, P. L., and CHANDLER, A. C., Host Parasite Relations of *Moniliformis dubius* in Albino Rats, and the Environmental Nature of Resistance to Single and Superimposed Infections with This Parasite, *Am. J. Hyg.*, **33**, D, 1–21 (1941).

GRASSI, B., and CALANDRUCCIO, S., Ueber einen *Echinorhynchus*, welcher auch in Menschen parasitirt und dessen Zweischenwirt ein Blaps ist, *Centr. Bakt. Parasitenk., Orig.*, **3**, 521–525 (1888).

KATES, K. C., Development of the Swine Thorn-Headed Worm, *Macracanthorhynchus hirudinaceus,* in Its Intermediate Host, *Am. J. Vet. Research,* **4**, 173–181 (1943).

MEYER, A., Acanthocephala. In *Bronn's Klassen u. Ordnungen d. Tierreichs,* 4, Abt. 2, 1933.

MOORE, D. V., Studies on the Life History and Development of *Moniliformis dubius* Meyer, 1933, *J. Parasitol.*, **32**, 257–271 (1946).

VAN CLEAVE, H. J., The Recognition of a New Order in the Acanthocephala, *J. Parasitol.*, **22**, 202 (1936).

Relationships of the Acanthocephala, *Am. Naturalist,* **75**, 31 (1941).

A Critical Review of Terminology for Immature Stages in Acanthocephalan Life Histories, *J. Parasitol,* **33**, 118–125 (1947).

Expanding Horizons in the Recognition of a Phylum, *J. Parasitol.,* **34**, 1–20 (1948).

WITENBERG, G., Studies on Acanthocephala, 3, Genus Oncicola, *Livro jubilar do Prof. Travassos,* 537, Rio de Janeiro, 1938.

CHAPTER 15

The Nematodes in General

The nematodes constitute a large group of worms of comparatively simple organization, nearly all of which are total strangers to everyone but zoologists, although they play extremely important roles in the economy of nature. Popular ignorance of these animals is, as Cobb has remarked, easy to understand since they are seldom if ever seen; they do not supply food, raiment, or other valuable material; they are not ornamental; they do not delight our ears with their songs or otherwise amuse us; and they fail even to furnish us with classic examples of industriousness, providence, or other virtues, although they might well be extolled by large-family enthusiasts. Thus avoiding the popular limelight, they do, nevertheless, unobtrusively leave their marks in the world. Probably every species of vertebrate animal on the earth affords harborage for nematode parasites, and Stoll (1947) estimated 2000 million human nematode infections in a world harboring 2200 million human inhabitants, a tribute, as he said, to the variety and biological efficiency of nematode life cycles.

About 50 species have been recorded as living in the human body, and about a dozen of these are common human parasites, some of which cause important diseases. In addition to this the soil of our farms and gardens is literally teeming with myriads of nematodes, some of which do inestimable damage to crops. As compared with these the parasitic nematodes, with which we are concerned, constitute a mere handful, both of species and of individuals.

Relationships. The nematodes show little relationship to any other group in the animal kingdom. The most primitive forms are the free-living species inhabiting soil and water. The majority of the parasitic species are relatively giants and are often much modified by their parasitic life. The free-living forms, often called " nemas," are barely visible to the naked eye, are transparent enough so that every structure in the body can be seen and its movements watched, and have extremely simple life cycles, whereas the parasitic ones, with a very few exceptions, are much larger, some up to several feet in length, are opaque, and may have relatively complex life cycles.

The parasitic forms have without doubt evolved from more than

365

one type of free-living form and do not, therefore, represent a single branch of the nematode phylum which can properly be classified independently of the free-living forms. This, however, is what has been done in the past, for students of the nematodes parasitic in vertebrate animals had little knowledge or interest in the free-living forms. Only since about 1935 have attempts been made to reconcile these two estranged sections of the nematode clan.

General Structure. A typical nematode is an elongated, cylindrical worm, tapering more or less at head and tail ends, and encased in a very tough and impermeable transparent or semitransparent cuticle. This cuticle is not chitin, like the cuticle of arthropods, since it is soluble in potassium hydroxide, but nematodes do have true chitin in the egg shells. Usually the cuticle is marked externally by fine transverse striations; it may have other inconspicuous markings and sometimes has bristles, spines, ridges, or expansions of various kinds. In some parasitic forms there are finlike expansions in the neck region, in others in the tail region of the males, the latter commonly supported by fleshy papillae; they are known respectively as cervical and caudal alae. In the Strongylata there is a bell-shaped expansion at the posterior end of the males supported by fleshy rays conforming in number and arrangement to a definite plan; this is called a bursa. The cuticle is secreted by a protoplasmic syncytial layer called the hypodermis, in which no separate cells can be distinguished. Nuclei are present only in four thickened chords or " lines," one dorsal, one ventral, and two lateral. In these chords run nerve fibers and, in some species, canals connected with the excretory system.

Between the chords there is a single layer of longitudinally spindle-shaped muscle cells of very peculiar structure. In small transparent worms the striated part of the muscle cell is limited to the part of the cell in contact with the hypodermis, and only a few, often only two, flat muscle cells are in each quadrant of a cross section. In larger and more opaque worms, however, the muscle cells in each quadrant become very numerous and in cross section have a flask-shaped appearance, with the striations along the " neck " of the flask as well as at the base of the cell (Fig. 121). Worms with these two types of musculature are said to be " meromyarian " and " polymyarian," respectively, but there are all gradations between them. Contraction of these elongated muscles causes a twisting or bending of the body. Special muscles occur in the esophagus, ovejector, etc., and for moving the spicules of the male.

Between the muscles and the gut wall is a relatively spacious body cavity in which the reproductive organs lie, unattached except at their external openings. This cavity is not lined by an epithelium as is a true celome. It contains a fluid which serves as a distributing medium for digested food and for collection of waste products. It is provided with a small amount of " mesenterial " tissue and a few large phagocytic cells called celomocytes.

The nervous system consists of a conspicuous " nerve ring " around the esophagus, from which longitudinal nerve trunks run forward and backward. A few special sensory organs are present; at the anterior end are a pair of supposedly olfactory receptors called amphids, and in some a similar pair, called phasmids, is situated on minute papillae behind the anus. These differ from ordinary tactile papillae in having canals connected with glandlike structures. There are tactile papillae about the mouth, a pair in the neck region of many forms (called deirids), and paired caudal or genital papillae in the males of many forms.

The excretory system is variable. Almost the only constant feature is a pore opening on the mid-ventral surface in the esophageal region; in some forms even this seems to be absent. A well-developed excretory system such as occurs in Rhabditis consists of an H-shaped system of tubes, the middle of the crossbar of the H being connected with the pore and the limbs lying in the lateral chords. In addition two subventral gland cells open into the pore. In Ascaris the posterior limbs are well developed; in some the system is reduced to an inverted U or is developed on one side only. In some free-living nematodes the excretory system is reduced to a single glandular cell. Mueller in 1929 expressed the opinion that excretion takes place through the cuticle and that the so-called excretory system is really secretory. There is no circulatory system, and respiration is through the cuticle or possibly through the alimentary canal.

The mouth is variously modified. The primitive type in free-living nematodes is a simple opening surrounded by three lips, one dorsal and two lateroventral. This is retained by many groups of parasitic forms, including Strongyloides, oxyurids, and ascarids. In some forms, e.g., the filariae and their allies, the lips have disappeared, but in others two lateral lips, sometimes with a dorsal and ventral one also, have replaced the primitive three. In still others, especially some of the Strongylata, the mouth has been highly modified into a " buccal capsule," which may be supplied with such embellishments as crowns of leaflike processes, cutting ridges, teeth, and lancets.

The mouth, or buccal capsule, leads into the digestive canal. This is a simple tube leading from the anterior mouth to an anus usually a short distance from the posterior end. It consists of two parts, an esophagus and an intestine. The esophagus has a chitinized triradiate lumen usually surrounded by muscle or gland cells (Fig. 121B), and ordinarily it has three esophageal glands embedded in its walls. In the suborder Trichurata, however, after a short anterior region the wall is

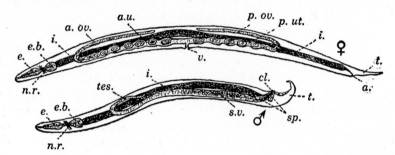

Fig. 120. Diagram of structure of a simple free-living Nematode of Rhabditis type, ♀ and ♂; a, anus; $a. ov.$, anterior ovary; $a.u.$, anterior uterus; $cl.$, cloaca; $e.$, esophagus; $e.b.$, esophageal bulb; $i.$, intestine; $n.r.$, nerve ring; $p. ov.$, posterior ovary; $p. ut.$, posterior uterus; $sp.$, spicules; $s.v.$, seminal vesicle and sperm duct; $t.$, tail; $tes.$, testis, $v.$, vulva.

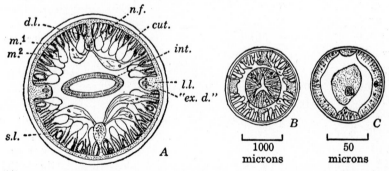

Fig. 121. A, Cross-section of Ascaris, a polymyarian nematode, in prevulvar region; $cut.$, cuticle; $d.l.$, dorsal line; "$ex. d.$," so-called "excretory duct"; $int.$, intestine; $l.l.$, lateral line; $m.^1$, striated contractile portion of muscle cell; $m.^2$, protoplasmic portion of muscle cell; $n.f.$, nerve fibers. (After Brandes, adapted from Fantham, Stephens, and Theobald.) B, Cross-section of esophageal region of Ascaris; C, of Trichuris. In Ascaris note the triangular lumen and thick muscular walls of the esophagus and the numerous muscle cells in body wall; in Trichuris note the greatly reduced esophagus imbedded in the protoplasm of a large cell, and broad, flat muscle cells on body wall. (Ascaris, original; Trichuris, after Chitwood.)

greatly reduced and the lumen of the esophagus appears to pass like a capillary tube through a column of large cells (Figs. 121C and 122). Chitwood showed that these cells open by minute ducts into the esophagus, and he interprets them as reduplicated esophageal glands. This column of glandular cells is called a stichosome. Sometimes the posterior end of the esophagus enlarges into a bulb provided with valves (Fig. 145A).

The intestine is a flat or cylindrical tube, usually straight, and is lined by a single layer of cells (Fig. 121A). In some forms, like the strongyles, it is lined by only 18 to 20 cells in all, whereas in Ascaris there are about a million. At the posterior end there is a chitinized rectum. In females the intestine has a separate anal opening, but in males the intestine and reproductive system open into a common cloaca.

Reproductive Systems. With rare exceptions parasitic nematodes have separate sexes, which are externally distinguishable; usually the males are smaller, and they differ in the form of the tail. In one instance the male lives as a parasite in the vagina of the female! In both sexes the reproductive system consists primitively of long tubules, part of which serve as ovaries or testes and part as ducts (Fig. 120). In all parasitic nematodes the male system is reduced to a single tubule, but the female system is double with rare exceptions and in a few cases is further reduplicated. The inner ends of the tubules are fine, coiled, threadlike organs closed at the ends, which produce the cells that ultimately become eggs or sperms. These sex glands open directly into a continuous part of the same tube, usually larger in caliber, called the uterus or vas deferens, as the case may be. The walls of the uterus appear to supply the yolk and shell material for the egg.

In the male the single vas deferens usually has an enlargement or seminal vesicle, followed by a muscular ejaculatory duct which opens into the cloaca. Males normally have a pair of chitinous "spicules," which lie in pouches dorsal to the ejaculatory duct near the cloaca. They are capable of exsertion and are used to guide the sperms into the vagina of the female at the time of copulation. There may be a third smaller chitinous body or accessory piece called a gubernaculum. The size and shape of the spicules vary greatly in different kinds of nematodes and are often very useful in identification. In a few forms one or both spicules may be missing.

In the females of simple types of nematodes the two uteri come together near the middle of the body and open into a single vulva (Fig. 120). In most parasitic forms, however, the uteri first unite into a common tube, the vagina. Frequently the vagina or the branches of the uteri have enlarged, thin-walled chambers which serve as seminal receptacles, and also muscular ovejectors which by a peristaltic action force the eggs through to the vulva one at a time. The vulva in different species may vary in position from just behind the mouth to a point just in front of the anus.

Development and Life Cycle. The development of nematodes is a comparatively simple process. The original egg cell, after being enclosed in a membrane or shell, segments into 2, 4, 8, 16, etc., cells, until it forms a solid morula. This then begins to assume a tadpole shape and become hollow inside, and then proceeds to form an elongated embryo provided with a simple digestive tract. After ten consecutive cell divisions, in the later ones of which not all the cells participate each time, the definitive form of the first larval stage is reached. Thereafter development proceeds more slowly and, as in insects, is punctuated by a series of moults, normally four, although in some forms one or two moults may occur in the egg before hatching. Although the successive stages differ in details of structure they are never totally unlike each other.

The state of development at the time the eggs are deposited varies greatly, apparently depending upon different oxygen requirements for development. Some leave the mother's body unsegmented (Ascaris and Trichuris) ; some in early stages of segmentation (hookworms and their allies) ; some in the tadpole stage (Enterobius), and some as fully developed embryos (Trichinella, Strongyloides, and filariae). Usually no further development occurs until the eggs or embryos have reached a new environment, either outside the body or in an intermediate host, except in the case of Trichinella the embryos of which find *their* new environment in the muscles of the parental host.   Having reached this new environment the embryo, either inside the egg or after hatching from it, commonly undergoes two moults, reaching the third stage, before it is infective for another definite host.   When it has reached that stage it ceases to grow or develop until transfer to a new host is accomplished.

The simplest type of life cycle is that in which the embryonated eggs are swallowed by the host. The embryos, usually in the third stage, hatch in the intestine and may develop to maturity there, only burying themselves temporarily in the mucous membranes, e.g., Enterobius and Trichuris, or they may make a preliminary journey through the host's body via heart, lungs, trachea, and esophagus, and thus back to the intestine, e.g., Ascaris. This life cycle may be modified by the first-stage embryos hatching outside the body and growing and developing to the infective stage as free-living larvae, then re-entering the definitive host by burrowing through the skin, e.g., hookworms, or being swallowed with vegetation, e.g., Haemonchus.

Strongyloides reproduces parthenogenetically and may intercalate a generation of morphologically different free-living males and females. Trichinella produces embryos which penetrate into the host's body and encyst in the muscles to await being eaten by another host, thus substituting the original host for the outside world as a place for preliminary partial development. The filariae and their allies (suborder

Spirurata) substitute insects or other invertebrates as a place for partial development, thus requiring a true intermediate host. A few, e.g., Gnathostoma, require two intermediate hosts, the larvae developing first in a Cyclops, continuing in a fish or other cold-blooded vertebrate, and reaching sexual maturity in a mammal. Some nematodes, after having reached an infective stage, can re-encyst if they get into an unsuitable host.

The methods of escaping from and re-entering a final host vary in accordance with the modifications in the life cycle.

Classification. The classification of nematodes is still in a very unsettled state. This is partly due to the process of promoting nematode groups to higher ranks as more and more species are described. Families or even genera of a few years ago are now superfamilies, suborders, or orders, according to the willingness of helminthologists to recognize the promotions. The classification has been subjected to a veritable earthquake by attempts, which must sooner or later be recognized, to combine the classification of free-living and parasitic groups in a single coordinated whole. Chitwood has done most in reconciling these two estranged groups and has evolved a classification which embraces them both, but Chitwood's conclusions will probably have to undergo some ripening and confirmation before parasitologists in general will accept this New Deal in nematode classification.

In the first place, he divides the entire class into two subclasses, Phasmidia and Aphasmidia, for the fundamental characters of which the student is referred to Chitwood (1937). The Phasmidia include the majority of soil nematodes, as well as most of the forms parasitic in insects and vertebrates, whereas the Aphasmidia include mainly aquatic forms and a few parasitic ones — the Trichurata, mermithids, and Dioctophymata. The further division of these subclasses into orders involves some unfamiliar names, which may not survive the limelight of publicity, so we omit them and give only the more or less familiar suborders and superfamilies. Just as a celebrated woman clings to her maiden name after marriage, we still adhere to a suborder Trichurata instead of accepting Chitwood's " Dorylaimata." As an *ad interim* classification the following is suggested:

Subclass **APHASMIDIA.** No phasmids (caudal sensory organs); amphids much modified externally except in parasitic forms; excretory system rudimentary or absent; celomocytes and mesenterial tissue well developed.

1. Suborder **Trichurata.** Esophagus a very long, fine tube embedded for most of its length in a column of glandular cells; females with one ovary; males with one spicule or none. Includes Trichuris, Trichinella, and Capillaria.

2. Suborder **Dioctophymata.** Large worms; esophagus cylindrical; female with one ovary; male with one spicule and a terminal sucker; no excretory system. Includes kidney worm (Dioctophyma).

Subclass **PHASMIDIA.** Phasmids present; amphids simple pores; excretory system present, not rudimentary; celomocytes (6 or less) and mesenterial tissue weakly developed.

1. Suborder **Rhabditata.** Small, transparent, meromyarian worms; esophagus usually with one or two bulbs; mouth simple or with three or six minute lips or papillae; no specialized ovejectors, and vagina transverse; majority free-living, some with an alternating generation of parthogenetic parasitic females. Includes Rhabditis and Strongyloides.

2. Suborder **Ascaridata.** Esophagus bulbed or cylindrical; vagina elongate; mouth usually with 3 or 6 lips; males usually with 2 spicules; tail of male not spirally coiled but usually curled ventrally; no true bursa, but alae may be present.

Superfamily 1. *Ascaridoidea.* Cervical papillae present; mostly large, stout polymyarian worms; males with 2 spicules; tail curled ventrally, with or without lateral alae; esophagus muscular, with or without a bulb. Includes Ascaris and Heterakis.

Superfamily 2. *Oxyuroidea.* Cervical papillae absent; mostly small or medium-sized transparent meromyarian worms; males with 1 or 2 spicules; esophagus bulbed; tail of female usually slender and pointed. Includes Enterobius.

3. Suborder **Strongylata.** Usually meromyarian; males with 2 spicules and with a true bursa supported by 6 paired rays and one dorsal one which may be divided; mouth simple, without lips, or with a buccal capsule; esophagus muscular, club-shaped, or cylindrical; eggs thin-shelled and colorless. Includes hookworms, strongyles, gapeworms, and lungworms.

4. Suborder **Spirurata.** Esophagus cylindrical, often part glandular and part muscular; males usually with 2 spicules and well-developed alae and papillae on spirally coiled tail; mouth either simple with no or rudimentary lips, or with 2 or 4 paired lips; vagina elongated and tubular; posterior part of esophagus with numerous nuclei; require intermediate host.

Superfamily 1. *Spiruroidea.* Mouth usually with a chitinized vestibule and 2 or 4 paired lips; vulva usually in middle or posterior part of body; males with spirally coiled tail with broad alae supported by papillae; eggs usually escape with feces and are eaten by intermediate host. Includes Gongylonema, Gnathostoma, and Physaloptera.

Superfamily 2. *Filarioidea.* Slender, delicate worms; mouth usually simple, without lips and rarely a vestibule; females with vulva far anterior; males small with coiled tails with or without alae, but always with papillae; usually give birth to embryos which swarm in blood or skin and develop in bloodsucking insects. Includes filariae and Onchocerca.

5. Suborder **Camallanata.** Mouth simple or with lateral jaws; posterior part of esophagus with 1 or 3 large nuclei; requires intermediate host.

Superfamily 1. *Dracunculoidea.* Mouth simple, surrounded by circlet of papillae; alimentary canal and vulva atrophied in adult females; males much smaller than females; embryos evacuated through burst uterus and mouth. Includes guinea worm (Dracunculus).

REFERENCES

ALICATA, J. B., Early Developmental Stages of Nematodes Occurring in Swine, *U. S. Dept. Agr., Tech. Bull.*, **489**, 1935.

BAYLIS, H. A., and DAUBNEY, R. A., *A Synopsis of the Families and Genera of Nematodes*, London, 1926

CHANDLER, A. C., The Nature and Mechanism of Immunity in Various Intestinal Nematode Infections, *Am. J. Trop. Med.*, **19**, 309 (1939).

CHITWOOD, B. G., A Revised Classification of the Nematoda, *Skrjabin Festschr.*, Moscow, 69 (1937).

CHITWOOD, B. G., and CHITWOOD, M. B., An Introduction to Nematology, Sect. I, Pts. I–III, and Sect. II, Pts. I and II so far published. Washington and Babylon, N. Y., 1937–1942.

CRAM, E. B., Bird Parasites of the Nematode Suborders Strongylata, Ascaridata, and Spirurata, *U. S. Natl. Museum Bull.*, **140** (1927).

HOEPPLI, R., Über Beziehungen zwischen dem biologischen Verhalten parasitischer Nematoden und histologischen Reaktionen des Wirbeltierkorpers, *Arch. Schiffs- u. Tropen-Hyg.*, **31**, 3 (1927).

LAPAGE, G., *Nematodes Parasitic in Animals*, London, 1937.

RAUTHER, R., Nematodes, in *Handbuch der Zoologie* (ed. by W. Kukenthal), Band II, Hälfte 1, Berlin, 1928–1933.

YORK, W. W., and MAPLESTONE, P. A., *The Nematode Parasites of Vertebrates*, London, 1926.

CHAPTER 16

Trichinella, Trichuris, and Their Allies

SUBORDER TRICHURATA

The worms belonging to the suborder Trichurata differ strikingly from all other nematodes in the appearance of the esophagus, which consists of a fine capillary tube embedded in a long column of single cells which form a structure called a stichosome, and which are believed to function as esophageal glands. The anterior portion of the body, containing only the esophagus, is always very fine and slender and in some forms is sharply demarkated from the relatively coarse posterior part of the body containing the intestine and reproductive organs. The vulva opens either at the end of the esophagus or anterior to this point. The eggs, if produced, are easily recognizable by their barrel shape with an opercular plug at each end. Trichinella, however, forms no egg shells, and the embryos hatch before birth.

The families and principle genera of this suborder are differentiated as follows:

Trichuridae. ♀ oviparous; ♂ with protrusible spiny spicular sheath and usually a spicule.
    Trichuris. Anterior portion of body much more slender than posterior; whipworms.
    Capillaria. Anterior portion slender but not sharply different from posterior; fine, hairlike worms.
Trichinellidae. ♀ viviparous; ♂ with no spicule or spicule sheath; contains Trichinella only.
Trichosomoididae. ♀ oviparous; ♂ parasitic in vagina of ♀; in urinary bladder of rodents; 1 genus, Trichosomoides.

Trichuris or Whipworms

The whipworm derives its name from its whiplike form, having a thick posterior part of the body containing the reproductive organs and a longer lashlike anterior part occupied only by the slender esophagus. The name Trichuris means " thread tail " and was given before it was recognized that the slender part was really a head and not a tail. Someone else more appropriately named the worm Trichocephalus (thread head), but since the other name was given first it must be used, in spite of its reflection on the inaccurate observation of its originator.

Whipworms are common inhabitants of the cecum and large intestine of many animals, including dogs, rodents, pigs, and all sorts of ruminants, as well as man and monkeys. Schwartz concluded in 1928 that the whipworms of pig and man are identical and that the whipworm commonly found in apes and monkeys is also the same species. The human species, *Trichuris trichiura*, has a world-wide distribution and is very common in the moist parts of warm countries. It usually inhabits the cecum but occasionally establishes itself in the appendix or upper part of the large intestine. It buries its slender head in folds of the intestinal wall, occasionally threading it into the mucous membranes.

Morphology. The whipworm has a length of 30 to 50 mm., of which the threadlike esophageal portion occupies about two-thirds. The mouth has no lips but is provided with a minute spear. The males are a little smaller than the females and can be distinguished by the curled tail end of the body (Fig. 122*C*). They have a single long spicule, retractile into a sheath with a spiny, bulbous end. Unlike the condition in most nematodes, the ejaculatory duct (distal part of the sperm duct) joins the intestine a long way from the anus, forming a cloacal tube. This joins the spicular tube, containing the spicule and its sheath, also at some distance from the anus (Fig. 122*D*). The vulva of the female is at the junction of the two parts of the body; the single uterus contains numerous eggs. The eggs (Fig. 122*B*) have opercular plugs and are brown; they measure about 50 by 22 μ and are unsegmented when they leave the host.

Life Cycle and Epidemiology. The life cycle is very simple. The eggs develop slowly; even when kept moist and warm they require 3 to 6 weeks for the embryo to reach the hatching point, and under less favorable conditions they may be delayed for months or even years. Spindler demonstrated experimentally that the eggs are less resistant to desiccation than are those of Ascaris, and nearly all die within 12 days when dried on a slide, even in a saturated atmosphere. Epidemiological evidence shows that a high incidence of Trichuris infection is always associated with an abundance of moisture in the soil, due either to a heavy and well-distributed rainfall or to dense shade. Infection may result from polluted water or from hand contaminations from polluted moist soil. In the United States Trichuris infections are more " spotty " in distribution than Ascaris and occur abundantly only in places where there is more or less dooryard pollution, dense shade close to the houses, a heavy rainfall, and a dense clay soil to conserve the moisture. These conditions are met in southwestern Louisiana and in the southern Appalachians.

When embryonated eggs are swallowed they hatch near the cecum, the embryos burrow into the villi for a few days and then take up their residence in the cecum, where they mature in about a month. The

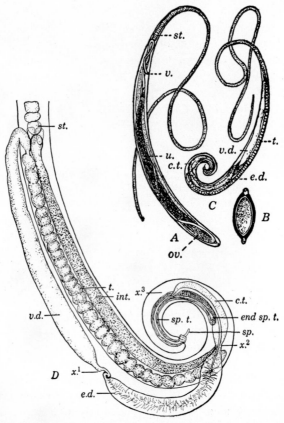

Fig. 122. Human whipworm, *Trichuris trichiura*. *A*, female, × 5; *B*, egg, × 280; *C*, male, × 5; *D*, posterior end of male with vas deferens and ejaculatory duct shown outside body contour, × 12; *c.t.*, cloacal tube; *e.d.*, ejaculatory duct; *int.*, intestine; *sp.*, spicule, with a little of spiny spicular sheath showing; *sp. t.*, spicular tube; *st.*, beginning of stichosome of esophagus; *t.*, testis; *u.*, uterus; *v.*, vulva; *v.d.*, vas deferens; $x.^1$, junction of vas deferens and ejaculatory duct; $x.^2$, junction of ejaculatory duct and intestine to form cloacal tube; $x.^3$, junction of cloacal tube with spicular tube.

worms live for a number of years, and therefore infections build up gradually and do not show seasonal fluctuations.

Pathology. Trichuris infections often produce no obvious symptoms, since frequently only a few worms are present, but sometimes the whole lower part of the colon and rectum may have a film of squirming Trichuris. Such heavy infections may be suggestive of severe hookworm disease. Symptoms observed are loss of appetite, nausea, diarrhea, blood-streaked stools, weakness, loss of weight, anemia, eosinophilia, abdominal discomfort, emaciation, and sometimes fever. Muscular aches and dizziness are also sometimes present. A few or all of these symptoms may be present, depending on the degree of infection and resistance of the host. The most frequent symptom, according to a study of uncomplicated cases in Louisiana by Swartz-welder (1938), is abdominal pain or discomfort, often suggestive of appendicitis. Children suffer severe infections much more frequently than adults.

Treatment. Trichuris is a particularly difficult worm to expel because of its position in the cecum, remote from either the mouth or the anus. Most of the ordinary nematode anthelmintics are relatively ineffective. Until recently best results were obtained with fresh or refrigerated latex of certain figs (Ficus), called by the Spanish name, lêche-de-higuerón, or an extract from it called ficin, containing a proteolytic enzyme. However, it has injurious effects on the mucous membranes (Thomen, 1939). Burrows, Morehouse, and Freed (1947) recommended enteric-coated " enseals " of emetin hydrochloride (see p. 104), which they considered at least as efficient as lêche-de-higuerón and less toxic, although it causes diarrhea with some blood in the stools and sometimes nausea and vomiting. Iron ammonium citrate (4 to 5 grams for 10 to 15 days) was reported by Vaquez Paussa (1937) (see Brown, 1949) as having cured 90 per cent of 300 cases with no untoward effects except diarrhea; it should be given further trial.

Other Trichuridae

Species of the genus Capillaria, with slender, delicate body and relatively short esophageal portion, are parasitic in a wide variety of vertebrates and exercise a remarkable choice of habitats.

Capillaria hepatica lives in the liver of rats and other rodents where its eggs accumulate in dry, yellow patches. Since the eggs require air to become embryonated, direct eating of the egg-burdened liver does not cause infection; the eggs must first be liberated and exposed to air by decomposition of the original host or preliminary passage through the intestine of a predatory animal. Two valid human cases, one from India and one from Panama have been reported, and a number of pseudo-infections in which the eggs were presumably eaten with livers of infected animals have been recorded.

Another species, *C.* (or *Eucoleus*) *aerophila* occurs in the respiratory system of cats, dogs, etc.; it is an important parasite of foxes, causing more harm than all other infections combined, except distemper. One human case has been reported from Moscow. Other species live in the esophagus and crop or in the intestine of birds, in the stomach of rats, in the urinary bladder of cats and foxes, and in the intestines of many animals.

The life cycles of most species are essentially the same as that of Trichuris except for migration via the blood stream of species living outside the alimentary canal. *C. annulata,* infecting the esophagus and crop, and *C. caudinflata,* infecting the intestine of chicks and turkeys, add an additional chapter, for the eggs fail to become infective until after ingestion by earthworms, which serve as true intermediate hosts (Morehouse, 1944). Consequently the fondness of poultry for earthworms is often penalized by Capillaria infection.

Trichinella spiralis and Trichiniasis

The trichina worm, *Trichinella spiralis,* though an intestinal parasite as an adult, is quite different in significance from other intestinal worms. The serious and often fatal results of trichiniasis are due to the offspring of the infecting worms and not to the adult worms in the intestine. Without a doubt this worm, with the pork tapeworm as an accomplice, was responsible for the old Jewish law against the eating of pork. Unlike most human helminths, this one is almost entirely absent from the tropics; it is primarily a parasite of Europe and the United States with moderate infection in Mexico and southern South America, particularly Chile; it is practically absent from San Francisco to Suez and from Africa and Australia.

Structure and Life History. The trichina worm infects many animals. In America hogs are most commonly infected, and infection is common in rats which have access to waste pork. Cats are frequently infected, dogs less often. Man is highly susceptible, and many rodents are easily infected if fed trichinized meat. Birds are very resistant.

The worms gain entrance to the digestive tract as larvae encysted in meat (Fig. 125). They are freed from their cysts in the stomach or intestine and penetrate into the mucosa of the small intestine. Here they undergo a series of moults of which, according to Weller, four seem to be required to bring them to the adult stage. They may reach sexual maturity and copulate as early as 40 hours after being swallowed. The females (Fig. 123) are from 3 to 4 mm. long, whitish, slender and tapering from the middle of the body toward the anterior end; the males are only 1.5 mm. long. The long capillary esophagus occupies one-third to one-half the length of the body. In the female the vulva opens near the middle of the esophageal region; the anterior part of the uterus is crowded with embryos, whereas the posterior part contains developing eggs. The males, aside from their minute size, are characterized by the presence of a pair of conical appendages at the posterior end. In both sexes the anus (or cloaca) is terminal. The males have no spicule.

The adult intestinal worms are essentially short-lived, usually disappearing within 2 or 3 months after infection. Many males pass out of the intestine soon after mating, though some live as long as the females.

Trichina embryos develop in the uterus of the mother and are scarcely 0.1 mm. in length when born. The mother worms usually bur-

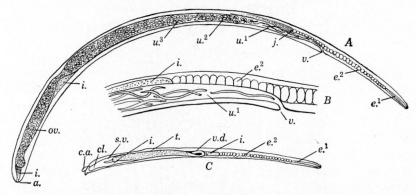

FIG. 123. Adult *Trichinella spiralis*. *A*, female; *B*, vulva region of female; *C*, male; *a.*, anus; *c.a.*, caudal appendages; *cl.*, cloacal tube; $e.^1$, anterior portion of esophagus; $e.^2$, posterior portion of esophagus, or stichosome; *i.*, intestine; *j.*, junction of esophagus and intestine; *ov.*, ovary; *s.v.*, seminal vesicle; *t.*, testis; $u.^1$, anterior portion of uterus with free embryos; $u.^2$, middle portion of uterus with embryos coiled in vitteline membrane; $u.^3$, posterior portion of uterus with ova; *v.*, vulva; *v.d.*, vas deferens. Entire worms × 40 in length, width × 80.

row into the mucous membranes far enough so that the young can be deposited in the tissues rather than into the lumen of the intestine. Embryos may be born within a week after the parents have been swallowed by the host and are most numerous in the circulating blood between the eighth and twenty-fifth days after infection.

The embryos enter lymph or blood vessels in the intestinal wall and are distributed over the entire body. They have been found in practically every organ and tissue but undergo further development inside the cells of the voluntary muscles. Active muscles containing a rich blood supply, such as those of the diaphragm, ribs, larynx, tongue, eye, and certain ones in the limbs, are particularly favored, but all the striated muscles in the body except the heart muscle are liable to invasion. Unlike many tissue-penetrating larvae, however, trichina embryos do not pass through the placenta and cause prenatal infections.

After entering muscle fibers the worms grow rapidly to a length of 1 mm., ten times their original size, and become sexually differentiated. They finally roll themselves into a spiral and are infected after about 17 or 18 days.

The inflammation caused by the movements and waste products of the worms results in the degeneration of the enclosing muscle fibers and

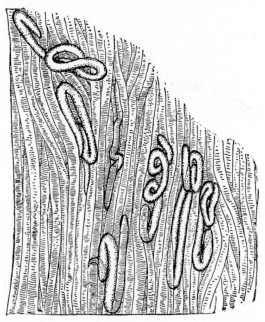

Fig. 124.   Larvae of trichina worms burrowing in human flesh before encystment. From preparation from diaphragm of victim of trichiniasis.   × 75.

in the formation of cysts around the young worms, beginning about a month after infection.   The cysts (Fig. 125), at first very delicate but gradually thickening, are lemon-shaped, from 0.25 to 0.5 mm. long, lying parallel with the muscle fibers; they are not fully developed until after 7 or 8 weeks.   As a rule only one or two worms are enclosed in a cyst but as many as seven have been seen.

After 7 or 8 months or sometimes much later, the cyst walls start to calcify, beginning at the poles.   After 18 months or longer the entire cyst becomes calcified and appears as a hard calcareous nodule (Fig. 126).   Even the enclosed worm, which usually degenerates and dies after some months, becomes calcified after a number of years.   At times, however, the trichina worms do not die and disintegrate so soon and the calcification process is much slower.   There are records of these worms found living in cysts in man 25 to 31 years after infection, but it is doubtful whether in some of these cases a fresh infection did

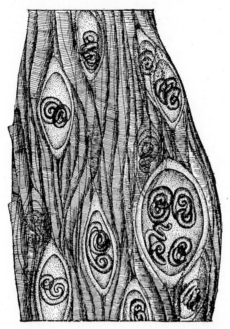

FIG. 125. Larvae of trichina worms, *Trichinella spiralis*, encysted in striated muscle fibers in pork. Camera lucida drawing of cysts in infected sausage. × 75.

not occur unknown to the patient or to the observers who made the records. Experimentally the calcification of well-formed cysts can be

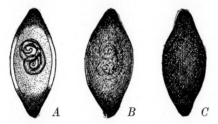

FIG. 126. Stages in calcification of trichina; *A*, ends calcified; *B*, thin layer of calcareous material over whole cyst, worm beginning to degenerate; *C*, complete calcification. (After Ostertag.)

hastened by administration of calcium and ergosterol or even more by large doses of parathormone.

Estimates of the number of encysted larvae that may be expected per female worm vary greatly, but experimental work with various animals indicates about 1500. An ounce of heavily infected sausage may contain more than 100,000 encysted larvae, over half of which are females, so the eating of it may result in more than a hundred million larvae distributing themselves throughout the body of the unfortunate victim. It has been estimated that for man ingestion of 5 trichina larvae per gram of body weight is fatal, for hogs 10, and for rats 30.

After encysting in the flesh no further development takes place until the flesh is eaten by a susceptible animal, whereupon the worms mature and begin reproducing in a few days. It will be seen that, whereas most worms begin the attempt to find new hosts at the egg or early embryo stage of the second generation, the trichina worm does not make a break from its parental host until it has reached the infective stage for another host.

Mode of Infection and Prevalence. Obviously man usually becomes infected from eating raw or imperfectly cooked infected pork. Under modern conditions hogs undoubtedly are most commonly infected by being fed on garbage containing pork scraps, as Hall pointed out in 1937. Nearly 40 per cent of cities of over 4500 population and 50 per cent of cities of over 15,000 dispose of garbage by feeding it to hogs. Stoll suggested calling Trichinella the " garbage worm."

Rats appear to play a very minor role in the epidemiology as compared with infected pork scraps, for hogs are not by nature rat-eaters; Hall says that in his experience hogs and rats usually live together on very friendly terms. Rats pass the disease among themselves by cannibalism, but in most cases it is a closed circuit.

Hall showed that the prevalence of the infection in both man and hogs is closely correlated with methods of raising hogs in different parts of the country. It is highest on the North Atlantic seaboard and in California where hogs are most extensively fed on garbage. In the Middle West, where a higher percentage are raised on pastures and fed on corn, the incidence is lower and it is still lower in the South where the hogs are generally allowed to roam the fields and woods, competing with the squirrels for acorns and without easy access to kitchen scraps or city garbage.

The incidence of human infection is astonishingly high; where examinations have been made in routine autopsies the infection ranges from about 5 per cent in New Orleans to 18 to 27 per cent in northern and western cities, with a general average of over 16 per cent in the entire United States; even these figures are apparently below the actual incidence. Stoll in 1947 called attention to the fact that the United States has three times as much trichiniasis as all the rest of the world combined.   The incidence in hogs in this country is about 1.5 per cent; at this rate, as Gould (1945) pointed out, an average pork-eating American might eat 200 meals of trichinous pork in his lifetime, so the 16 per cent infection is not so surprising.   Fortunately, in contrast to this high incidence of infection, outbreaks since 1900 have been mild, with low mortality; less than 600 clinical cases a year are reported, with a mortality of less than 5 per cent.

The most serious outbreaks occur among Germans, Austrians, and Italians who are fond of various forms of uncooked sausage and " wurst."   Nearly all serious outbreaks can be traced back to animals slaughtered on farms or in small butchering establishments, since in sausage made in large slaughterhouses the meat of an infected animal is almost certain to be diluted with the meat of uninfected animals. Moreover, in federally inspected establishments pork destined for raw consumption is refrigerated long enough to destroy the infection (see below).   There is a particularly high death rate among rural school teachers and preachers, who are invited by their hospitable neighbors to sample and praise new batches of delicious, freshly made sausage.

The Disease.   As we have seen, the vast majority of human infections are never diagnosed or suspected unless the diaphragms are examined microscopically or by artificial digestion after death.   Hall and Collins call attention to the fact that in not one of 222 infections found post-mortem had a diagnosis of trichiniasis been made, although in some there were almost 1000 worms per gram of muscle, and no person harboring that many worms could by any stretch of the imagination be considered free of symptoms.   Clinical symptoms are certainly far commoner than the number of reported cases would indicate.   Some cases are mistaken for typhoid, ptomaine poisoning, " intestinal flu," or what not, but in many cases the patients probably just didn't feel well.   The severity of the symptoms is largely dependent on the number of living worms eaten, although it is undoubtedly influenced also by the general state of health and resistance and by immunity due to prior infections.

The clinical course of trichiniasis is very irregular.   Characteristically, the first symptoms are diarrhea, abdominal pains, nausea, and other gastro-intestinal symptoms, with or without fever, flushing, etc., caused by irritation of the intestine by the growing and adult worms burrowing into its walls.   There is often a sort of general torpor accompanied by weakness, muscular twitching, etc.   As the larvae become numerous in the blood and tissues eosinophilia develops, in extreme cases reaching 50 per cent and even 90 per cent.

The second stage is the period of migration of larvae and penetration of muscles; it is frequently fatal.   One of the earliest symptoms in this stage is a marked puffiness under the eyes and in the lids.   The characteristic symptoms are intense muscular pains and rheumatic aches. Disturbances in the particular muscles invaded cause interference with movements of the eyes, mastication, respiration, etc.   The respiratory troubles become particularly severe in the fourth and fifth weeks of the disease, in fact sometimes so severe as to cause death from dyspnea or asthma.   Profuse sweating and more or less constant fever, though sometimes occuring in the first stage also, are particularly characteristic of the second stage.   The fever is commonly absent in children. Eosinophilia and leucocytosis are nearly always present.

The third stage, accompanying the encystment of the parasites, begins about 6 weeks after infection.   The symptoms of the second stage become exaggerated, and in addition the face again becomes puffy, and the arms, legs, and abdominal walls are also swollen.   The patient becomes anemic, skin eruptions occur, the muscular pains gradually subside, and the swollen portions of the skin often scale off.   Pneumonia is a common complication.   In fatal cases death usually comes in the fourth to sixth week, rarely before the end of the second or after the seventh.

Numerous variations from this course involve both omissions and additions.   In America a more or less persistent diarrhea accompanied by eosinophilia, fever, puffy eyes, and muscular pains should always suggest trichiniasis.   Sometimes the characteristic symptoms are overshadowed by others, involving the heart, eye, or nervous system, where the larvae burrow but do not develop.   Sometimes even the gastrointestinal symptoms fail to appear, and when there are accompanying bacterial infections there may be no eosinophilia.

Recovery usually does not occur in less than from five to six weeks after infection and often not for several months.   Recurrent muscular pains and weakness may continue for a year.   Commonly cases in which a copious diarrhea appears early in the disease are of short duration and mild in type.   Young children, owing either to smaller quantities of pork eaten or to greater tendency to diarrhea, are likely to recover quickly.

Diagnosis.   To confirm a diagnosis is not easy.   Search for adult worms in feces is unreliable, and larvae in blood or cerebrospinal fluid, though present after 8 to 10 days, are difficult to find.   The removal of a bit of muscle and examination of it pressed out between two slides is of no use early in the infection but is often diagnostic later.

Bachman (1928) devised a skin test and a precipitin test which have proved helpful.   The antigen consists of dried and powdered larvae obtained by artificial digestion of the meat of heavily infected animals. The skin test is made by injecting 0.1 cc. of a 1:10,000 dilution of the antigen in saline into the forearm; in positive cases a blanched wheal appears in 5 minutes and reaches a diameter of 1 to 2 cm. in an hour. The precipitin test consists in overlaying a patient's serum with a 1:100 dilution of the antigen and looking for a white ring. The skin test is seldom positive before about 11 to 14 days, however, and may remain positive for at least 7 years after infection, so might be misleading. It may, however, be put to practical use in the detection of infected hogs (see below). There is a difference of opinion as to whether the precipitin test develops earlier or later. After 2 weeks negative skin or precipitin tests are valuable in ruling out trichiniasis, whereas a positive one is valuable as corroborative evidence. Positive reactions sometimes occur in Trichuris infections. In view of the difficulty in making a correct diagnosis, it is not surprising that trichiniasis has been mistaken for at least 50 other disease conditions.

Treatment. The search for a good anthelmintic to kill the larvae in the muscles has not yet been fruitful, and until recently little progress had been made in finding a drug that would dislodge the adult worms in the intestine. Oliver-Gonzalez and Hewitt, however, found that in experimental animals hetrazan administered by stomach tube at the rate of 200 mg. per kg. 3 times a day for 5 to 10 days reduced the worms recovered from the intestine over 80 per cent.

Often, however, diagnosis is not made until the critical stage, when millions of embryos are migrating through the body and developing in muscle fibers. The treatment employed then can be only symptomatic.

Immunity. Considerable resistance to infection is produced by prior exposure. McCoy showed that this resistance was effective against worms developing in the intestine as well as larvae migrating parenterally. Previously infected rats develop a diarrheic condition that McCoy interpreted as allergic; they evacuate most of the larvae fed before they begin development. Culbertson (1942) corroborated this in mice, showing that in previously infected mice fewer adults develop in the intestine and fewer larvae per adult in the muscles, presumably few or none resulting from the later infective feeds. Roth in 1943, by infecting animals with larvae of one sex only, showed that a marked degree of immunity was developed by the intestinal phase alone, though not as much as when the host was invaded by larvae.

A far smaller degree of protection results from injection of vaccines or immune serum, corroborating results obtained by the writer in another nematode infection. When either adults or larvae are placed in immune serum a precipitate forms at mouth and anus, as

Taliaferro and Sarles first demonstrated in the case of Nippostrongylus. This seems to uphold the writer's idea, expressed in 1939, that the immune reaction is directed mainly against the nutritional enzymes or their metabolic products.

From the evidence available it may be presumed that human beings may often be protected from the ill effects of eating heavily trichinized meat by having eaten more lightly infected meat at some earlier date. Data are lacking, however, on how long the immunity is effective.

Prevention. Personal preventive measures against trichiniasis are easy and consist simply in abstinence from all pork that is not thoroughly cooked. Trichinae are quickly destroyed by a temperature of 55° C. (131° F.), but pork must be cooked for a length of time proportionate to its weight in order to insure the permeation of heat to the center. At least 30 to 36 minutes' boiling should be allowed to each kilogram of meat (2¼ lb.). Hurried roasting does not destroy the parasites as long as red or raw portions are left in the center.

Augustine (1933) showed that quick cooling to −34° C., or quick cooling to −18° C. followed by storage at that temperature for 24 hours, or at −15° C. for 48 hours, renders the trichinae noninfective. Cold storage for 20 days at a temperature of −15° C. is required by the U. S. Bureau of Animal Industry for pork products to be used uncooked, unless cured in accordance with certain specified processes, but this appears to be an unnecessarily long time. Salting and smoking are not efficacious unless carried out under certain conditions.

From a public health standpoint little has been accomplished by propaganda against eating uncooked pork or by special treatment in government-inspected slaughterhouses of pork destined to be eaten uncooked. Prevention by meat inspection methods is expensive and at best only partial. It would not touch the most dangerous source of infection — pork butchered on farms and in small local establishments. The same objection applies to the use of a skin test on hogs just before slaughtering, with a view to refrigeration of all positive reacting hogs.

The most feasible and practical plan for the control of trichiniasis consists in the adoption of propaganda, laws, and economic coercion to do away with the widespread custom of feeding raw garbage to hogs. The swine industry is far behind the dairy and poultry industries in modern sanitation and is unorganized and difficult to deal with, but much pressure can be brought to bear through the medium of the meat-packing industry.

In places where it is economically desirable to feed garbage to hogs it is feasible to cook it with steam or boiling water. City health departments should not only prohibit the feeding of uncooked city garbage on municipal hog farms but should also prohibit its sale to private contractors. Local and state-wide control over feeding of garbage to hogs, which could gradually be extended to the small home producers, is undoubtedly the most important method by which trichiniasis can be reduced. Rat destruction and keeping of dead rats from hogs is a factor of minor importance, but desirable.

Other Aphasmidia

Suborder Dioctophymata. The Giant Kidney Worm

The only aphasmid nematodes other than the Trichurata which are normally parasitic in vertebrates are the Dioctophymata. The females have one ovary, anterior vulva (in Dioctophyma), and terminal anus; the males have a terminal bell-shaped bursa without rays, and a single spicule. The eggs have thick, pitted shells.

The only species of importance is *D. renale*, the giant kidney worm, found in the pelvis of the kidney or in the abdominal cavity of dogs and occasionally in many other animals, including man. In Canada it is an important parasite of mink. It is a huge, blood-red worm, the female of which sometimes exceeds 3 ft. in length, with the diameter of a small finger, whereas the male may be from 6 to 16 in. long.

Woodhead (1945) reported a remarkable life cycle for this worm involving a first stage of development in a leech parasitic on crayfish and a second one in a fish, *Ameiurus melas* (bullhead), before reaching the adult stage in a mammal. The stages described are strikingly similar to those of the Gordiacea (see p. 239). It has generally been assumed that the parasite invades one of the kidneys first and enters the abdominal cavity after the kidney has been more or less destroyed, but Stéfanski and Strankowski (1936) think it develops in the body cavity and later penetrates the kidney by means of a histolytic secretion from its highly developed esophageal glands.

REFERENCES

Trichuridae

ALLEN, R. W., and WEHR, E. E., Earthworms as Possible Intermediate Hosts of *Capillaria caudinflata* of the Chicken and Turkey, *Proc. Helminthol. Soc. Wash., D. C.,* **9,** 72 (1942).

BROWN, H. W., Recent Developments in the Chemotherapy of Helminthic Diseases, *Proc. 4th Intern. Congr. Trop. Med. and Malaria,* **2,** Sect. VI, 966–974 (1948).

BURROWS, R. B., MOREHOUSE, W. G., and FREED, J. E., Treatment of Trichuriasis with Enseals of Emetin Hydrochloride, *Am. J. Trop. Med.,* **27,** 327–338 (1947).

CHANDLER, A. C., Specific Characters in the Genus Trichuris, *J. Parasitol.,* **16,** 198 (1930).

CHRISTENSON, R. O., Life History and Epidemiological Studies on the Fox Lungworm, *Capillaria aerophila*, *Livro jubilar do Prof. Travassos*, **119**, Rio de Janeiro, 1938.

FÜLLEBORN, F., Über die Entwicklung von Trichozephalus in Wirte, *Arch. Schiffs- u. Tropen-Hyg.*, **27**, 413 (1923).

GETZ, L., Massive Infection with *Trichuris trichiura* in Children. Report of Four Cases, with Autopsy, *Am. J. Diseases Children*, **70**, 19–24 (1945).

NOLF, L. O., Experimental Studies on Certain Factors Influencing the Development and Viability of the Ova of the Human Trichuris, *Am. J. Hyg.*, **16**, 288 (1932).

OTTO, G. F., Ascaris and Trichuris in Southern United States, *J. Parasitol.*, **18**, 200 (1932).

SWARTZWELDER, J. C., Clinical *Trichocephalus trichiurus* Infection. An Analysis of 81 Cases, *Am. J. Trop. Med.*, **19**, 473 (1938).

THOMEN, I. J., The Latex of Ficus Trees and Derivatives as Anthelmintics: Historical Account, *Am. J. Trop. Med.*, **19**, 409–418 (1939).

Trichinella spiralis

AUGUSTINE, D. L., Effects of Low Temperatures upon Encysted *T. spiralis*, *Am. J. Hyg.*, **17**, 697 (1933).

BACHMAN, G. W., Precipitin Test in Experimental Trichinosis, *J. Preventive Med.*, **2**, 35; An Intradermal Reaction in Experimental Trichinosis, *ibid.*, **2**, 513 (1928).

CULBERTSON, J. T., Active Immunity in Mice against *Trichinella spiralis*, *J. Parasitol.*, **28**, 197 (1942).

GOULD, S. E., *Trichinosis*, Springfield, Ill., 1945.

McCOY, O. R., Artificial Immunization of Rats Against *Trichinella spiralis*, *Am. J. Hyg.*, **21**, 200 (1935); Rapid Loss of Trichinella Larvae Fed to Immune Rats and Its Bearing on the Mechanism of Immunity, *ibid.*, **32**, D, 105 (1940).

National Institute of Health (Hall, Wright, Bozicevich, *et al.*) I–XV, Studies on Trichinosis, *Publ. Health Repts.*, **52**, 468, 512, 539, 873 (1937); **53**, 652, 1086, 1472, 2130 (1938); **55**, 683, 1069 (1940); **56**, 836 (1941); **58**, 1293 (1943); *J. Am. Vet. Med. Assoc.*, **94**, 601 (1939); *Am. J. Publ. Health*, **29**, 119 (1939).

SHOOKHOFF, H. B., BIRNKRANT, W. B., and GREENBERG, M., An Outbreak of Trichinosis in New York City, with Special Reference to Intradermal and Precipitin Tests, *Am. J. Publ. Health*, **36**, 1403–1411 (1946).

SPINK, W. W., and AUGUSTINE, D. L., The Diagnosis of Trichinosis, *J. Am. Med. Assoc.*, **104**, 1801 (1935).

STOLL, N. R., This Wormy World, *J. Parasitol.*, **33**, 1–18 (1947).

Dioctophyma

STÉFANSKI, W., and STRANKOWSKI, M., Sur un cas de penetration du strongle géant dans le rein droit du chien, *Ann. parasitol. humaine et comparée*, **14**, 55 (1936).

UNDERWOOD, P. C., and WRIGHT, W. H., A Report of the Giant Nematode, *Dioctophyme renale*, from a Dog, with a Summary of American Records, *J. Am. Vet. Med. Assoc.*, **85**, 256 (1934).

WOODHEAD, A. E., The Life History Cycle of *Dioctophyma renale*, the Giant Kidney Worm of Man and Many Other Mammals (Abstract), *J. Parasitol.*, **31**, 12 (1945).

CHAPTER 17

The Hookworms and Their Allies

SUBORDER STRONGYLATA

No group of the nematodes causes more injury to man or greater economic loss through attacks on his domestic animals than the members of the suborder Strongylata, the great majority of which are parasites of mammals. They are bloodsuckers and cause severe injury to their hosts by loss of blood sucked by them or wasted from hemorrhages; the result is anemia, loss of vitality, and general unthriftiness. The worms of this suborder have one easily recognizable character

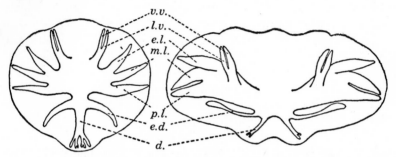

Fig. 127. Diagrams of bursas (spread out flat) of *Ancylostoma duodenale* (left) and *Necator americanus* (right), showing arrangement of rays; *d.*, dorsal ray; *e.d.*, externo-dorsal; *e.l.*, externo-lateral; *l.v.*, latero-ventral; *m.l.*, medio-lateral; *p.l.*, postero-lateral; *v.v.*, ventro-ventral. (After Chandler, *Hookworm Disease.*)

which is constant and peculiar to them, namely, a bursa surrounding the cloaca of the male. This is a sort of umbrella-like expansion of the cuticle at the end of the body which is supported by fleshy rays comparable with the ribs of an umbrella. The arrangement of the rays is remarkably constant, and each ray is given a name. Usually the bursa consists of three lobes, two lateral and one dorsal, and it may or may not be split ventrally; in some species it is small, in others very large. The dorsal lobe is supported by a dorsal ray which may be bifurcated only at its tip or may be split almost to the base. From its root there arise a pair of externo-dorsal rays which usually enter the lateral lobes. The latter are supported by three pairs of lateral rays arising from a common root and two pairs of ventral rays arising from another common root. The names and arrangement of these rays as they occur in hookworms are shown in Fig. 127.

Other characteristics of the group are the club-shaped or cylindrical muscular esophagus and the absence of distinct lips; the mouth is either a simple opening at the end of a fine slender head or is provided with a more or less highly specialized buccal capsule. The eggs always have thin transparent shells that do not become bile stained and are therefore colorless. They are in some stage of segmentation or contain embryos when laid. The eggs hatch outside the body into free-living larvae which, after reaching a certain stage of development, enter a new host either by burrowing through the skin or by being ingested with water or vegetation.

The suborder has commonly been divided into three superfamilies, Strongyloidea, Trichostrongyloidea, and Metastrongyloidea, the first two being mostly intestinal forms with and without a well-developed mouth capsule, respectively, and the third being parasites of the respiratory system without mouth capsules and with stunted bursas. Doughety (1945), however, pointed out that habitat is a poor criterion for classification and that the best morphological character separating most of the members of the two groups without mouth capsules is the presence of a long vagina and simple parallel uteri in the metastrongylids, and a short transverse vagina and divergent uteri with specialized ovejectors in the trichostrongylids (Fig. 140). This, however, throws some of the respiratory forms with the intestinal ones, so it seems best to follow Doughety and not recognize superfamilies at all. We shall consider the following families which have important representatives in man and domestic animals:

I. Eustomatous forms, i.e., with well-developed mouth capsule.
   1. **Ancylostomidae** (hookworms). Capsule with ventral teeth or plates inside opening (Fig. 129).
   2. **Strongylidae.** With crown of leaflike processes (corona radiata) (Fig. 136).
   3. **Syngamidae** (gapeworms). Capsule hooped by large chitinous ring (Fig. 138).
II. Meiostomatous forms, i.e., with reduced or vestigial mouth capsule.
   1. **Trichostrongylidae.** Intestinal forms or lungworms with ovejectors (Fig. 140B); bursa well-developed except in lungworms of subfamily Skrjabingylinae.
   2. **Metastrongylidae.** Lungworms with long vagina and simple parallel uteri (Fig. 140A) and reduced bursa.

Hookworms of Man

Importance. No human worm infection has attracted so much attention and has been the subject of so much investigation as hookworm. This is justifiably true, for no other worm infection is as significant to the human race as a whole, although, at least in civilized parts of the world, it is not the scourge it was up to about 1920. Hookworm is never spectacular like some other diseases, but is essentially insidious; year after year, generation after generation, it saps the vitality and undermines the health and efficiency of whole communities. In the course of a few summers a healthy family may become pale and puny; once industrious, they become languid and backward in work; once prosperous, they fall into debt; once proud, property-owning people, they are reduced to tenancy and poverty; the

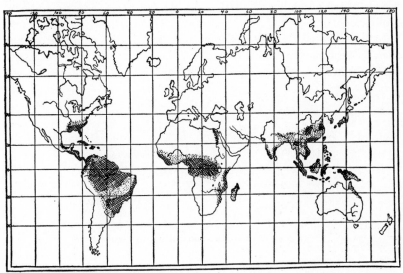

Fig. 128. Map showing distribution of hookworm infections. Crossed lines represent areas with heavy or moderately heavy infections. Stipple represents areas of light infections in a high percentage of individuals.

children, once bright and intelligent, become dull and indifferent, and soon fall hopelessly behind in school and drop out. For years the " poor white trash " of some rural parts of our South were considered a shiftless, good-for-nothing, irresponsible people, worthy only of scorn and of the sordid poverty and ignorance which they brought upon themselves as the fruits of their supposedly innate shiftlessness, but the discovery that these unfortunate people were the victims of hookworms which stunted them physically and mentally made them objects of pity rather than scorn. Fortunately, their unhappy lot has been greatly improved since the early part of the present century.

Distribution. The general distribution of hookworm infection is shown in Fig. 128, the crossed lines representing areas where it is known or thought to be an important public health problem, and the dotted areas representing places where hookworm is common but is of less importance because the infections are for the most part light. Localities which have particularly severe infections in at least some large element of the population include the Gulf Coast states of America, some of the West Indies (especially Puerto Rico), Central America, the Amazon valley, and the southeast coast of Brazil in the New World, and Egypt, west and central Africa, a few localities in southeastern Asia and China, and some of the East Indies in the Old World. Hookworm also occurs outside of the warm, moist parts of the world in mines, where suitable conditions exist, even as far north as England and Holland.

In the United States hookworm is practically confined to the southeastern coastal states from Virginia to eastern Texas, together with Tennessee, Kentucky, southeastern Missouri, and Arkansas.

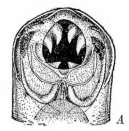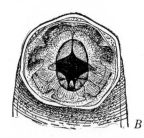

Fig. 129. Buccal cavity and mouth of *Ancylostoma duodenale* (*A*), and *Necator americanus* (*B*), showing teeth in former and cutting ridges in latter. Dorsal view. *A*, × 100; *B*, × 230. (After Looss.)

Surveys by Leathers, Keller, *et al.* have shown that there has been a remarkable decrease in both the incidence and intensity of infection since the first surveys were made. In 6 of 8 southern states the average incidence, by techniques that miss very light cases, was 36.6 per cent in 1910–1914 and 11.2 per cent in 1930–1938. In 1940 the incidences varied from 50 per cent in western Florida to 7 to 9 per cent in Tennessee and Kentucky, the areas of important infection being largely localized. The highest incidence is in whites in the 15- to 19-year age group. Only a small percentage of those infected have enough worms to cause clinical symptoms.

Species. Two species of hookworms are common human parasites, *Ancylostoma duodenale* and *Necator americanus*. They are similar in general appearance and in most details of their life cycle, habits, etc., but *A. duodenale* is much more injurious to its host and is harder to expel by means of anthelmintics. All hookworms, including many species found in dogs, cats, herbivores, and other animals, are rather stocky worms, usually about half an inch in length, with a well-developed bursa, very long-needle-like spicules, and with a conspicuous goblet- or cup-shaped buccal capsule, guarded ventrally by a pair of chitinous plates which either bear teeth, as in the ancylostomes, or have a bladelike edge, as in the necators and their allies (Fig. 129). The human ancylostome, *A. duodenale,* has two well-developed teeth on each plate, with a rudimentary third one near the median line; *A. caninum,* common in dogs and cats, has three pairs of teeth, and *A. braziliense,* also common in cats and dogs, especially in the tropics,

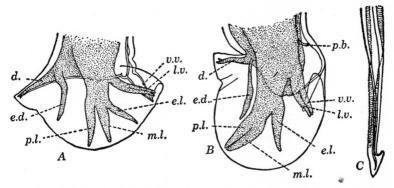

Fig. 130.   Side view of bursas of *Ancylostoma duodenale* (*A*) and *Necator americanus* (*B*), and terminal portion of spicules of Necator (*C*).   Abbreviations as in Fig. 127. (After Looss from Chandler, *Hookworm Disease.*)

has one large tooth and a rudimentary one on each side.   The latter species is an occasional human parasite, and its larvae are a frequent cause of " creeping eruption."

Ancylostoma.   *Ancylostoma duodenale* (Fig. 131) is primarily a northern species and predominates only in Europe, North Africa, western Asia, northern China, and Japan, but it has accompanied infected mankind to all parts of the world; it is possible that it may have been the original species in at least a part of the American aborigines.   It is larger and coarser than Necator, the females averaging about 12 mm. and the males about 9 mm. in length.   Freshly expelled specimens have a dirty rust color.   The vulva of the female is behind the middle of the body, and the tail is tipped by a minute spine.   The males are easily recognizable by their broad bursas, which have the rays arranged as shown in Figs. 127 and 130*A*.   The single dorsal ray and the nearly equal spread of the three lateral rays are good marks for distinguishing this species from Necator, but after a little experience the two genera of either sex can be distinguished with the naked eye by the form of the head, which in ancylostomes is coarse and only slightly bent dorsally,

whereas in necators it is much finer and sharply bent (Fig. 131).   The
structure of the mouth capsule of this species is shown in Fig. 129.

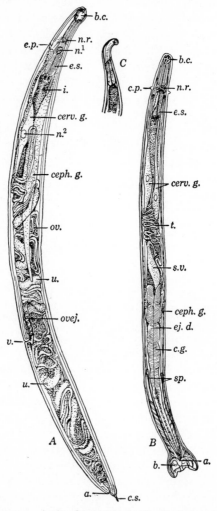

FIG. 131. Hookworms.   *A, Ancylostoma duodenale; B,* ♂ of same; *C,* head of *Necator
americanus,* same scale; *a.,* anus; *b.,* bursa; *b.c.,* buccal capsule; *ceph. g.,* cephalic gland;
cerv. g., cervical gland; *c.g.,* cement glands; *c.p.,* cervical papilla; *c.s.,* caudal spine; *e.p.,*
excretory pore; *ej. d.,* ejaculatory duct; *es.,* esophagus; *i.,* intestines; *n.*[1], nucleus of
cephalic gland; *n.*[2], nucleus of cervical gland; *n.r.,* nerve ring; *ov.,* ovary; *ovej.,* ovejector;
sp., spicules; *s.v.,* seminal vesicle; *t.,* testis; *u.,* uterus; *v.,* vulva.   (Adapted from Looss.)

A. duodenale is primarily a human parasite but on rare occasions has
been found in pigs and experimentally can be reared occasionally in
dogs, cats, and monkeys.

A. braziliense is a smaller and more slender worm, dead white or ivory-colored, with a strikingly clear esophageal region in fresh worms. In some places in the tropics practically every cat and most dogs are infected with it, and in some localities, especially in Burma and some East Indian Islands, about 1 to 2 per cent of the hookworms harbored by man are of this species. Particular interest attaches to it, however, from its connection with " creeping eruption " (see p. 402). Fülleborn found creeping eruption to be produced also by the European dog hookworm, *Uncinaria stenocephala*, which is more nearly related to Necator.

Necator. *Necator americanus* is primarily a tropical worm. It is now the predominant species in all parts of the world except those mentioned in the section on ancylostomes. In our southern states 95 per cent or more of the hookworms are of this species. It is often called the " American " hookworm because it was first discovered here, but it is probably African in origin, having spread from there to India, the Far East, and Australia, and also to America. Interesting evidence of past and present migrations of mankind can be traced in the hookworm fauna of various countries.

Necator is smaller and more slender than *A. duodenale;* the females average 10 to 11 mm. in length and the males 7 to 8 mm. The vulva of the female is anterior to the middle of the body, and there is no caudal spine. The bursa is longer and narrower than in the ancylostomes (Figs. 127 and 130*B*), and is distinguished by the split dorsal ray and approximation of two of the lateral rays. The struture of the mouth capsule is shown in Fig. 129*B*. *N. americanus* is primarily a human parasite, though capable of development in apes and monkeys, but a very similar form has been found in pigs in tropical America. Although regarded by its discoverers, Ackert and Payne, as a separate species, *N. suillus*, it is thought by others to be the human species, slightly modified by its development in a strange host. Other species of Necator have been described from chimpanzees.

Life Cycle. The adult hookworms of both genera reside in the small intestine, where they draw a bit of the mucous membrane into their buccal capsules and nourish themselves on blood and tissue juices which they suck (Fig. 132). Their main business in life is the production of eggs, and they tend strictly to business! Careful estimates show that each female necator produces from 5000 to 10,000 eggs per day, and ancylostomes over twice that many. Yet the bodies of the worms contain on the average only about 5 per cent of this number of eggs at any one time.

The eggs average about 70 by 38 μ in necators and 60 by 38 μ in ancylostomes, but the species cannot be identified reliably by eggs in the feces. They are in the four-celled stage when freshly passed and do not develop further until exposed to air. They require moisture and warmth also, and if these conditions are present, and there are no injurious substances in the feces, development proceeds so rapidly that an embryo hatches in less than 24 hours. Usually feces in the tropics are not left undisturbed but are stirred up, aerated, and mixed with soil by dung beetles and other insects, which greatly improves the environment for the eggs and larvae of hookworms.

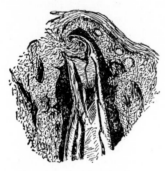

FIG. 132. American hookworm; section showing manner of attachment to intestinal wall. (After Ashford and Igaravidez, from photo by Dr. W. M. Gray.)

The hatched larvae (Fig. 133, 8) are of the " rhabditiform " type, i.e., they have an esophagus with an anterior thick portion connected by a necklike region with a posterior bulb, a character which distinguishes these larvae from " filariform " larvae, which have a long cylindrical esophagus typically without a terminal bulb. After the second moult the larvae of hookworms lose their typical rhabditiform esophagus, but they never become truly filariform, although often so called; a preferable name is " strongyliform." The free-living larvae of hookworms in all stages are distinguishable from the rhabditiform larvae of Strongyloides by the long mouth cavity (cf. Figs. 133, 8 and 9). Larvae of many Strongylata of domestic animals, e.g., esophagostomes and trichostrongyles, are distinguishable by their long, filamentous tails.

The larvae feed on bacteria and perhaps other matters in the feces, and grow rapidly. At the end of about 2 days they moult, grow some more, and at the end of about 5 days they moult again. This time, however, the shed cuticle is retained as a protecting sheath (Fig. 133, 11), which may remain until the larva penetrates the skin of a host or may be torn or worn away by the movements in the soil. A small oval body, the genital primordium (Fig. 133, 11, g.r.), is visible near the middle of the body. These larvae are easily distinguishable from the more typically filariform infective larvae of Strongyloides (Fig. 147) by the shorter and bulbed esophagus and the pointed tail (notched in Strongyloides).

These larvae are now in the infective stage. They eat no more but subsist on food material stored up as granules in the intestinal cells

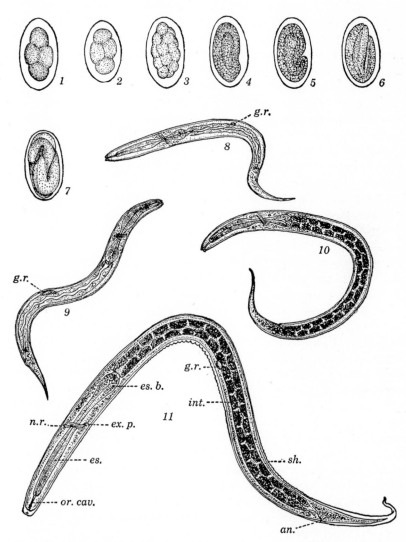

Fig. 133. Stages in life cycle of hookworms from egg to infective larva. *1*, egg of *Necator americanus* at time of leaving body of host; *2*, same of *Ancylostoma duodenale;* *3* to *7*, stages in segmentation and development of embryo in the egg; *8*, newly hatched embryo; *9*, same of Strongyloides for comparison (note difference in length of oral cavity and size of genital rudiment, *g.r.*); *10*, second stage larva; *11*, third stage (infective) larva; *an.*, anus; *ex. p.*, excretory pore; *g.r.*, genital rudiment; *int.*, intestine; *n.r.*, nerve ring; *es.*, esophagus; *es. b.*, esophageal bulb; *or. cav.*, oral cavity; *sh.*, sheath. × 285. (After Looss from Chandler, *Hookworm Disease.*)

during their 5 days of feasting. The optimum temperature for development is between 70° and 85° F.; lower temperatures retard and finally stop it, and in frosty weather the eggs and young larvae are destroyed; higher temperatures decrease hatching and increase larval mortality. The infective larvae of hookworms are about 500 to 600 μ in length, with characteristic form, color, and movements which make them recognizable after some experience. Minute details of anatomy also make it possible to distinguish necator from ancylostome larvae.

Biology of Larvae. Accurate knowledge of the biology of hookworm larvae was gained after the discovery of a method of extracting the larvae from soil by Baermann in 1917 and its improvement by Cort and his colleagues (1922). Important contributions were made by Cort, Payne, Riley, Augustine, Ackert, and Stoll in the West Indies (1921–1925), by the writer in India (1924–1928), and by Svensson (1926) in China.

The larvae normally live in the upper half inch of soil, and commonly climb up to the highest points to which a film of moisture extends on soil particles, dead vegetation, etc., and extend their bodies into the air to await an opportunity to apply themselves to a human foot which is unfortunate enough to come in contact with them. When exposed to a hot sun or to superficial drying of the soil they retreat into crevices in the upper layer.

They do not migrate laterally to any great extent, but are dispersed by rain, insects, etc. In loose-textured soil they can migrate vertically, even to the extent of 2 or 3 ft., but in trenches or pits they do not climb the walls, since, from the standpoint of the larvae, the soil walls are very rugged paths. Before they have climbed more than a few inches they reach the top of some projecting particle from which they extend themselves, unaware that they have not reached a vantage point at the top, and are thus trapped. The larvae are strongly attracted by moderate heat and are stimulated to activity by contact with objects; it is these reactions which cause the larvae to burrow into the skin of animals.

Since the larvae have only the stored food granules on which to subsist until a suitable host is reached, the more active they are the sooner their food supply is used up and the sooner they die. Vertical migration through even a few inches of soil is an expensive process for them. Under tropical conditions, where alternations of sun and shade, of heat and coolness, and also disturbance by rain, insects, etc., stimulate them to frequent movement, their span of life is not nearly so long as it was thought to be; about 90 per cent of the larvae succumb in

2 to 3 weeks, and almost all are dead in 6 weeks. On the other hand, larvae kept in water in a cool place and left undisturbed may live for 18 months or more. Larvae that have had their reserve food greatly depleted, although still alive, may not have enough energy to penetrate the skin of a host.

Mode of Infection. Infection normally takes place by penetration of the skin by the larvae; this important discovery was first made by Looss in 1898 when he accidentally spilled some water containing larvae on his hands and acquired an infection. Skin penetration usually results from contact with infested soil but may come from handling feces-soiled clothing, etc., if left damp for 4 or 5 days. The larvae burrow until they enter a lymph or blood vessel and are then carried by the blood stream to the right side of the heart and thence to the lungs, where they are usually caught in the capillaries and again proceed to burrow, this time into the air spaces of the lung. The ciliary movement of the epithelium of the bronchial tubes and trachea carries them to the throat, whence they are either expectorated with sputum or swallowed. If they are swallowed, they go to the intestine and bury themselves between the villi and in the depths of glands for a brief period until the third moult is completed, after which they acquire a provisional mouth capsule and can successfully adhere to the mucosa.

It is also possible for the larvae to cause infection when swallowed with food or water, though in nature this must be of relatively rare occurrence. Although in normal hosts some swallowed larvae bury themselves in the glands of the stomach and intestine for a few days and then establish themselves directly in the intestine, the majority enter the circulation and go by the roundabout path through the body.

The third moult may occur as early as 3 days after infection, but it may be delayed for several days longer. The larvae grow rapidly to a length of 3 to 5 mm. and then moult for the fourth and last time, with the acquisition of the definitive mouth capsule and the development of reproductive organs. In man the eggs first begin to appear in the feces usually about 6 weeks after infection.

Longevity. The length of life of the adult worms in the intestine may be 5 years or more but is much shorter in the majority of the worms. There is evidence that in natural infections, when repeated reinfections occur, the peak of egg production of newly acquired worms may occur after about 6 months, after which there is a rapid falling off in number of worms. A high percentage of newly acquired worms in repeatedly infected individuals is probably lost within a year. In places where there are prolonged unfavorable seasons little cumulative increase in worms can occur on account of the large annual reduction in worms during the season when reinfection is largely stopped.

Epidemiology. Many environmental factors influence the amount of hookworm infection in a community. Temperature, as already intimated, is a prime controlling factor. Rainfall is also of fundamental importance. Heavy hookworm infections are never common in localities having less than 40 inches of rain a year, and with larger annual rainfall much depends on the seasonal distribution and on the distribution within each month, for hookworm larvae will not withstand complete desiccation. Excessive rainfall, resulting in saturated soil, may exert an even greater check on hookworm infection. Such local factors as humidity, drainage, and hygroscopic nature of the soil also influence the effectiveness of short rainless periods.

The nature of the soil is very influential; hookworm never thrives in regions of heavy clay soil, whereas in adjoining areas with sandy or humus soil it may constitute an important problem. Salt impregnation of soil is also injurious. Vegetation exerts an influence, since dense shade is far more favorable for the development and longevity of larvae than light shade or exposure to sun. Irrigation may make rainless regions favorable for hookworm if moistened soil is selected for defecation.

Animals, such as pigs, dogs, and cattle, which devour feces, especially in the tropics, exert an influence, since in pigs and dogs the eggs in fresh feces pass through the animals uninjured and may be voided with the feces of the animals in places where they are more, or less, likely to cause infection. In chickens, on the other hand, and probably in cattle also, most of the eggs are destroyed when ingested. Insects play an important role. Dung beetles are allies of hookworms since they mix feces with soil and render the cultural conditions far more favorable; cockroaches, on the other hand, destroy most of the eggs in their " gizzards " and were found by the writer to play an important part in keeping down hookworm infections in Indian mines.

Many human factors also affect the amount of hookworm. Some races are more susceptible than others. The white race is particularly susceptible, and Negroes very slightly so. The other races appear to occupy various intermediate positions. Age and sex and the corresponding differences in habits influence the amount of infection and also affect the injury done by a given number of worms, for females are more injured than males and children more than adults.

Occupation is often a determining factor, in so far as it leads to habits which render the acquisition of worms more likely. In most countries agriculture and mining are the main hookworm occupations, but in most places the infection is not strictly agricultural but merely rural. The raising of such crops as coffee, tea, sugar, cacao, and bananas is particularly conducive to hookworm in soil-pollution countries since they are grown in moist, warm climates under conditions affording an abundance of shade and suitable soil; cotton and grain raising are much less dangerous since these crops are grown in drier areas, and cotton in unfavorable soil. Raising of rice and jute, mainly on flooded ground, is not associated with heavy hookworm infections. In China and Japan, where night soil is used as fertilizer, hookworm infection is more strictly agricultural and varies greatly with the type of crop produced and the manner in which the night soil is used. Especially heavy infections occur in mulberry-raising districts, since ideal conditions for hookworm propagation are afforded.

Defecation habits are also of great importance. In soil-pollution countries the greater part of the infections are acquired while standing on previously polluted ground during the act of defecation. The concentration of the defecation areas, the extent to which people mingle in common areas around villages, the type of places selected, etc., are all influential factors. Wherever simple soil pollution is modified by the use of standing places or primitive latrines that keep the feet off the polluted ground and bring about an unfavorable concentration of fecal material, hookworm infections are light.

Shoe wearing also affords a high degree of protection; in southern United States and Queensland hookworm infection is almost entirely limited to children who are less than 14 to 16 years of age, since after the age of 14 shoes are habitually worn. Even simple sandals or wooden soles without uppers, as worn in parts of India, are effective.

Expectoration habits also have an important effect; those individuals who habitually spit out phlegm collecting in the mouth get rid of many of the hookworms which invade the body. From Suez to Singapore the Orient is polka-dotted with the red expectorations of betel-nut chewers; this prevalence of chewing and consequent expectoration is probably an important factor in keeping hookworm infections at a relatively low level in Far Eastern countries. There is a prevalent notion in our southern states that tobacco chewing is conducive to health. This is not due to any virtue in tobacco juice *per se* but to the constant spitting entailed.

Effect of Diet. Diet is of profound importance. As we shall see, most of the injury done by hookworms is the result of blood loss, for the replacement of which large amounts of iron, protein, and vitamins are required in the diet. If these are present in adequate amounts the host soon develops a partial immunity which results both in resistance

to reinfection and in loss of worms already harbored — the so-called
" self-cure " which Stoll in 1929 demonstrated in a striking manner in
Haemonchus infections in sheep and which has since been shown to
be a common phenomenon among intestinal nematodes and trematodes.
In other words, a good diet, as Foster and Cort demonstrated long
ago (1932), does not permit serious damage from hookworm infection
to occur except when there are overwhelming initial infections with
the blood loss so great that *no* diet can compensate for it (Cort and
Otto, 1940). Except in such cases a good diet permits an immune
response to develop which reduces an existing infection and protects
against severe reinfections; with a poor diet, on the other hand, the
bloodsucking of the worms already present lowers the vitality of the
host to such an extent that no immune response can develop or if
developed will break down. In an endemic area this results in an
increasing worm burden, causing still further injury to the host, etc. —
a vicious cycle that is ultimately fatal. As Cruz (1948) pointed out,
hookworm disease is essentially associated with malnutrition. The
severity of hookworm disease in a community is measured far more
by the adequacy of the diet than it is by the average number of hookworms harbored.

Pathology. *Preintestinal Phase.* When human hookworms enter
the skin they may cause " ground itch " or " water sore," characterized
by itching and inflammation, and often development of pustular sores
from secondary bacterial invasion. Ancylostomes less consistently
cause these effect than necators.

Some " foreign " species of hookworms, particularly *Ancylostoma
braziliense,* commonly fail to find their way below the germinative
layer of skin, thus failing to reach blood or lymph vessels. They
then wander aimlessly just under the surface, sometimes for 3 months
or more, causing tortuous channels — a condition known as " creeping
eruption " (Fig. 134). The severity of the reaction is conditioned by
previous sensitization and the allergic responsiveness of the victim.
In highly allergic individuals *A. caninum* and the European Uncinaria
cause severe skin reactions, though not typical creeping eruption.
Creeping eruption is common on the coasts of southern United States
and tropical America, where children play in sandpiles or adults on
bathing beaches that are the chosen defecation sites of dogs and cats
infected with *A. braziliense.* It could be prevented by excluding
dogs and cats from such places, or bathers from beaches that are not
washed by tides. Millspaugh and Sompayrac (1942) reported that in
Florida creeping eruption incapacitated a considerable number of naval
personnel. They recommended treatment by an ethyl chloride spray

shortly ahead of the end of the inflamed burrow or treatment by electric cautery after injection of procaine.

The next effect of *human* hookworms is in the lungs, where the burrowing larvae may predispose to pulmonary infection or even cause pneumonia symptoms themselves, if numerous.

In repeatedly infected cases many larvae are frustrated in their migration through the body by the development of immunity. Immunized serum causes precipitates to form about the mouth, intestine, anus, and excretory pore of migrating larvae, probably directed against digestive enzymes or metabolic products of some kind. The larvae are also immobilized, and many are destroyed by encapsulation and phagocytosis in the skin, lymph glands or lungs. The eosinophilia and occasional leucocytosis associated with hookworm infection probably result from liberation of proteins from such captured worms in partially immune persons. This larval phase of infection was emphasized by Ashford, Payne, and Payne (1933).

Intestinal Phase. After several weeks, as the worms are developing in the intestine, local symptoms may appear. Occasionally the worms bury themselves in the mucosa. The principal effects, however, are from anemia from the constant sucking of blood.

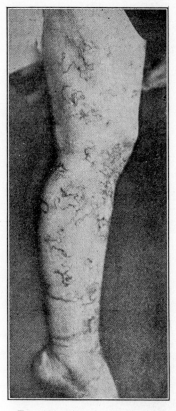

FIG. 134. A case of "creeping eruption," about two weeks after infection. (After Kirby-Smith, Dove, and White.)

Wells (1931) calculated that 500 *A. caninum* in a dog may suck nearly a pint of blood per day. The permanent loss of most of the iron causes reduction in number and size of corpuscles and in their hemoglobin content unless the iron is adequately replaced in the diet. In children the diversion of nutriment to keep the hemoglobin up to standard interferes with normal growth, thus causing a stunting in size.

When the repair cannot keep pace with the damage and immunity fails to develop, symptoms appear. In severe cases the hemoglobin may be reduced to 30 per cent or less, with 2,000,000 or less corpuscles per c.mm. The most noticeable symptoms are a severe pallor; extreme languor and indisposition to play or work, popularly interpreted as laziness; a flabbiness and tenderness of the muscles; breathlessness after slight exertion; enlargement and palpitation of the heart, with weak and irregular pulse; edema, making the face puffy and the abdomen " pot-bellied "; a fishlike stare in the eyes; reduced perspiration; more or less irregular fever; and heartburn, flatulence, and abdominal discomfort. The appetite is capricious, and frequently there is an abnormal craving for coarse " scratchy " substances such as

Fig. 135.   Hookworms on wall of intestine, showing lesions.   (After International Health Board.)

soil, chalk, and wood. Severe hookworm cases in our southern states a few decades ago were often " dirt-eaters," though they rarely admitted it.

Children may suffer several years' retardation in physical and mental development, with puberty long delayed. The mental retardation results in stupidity and backwardness in school, and there are sometimes other nervous manifestations, such as dizziness, insomnia, optical illusions, general nervousness, and fidgety movements.

The effects of hookworm infection are particularly severe during pregnancy, when the demand for iron by the developing fetus puts an extra drain on the mother. Hookworm is the cause of a tremendous number of stillbirths and is believed by some to be a more serious complication of pregnancy than even syphilis or eclampsia. The reduction of labor efficiency from hookworm infection may amount to 25 or even 50 per cent, and there may be additional loss from sickness and death.

Grades of Infection. In earlier days all infected individuals were lumped together in contrast to those in whom infection was not demonstrated by methods of examination then in vogue. The amount of hookworm in a locality was judged by the percentage infected, and evidence was obtained which demonstrated the greater healthiness and efficiency of the uninfected group. Darling in 1918 was the first to emphasize the importance of the *number* of hookworms harbored, though now we know that even the number may not mean much without considering the adequacy of the diet as well. The first efforts to estimate the number of hookworms harbored were based on worm counts after treatment, but the technical difficulties were too great. In 1923 Stoll devised an easy method of counting the eggs per gram in the feces of infected people and demonstrated that there was a rough correlation between eggs per gram and number of worms harbored. This method, or modifications of it by Stoll and Hausheer and by the Caldwells, both in 1926, has been a valuable yardstick not only for measuring the hookworm burden of communities and the efficacy of control measures, but also for demonstrating the effect of different degrees of infection under varying conditions.

Slight infections with 50 worms or less are practically harmless except in a person who needs additional food much more than he needs hookworm treatment; ordinarily such infections can safely be ignored. Even several hundred worms may produce no measurable symptoms in a person on an excellent diet, not pregnant, and not suffering from overwork or chronic disease, but Hill and Andrews (1942) in Georgia found a falling off in hemoglobin in the group with 2000 to 4000 eggs per gram (about 60 to 120 worms), which became marked in the 4000 to 8000 group and severe in cases with over 15,000 e.p.g. It is not possible to set any definite limits to these grades of injury in the case of any individual, but in communities the percentage falling into different egg-count groups gives a useful index to the hookworm burden, and correlation with hemoglobin percentages gives valuable information on susceptibility to injury under existing dietary and environmental conditions.

The erroneousness of judging hookworm infection by the percentage of people infected is nowhere better demonstrated than in Bengal, where an average of at least 80 per cent of the 46,000,000 inhabitants are infected, a condition which some years ago was spoken of as " staggering." But egg counts show that in 90 per cent of the area of Bengal the average number of worms harbored per person is less than 20, and not more than 1 per cent of the people are estimated to have over 160 worms and almost none over 400. In other words, instead of being a staggering problem involving the health of over **35,000,000** people, it is negligible from the public-health point of view.

Diagnosis. Hookworm infection can rarely be diagnosed with certainty by symptoms, but a positive diagnosis is easily obtainable by modern flotation methods of finding eggs in the stools. If it is only desired to find infections which need treatment the simple smear method suffices, but more accurate diagnosis can be made by the Willis, D.C.F., or A.E.X. methods (see p. 251). Community diagnosis, i.e., the relative degree of severity of the disease in a community, can be indicated by ascertaining the weighted mean egg count as described by the writer (1929).

The collection of fecal samples for diagnosis on a large scale can be made in bottles containing a few cubic centimeters of antiformin as described by Maplestone in 1929, or with 1 per cent NaCl added in the proportion of 30 : 1 as suggested by Maplestone and Mukerji in 1943. In either case the specimens can be sent to a central laboratory for examination, thus eliminating the necessity for a moving field laboratory, for the specimens are useful for both diagnosis and egg counts even after several days.

Treatment. The treatment of hookworm infection has undergone an interesting evolution, and more advance has been made towards the goal of an ideal anthelmintic for hookworms than for any other common helminthic infection.

Thymol, introduced in 1880, was the classical treatment for many years but has been almost completely discarded for safer and more effective drugs. Oil of chenopodium replaced thymol during World War I but is more effective for Ascaris than for hookworm; it is frequently combined with tetrachloroethylene when both worms are present. The maximum dose should be 3 cc. divided into three doses; combined with other drugs, 1 cc. is used.

In 1921 Hall found carbon tetrachloride, previously best known as a fire extinguisher, to be highly effective for extinguishing hookworms. Within a few years it was being widely used all over the world, but a few unfortunate results occurred, since it developed that the drug is injurious to the liver and may be dangerous where there is a calcium deficiency.

Since 1925 tetrachloroethylene, which is highly efficient and of very low toxicity, has largely replaced carbon tetrachloride. The only effects are a brief burning sensation in the stomach, slight nausea, and a drunken sensation. A dose of 3 to 4 cc. removes 75 to 90 per cent of the hookworms, with complete cures in about two-thirds of the cases. Treatment may need to be repeated once or twice at intervals of a week. Best results are obtained if the patients are given salts the night before and again 2 hours after the drug, with food only after the purge has worked. The drug can be given in capsules or in a spoon with sugar. When Ascaris is also present tetrachloroethylene should be accompanied or preceded by oil of chenopodium or hexyl-resorcinol, since it irritates but does not kill these worms, and they may tangle themselves into masses that block the intestine.

Caprokol, or hexylresorcinol crystoids in hard gelatin capsules containing 0.2 gram, is somewhat less effective, but it is nontoxic and can be repeated at 3-day intervals. It is valuable during pregnancy and illness, for school children, etc. The dose is 5 capsules for an adult, 4 for a school child, and 3 for a preschool child, given on an empty stomach in the morning, with food 5 hours later.

Another drug that has shown promise in dogs is n-butyl chloride, which is effective against Ascaris and whipworms also, but has not yet come into general use for human infections.

Improvement after deworming is very slow, whereas administration of iron, e.g., Blaud's pills, with a diet rich in protein and vitamins, causes rapid improvement. In weak, anemic cases, and in pregnancy, the blood should be built up by iron therapy before an anthelmintic is given. For dosage see pp. 408–409.

Mass Treatment. Mass treatment, first advocated by Darling, greatly speeds up hookworm campaigns. By this is meant the treatment, without preliminary diagnosis, of an entire community at one time, when the great majority of the individuals are found to be infected. The diagnosis itself does not require so much time, but the difficulty in obtaining fecal samples from primitive people is well known to anyone who has tried it; in many cases it is quite impossible. If all the members of a community are treated at once, preferably in a dry or cold season when rapid reinfection from an already badly infested soil cannot occur, the reduction in infection is striking and durable. In Fiji practically the entire population was treated in two years, a feat which could not have been accomplished in *any* length of time by the older methods, for, long before even a fair percentage of the people could have been covered by diagnostic measures, those first treated would again have been infected from their untreated neighbors. The original mass treatment in Fiji was made in 1922 and 1923 and was followed by improvement in the sanitary conditions of the soil. In 1935 Lambert reported that clinical hookworm disease was still rare in Fiji; the people were healthier, happier, and more prosperous, and hookworm had been eliminated as an important economic factor.

Prevention. Theoretically, few if any diseases can be as simply, as certainly, and as easily controlled as hookworm. Diagnosis is easy and accurate, treatment reduces existing infections to a negligible point, and reinfection can be prevented by stopping soil pollution, for no other animals, except possibly pigs and apes, and these only in some localities, harbor human hookworms. But in the prevention of soil pollution the sanitarian runs into a snag. The difficulties involved in this seemingly simple procedure are infinitely greater than the average inhabitant of a civilized sanitary country would suspect. It involves an attempt to induce hundreds of millions of people in tropical and subtropical countries to abandon habits which have been ingrained in them for countless generations and in some instances dictated by religion, and to adopt in their place unfamiliar habits that seem to them obnoxious and undesirable and the reasons for which they cannot readily grasp.

Even in our own southern states a survey in the early part of the present century showed that in the hookworm belt about 68 per cent of the rural homes were unprovided with privies of any kind. Fortunately there has been much improvement in this respect, but in many rural districts where privies do exist, their use is restricted to the women and children or to the family of the manager. Among the "jibaros" or plantation laborers of Puerto Rico, of 61 hookworm patients who were questioned, 55 never had used privies of any kind, and of the 6 who did occasionally use them, only 2 lived in rural districts.

Five weapons are available for use in the control of hookworm: treatment, dietary supplements, protection of the feet, disinfection of feces or soil, and prevention of soil pollution. Mass treatment gives immediate relief and slows up the rate of reinfection on account of the great reduction in number of eggs reaching the soil, but treatment alone, unless consistently repeated, is inadequate, since it has never yet been and probably never will be found feasible to eliminate all the worms, and reinfection inevitably follows. In Puerto Rico, Hill in 1927 treated 1000 people in an isolated valley and eliminated 97.5 per cent of the worms. In one year the residual infection increased to 500 per cent and was nearly 20 per cent of the infection before treatment.

Cruz and de Mello (1945), recognizing the extent to which hookworm disease is influenced by diet, suggested the wholesale addition of iron to food as a preventive measure, just as iodine is added to water to prevent goiter. It is more difficult, since the iron used must be in a cheap, stable form and must not markedly discolor food or give objectionable tastes. In Brazil they suggested ferrous sulfate added to cassava meal, or iron and ammonium citrate to beans. For people with hookworm anemia they recommended 1 gram per day until the hemoglobin is normal, then 0.5 gram for 80 days, and then 0.25 gram for 80 days more. Such a program not only would eliminate symptoms but also would permit development of immunity, reduce the number of eggs reaching the soil, and eventually lead to a much lower hookworm burden even without improvement in sanitary conditions.

Wearing of footgear is a valuable measure when it can be consistently enforced; it is essential for individuals in infected areas who desire to protect themselves. However, the wearing of footgear is often as difficult to enforce in the tropics as is sanitary disposal of feces, and it is far less effective in ultimate control. It is a valuable temporary measure, comparable with the use of mosquito screens for the control of malaria, but it does not get at the root of the trouble.

Disinfection of soil or feces is difficult. Salt can be effectively used under certain conditions, especially in mines, and lime added to feces is an effective method of killing hookworms in night soil. Recent experiments indicate that cyanamides applied at the rate of 1000 lb. per acre is beneficial. Orthodichlorobenzene at 120 gallons or more per acre is highly effective. In general, however, disinfection methods are not feasible. Methyl bromide applied to the ground under an airtight covering of glue-coated paper (1 lb. to 64 sq. ft.) kills all worm larvae and eggs, and protozoan cysts as well, but it is too expensive except for small areas, for valuable breeding stock, zoos, etc.

Prevention of soil pollution, then, remains as the only dependable method of hookworm control under most conditions. It is significant that the domestic cat, which sanitarily covers up its excreta, has on the average far fewer intestinal parasites of those species acquired from contamination of food or water than has the less careful dog.

The efforts of sanitarians are not so prone to be too little and too late as to be too much and too soon; we are likely to try to force on tropical natives our own ideas of sanitary arrangements, just as we try to force on them our ideas of ethics, religion, clothing, and food habits. It is better as a beginning to teach the coolie to defecate into a trench, from a log over a ditch, or from a low branch or root of a tree or even from a projecting stone, than to build an enclosed flyproof latrine, which he promptly befouls and which prejudices him against latrines in general. Meanwhile education will gradually alter prejudices, and eventually really sanitary privies to control such diseases as dysentery and typhoid as well as hookworm will be possible.

In the United States Andrews (1942), in Georgia, pointed out that hookworm work should be directed toward the detection, prevention, and control of clinical infections. Most of these could be found by examination of large, white, low-income families living on sandy or sandy-loam soil, without sanitary conveniences, and showing evidence of anemia. Attention should, he thinks, be concentrated on these families, omitting work where there is good sanitation, clay soil, good income, or a Negro population. The bulk of hookworm morbidity would then be revealed at a minimum of time and expense.

The campaign against hookworm disease, which has been sponsored especially by the International Health Board, although a most worthy end in itself, leads to even greater benefits, for the work, while bringing relief to hundreds of thousands of suffering people, is at the same time serving the more useful purpose of creating a popular sentiment in support of permanent agencies for the promotion of public health. In the United States it has led to rapid advances in rural hygiene and the establishment of county health organizations all over the country, and similar local organizations have been brought to life in many other countries. Schools of hygiene have been established in various parts of the world to provide trained men to carry on the work. The ultimate results which may come from the simple beginnings centered on the eradication of hookworm disease are impossible to estimate, but in the light of the tremendous accomplishments which we have seen realized since the inception of the work of the International Health Board about 1910 the outlook for the future is bright indeed.

Other Strongylata

Other Hookworms. *Ancylostoma caninum* and *A. braziliense*, important parasites of dogs and cats, were discussed on pp. 393 and 395. In Europe dogs commonly harbor *Uncinaria stenocephala*, a hookworm related to Necator but with only one pair of lancets in the depth of the mouth capsule. The hookworms of cattle, sheep, and other ruminants belong to the genus Bunostomum, also related to Necator but with the dorsal lobe of the bursa asymmetrical.

Family Strongylidae. The members of this family have globular, goblet-shaped or cylindrical deep or shallow mouth capsules, with a crown of leaflets (corona radiata) guarding its entrance (Fig. 136). The family contains a number of species which are injurious to domestic animals and a few which are more or less frequent parasites of man. Among the more important forms are species of Oesophagostomum in pigs, ruminants, and primates; Strongylus and members of the subfamily Cyathostominae (also called Trichoneminae or Cylicostominae) in horses; Chabertia in sheep and goats; and Stephanurus (kidney worm) in pigs.

The esophagostomes of pigs and ruminants and the strongyles of horses, as well as many of the trichostrongylids (discussed on pp. 414

to 417), are very susceptible to treatment with phenothiazine, but this drug is relatively ineffective for worms of the hookworm type.

All the members of the Strongylidae have a life cycle similar to that of the hookworms except that the infective larvae of most genera do not penetrate the skin but are ingested with vegetation. The larvae have long pointed tails and are protected from desiccation by their sheaths.

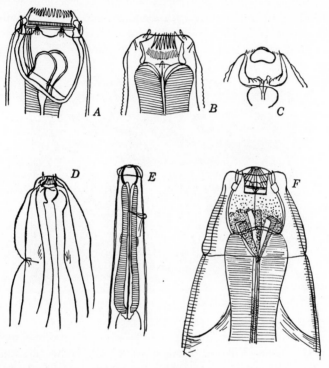

Fig. 136. Heads of various types of Strongylata. *A*, *Strongylus vulgaris*; *B*, *Trichonema tetracanthum*; *C*, *Stephanurus dentatus*; *D*, *Oesophagostomum bifurcum*; *E*, fourth-stage larva of Oesophagostomum; *F*, *Ternidens deminutus*. (*A*, *B*, *C*, and *F* after Yorke and Maplestone; *D* after Travassos and Vogelsang; *E* after Mönnig.)

They are frequently found in an apparently dry state, but viable, curled up on the under side of grass or leaves. Many species retreat to the upper layers of the soil during the heat of the day. They are susceptible to excessive heat or direct sunlight but not to freezing. Some of the species, e.g., *Strongylus* spp. (Fig. 136*A*), go on a roundabout tour through the body before growing to maturity in the intestine, but most of them spend their apprenticeship in nodules in the walls of the gut.

The Cyathostominae or " small strongyles " (Fig. 136*F*) of horses also pass the first part of their parasitic life as larvae in nodules in the walls of the large intestine and cecum, but the nodules are smaller. One species of Strongylus (*S. vulgaris*) frequently causes aneurisms of the mesenteric arteries in horses and appears to be a cause of colic.

The esophagostomes or nodular worms are common and injurious parasites of pigs, sheep, goats, cattle, apes, and monkeys, and are occasional parasites of man. They are about the size of hookworms but have a shallow mouth capsule with a corona, and a groove behind the head on the ventral side. When the infective larvae are eaten and liberated from their sheaths they do not at once establish themselves

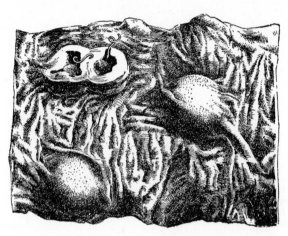

FIG. 137.   Tumors or nodules of *O. bifurcum* in the large intestine of an African. ¾ natural size.   (After Brumpt's *Précis de parasitologie*.)

in the lumen of the intestine but first burrow into the lining of the large intestine where the host forms a tumor-like nodule around them (Fig. 137).

In young nonimmune animals the worms return to the lumen of the intestine in 5 to 8 days and grow to maturity, but, as immunity develops, the tissue reaction becomes greater and many of the worms remain imprisoned in the nodules, even for months. Older animals may have the large intestine covered with nodules but have very few adult worms. The nodules are ½ to 1 inch in diameter and contain a greenish pus-like substance surrounding the immature worm. Progressive weakness and loss of weight are characteristic, with diarrhea in earlier stages.

Several species of these worms, normally inhabiting apes and monkeys, have been found on rare occasions in man, but since the eggs are indistinguishable from those of hookworms and diagnosis of the encysted worms can be made only at autopsy, human cases may be much commoner than is suspected. Opinions differ as to the species involved. A single human case in Brazil was due to a species parasitic in apes, *Oesophagostomum stephanostomum*, and *O. bifurcum* (=*O. brumpti*) (Fig. 136*D, E*) has been recorded from man once in East Africa and once in New Guinea; it is probably this species that was found infecting about 4 per cent of the prisoners in a Nigerian jail and which Leiper in 1911 referred to the species *O. apiostomum*. Most of these cases were light, but the Brazilian case was severe, and probably the parasites were the cause of death.

In ruminants and apes the infection commonly produces severe emaciation and prolonged dysentery, and sometimes fatal peritonitis. In the encysted stage the worms are unaffected by anthelmintics, and they are difficult to dislodge even when free on account of their location in the large intestine.

A related worm, *Ternidens deminutus*, is a common parasite in natives of parts of southern East Africa; Sandground (1931) found it in 50 to 65 per cent of natives examined in two villages in southern Rhodesia, but he found it rare or absent in neighboring countries. Most of the infections are light, but the worm is doubtless capable of considerable pathological damage by the formation of nodules. The eggs resemble those of hookworms but are distinctly larger, averaging about 84 μ by 51 μ, and are usually in the 8-celled stage when passed. The infective larvae are similar in form and habits to those of other Strongylidae. The adult worms were found in monkeys in Rhodesia by Blackie. They superficially resemble hookworms but have a deep goblet-shaped buccal capsule with three teeth in its depths (Fig. 136*F*).

A strongylid which causes much damage in the colon of sheep is *Chabertia ovina*, a rather large worm, the females measuring up to 20 mm. long and having a globular mouth capsule with no teeth but with two crowns of extremely fine leaflets. It is a northern parasite; its larvae are capable of development at very low temperatures. In sheep it is 9 to 10 weeks after infection before eggs appear.

Stephanurus dentatus, the kidney worm of pigs, has a globular capsule with a very feeble corona (Fig. 136*C*) and a poorly developed bursa that is subterminal. After developing to the infective stage outside the body the larvae enter the body either by mouth or through the skin and go by way of the bloodstream to the liver, where they live and grow for a few months, eventually making their way to the kidneys. Here they become embedded, the eggs reaching the ureters and being excreted with the urine. It is rather injurious to pigs and entails considerable economic loss from condemned liver and kidneys.

Family Syngamidae.   This family (see p. 390) includes bloodsucking worms that live in the trachea and bronchi of birds and mammals.

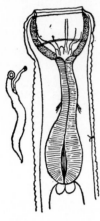

The worms are called gapeworms or forked worms because the male remains permanently attached to the vulva of the female by its bursa, giving a forked appearance (Fig. 138); the females are 15 to 20 mm. long and red in color.   The eggs measure about 85 to 50 μ and are in early stages of segmentation when oviposited.   From the air passages they are coughed up and swallowed, passing out with the feces.   Although direct infection with embryonated eggs is possible, the eggs are frequently eaten by various invertebrates, in which the embryos hatch and become encapsulated, the invertebrates thus becoming " transport " hosts.   Earthworms are particularly important hosts and may harbor the infection for years, but slugs, springtails, maggots, and others are also involved.   When swallowed, the infective larvae penetrate the mucous membranes and are carried to the lungs by the bloodstream.

FIG. 138.   *Right,* head of female *Syngamus kingi* (after Leiper); *left,* a pair of worms in copula.

One species, *Syngamus trachea,* is an injurious parasite of turkeys, young chickens, and pheasants, and a related worm affects geese. Many passerine birds such as robins, blackbirds, crows, and starlings also harbor gapeworms; although Goble and Kutz in 1945 showed that several species are involved, these birds can serve as carriers of the poultry parasite.   A number of instances of human infection with gapeworms have been recorded, all but one of them in tropical America; in most of these cases the species concerned was *S. laryngeus* of cattle. The worms attack the pharynx, trachea, or neighboring air spaces in the head or throat, often causing nodules at the point of attachment. Coughing and gaping are the usual symptoms, and chicks may die from obstruction of the trachea.   Immunity develops quickly, but chicks lose their worms much more rapidly than turkeys.   Barium antimonyl tartrate, inhaled as a dust, is recommended for treatment.

Family Trichostrongylidae.   These worms, recognizable by the finely drawn-out head without a large buccal capsule, together with a well-developed bursa in the male (Fig. 139), are very important parasites of domestic animals.   Sheep, goats, and cattle suffer severely from the stomach worm, *Haemonchus contortus,* and to a less extent from species of Trichostrongylus, Cooperia, Nematodirus, and Ostertagia.   *Trichostrongylus axei* also lives in the stomach of horses.   Pigs are infected with Hyostrongylus. These genera have the following characters:

1. *Haemonchus:* length, ♀ 20–30 mm., ♂ 10–20 mm.; small buccal cavity with a lancet; ♀ with conspicuous vulvar flap; ♂ with short, stout spicules and small asymmetrical dorsal lobe on bursa (Fig. 139*D*).
2. *Ostertagia:* length, ♀ 8–9 mm., ♂ 6–8 mm.; head with very small buccal cavity; ♂ with short spicules and small accessory bursal membrane dorsally.
3. *Cooperia:* length, ♀ about 6–7 mm., ♂ about 5–6 mm.; head 25 μ in diameter; no cervical or prebursal papillae; ♂ with short spicules, branches of dorsal ray lyre-shaped.
4. *Nematodirus:* length, ♀ 15–20 mm., ♂ 10–15 mm.; extremely slender; ♀ tail truncated with spinelike process; ♂ with filiform spicules, dorsal ray split to base.
5. *Trichostrongylus:* length, ♀ 5–6 mm., ♂ 4–6 mm.; head 10 μ in diameter; ♂ with short spicules, dorsal ray split only near tip.
6. *Hyostrongylus:* length, ♀ 5–8 mm., ♂ 4–5 mm.; very similar to Trichostrongylus but found only in pigs.

The life cycles of all these worms are essentially the same; the eggs develop outside the host's body into long-tailed, sheathed larvae most of which are capable of withstanding considerable desiccation and live for a long time. They gain access to their hosts by being ingested with vegetation. They grow to maturity directly in the intestine, although some species burrow into the mucous membrane before becoming established in the lumen of the intestine, and some, e.g., Ostertagia and Cooperia, like esophagostomes, become enclosed in nodules in partly immune animals.

All these worms cause a condition known as " verminous gastro-enteritis " by veterinarians, but more often as " black rush," " black scours," etc., by sheep men. As with hookworms, severe infection is the result of poor nutrition or of overwhelming initial infections, for otherwise the animals soon build up an immunity resulting in " self-cure " by expulsion of the worms and resistance to reinfection. Even moderate infections, however, may cause diarrhea, failure to gain weight, poor wool production, and general unthriftiness. *Haemonchus contortus* is a bloodsucker like the hookworms and may cause severe anemia, but unlike other Trichostrongylidae it causes constipation rather than diarrhea. All the other smaller species of the family cause diarrhea, weakness, and emaciation but little or no anemia. The emaciated appearance is due in part to interference with appetite and nutrition and in part to dehydration from diarrhea. All these infections in animals are very successfully treated with phenothiazine.

Haemonchus contortus (stomachworm or wireworm) (Fig. 139*C, D*) lives in the stomach (abomasum) of sheep, goats, and cattle, and may play havoc with young animals. It is much larger than other trichostrongylids, the females being about 1 inch long and the males about ½ inch. It has a world-wide distribution. One human case has been reported from Brazil.

Ostertagia are also stomach parasites; they are brownish hairlike worms less than ½ inch long. *O. ostertagi* is commoner than Haemonchus in cattle in western United States.

Trichostrongylus (Fig. 139*A, B*) contains many species of minute reddish hairworms only about ¼ inch in length. *T. axei* lives in the stomach of ruminants and horses, and rarely in man. Sheep and goats suffer from a number of species, *T. colubriformis, vitrinus,* and *capri-*

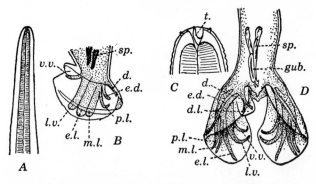

FIG. 139. *A* and *B*, head and bursa of *Trichostrongylus colubriformis; C* and *D*, head (greatly enlarged) and bursa of *Haemonchus contortus; t.,* buccal tooth; *d.l.,* dorsal lobe; *gub.,* gubernaculum, other abbreviations as in Fig. 127. (*A* original; *B* after Looss; *C* after Yorke and Maplestone; *D* after Ransom.)

cola being the commonest. Andrews (1939) showed that in pure experimental infections Trichostrongylus produces a profuse, continuous diarrhea. Animals with very heavy infections die after several weeks.

Human Trichostrongylus infections are fairly common in parts of the Far East and the tropics. In Korea *T. orientalis,* so far known only from man, infects over 25 per cent of children and soldiers. In India from 1 to 25 per cent infections have been recorded, and in Congo 10 per cent. The eggs are probably often mistaken for those of hookworms, although they are larger, more slender, and more pointed at one end. Since hookworm remedies do not expel these worms, the efficacy of treatment is sometimes underrated because of mistaken diagnosis. Human infections are otherwise of no consequence, since they are always light.

Nematodirus and Cooperia also contain species parasitic in the duodenum of sheep and goats, and the latter also in cattle. Nematodirus is remarkable for its large eggs, up to 200 μ or more long, and for its larvae, which undergo two moults in the egg before they hatch and climb to a vantage point on grass. Hyostrongylus, the red stomachworm of pigs, is only ⅕ inch long and red in color. In poorly nourished pigs it produces effects similar to those of most other tricho-strongyles.

Mention should also be made of the subfamily Heligmosominae, which are parasites of rodents; they are tiny red worms which have a single ovary and uterus and which roll their bodies in spirals.

Lungworms

Formerly placed in a separate superfamily Metastrongyloidea (see p. 390), these slender worms, inhabiting various parts of the respiratory system of mammals, are now split between a subfamily of Tricho-strongylidae (Skrjabingylinae) and the family Metastrongylidae. Most of these worms inhabit the fine branches of the bronchial tubes of the lungs, but one species lives in the heart and pulmonary arteries of dogs, and others in the frontal sinuses of tigers and skunks.

The subfamily Skrjabingylinae includes several species of Dictyo-caulus. They are threadlike worms several inches in length. Unlike the Metastrongylidae these have very short, robust spicules, a vulva near the middle of the body, and well-developed ovejectors. The larvae hatch in the bronchi of the host and are either coughed out or swallowed and passed in the feces. They are peculiar in not feeding at all in the free-living phase; they moult twice, and both shed cuticles are retained for a time. They infect by being swallowed, and they reach the lungs via the lymph system. Species of this genus occur in sheep, cattle, and horses; in all of these they cause coughing and bronchitis, but in sheep they may block off so much of the lungs as to be fatal.

The Metastrongylidae have medium or very long spicules, and the vulva is a short distance in front of the anus (Fig. 140A). In the genera Metastrongylus and Choerostrongylus, important parasites of pigs, the spicules are very long and the female has a fingerlike tail (Fig. 140D). These pig parasites produce thick-shelled embryonated eggs which hatch when ingested by certain species of earthworms, in which they develop to the infective stage. Members of the subfamily Protostrongylinae (Protostrongylus and Muellerius of ruminants, Aelurostrongylus of cats, and several genera in deer) develop in mol-lusks. The embryos hatch before leaving the body and burrow into the foot of various land snails and slugs, where they become encap-sulated. As Hobmaier remarked, the utilization of mollusks as intermediate hosts by these worms probably grew out of their habit of seeking protection from desiccation in the slime of the mollusks.

Only one species of lungworm, *Metastrongylus elongatus* (Fig. 140) of pigs, has been found in man, and this only three times.

Attempts at treatment of lungworms in animals have been made by tracheal injection of various substances and by inhalation of chloro-

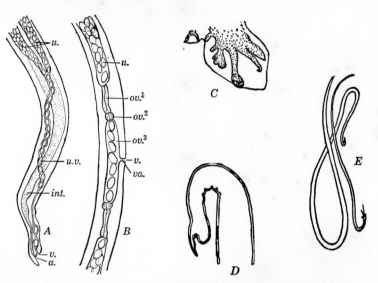

FIG. 140. *A* and *B*, comparison of female reproductive system of a metastrongylid (*A*) and a trichostrongylid (*B*); *a.*, anus; *int.*, intestine; *ov.*^{1}, ejector of ovejector; *ov.*^{2}, sphincter of ovejector; *ov.*^{3}, chamber of ovejector; *u.*, uterus; *u.v.*, uterine vagina; *v.*, vulva; *va.*, vagina. *C*, *D*, and *E*, *Metastrongylus elongatus;* *C*, bursa of male; *D*, posterior end of female; *E*, male and female worms, × 3. (Adapted from various authors.)

form or fumes of tar, sulfur, etc., but with good care the animals resist the infection and soon lose their worms.

Of very great interest for helminthology in general is the demonstration by Shope (1939) that swine influenza is caused by a combination of certain influenza bacteria and a virus, and that the virus is harbored by the larvae of lungworms (Metastrongylus), which serve as vectors for it. The virus survives as long as three years in lungworms encapsulated in earthworms; it is thus perpetuated from one outbreak to another. Species of Strongylus have likewise been found to harbor the virus of swamp fever of horses, and Trichinella has been shown to act as a vector for the virus of lymphocytic choriomeningitis. Heterakis (p. 428) is a carrier of Histomonas, a protozoan parasite of turkeys (p. 131). The role of helminths as vectors for viruses and other disease agents is still an almost virgin field.

REFERENCES

Hookworms

ANDREWS, J., New Methods of Hookworm Disease Investigation and Control, *Am. J. Publ. Health*, **32**, 382 (1942).

ASHFORD, B. K., PAYNE, G. C., and PAYNE, F., The Larval Phase of Uncinariasis, *Puerto Rico J. Pub. Health Trop. Med.*, **9**, 97 (1933).

CHANDLER, A. C., *Hookworm Disease*, New York, 1929.

CORT, W. W., Investigations on the Control of Hookworm Disease. XXXIV. General Summary of Results, *Am. J. Hyg.*, **5**, 49 (1925).

CORT, W. W., and OTTO, G. F., Immunity in Hookworm Disease, *Rev. Gastroenterol.*, **7**, 2–11 (1940).

CRUZ, W. O., Hookworm Anemia — A Deficiency Disease, *Proc. 4th Intern. Congr. on Trop. Med. and Malaria*, **2**, Sect. VI, 1045–1054 (1948).

CRUZ, W. O., and DE MELLO, R. P., Profilaxia da anemia ancilostomótica — sindrome de carencia, *Mem. inst. Oswaldo Cruz.*, **42**, 401–448 (1945).

DOVE, W. E., Further Studies on *Ancylostoma braziliense* and the Etiology of Creeping Eruption, *Am. J. Hyg.*, **15**, 664 (1932).

FOSTER, A. O., and CORT, W. W., The Relation of Diet to the Susceptibility of Dogs to *Ancylostoma caninum*, *Am. J. Hyg.*, **16**, 582–601 (1932).

FOSTER, A. O., and LANDSBERG, J. W., The Nature and Cause of Hookworm Anemia, *Am. J. Hyg.*, **20**, 259 (1934).

HILL, A. W., and ANDREWS, J., Relation of the Hookworm Burden to Physical Status in Georgia, *Am. J. Trop. Med.*, **22**, 499 (1942). International Health Div., Rockefeller Foundation, Annual Reports.

HUNTER, G. W., III, and WORTH, C. B., Variation in Response to Filariform Larvae of *Ancylostoma caninum* in the Skin of Man, *J. Parasitol.*, **31**, 366–372 (1945).

KELLER, A. E., LEATHERS, W. S., and DENSEN, P. M., The Results of Recent Studies of Hookworm in Eight Southern States, *Am. J. Trop. Med.*, **20**, 493 (1940).

LAMBERT, S. M., A Resurvey of Hookworm Disease in Fiji in 1935, Ten Years after Mass Treatment, *J. Trop. Med. Hyg.*, **39**, 19 (1936).

LANDSBERG, J. W., Hookworm Disease in Dogs, *J. Am. Vet. Med. Assoc.*, **94**, 389 (1939).

MAPLESTONE, P. A., and MUKERJI, K., Further Experience with Tetrachlorethylene, *Indian Med. Gaz.*, **72**, 650 (1937).

MILLSPAUGH, J. A., and SOMPAYRAC, L. M., Creeping Eruption. Infestation with *Ankylostoma braziliense* larvae, *U. S. Naval Med. Bull.*, **40**, 393 (1942).

WELLS, R. S., Observations on the Blood-Sucking Activities of the Hookworm, *Ancylostoma caninum*, *J. Parasitol.*, **17**, 167 (1931).

Other Strongylata

ANDREWS, J. S., Experimental Trichostrongylosis in Sheep and Goats, *J. Agr. Research*, **58**, 761–770 (1939).

CAMERON, T. W. M., *The Internal Parasites of Domestic Animals*, London, 1934.

CLUNIES, R. I., and GORDON, H. M., *The Internal Parasites and Parasitic Diseases of Sheep; Their Treatment and Control*, Sydney, Australia, 1936.

DOUGHETY, E. C., A Review of the Genus *Crenosoma* Molin, 1861 (Nematoda: Trichostrongylidae); Its History, Taxonomy, Adult Morphology, and Distribution, *Proc. Helminthol. Soc. Wash., D. C.*, **12**, 44–62 (1945).

FOSTER, A. O., A Quantitative Study of the Nematodes from a Selected Group of Equines in Panama, *J. Parasitol.*, **22**, 479 (1936).

HOBMAIER, M., Lungenwurmlarven in Mollusken, *Z. Parasitenk.*, **6**, 642 (1934).

MAYHEW, R. L., Studies on Bovine Gastro-Intestinal Parasites: V. Immunity to the Stomach Worm, *Haemonchus contortus*, with a Note on the Prepatent Period (Abstract), *J. Parasitol.*, **26**, Suppl., 17 (1940).

PAVLOV, P., Recherches sur le cycle évolutif de *Metastrongylus elongatus* et de *Dictyocaulus filaria, Ann. parasitol. humaine et comparée*, **13**, 430 (1935).

PORTER, D. A., Incidence of Gastro-Intestinal Nematodes of Cattle in the Southeastern United States, *Am. J. Vet. Research*, 304–307 (1942).

SANDGROUND, J. H., Studies on the Life History of *Ternidens deminutus*, with Observations on its Incidence in Certain Regions of Southern Africa, *Ann. Trop. Med. Parasitol.*, **25**, 147 (1931).

SCHWARTZ, B., Controlling Kidney Worms in Swine in the Southern States, U. S. Dept. Agr. Leaflet 108 (1934).

SHOPE, R. E., The Swine Lungworm as a Reservoir and Intermediate Host for Swine Influenza Virus, I–IV, *J. Exptl. Med.*, **73** (1940); **74**, 49 (1941); **77**, 111, 127 (1942).

TAYLOR, E. L., *Syngamus trachea, J. Path. Ther.*, **48**, 149 (1935).

TRAVASSOS, L., and VOGELSANG, E., Contribucão as conhecimento does especies de Oesophagostomum does primatos, *Mem. inst. Oswaldo Cruz*, **26**, 251 (1932).

U. S. DEPT. OF AGRICULTURE, Keeping Livestock Healthy, *Yearbook*, 1942.

WATSON, J. M., The Differential Diagnosis of Hookworm, Strongyloides, and Trichostrongylus, with Special Reference to Mixed Infections, *J. Trop. Med. Hyg.*, **49**, 94–98 (1946).

WEHR, E. E., and OLIVIER, L., The Efficiency of Barium Antimonyl Tartrate for the Removal of Gapeworms from Pheasants, *Proc. Helminthol. Soc. Wash., D. C.*, **10**, 87–89 (1943).

CHAPTER 18

Other Intestinal Nematodes

ASCARIDATA. I. ASCARIDOIDEA

As noted on p. 372, the suborder Ascaridata consists of two super-families, the Ascaridoidea and the Oxyuroidea. The former contains for the most part relatively large, opaque, Ascaris-like worms of which

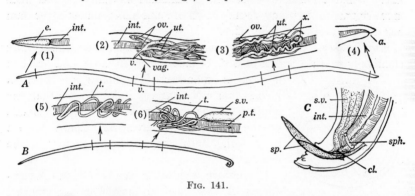

Fig. 141.

Fig. 141. *Ascaris lumbricoides.* A, ♀, $\frac{1}{4}$ nat. size, with enlargements of regions of (1) esophagus, (2) vulva, (3) junction of uteri and ovaries, and (4) anus. B, ♂, $\frac{1}{4}$ nat. size, with enlargements of regions of (5) anterior end of testis, and (6) junction of testis and seminal vesicle. C, posterior end of ♂, much enlarged. Abbrev.: *a.*, anus; *cl.*, cloaca; *e.*, esophagus; *int.*, intestine; *ov.*, ovary; *p.t.*, posterior end of testis; *sp.*, spicules; *sph.*, intestinal sphincter; *s.v.*, seminal vesicle; *t.*, testis; *ut.*, uterus; *v.*, vulva; *vag.*, vagina; *x.*, junction of uteri and ovaries.

there are numerous species parasitic in all kinds of vertebrates, whereas the latter contains smaller, transparent, Oxyuris-like worms which are parasitic, mostly in the cecum and colon of vertebrates and also of insects.

Ascaris lumbricoides

General Account. *Ascaris lumbricoides* has undoubtedly been one of man's most faithful and constant companions from time immemorial, probably since he began domesticating pigs and by his habits made possible the development of a special strain particularly adapted for residence in his own intestine. This worm has clung to mankind successfully through the stone, copper, and iron ages, but plumbing threatens eventually to dissolve the partnership if children can be " yard-broken " early enough. Wherever soil pollution prevails, if

421

only by toddlers in the dooryards, and wherever there is warmth and moisture, Ascaris infections are common.

Although Ascaris is one of the longest-known human parasites, it is a remarkable fact that important details of its life cycle were unknown before 1916, and the factors influencing its epidemiology were not elucidated until after 1930.   One reason for this is that Ascaris infections have in general not been taken very seriously and their injurious effects have been minimized, whereas the effects of hookworm have often been exaggerated.   Early in the present century Ascaris came into the limelight as an injurious and sometimes dangerous parasite.   When a parasite steps into prominence nowadays it has little more chance to keep any details of its life and habits under cover than has a candidate for public office.

Morphology.   *Ascaris lumbricoides* is a large nematode; the females commonly reach a length of 8 to 14 inches or even more, and are 4 to

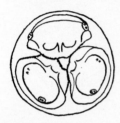

FIG. 142. Lips of *Ascaris lumbricoides*, end-on view. (After Yorke and Maplestone.)

6 mm. in diameter.   The males are 6 to 12 inches long but distinctly more slender than the adult females; they are always distinguishable by the curled tail, whereas the females have a blunt tail.   Both sexes are more slender at the head end.

In common with other members of the Ascaridoidea, *A. lumbricoides* has the mouth guarded by three lips, one dorsal and two latero-ventral, each with minute papillae (Fig. 142).   The esophagus is nearly cylindrical and is followed by a flattened, ribbonlike intestine.   The vulva is situated about one-third the distance from head to tail.   The coiled tail of the male is short and provided with a characteristic number and arrangement of papillae but no alae.   This worm is a favorite object for the study of nematode anatomy, since it is always easily obtainable and is easily dissected.

Relation to Pig Ascaris.   An Ascaris which is indistinguishable morphologically or even serologically from the human species is a very common parasite of pigs, and was long regarded as identical, but the eggs derived from the pig Ascaris do not ordinarily develop to mature worms in man, or vice versa, and that there is little epidemiological relationship between infection in these two hosts.   It is preferable, therefore, to distinguish the pig Ascaris as *A. lumbricoides* var. *suum*. A form found in a chimpanzee seems to represent a still different biological strain.   In nature human Ascaris infection ordinarily spreads from man to man, and pigs are negligible as reservoirs.   Both they and dogs may, however, be important in the dissemination of eggs which they have ingested with human feces.

Life Cycle. The adult Ascaris normally lives in the small intestine, where it is supposed to feed on the semidigested food of the host, but there is evidence that it commonly bites the mucous membranes with its lips and sucks blood and tissue juices to some extent. Reid (1945) showed that a related worm, *Ascaridia galli* of chickens, is highly susceptible to host starvation for 48 hours, just as are tapeworms, and that many are expelled when their stored glycogen supply is depleted.

The egg production of Ascaris is astounding. Cram (1925) estimated the number of eggs contained in a mature female worm to be as high as 27,000,000, and the eggs per gram of feces for each female worm may be in excess of 2000. This would indicate a daily production of something like 200,000 eggs! Evidently the chances against the offspring of an Ascaris reaching a comfortable maternity ward in a human intestine are many millions to one.

The eggs (Fig. 143*A*, *B*) have a thick, clear, inner shell covered over by a warty, albuminous coat which is stained yellow or brown in the intestine; they usually measure about 60 to 70 μ by 40 to 50 μ. Unfertilized

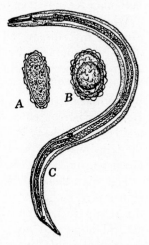

Fig. 143. *Ascaris lumbricoides.* *A*, infertile egg; *B*, fertile egg; *C*, larva from lung of rabbit 10 days after infection. × about 65. (After Ransom and Foster.)

eggs are more difficult for a beginner to identify, since they are more elongate and less regularly oval in shape and have amorphous contents instead of the well-defined round cell of the fertilized eggs. The warty, albuminous coat dissolves off in sodium hydroxide, so in feces examined by Stoll's egg-count method the eggs have only the thick inner shell.

The eggs are unsegmented when they leave the host. In order to develop they require a temperature lower than that of the human body, at least a trace of moisture, and oxygen. They are very resistant to chemical substances and will develop readily in weak formalin solutions or in sea water, but they can be killed by methyl bromide (see p. 409). They gradually degenerate at temperatures above 38° C. and cease development below about 16° C.; about 30° C. is the most favorable temperature. Martin found eggs viable after storage for 4 years in an icebox. Absence of oxygen retards or stops development; complete drying is lethal. In pit latrines the eggs die in 6 months if exposed, in about a year if buried, but under favorable conditions in soil they may remain alive for years.

Under favorable conditions of temperature, moisture, and air the eggs develop active embryos within them in 10 to 14 days, but the embryos are not infective until they have moulted inside the egg, becoming second-stage larvae; this requires an extra week.

When the eggs are swallowed the larvae hatch in the small intestine. Stewart first discovered in 1916 that these larvae do not develop directly to maturity in the intestine but first go on a 10-day tour, a sort of homeseeker's trip, through the body in the same manner as do hookworms. They penetrate the mucous membranes and are carried by the blood stream to the liver, then the heart, and then the lungs. Here they burrow out and make their way through the trachea, throat, and esophagus back to the intestine, meanwhile having benefited from the trip by a growth from an initial length of about 200 to 300 μ to about ten times this length (Fig. 143C).

The migration through the lungs takes place readily in rats, mice, guinea pigs, and other rodents as well as in the natural hosts, but after the return to the intestine the worms pass right on through in unnatural hosts and are voided in the feces. Even in natural hosts experimental infection with thousands of eggs, although it sets up a severe pneumonia, results in the establishment of only a very small percentage of the worms in the intestine and sometimes none at all. It is possible that the heavy experimental infections may be unfavorable for the final establishment of the worms, whereas the occasional ingestion of two or three eggs, such as would occur in nature, might enable a large number of worms to " sneak in," as it were, in the course of time. After reaching the intestine, the young worms, 2 to 3 mm. long, grow to maturity in 2 to 2½ months. The length of life in the host is rather short and probably averages less than a year.

Epidemiology. Since a combination of heat and dryness is injurious to them, Ascaris eggs in feces passed on sandy soil exposed to the sun in a hot climate die before the embryos can develop. Ascaris thrives best where there is abundant moisture and shade.

Infection ordinarily results from swallowing embryonated eggs, which are more frequently conveyed to the mouth by fingers than by other methods. In some places in India heavy infection is directly correlated with polluted water supplies, but in other localities the water could not be involved. Brown in 1927 observed that in Panama the infection is distinctly of household nature and is derived from contamination of hands and food by eggs developing in the soil on the floors and dooryards of huts polluted by young children. Samoans become infected by dunking food in sea water, in which the eggs develop readily.

In the United States Ascaris infection is largely limited to the mountainous areas of the southeastern states and is concentrated in young children; here the presence of shelter in the immediate vicinity of the dooryards leads to close-in pollution, whereas in more open and flat country there is a tendency to go farther away. This is believed by Otto and Cort (1934) to account for the lower incidence of infection in the coastal plains, although the exposure of eggs to sun and dryness in sandy soil as compared with clay soil is also a factor. The playing of children on polluted ground near their homes, tracking of pollution into the houses, and eating with dirty hands, are the most important factors in the epidemiology. It has been widely believed that in the Orient vegetables fertilized with night soil constituted the most prolific source of infection, but work by Winfield (1937) indicates that in China, as elsewhere, soil pollution in or near the homes and eating with dirty hands are of greater importance.

Considerable Ascaris infection may occur in the riffraff living in crowded quarters on the edges of southern cities, when there are dense shade, abundant rain, and children who are careless in their defecation habits. Such an endemic center was found in Tampa.

Pathology. In heavy experimental infections the migration of the larvae through the lungs causes hemorrhages and sets up a severe pneumonia which may be fatal. The invasion may be accompanied by a fever, a temporary anemia and leucocytosis, and an eosinophilia. Pigs frequently show lung symptoms known as " thumps," and similar conditions have been observed in human beings preceding an Ascaris infection; ordinarily in nature, however, not enough eggs are ingested at a time to cause serious pneumonia.

After reaching maturity in the intestine, Ascaris may or may not disturb the peace of the host, but vague abdominal discomfort and acute colick pains are frequently felt, sometimes with vomiting, diarrhea, and mild elevations of temperature. Light infections may be entirely unsuspected until the eggs are found in the feces. On the other hand the parasite is not always so docile. In heavy infections, especially if made uncomfortable by some food or drug taken by the host, the worms are likely to tangle themselves in masses and completely block the intestine. One thousand to five thousand worms have been recorded in some cases, but even less than a hundred worms may cause a blockage that is fatal if not surgically removed. A number of cases of death after carbon tetrachloride treatment for hookworm are known, due to obstruction of the intestine by squirming masses of irritated Ascaris.

Sometimes irritation of the mucous membranes may cause dangerous spasmodic contractions or permanent nervous constrictions of the intestine. The worms sometimes cause appendicitis by blocking the appendix. Toxic products may cause effects resembling anaphylactic shock and such nervous symptoms as convulsions, delirium, general nervousness, and coma. Sang in 1938 demonstrated a substance excreted by Ascaris which combines with trypsin, and he believes that when numerous Ascaris are present enough destruction of trypsin may occur to interfere with digestion of proteins and account for the loss of condition and stunting growth often seen in infected animals. Japanese workers found that Ascaris-infected school children were shorter than uninfected ones and had less memory and thinking capacity. Simonin in 1922 collected clinical evidence of serious effects on glands of internal secretion.

The list of dangerous complications of Ascaris infection is greatly enlarged by the fact that the worms have a " wanderlust " and tend to explore ducts and cavities. They frequently invade bile or pancreatic ducts and may enter the gall bladder or even go on into the liver; when children too young to have gallstones have symptoms of disease of the biliary tract, a misplaced Ascaris may well be suspected. Occasionally an Ascaris creeps forward through the stomach and is vomited or emerges through the nose of a horrified patient; it may even enter the trachea and cause suffocation. Ascaris sometimes passes through the intestinal wall and causes fatal peritonitis or may even come through the umbilicus or groin, or the worms may make their way into the pleural cavity, urinogenital organs, etc. It is evident, therefore, that these worms, so far from being the " guardian angels " of children, as they were once considered, are more like bulls in a china shop.

Treatment and Prevention. Ascaris, as long as it stays in the intestine, is fairly easily expelled by some anthelmintics, but some, e.g., tetrachloroethylene, merely irritate the worms and cause intestinal blockage. Therefore, when different treatments for Ascaris and some other worm infection are indicated, the Ascaris treatment should usually be given first. Brown in 1946, however, found no irritating action from gentian violet.

Oil of chenopodium and santonin are efficient drugs for ascariasis, but both are very toxic. However, a mixture of oil of chenopodium and tetrachloroethylene, as described on p. 406, is usually successful. Lamson *et al.* showed that hexylresorcinol gives excellent results, especially if given as " crystoids " in hard gelatin capsules. A single treatment with 0.6 gram for young children to 1 gram for adults, followed by a purge, removes 95 per cent of the worms and makes a clean sweep in 90 per cent of cases, with little discomfort to the patient.

In endemic localities treatment without sanitary improvement does little good, for a treated population usually gets back to the pretreatment level of infection within a year. On the other hand, when reinfection is stopped the worms are lost in from 12 to 15 months even without treatment. Prevention must depend mainly upon doing away with soil pollution near homes, even by very young children, and teaching children early in life to wash their hands before eating. The installation of privies is not always as successful as anticipated, because of only partial use of them. Careful washing of vegetables grown in polluted or night-soil-treated ground is desirable, for, although not as important as soil-to-mouth infection by children's dirty hands, such vegetables may cause infection in more fastidious adults.

Other Ascaridoidea

Ascaris lumbricoides var. *suum* is a very common parasite of pigs; about 75 per cent of pigs in the United States and Canada harbor it before they are 6 months old. The principal effect is stunting of growth. Spindler found that pigs infected with 20 or more worms at 8 weeks of age failed in gain of weight in proportion to the number of worms. One pig with 109 worms gained no weight at all, while uninfected pigs gained an average of 100 lb. Loss results also from condemnation of carcasses for jaundice owing to blockage of bile ducts. Sodium fluoride is highly efficient for removal of Ascaris and stomachworms of pigs (see p. 463) when 1 per cent is added to 1 lb. of dry ground feed for one day for a 25-lb. pig; for heavier animals additional medicated feed up to a total of 4 lb. may be given at 12- to 24-hour intervals.

Other ascarids found in domestic animals are *Ascaris vitulorum* in calves and *A. equorum* (*megalocephala*) in horses.

The related genera Toxocara and Toxascaris contain the common ascarids of dogs and cats — *Toxocara canis* in dogs, *T. cati* (*Belascaris mystax*) in cats, and *Toxascaris leonina* in both. They are smaller than the Ascaris of pigs and man, the females measuring 7 to 18 cm. and the males 5 to 10 cm.; they have conspicuous cervical alae giving the anterior end an arrowhead shape (Fig. 144A). Toxocara males have a small fingerlike process at the tip of the tail, lacking in Toxascaris (Fig. 144B, C). Toxocara eggs are delicately pitted, and those of Toxascaris are smooth. The life cycle of Toxocara is like that of Ascaris, but Toxascaris differs in passing its early stages in the host in the intestinal wall. A few cases of human infection with the species of Toxocara have been recorded.

Another rare ascarid found in man is *Lagochilascaris minor,* normally found in the cloudy leopard. In several cases in Trinidad and Guiana sexually mature specimens have been found in subcutaneous or tonsillar abscesses about the head. The adults are about the size of hookworms and are identifiable by their lips and a keel-like expansion of the cuticle extending the whole length on each side.

Poultry are subject to two common types of ascarids, *Ascaridia galli* in the small intestine, and species of Heterakis or cecal worms in the

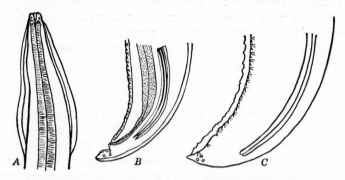

FIG. 144.   *A,* head of *Toxocara canis; B,* tail of male of same; *C,* tail of male of *Toxascaris leonina.* (After Yorke and Maplestone.)

ceca. The former, a worm about 2 to 4 inches long with a muscular preanal sucker on the male, causes retarded growth and droopiness in heavy infections in young chickens. Older birds develop a marked age immunity due to an increase in number of mucin-producing goblet cells (see p. 22). Phenyl mecuric compounds (50 mg.) plus 0.5 gram phenothiazine removes most of these worms. *Heterakis gallinae* is 7 to 15 mm. long with a chitin-rimmed preanal sucker and conspicuous caudal alae in the males. It seems to be harmless, even when the ends of the ceca contain swarming masses of them, except for its role as a carrier of the protozoan, *Histomonas meleagridis,* that causes "blackhead" in turkeys (see p. 131). Chickens become infected with ascarids by swallowing embryonated eggs; there is no migration through the body, but Ascaridia temporarily bury themselves in the intestinal wall.

Ascarids in fish-eating mammals, birds, and fish have more complicated life cycles involving first and second intermediate hosts, which are aquatic invertebrates and small aquatic veterbrates, respectively.

ASCARIDATA. II. OXYUROIDEA

As already noted, the Oxyuroidea are almost exclusively parasites of the cecum or colon of their hosts, not only of vertebrates but also of insects. Only a single oxyurid, *Enterobius vermicularis,* occurs commonly in man.

Enterobius vermicularis

Most members of the Caucasian race, even in highly sanitated countries, fail to get through life without affording food and shelter for oxyuris, also popularly called the pinworm or seatworm (*Enterobius vermicularis*). It is found all over the world but unlike most helminthic infections is relatively rare in the tropics. Its great stronghold is in Europe and North America, but according to Neghme 60 per cent of schoolboys in Chile are infected. As Stoll (1947) remarked, there seem to be factors in our modern way of living which are very favorable for the spread of Enterobius in high as well as low social levels. In North America the general incidence in white children probably averages over 40 per cent. Sample surveys have shown a general incidence of 41 per cent in whites in Washington, D. C. (50 per cent in school children, 35 per cent in preschool children, 22 per cent in adults); 39 per cent in school children in South Dakota; 29 per cent in boys and 34 per cent in girls in San Francisco; 52 per cent in adults and 60 per cent in children in Toronto. Colored races are far less susceptible. Negroes in Washington had less than 16 per cent infection; in Honolulu, children of Caucasian ancestry had 40 per cent infection, those of Oriental ancestry 21 per cent. *Enterobius vermicularis* is strictly a human parasite, although closely related species occur in apes and monkeys.

Morphology. The adult worms live in the cecum, appendix, and neighboring parts of the intestine, from which the gravid females migrate to the rectum. These are little white worms, often seen wriggling actively in stools passed after a purge or enema. Through the semitransparent cuticle can be seen the esophagus with a bulb at its posterior end, and the uteri and coiled ovaries. The head has three small lips and is set off by lateral expansions of the cuticle. The females, 8 to 13 mm. long, taper at both ends, but the tail is drawn out into a long, fine point. The minute males, only 2 to 5 mm. long, are less numerous than the females and are seldom noticed. The tail is curled and has a small bursa-like expansion; there is only one spicule (Fig. 145).

Life Cycle. As the uteri of the females fill with eggs, the worms migrate down to the anus; according to MacArthur they may make regular nightly trips, deposit eggs in the peri-anal region, and retreat into the rectum, but many worms creep out of the anus, and others are passed in the feces. Their movements cause intense itching. Contact with air stimulates the worms to deposit eggs, and a trail of these is left behind as the worms crawl. Eggs are seldom found in the feces before the worms have disintegrated but can be obtained from scrapings from about the anus or lower part of the rectum. The worms eventually dry

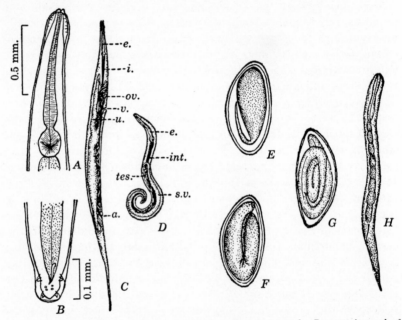

FIG. 145. Pinworm, *Enterobius vermicularis.* *A*, anterior end; *B*, posterior end of male; *C*, female (× 8); *D*, male (× 8); *E*, newly laid egg with " tadpole " embryo; *F*, *G*, development of infective embryo; *H*, newly hatched embryo; abbrev. as in Fig. 120. (Figs. *A* and *B* after Yorke and Maplestone; *C* and *D* after Claus from Braun; *E* and *F* after Braun; *G* and *H* after Leuckart.)

and explode, liberating all the remaining eggs in showers. The eggs when first laid contain partially developed embryos in the " tadpole " stage (Fig. 145*E*); they quickly mature but remain in the egg shell until swallowed. The eggs are clear and unstained, measuring about 55 by 30 μ, and are flattened on one side. Reardon estimated the average number of eggs in a female oxyuris to be about 11,000. After being swallowed the larvae hatch and temporarily burrow into the mucous membranes in the region of the cecum before growing to maturity in the lumen.

Mode of Infection and Epidemiology. The eggs regain access to the same or another person in various ways, but are probably most often air-borne or conveyed by the hands. The itching caused by the emigration of the worms from the anus results in scratching, and the eggs lodged under the fingernails may eventually reach the mouth in children or others who are careless in their habits. The eggs are easily liberated into the air when sheets, clothing, etc., contaminated with them are shaken or rubbed, and may be inhaled or may settle as dust which may be inhaled later.

The extent to which the eggs become scattered in infected households is almost incredible. Not only are they present on the hands, clothing, bed linen, towels, washcloths, and soap, but also on floor, upholstery, and furniture. Nolan and Reardon (1939) collected eggs, some of them viable, from dust in every room of seven houses which were occupied by one or more heavily infected cases; the eggs were found at all levels, including light fixtures and moldings over doors. Schuffner (1944) studied the distribution of eggs in infected institutions in Holland and found that the smaller the enclosed space the greater the number of eggs; in 1 square foot in a large dining hall he found 119 eggs, in a smaller classroom 305, in a toilet 5000. He pointed out that half the life of an infected child is spent in a still smaller enclosed space — that between bed sheets, where the eggs are disseminated by movements of the sleeper. He believes, however, that very heavy infections result only from transfer of eggs by fingers after scratching.

Cram has called attention to the familial nature of pinworm infections, and numerous observations point to its ready spread in schools and institutions. The eggs survive longest (2 to 6 days) under cool humid conditions, but their life span in dry air above 25° C. is greatly shortened, few surviving as long as 12 hours. In dry air at 36 to 37° C. less than 10 per cent survive for 3 hours and none for 16 hours. Since the worms have a life span of only 37 to 53 days, the infection would die out in this period if reinfection could be stopped; the periodic appearance of increased numbers of worms often observed at 4- or 5-week intervals is due to the maturation of new generations of worms from reinfections.

Diagnosis. No dependence can be placed upon examinations of the feces for the eggs of oxyuris. Direct fecal smears show less than 1 per cent of the actual infections, and flotation methods less than 25 per cent; even heavy infections often fail to be detected.

Far better results are obtained by scraping the perianal region. Of various devices for this purpose, the most widely used is the " N I H " swab described by Hall (1937). It consists of a piece of cellophane, small enough to go under a cover glass, wrapped around the end of a 4-mm. glass rod and fastened with a rubber band cut from a piece of tubing. The rod is first pushed through a perforated rubber cork which fits a test tube, so that after use it can be kept and handled easily. When the anal region is scraped with this the eggs adhere and can be found when the piece of cellophane is flattened out in decinormal sodium hydroxide solution under a cover glass. Another device is a loop of Scotch tape held at the ends by a pair of forceps, the sticky side being applied to the perianal skin and then flattened on a slide.

The success of the swabbing method is affected by bathing, personal cleanliness, and irregular periodicity in the migration of the worms, so the number of eggs found has no relation to the size of the infection and one negative examination cannot be considered conclusive.

Pathology. The itching caused by migration of the worms in the anal region and by allergic irritation of the skin may be intense, causing loss of sleep, restlessness, nervousness, and even sexual disorders. In girls the worms may cause vaginitis by entering the vulva, and they may even wander into the Fallopian tubes or to the peritoneal cavity, where they become encysted.

Immature burrowing worms may cause inflammation in the cecal region, with some abdominal pain and digestive disturbances. Since the males and young females are often found in removed appendices they are often accused of causing appendicitis, but there is very little to support this view, since they are about equally common in healthy and inflamed appendices.

Treatment and Prevention. Treatment is difficult because of the situation of the worms in the cecal region far from either mouth or anus, and because if all the worms are not expelled the infection may soon build up again; this frequently happens anyway unless all the members of the family are treated.

Many of the nematode group of anthelmintics, especially tetrachloro-ethylene and hexylresorcinol, remove some of the worms, but the only really efficient drug until recently has been gentian violet, with which up to 90 per cent of cures can be obtained. It has to be given in enteric-coated capsules (" Seal-Ins " or " Enseals ") in repeated small doses of ½ to 1 grain 3 times a day with meals or an hour before meals for 8 days or for a number of consecutive days with rest periods in between. Small $\frac{3}{20}$- or $\frac{1}{5}$-grain tablets are available for infants. No serious reactions develop, although some patients may lose appetite or have cramps or nausea at some time during treatment. In 1947 a report on a few cases indicated that acranil (see p. 323) may be even more effective, and in a single dose.

Phenothiazine in daily doses of 0.5 to 1 gram for 6 to 10 days is also very successful in curing oxyuriasis, but it sometimes causes a severe or even fatal anemia in children which develops after the treatment is completed; it is considered too dangerous to be used routinely. Lubisan, a resorcin compound, was reported by Sisk in 1946 to have cured 37 of 51 cases (1.2 gram on 3 successive mornings, repeated after a rest of 4 days, with reduced doses for children under 12). There were no toxic effects, and it was suggested that larger doses might be safe.

If reinfection could be stopped the infection would disappear without treatment in a few weeks, but, even with the most meticulous care in cleanliness, prevention of reinfection without treatment usually fails. It requires closed pajamas of nonporous material, daily changing and sterilization of bedclothes, towels, and underwear, use of anal bandages and disinfecting ointments, frequent washing of hands, close-clipped fingernails, a dustless house, and unrelaxing parental vigilance. Treatment is easier! Schuffner (1944) believes that 100 per cent of the children in Holland are infected in spite of the proverbial Dutch cleanliness. He thinks that efforts to eliminate the infection completely may lead to a " pinworm neurosis " that is worse than a mild pinworm infection. In light infections a small enema of 1 or 2 ounces of water and removal of worms from the anal folds will relieve symptoms; and wearing closed bathing trunks, which will prevent picking up eggs by scratching although it will not entirely eliminate dust infection, will convert an active into a latent case. Light dust-borne infections can be minimized by using anal ointments at night and washing immediately after rising in the morning.

Other Oxyuroidea. The only domestic animal that suffers from oxyuris infection is the horse, which harbors a large species known as *Oxyuris equi*. Rodents harbor numerous species, and one of these, *Syphacia obvelata* of mice and rats, was found once in a child in the Philippines. Its eggs are shaped like those of Enterobius, but are 110 to 142 μ long. Common oxyurids for class study can nearly always be found in large cockroaches.

RHABDITATA

The suborder Rhabditata is of particular interest from an evolutionary standpoint since it contains nematodes showing every imaginable gradation from free-living, saprophagous forms to strict parasites. It presents a sort of pageant of parasites in the making. The genus Rhabditis alone contains many species which appear to be experimenting with parasitism. Some species have been found breeding in the feces-soiled hair of the perianal region of dogs; the larvae of the common soil nematode, *R. strongyloides,* have been found repeatedly in itching pustules in the skin of dogs and other animals after lying on soiled straw bedding; members of a closely related genus, Longibucca, have been found breeding in the stomach and intestine of snakes and bats; another member of the same family, *Diploscapter coronata* (see p. 439), is an opportunist which is capable of establishing itself in the human stomach or female urinogenital system when abnormal conditions make these environments favorable.

Members of the families Strongyloididae and Rhabdiasidae have bridged the gap between free-living and parasitic existence by a method peculiar to themselves — a true alternation of generations. There is a free-living generation consisting of males and females which are hardly distinguishable from Rhabditis, and a parasitic generation of parthenogenetic females which have a markedly different appearance. The eggs produced by one generation give rise to worms of the alternate generation. This routine is, however, short-circuited by many of the individual worms by omission of the free-living bisexual generation entirely, in spite of the fact that this is unquestionably the ancestral type. By this process we arrive at a form which is as truly parasitic as a hookworm.

The Strongyloididae pass the parasitic phase of their lives in the intestine of mammals, while the Rhabdiasidae pass theirs in the lungs of amphibians and reptiles. *Strongyloides stercoralis* is the only common and important human parasite in the Rhabditata, but Rhabditis (see p. 440) is frequently found in human stools, to the confusion of technicians examining them.

Strongyloides stercoralis

General Account. This, the smallest nematode parasitic in the human body except the male Trichinella, is a very common human parasite in moist tropical or subtropical climates, having much the same distribution as hookworms. Faust found it in 20 per cent of hospital and village populations in Panama and in 4 per cent of cases examined in New Orleans hospitals and clinics. It is a common parasite in soldiers returning from the South Pacific. Statistics based on ordinary stool examinations do not give a correct idea of the prevalance of this parasite.

There has been some dispute about whether the slender parasitic females of Strongyloides are really parthenogenetic, hermaphroditic, or actually bisexual, since Kreis (1932) and Faust (1933) found a few male worms in the lungs of infected dogs and suspected them of fertilizing the females before the latter reached the intestine. There is

no longer any doubt that the parasitic females are really parthenogenetic and it seems evident that the so-called parasitic males are really
free-living males precociously developed in the lungs, where some
reproduction by the parasitic females sometimes occurs. There is one
species of Strongyloididae, *Parastrongyloides winchesi*, which *is* bisexual in the parasitic generation, but the males are filariform like the
females, whereas the males found by Kreis and Faust are rhabditiform,
like the free-living males.

Morphology. The parasitic females (Fig. 146, *1*) are extremely
slender worms 2 to 2.5 mm. long by only 40 to 50 μ in diameter, with a
bulbless esophagus about one-fourth the length of the body. The uteri
diverge from the vulva in the posterior third of the body; each contains
a few developing eggs in single file.

Life Cycle (Fig. 146). The adult females burrow in the mucous
membranes of the intestine anywhere from just behind the stomach to
the rectum, although the upper part of the small intestine is their
favorite spot. A few mature even in the bronchial tubes. The eggs,
measuring about 50 by 32 μ, are deposited in the mucous membranes
where they undergo development and hatch, the larvae then making
their way into the lumen of the intestine, to be voided with the feces.
Only exceptionally, in cases of severe diarrhea, do embryonated eggs
appear in the feces. The egg output per worm is relatively small, not
more than 50 per day.

The passed larvae are rhabditiform (see p. 396) and have usually
grown to a length of 300 to 800 μ. They resemble hookworm larvae
but can be distinguished by the very short mouth cavity (Fig. 133, *9*).

The course of development of these larvae may follow either one of
two lines: (1) direct or " homogonic," or (2) indirect or " heterogonic."
In the *indirect course* of development the rhabditiform larvae develop,
in 36 hours or more and after four moults, into free-living males
and females (Fig. 146, *2*), which closely resemble soil nematodes of the
genus Rhabditis; they are about 1 mm. in length and 40 to 60 μ broad.
These adults produce eggs which hatch into rhabditiform larvae very
similar to the offspring of the parasitic females, which then ordinarily
transform after two moults into slender filariform larvae characterized
by a very long, slender esophagus and a long tail notched at the tip
(Fig. 147). The small oval genital primordium is midway between
the end of the esophagus and the anus. These larvae, 600 to 700 μ
long, remain, like infective hookworm larvae, ensheathed by the
moulted cuticles of the rhabditiform larvae, and are now in the infective stage. They may appear in less than 48 hours, and they become

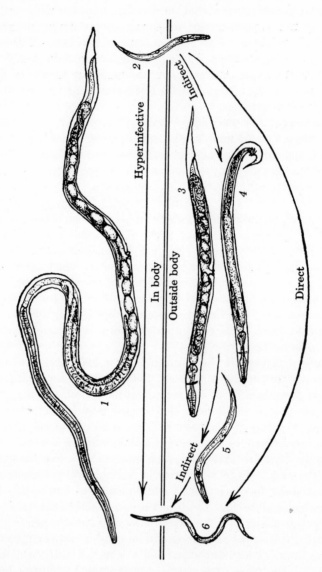

FIG. 146. Life cycle of *Strongyloides stercoralis* showing direct, indirect, and hyper-infective methods. *1*, adult parasitic ♀ ; *2*, first rhabditiform larva; *3*, adult free-living ♀ ; *4*, adult free-living ♂ ; *5*, second rhabditiform larva (offspring of free-living adults; *6*, filariform (infective) larva. × 100.

numerous in 5 or 6 days. They infect by penetrating the skin or mucous membranes as do hookworm larvae. Occasionally, according to Beach (1936), more than one free-living generation may develop.

In the *direct* course of development the rhabditiform larvae produced by the parasitic females, usually after a brief period of feeding and growth, metamorphose directly into infective filariform larvae at the second moult. These penetrate the skin as do those produced indirectly.

A third possible course of development, called the *hyperinfective* method, occurs in exceptional cases when the larvae of the parasitic females rapidly undergo two moults inside the intestine without feeding

Fig. 147. Mature filariform larva of *Strongyloides stercoralis*, × 180. (Modified from Looss.)

or growing, transforming into filariform larvae which then burrow through the mucous membranes or perianal skin, causing reinfection without any outside existence (see Faust and de Groat, 1940).

The larvae of Strongyloides are rather delicate, are easily destroyed by cold, desiccation, or direct sunlight, and are rather short-lived even under the most favorable conditions. This probably accounts for the infrequence of Strongyloides infections outside warm moist climates.

After penetration some larvae remain in the skin for a long time, but they appear in the lungs from the third day onward. The larvae undergo development to adolescence in the lungs, and then migrate to the alimentary canal via the trachea and throat, although a few mature and reproduce in the lungs and bronchioles. Larvae begin to appear in the feces about 17 days or more after infection in man, but in dogs the prepatent period is only 12 days and in rats 6 days. The numbers rise rapidly but decrease again after some months, when immunity begins to develop.

Biology of Direct and Indirect Development. The apparently willy-nilly appearance of the direct and indirect modes of development of Strongyloides has been very puzzling. Attempts have been made to explain it on the basis of environmental effects inside and outside the host, age of worms, fertilization by parasitic males, and biologically different strains.

Sandground (1926) found that in rats mass infections with *Strongyloides ratti* larvae of direct or homogonic type gave a higher percentage of homogonic progeny than did infections with heterogonic larvae. Graham (1936–1939) started two pure lines of *S. ratti* in rats from original single-larva infections of the homogonic and heterogonic types, respectively, and found marked inherent differences between them. In each line over 85 per cent of the total progeny were of its own type, with an extreme difference in the number of free-living males produced. Meanwhile Beach (1935, 1936) showed conclusively that the course of development can be influenced by nutritional conditions; as these become less favorable more and more of the rhabditiform larvae undergo direct transformation into filariform larvae instead of becoming males and females. The conclusion seems warranted, therefore, that the course of development is dependent upon nutrition or other environmental influences and not on genetic constitution, but that there are genetic differences in the extent to which different strains are influenced toward homogony by given degrees of unfavorableness in the environment.

Diagnosis. The infection must be diagnosed by the finding and identification of the larvae in the stools. Usually the larvae can be found in simple fecal smears and can be floated satisfactorily in zinc sulfate solution (see p. 91), but they shrink badly in saturated sodium chloride. If scanty they can be found readily by culturing the stool mixed with an equal part of charcoal or sterilized earth. The rhabditiform larvae, as already noted, can be distinguished from those of hookworms by the very short mouth cavity, but are difficult to distinguish from coprophagic Rhabditis larvae in stale or contaminated stools unless cultured for 2 to 5 days, and the filariform larvae found by extraction into warm water. Embryonated eggs are occasionally found in cases of severe diarrhea. In examining stale stools there may be confusion with hookworm infections, but an excess of larvae over eggs in uncultured stools is indicative of Strongyloides. The eggs, if present, are decidedly smaller and always embryonated.

Pathology. Skin penetration by the larvae often causes redness and intense itching, with lesions resembling ground itch. Invasion of the lungs sometimes causes acute inflammation. The adults burrowing in the intestinal mucosa cause a catarrhal inflammation with so much erosion in severe cases as to give the appearance of raw beefsteak. In very light infections there may be no demonstrable symptoms; in moderate and chronic cases there are usually intermittent diarrhea and epigastric pain; in severe cases there may be uncontrollable diarrhea with blood and undigested food in the liquid stools. The loss of food and continued drain of liquids cause severe emaciation. In the tropics there is often evidence of toxic effects as well; de Langen described cases in Java with high eosinophilia, leucocytosis, anemia, slight fever, edema, and bronchial pneumonia in addition to the intestinal symptoms, and Faust called attention to the frequency of nervous symptoms in chronic infections. These are probably due to the toxic effects of disintegration of numerous larvae invading the bodies of people who have developed immunity. Lawler (1941) showed that in rats development of immunity is weakened by a Vitamin A deficiency.

Treatment and Prevention. Gentian violet is a specific for Strongyloides infections. It stains the intestinal mucosa and kills the adult worms buried in it. Faust recommends for children ½-grain enteric-coated tablets 3 times a day before meals for a week, and twice that dose for adults. Sometimes one course is sufficient to effect a complete cure, but often several are needed. Hexylresorcinol is very toxic to Strongyloides *in vitro* but may not be effective *in vivo*. In 1948 hetrazan by stomach tube was reported to have given favorable results.

Control is much the same as in hookworm infections, except that the delicacy of the Strongyloides larvae should make it easier.

Other Strongyloides. *Strongyloides stercoralis* is infective for dogs and cats as well as man but usually dies out in a number of weeks. In India, however, the writer found a high percentage of cats naturally infected with a Strongyloides which was very similar to, if not identical with, the human species. Other species occur in monkeys, sheep, rodents, pigs, and other animals. One human infection with *S. fülleborni* of monkeys has been reported. Most of the species in herbivorous animals differ from those in man and carnivores in that the eggs do not usually hatch until after they have left the body of the host.

Diploscapter coronata

Some nematodes found in the aspirated stomach contents of nine patients who were suffering from complete or almost complete lack of

Fig. 148. *Diploscapter coronata*, adult female from human stomach.

hydrochloric acid were examined by the writer (1938) and found to be *Diploscapter coronata* (Fig. 148). This nematode was previously known only as an inhabitant of soil or sewage beds; a related species is parasitic on living roots of plants. The worms from the stomach were abundant in some cases and scanty in others; they were in all stages of development, but no males were found. This corresponds with most previous observations on this worm; apparently, like Strongyloides and some species of Rhabditis, it can get along very well without the presence of the male sex. Adult females are about 420 μ long.

All the cases were discovered in a Houston clinic, and similar cases are reported as having been seen frequently before but incorrectly diagnosed as Strongyloides. In one case a re-examination four days later showed the worms still present, so they were undoubtedly established in the stomach. Oddly enough only a single prior case of similar nature has been recorded in the literature. The same worm was, however, found by Yokogawa in 1936 and in the urine of a Japanese woman who was suffering from pyelitis and who apparently had acquired the infection from soil on which she had sat. Whether or not the worm has any pathogenic effect has not been determined.

Rhabditis

The genus Rhabditis contains numerous species of nematodes normally found in soil, organic matter, or water, and frequently in feces of man or animals. They closely resemble the free-living generation of Strongyloides but have no alternation of generations.

Rhabditis pellio is a species which has on a few occasions been found living in the human vagina, the larvae escaping in the urine. Another species, *R. hominis,* has been recorded from both Japan and the United States in stools of man and animals, and several other species have been found in human stools in Russia. In most of these cases there was suspicion of their being true parasites, but the worms have not been found on re-examination, and in some cases clear evidence of contamination with soil or water was obtained. There is as yet no conclusive evidence that any of these species are more than coprophagous. Other pseudo-infections with Rhabditis were mentioned on pp. 433–434. Their only importance is their possible confusion with Strongyloides.

REFERENCES
Ascaridoidea

ACKERT, J. E., The Morphology and Life History of the Fowl Nematode *Ascaridia lineata* (Schneider), *Parasitol.*, **23**, 360 (1931).

CRAM, E. B., Ascariasis in Preventive Medicine, *Am. J. Trop. Med.*, **6**, 91 (1926).

HEADLEE, W. H., The Epidemiology of Human Ascariasis in the Metropolitan Area of New Orleans, La., *Am. J. Hyg.*, **24**, 479 (1936).

LANE, C., The Prevention of Ascaris Infection: A Critical Review, *Trop. Diseases Bull.*, **31**, 605 (1934).

OTTO, G. F., and CORT, W. W., The Distribution and Epidemiology of Human Ascariasis in the United States, *Am. J. Hyg.*, **19**, 657 (1934).

REID, W. M., The Relationship between Glycogen Depletion in the Nematode *Ascaridia galli* (Schrank) and Elimination of the Parasite by the Host, *Am. J. Hyg.*, **41**, 150–155 (1945).

Scott, J. A., Observations on Infection with the Common Roundworm, *Ascaris lumbricoides,* in Egypt, *Am. J. Hyg.,* **30,** D, 83–116 (1939).

Winfield, G. F., *et al.,* Studies on the Control of Fecal-borne Diseases in North China, II, IV. *China Med. J.,* **51,** 502, 643, 919 (1937).

Oxyuroidea

Gordon, H., Appendical Oxyuriasis and Appendicitis Based on a Study of 26,051 Appendices, *Arch. Path.,* **16,** 177 (1933).

Lentze, F. A., Zur Biologie des *Oxyuris vermicularis, Zentr. Bakt. Parasitenk.,* I Abt., Orig., **135,** 156 (1935).

MacArthur, W. P., Threadworms and Pruritis Ani, *J. Roy. Army Med. Corps,* **55,** 214 (1930).

Miller, M. J., and Allen, D., Studies on Pinworm Infections, III, Tests with Phenothiazine in the Treatment of Pinworm Infections, *Can. Med. Assoc. J.,* **46,** 111 (1942).

National Institute of Health, Studies on Oxyuriasis, I–XXVIII (Papers by Hall, Wright, Bozicevich, Cram, Jones, Reardon, Nolan, Brady, *et al.*), 1937–1943; XXVIII, Summary and Conclusions (by Cram, E. B., *Am. J. Diseases Children,* **65,** 46, 1943) contains references to entire series.

Schüffner, W., Die Bedeutung der Staubinfektion für die Oxyuriasis, Richtlinien der Therapie und Prophylaxe, *Münch. med. Wochenschr.,* **44,** 411–414 (1944); Review in *Trop. Diseases Bull.,* **43,** 233–236 (1946).

Stoll, N. R., This Wormy World, *J. Parasitol.,* **33,** 1–18 (1947**)**.

Rhabditata

Beach, T. D., Experimental Studies on Human and Primate Species of Strongyloides, V, The Free-living Phase of the Life Cycle. *Am. J. Hyg.,* **23,** 243 (1936).

Chandler, A. C., *Diploscapter coronata* as a Facultative Parasite of Man, with a General Review of Vertebrate Parasitism by Rhabditoid Worms, *Parasitol.,* **30,** 44 (1938).

Faust, E. C., The Symptomatology, Diagnosis and Treatment of Stronglyoides Infection, *J. Am. Med. Assoc.,* **98,** 2276 (1932).

Experimental Studies on Human and Primate Species of Strongyloides. II, *Am. J. Hyg.,* **18,** 114 (1933); III and IV, *Arch. Path.,* **18,** 605 (1934); **19,** 769 (1935).

Faust, E. C., and de Groat, A., Internal Autoinfection in Human Strongyloidiasis, *Am. J. Trop. Med.,* **20,** 359 (1940).

Graham, G. L., Studies on Strongyloides, I, II, *Am. J. Hyg.,* **24,** 71 (1936); **27,** 221 (1938); III, *J. Parasitol.,* **24,** 233 (1938); IV, *Am. J. Hyg.,* **30,** Sect. D., 15 (1939); V, *J. Parasitol.,* **25,** 365 (1939).

Kreis, H. A., Studies on the Genus Strongyloides. *Am. J. Hyg.,* **16,** 450 (1932).

Lawler, H. J., The Relation of Vitamin A to Immunity to Strongyloides Infection, *Am. J. Hyg.,* **34,** D, 65–72, (1941).

Napier, L. E., *Strongyloides stercoralis* Infection, Parts 1 and 2, *J. Trop. Med. Hyg.,* **52,** 25–30, 46–48 (1949).

Sandground, J. H., Observations on *Rhabditis hominis* Kobayashi in the United States, *J. Parasitol.,* **11,** 140 (1925).

Biological Studies on the Life Cycle in the Genus Strongyloides Grassi, 1879, *Am. J. Hyg.,* **6,** 337 (1926).

CHAPTER 19

Filariae, Spiruroids, and Guinea Worm
(Suborders Spirurata and Camallanata)

I. Filariae (Superfamily Filarioidea)

The filariae, constituting the superfamily Filarioidea, are slender threadlike worms which inhabit some part of the blood or lymphatic system, connective tissues, body cavities, eye sockets, nasal cavities, etc. They have simple mouths without lips and rarely a vestibule; the females nearly always have the vulva forward near the mouth, and the relatively small males have spirally coiled tails, with or without alae but always with papillae. Many of them — all those that concern us here except Parafilaria in horses — produce embryos that live in the blood or skin, whence they are sucked out by bloodsucking arthropods which serve as intermediate hosts; they gain access to a new host through the skin when these arthropods bite.

The classification into families and subfamilies is still controversial. We shall follow Wehr's (1935) arrangement. He recognized four families; of these three, Stephanofilariidae, Filariidae, and Dipetalonematidae, contain parasites of medical or veterinary interest. The first contains a single genus, Stephanofilaria, a skin parasite of horses (see p. 461), with a row of small spines around the mouth. The other two, Filariidae and Dipetalonematidae, are distinguished mainly by the first-stage larvae, which are usually short and stout with spiny anterior ends in the Filariidae and long and slender with no spines in the Dipetalonematidae. Except Parafilaria and Setaria in horses and cattle, all the species parasitic in man or domestic animals belong to the Dipetalonematidae. There are two subfamilies: Dirofilariinae, including Dirofilaria and Loa, which have well-developed caudal alae and the esophagus externally divided into separate muscular and glandular parts; and the Dipetalonematinae, which have very narrow caudal alae, if any, and no external division of the esophagus; in this subfamily are included Wuchereria, Onchocerca, Acanthocheilonema, and Mansonella. Guinea worms, Dracunculus, were formerly classed with filariae but are now placed in an entirely distinct suborder (see p. 468). At one time all the filariae were placed in the single genus Filaria and are sometimes still so referred to in medical and veterinary books.

Microfilariae. Many filarial infections are practically impossible to diagnose except by the embryos or " microfilariae," and it is therefore important to be able to distinguish them. When living, they are colorless and transparent and may or may not be enclosed in " sheaths." In order to identify them it is usually necessary to stain them. The body will then be found to contain a column of nuclei, broken in definite places which serve as landmarks (Fig. 149). The principal ones are a nerve ring anteriorly, an excretory pore or " V " spot, an excretory cell somewhat farther back, a few genital cells posteriorly, and an anal pore or " tail spot." The spacing of these landmarks is fairly constant in

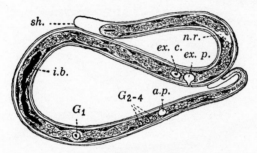

Fig. 149. Anatomy of a microfilaria, *Mf. bancrofti;* *a.p.*, anal pore or " tail spot "; *ex. c.*, excretory cell; *ex. p.*, excretory pore or " v " spot; *i.b.*, " inner body "; G_1, G_{2-4}, genital cells; *n.r.*, nerve ring; *sh.*, sheath. × 600. (After Fülleborn.)

different species. The presence or absence and arrangement of nuclei in the head and tail ends and the shape of the tail are also useful identification marks. The following table shows the outstanding characters of the microfilariae found in human blood or skin (see also Fig. 150).

Sheathed forms.

 Mf. bancrofti: about 225 to 300 μ by 10 μ; sheath stains red with dilute Giemsa stain; tail end tapers evenly; no nuclei in tail; does not stain with 1 : 1000 methylene blue when alive; lies in graceful coils when dried; nocturnal or nonperiodic; in blood or urine.

 Mf. loa: same size; sheath unstained in Giemsa; tail short and recurved, with nuclei to tip; stains with methylene blue when alive; lies in kinky scrawls when dried; diurnal; in blood.

 Mf. malayi: about 160 to 230 μ by 5 to 6 μ; tail sharp-pointed, with a single nucleus at its tip and another 10 μ in front of it; nocturnal.

Unsheathed forms.

 Mf. perstans: about 200 μ by 4 μ; tail ends bluntly, with nuclei to its tip; stains with methylene blue when alive; no periodicity; in blood.

 Mf. streptocerca: about 215 μ by 3 μ; tail ends in a crook and terminates bluntly with nuclei to tip; does not stain with methylene blue when alive; no periodicity; in skin.

Mf. ozzardi: about 200 μ by 5 μ; tail sharply pointed, with no nuclei at its tip; stains with methylene blue when alive; no periodicity; in blood.

Mf. volvulus: about 300 to 350 μ by 5 to 8 μ; tail sharply pointed, with no nuclei at its tip; no periodicity; in skin.

Wuchereria (Filaria) bancrofti

Distribution. This worm is a very widespread and important human parasite in warm countries but is not evenly distributed or uniformly

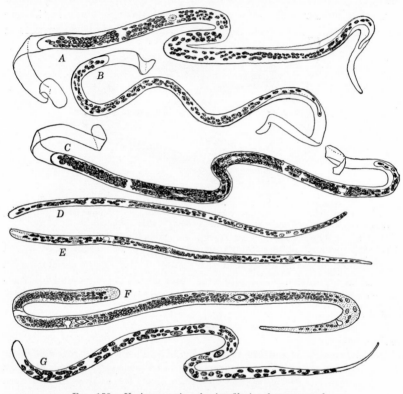

FIG. 150. Various species of microfilariae drawn to scale.

A, Wuchereria bancrofti; sheathed, no nuclei in tip of tail, 270 × 8.5 μ.
B, W. malayi; sheathed, 2 nuclei in tail, 200 × 6 μ.
C, Loa loa; sheathed, nuclei to tip of tail, 275 × 7 μ.
D, Acanthocheilonema perstans; no sheath, tail blunt with nuclei to tip, 200 × 4.5 μ.
E, Mansonella ozzardi; no sheath, pointed tail without nuclei at tip, 205 × 5 μ.
F, Onchocerca volvulus; no sheath, no nuclei in end of tail, 320 × 7.5 μ.
G, Dirofilaria immitis; no sheath, sharp tail without nuclei in end, 300 × 6 μ.

prevalent throughout any country. As Augustine (1945) pointed out, it occurs almost entirely in coastal areas and islands where there is a fairly long hot season with high humidity. In Africa it is found on the Mediterranean and east and west coastal areas but not in the interior of Central Africa. In Asia it is prevalent on the coasts of Arabia, India, Malaya, and north to China and the southern parts of Korea and Japan. It is prevalent in practically all the East Indian and South Pacific islands and on the coasts of Queensland.

In the Western Hemisphere, where it was almost certainly introduced by whites or Negroes, it is prevalent throughout the West Indies and on the northern coast of South America from northern Brazil to Colombia, but it is strangely scarce or absent on the Caribbean shores

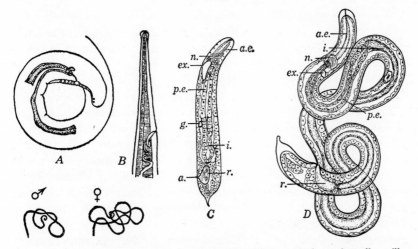

Fig. 151. *Wuchereria bancrofti;* *A*, tail of male, showing spicules and small papillae on narrow alae; *B*, anterior end, showing bulbous head and position of vulva; *C*, " sausage " stage of larva; *D*, infective larva from mosquito; under *A* and *B*, ♂ and ♀ shown natural size; *a.*, anus; *a.e.*, anterior portion of esophagus; *ex.*, excretory pore; *g.*, genital rudiment; *i.*, intestine; *n.*, nerve ring; *p.e.*, posterior portion of esophagus; *r.*, rectum. (*A* and *B*, adapted from Maplestone; *C* and *D*, adapted from Looss.)

of Central and North America. In the United States it was endemic for a long time in Charleston, S. C., but failed to become established elsewhere and has apparently died out there. Throughout this area it is almost completely restricted to towns and sometimes even to parts of them, but in some places it affects 80 per cent or more of the local population.

Morphology. The adult worms (Fig. 151) live in the lymph glands or ducts, often in inextricable tangles. The females are 65 to 100 mm. long and only 0.25 mm. in diameter — about the caliber of coarse sewing thread; the males are about 40 mm. long and 0.1 mm. in diameter. The body tapers to a fine head slightly swollen at the end, with a simple pore as a mouth. The esophagus is partly muscular and partly glandular, with the vulva opening a little behind its middle.

The males have the tail coiled like the tendril of a vine, with numerous pairs of papillae; there is one long and one short spicule.

Life Cycle. The female worms give birth to microfilariae which are surrounded by delicate membranes or sheaths. These have usually been assumed to represent the vitelline membranes, but Augustine (1937) thinks the sheaths are really shed cuticles and are not discernible structures while the embryos are still in the circulating blood. If this is so, they would not, as was formerly supposed, act as muzzles to keep the embryos in the blood vessels.

The further development of the microfilariae depends on their being sucked with blood by certain species of mosquitoes which serve as intermediate hosts (see p. 695). Unlike malaria and yellow fever, *Wuchereria bancrofti* is not limited to transmission by species of one genus or group of mosquitoes; it is transmitted by certain species of Culex, Aëdes, Anopheles, and others, but sometimes nearly related species fail to function; e.g., in the United States *Culex quinquefasciatus, C. pipiens,* and *C. restuans* are good transmitters of the nocturnal strain (see following section on periodicity), but *Aëdes vexans* fails entirely. There is evidence that the nonperiodic Pacific strain normally transmitted by *Aëdes scutellaris* does *not* develop readily in Culex. Byrd, St. Amant, and Bromberg (1945) succeeded in rearing this strain from Samoa in only 1 of 200 *C. quinquefasciatus,* whereas 80 per cent of *Aëdes scutellaris* became infected. The principal transmitters in various parts of the world are considered on p. 695. In order to infect mosquitoes there must be about 15 or more microfilariae per drop of blood (20 c.mm.); a high concentration of 100 or more per drop is fatal to the mosquitoes. Sometimes the blood contains up to 600 in a drop.

Within a few hours or sometimes even a few minutes after being ingested by a mosquito the embryos have penetrated the stomach and migrated to the breast muscles, where they lie lengthwise between the muscle fibers (Fig. 152). Here the body shortens to half its original length but grows several times as thick, thus changing from a graceful snakelike animal to a sausage-shaped creature (Fig. 151C). Then the digestive tract differentiates and the worms begin to grow in length as well as girth, eventually measuring about 1.5 to 2 mm. by 20 to 30 μ (Fig. 151D). During this time there have been two moults and the larvae have reached the infective stage. The worms now become active again and leave the thoracic muscles to make their way down into the proboscis in the interior of the labium, although some get lost and end up in other parts of the body.

This development to the infective stage in the mosquito takes a minimum of 8 to 10 days but more frequently 2 weeks or more.   The optimum conditions are 80° F. and 90 per cent humidity.   At best only a small percentage of the microfilariae ingested develop into infective larvae.

When the mosquito bites a warm moist skin the larvae break free from the labium where the labellum is joined, creep out on the skin of the host, and penetrate through the mosquito bite or other abrasions. This happens successfully only in warm moist weather, for cold makes the larvae inert and dryness destroys them.   Pratt and Newton in 1946, in experimentally infected *Culex quinquefasciatus*, found that after the larvae had matured they gradually decreased in number by

FIG. 152.   Mature larvae of *Wuchereria bancrofti* in thoracic muscles and proboscis of a mosquito.   (Adapted from Castellani and Chalmers.)

loss from the proboscis; they escaped when the proboscis was dipped into saline or even spontaneously, sometimes 8 or 10 within a minute; in 25 days practically all were gone.

Nothing is known of the course pursued by the larvae after they enter the skin and very little as to the time required for sexual maturity to be reached.   The large heart filaria of the dog, *Dirofilaria immitis,* matures 9 months after infection, and it is unlikely that the human filaria takes longer.   The fact that in India children seldom show microfilariae in their blood under 5 years of age and Europeans only after many years of residence in an infected locality is due either to the scarcity of the embryos in the blood or to failure of the males and females to meet each other in the same glands or lymph ducts.   Probably the adults live at least 4 or 5 years.

Periodicity.   One of the most interesting and puzzling facts about the microfilariae in the blood is their " periodicity," i.e., their periodic appearance at night, chiefly from 10 P.M. to 4 A.M., in the peripheral blood, and their almost complete disappearance in the daytime.   This happens in most parts of the world, but in many islands in the South Pacific, including all those east of 180° longitude, where the main transmitter is the day-biting *Aëdes scutellaris*, there is no periodicity or, according to Eyles, Hunter, and Warren, there is a slight diurnal periodicity.   Because of this peculiarity of periodicity and difference in vectors Manson-Bahr (1941) considered this a separate species, *W. pacifica.* Although scarce, the microfilariae of *W. bancrofti* are usually discoverable in day blood if 1 cc. is laked in 10 cc. of 2 per cent formalin, let settle 12 to 24 hours, decanted, and the sediment stained with methylene blue and eosin.

The stimulus which times the appearance of the embryos in the blood is in some way connected with periods of activity of the host, for it is gradually reversed in people who sleep by day and work by night; yet sleep itself is not the factor, since the embryos begin to appear before the usual sleeping hours.

Two general hypotheses have been proposed to explain the periodicity of microfilariae. Manson, who first observed the development of filarial larvae in mosquitoes in China in 1878, believed that the microfilariae were relatively long-lived, being concentrated in internal organs of the body during the day but appearing in the skin capillaries at night, to keep a sort of tryst with their night-biting transmitter, Culex. Lane in 1929, on the other hand, proposed a " cyclical parturition " hypothesis, in which he explained the periodicity by assuming that all the females in a host give birth to their embryos each day at approximately the same hour, and that all these embryos are then destroyed in the host within the next 24 hours. There are strong arguments against either of these hypotheses, and there is still no adequate explanation for the phenomenon. For blow-by-blow accounts of the contest over rival theories see Hinman (1937) and Lane (1937, 1947).

Pathology. Filarial symptoms are caused by the adult worms; the microfilariae usually produce no symptoms. The so-called signs and symptoms are due either to inflammatory reactions or to lymphatic obstruction.

It is very likely that the inflammatory effects are due largely to allergic reactions in sensitized tissues. They consist primarily in inflammation of lymph glands (lymphadenitis) and lymph channels (lymphangitis), particularly of the male genital organs (scrotum, spermatic cords, epididymis, and testes), and of the arms and legs. The attacks are usually recurrent, often being precipitated by exercise, and may be accompanied by chills, fever, aches, and general malaise. It is believed that the allergic irritation may be due either to fluid in which the embryos of the worms are discharged, or other metabolic products, or to proteins liberated from dead and phagocytized worms. Some workers, e.g., Grace, believe that hypersensitiveness to accompanying chronic Streptococcus infections is largely responsible for the symptoms. Failure of penicillin and sulfonamides to affect filarial lymphangitis is against this theory.

Obstruction of lymph channels may play a prominent part in the symptoms, especially in old infections. The dramatic end result of this is elephantiasis (Fig. 153), which, as Brown (1945) says, is popularly but mistakenly believed to be the inevitable final termination of every filarial infection. This belief caused a tremendous amount of

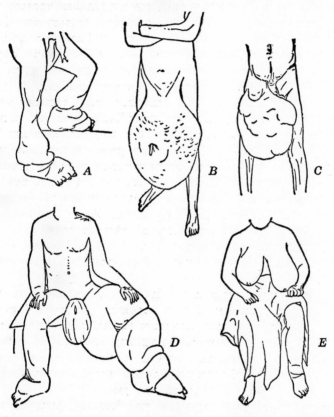

Fig. 153. Some extreme cases of elephantiasis; *A*, of legs and feet; *B*, of scrotum; *C*, varicose groin gland; *D*, scrotum and legs; *E*, of mammary glands. (*A* and *B* sketched from photos from Castellani and Chalmers; *C*, *D*, and *E* from Manson.)

unnecessary mental anguish and psychoneurosis during World War II among infected American troops in the South Pacific, who had visions of themselves ending up with anything from sterility to being attached to a 200-pound scrotum or leg.

The earliest obstructive effects are varicose lymph or chyle vessels behind places where lymph glands or channels are blocked by inflammatory tissue reactions. Such varices may burst and divert large amounts of lymph or chyle into the scrotum, bladder, kidney, or peritoneum, or even into the intestine. When obstruction occurs in the smaller lymph channels in the subcutaneous system and skin, especially in scrotum, limbs, breast, or vulva, the tissues become swollen and "blubbery." Eventually fibrous tissue increases and the skin becomes dense, hard, and dry, since the sweat glands also degenerate. This process may gradually increase until true elephantiasis appears, when certain parts of the body develop to monstrous proportions. It is a characteristic feature of obstructive forms of filariasis that microfilariae are commonly absent from the blood, either because they are dammed up in the lymph system or because the parental worms have died. There is a positive correlation between incidence of filarial disease and microfilaria rate in a community but a negative correlation between elephantiasis and blood microfilariae in an individual.

As Brown pointed out, any disease that may run its course for a period as long as 50 years is likely to vary greatly in its clinical course in different human hosts. Such factors as number of worms, speed with which they are acquired, and allergic sensitivity of the individual must be taken into account. Many cases never show any obvious symptoms. In a large group in the Virgin Islands, 20 per cent had microfilariae in the blood, yet practically all were unaware of infection. One had 23,240 microfilariae per cc. of blood yet had no signs or symptoms of filarial infection except a slight general glandular enlargement.

It has been common experience in India and other parts of the world that filarial symptoms are slow in appearing; in India, Europeans seldom show symptoms until they have resided in endemic localities for 10 to 15 years, and even native children seldom show symptoms until half grown. Sometimes, however, elephantiasis, once started, may develop rapidly. Brown saw a patient whose scrotum grew from normal size to a weight of 14 pounds in a year.

In contrast to all prior experience with filariasis, American troops exposed to the nonperiodic strain in Samoa and other South Pacific islands during World War II developed filarial symptoms in as short a time as $3\frac{1}{2}$ to 6 months and in an average of 9 months (Dickson, Huntington, and Eichold, 1943). This disease, called by the native name "mu-mu," was characterized by lymphangitis, enlarged glands, swelling, and redness, most frequently in the genitals or arms and less often in the legs. Headache, backache, fatigue, and nausea were common, but fever and malaise were unusual; physical and mental depression was very pronounced. Microfilariae appeared in the blood in very few cases.

It seems probable that the differences between this rapidly developing disease and the slow-developing filariasis of other parts of the world was due to intensity of infection and consequent early development of strong allergic reaction. In most places in the tropics Europeans are segregated from infected natives at night and protect themselves from mosquitoes sufficiently to escape heavy infections. In the Pacific islands, where the abundant day-biting *Aëdes scutellaris* is the transmitter, men working or fighting in or near native villages may get as many infective bites in a month as they would get in India in years. A very interesting and possibly significant fact is that in islands where only the nocturnal strain exists, e.g., New Guinea, few or no cases developed among white troops.

Diagnosis. If microfilariae are present they can usually be demonstrated (in night blood in the nocturnal strain) by examination of a fresh drop of blood for squirming embryos, or of a dehemoglobinized thick smear for stained embryos (see p. 205). A more accurate method in case the embryos are scanty is to take 1 cc. of blood in 10 cc. of 2 per cent formalin, centrifuge, and examine the sediment. For specific identification the embryos should be stained by Giemsa or Wright methods.

Since microfilariae are frequently absent, especially in elephantiasis cases, clinical signs and symptoms must be relied on to a considerable extent. Skin tests with antigen prepared from *Dirofilaria immitis* (or other filariae since there is very little specificity) are very helpful. Injection of 0.01 cc. of a 1 : 8000 dilution gives positive reactions in most cases and a minimum of false positives, though many of the positives are not clinically active cases. False positives are probably due, as Augustine and Lherisson (1946) pointed out, to sensitization of man by larvae of nonhuman filarial worms, to which he must often be exposed. Negative skin reactions are helpful in ruling out filarial infections, though they sometimes occur in active cases, probably due to desensitization (Huntington, 1945).

Treatment and Prevention. Filariasis apparently balked all efforts to treat it until World War II, when several American workers (Brown, 1944, and Culbertson *et al.*, 1945, 1947), following up successful experiments on Dirofilaria in dogs and on Litomosoides in cotton rats, found that a number of antimony compounds, both trivalent and pentavalent, and also some arsenic compounds, when given over a period of several weeks, greatly reduced or completely eliminated the microfilariae of *W. bancrofti* in man. In some instances, however, it was a year or more before the beneficial effects became evident, which is why the value of these drugs had not previously been realized.

Of the antimony compounds the pentavalent neostibosan gives the best results, reducing the microfilariae 99 per cent and eliminating them entirely in 75 per cent of patients. Of the arsenicals, arsenamide gives comparable results without being too toxic. However, the disadvantage of numerous injections are obvious, so a search has been made for a nontoxic drug that would be effective when taken by mouth. Hetrazan, a piperazine derivative, shows promise of being such a drug, comparable in its effects to the best antimony or arsenic injection treatments. It, like some of the metal compounds, e.g., anthiomaline and arsenamide, has a direct lethal effect on the microfilariae as well as on the adult worms, so that the microfilariae disappear quickly and do not return. Some of the metal compounds, on the other hands, e.g., neostibosan and melarsen oxide, cause the microfilariae to disappear slowly over a period of months, indicating an effect on the adults but not directly on the microfilariae (Brown, 1948).

Some workers believe that elephantiasis is brought on by dead filariae, so the wisdom of killing the adult worms by chemotherapy has been questioned, but no evidence of elephantiasis has appeared in cured patients. In some cases of elephantiasis Knott (1938) has obtained good results from pressure bandaging. In some cases surgery can be used to advantage, as Auchincloss showed in 1930.

Control, of course, consists in avoiding infected mosquitoes and, so far as possible, in keeping persons with microfilariae away from mosquitoes. It happens that many of the important transmitters are mosquitoes of short flight range which can be locally controlled, e.g., *Culex quinquefasciatus, C. pipiens,* and *Aëdes scutellaris.* White residents, troops, etc., in endemic areas are largely protected by segregation from natives, avoidance of servants with microfilariae in their blood, and protection against mosquitoes by screens, sprays, and repellents. Danger of introduction of the disease to new areas, e.g., into the United States by return of filariated troops, is minimal. Since only one or two worms are transmitted at an infected bite, the chances would be against any one person's being bitten often enough by infected mosquitoes to develop either microfilariae or symptoms unless there was a whole group of people living close together from whom the mosquitoes could acquire infection.

Wuchereria malayi

Although *Wuchereria bancrofti* was long thought to be the only filaria that was commonly responsible for lymphangitis and elephantiasis, it has been found that in many places this species plays a very subdued second fiddle to another species that was long known only by the embryo, *Microfilaria malayi* (see p. 443 and Fig. 150*B*). The adults, which resemble *W. bancrofti* closely, were first found by Rao and Maplestone (1940) in India.

W. malayi is common in many places in India and in southeastern Asia and the East Indies, sometimes along with *bancrofti*, sometimes alone; it may affect up to 50 per cent of the rural population.

The transmitting mosquitoes are mainly species of Mansonia (see p. 696). Since these live in swamps, with the larvae and pupae attached to the roots of water plants, the disease is strictly rural. *W. bancrofti* infections increase toward the center of towns, *malayi* infections peripherally. In India *Mansonia annulifera* is the principal vector, and so the disease can be controlled by the delightfully simple method of removing Pistia (water lettuce) on which this mosquito lives almost exclusively (Iyengar, 1938). In Malaya, however, the chief vector is *M. longipalpis*, which pierces the fine roots of swamp-loving trees, and so only extensive drainage is effective.

The pathogenic effects of *malayi* infection are similar in most respects to those of *bancrofti* infection, but the elephantiasis is more frequently in the legs, and the genital organs are rarely affected. In Travancore, microfilariae were occasionally found in children only 2 years old, and elephantiasis was seen in a child of 6.

The African Eye Worm, Loa loa

This worm is a common parasite in west and central Africa. The same or a closely related species has been found a few times in monkeys. The adults live in the subcutaneous tissue of man and make excursions from place to place under the skin, causing itching and a creeping sensation; they show a special preference for creeping in and about the eyes (Fig. 154*D*), and are responsive to warmth. In a person sitting before a fire the worms become active and move to exposed parts; they have been observed to travel at the rate of about an inch in 2 minutes.

The adult worms resemble pieces of surgical catgut, the female varying from about 20 to 70 mm. in length, whereas the males measure about 20 to 35 mm. The general anatomy is not unlike that of *Wuchereria bancrofti*, but the cuticle is provided with numerous little dewdrop-like warts along the lateral lines (Fig. 154).

Loa loa produces sheathed embryos (see p. 443 and Fig. 150*C*) which make their way to the blood stream. They have a diurnal periodicity, swarming in the blood in the daytime and disappearing at night. The intermediate hosts are certain species of Chrysops (*C. dimidiata, C. silacea,* and possibly others), known as mango flies (see p. 639). The larvae develop in the fly's abdomen, sometimes by hundreds, and invade the proboscis after development to the infective stage, which takes 10 to 12 days. When the fly bites, dozens of the larvae may file out of the proboscis and quickly penetrate the skin.

Loa worms cause annoyance by creeping under the skin and about the eyes. They seem especially active in their youth, later showing a tendency to retire to deeper parts of the body. In the eye they are painful, but it is here that they can most easily be extracted. The extraction, however, has to be done expeditiously, before the disturbed worm flees to hiding places deeper in the body.

Loa infections are usually accompanied by painless though sometimes itchy edematous swellings, commonly as large as pigeon eggs,

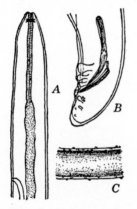
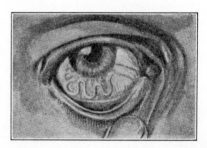

Fig. 154. *Loa loa; A*, anterior end, showing muscular and glandular parts of esophagus and position of vulva (× 20); *B*, tail of male, showing spicules, narrow alae, and papillae (× 100); *C*, portion of body showing dewdrop-like warts on cuticle along lateral lines; *D*, *Loa loa* in eye. (*A* after Yorke and Maplestone; *B* after Vogel; *C* and *D* after Fülleborn.)

which appear suddenly, last a few days, and then disappear to reappear later somewhere else. These "Calabar swellings" are often more troublesome a few months after removal to a cold climate than they are in west Africa, so much so that they take the joy out of leave trips home for some Europeans. Manson-Bahr tells of one patient who went on having Calabar swellings for 17 years until the microfilariae disappeared. The swellings are undoubtedly allergic reactions to metabolic products of the worms or to proteins liberated from injured or expired worms. Chandler, Milliken, and Schuhardt (1930) produced a large swelling by injection of a minute amount of Dirofilaria antigen into the skin of a patient.

Culbertson (1947) reported some work by Rose indicating that antimony compounds are effective in treatment.

Acanthocheilonema perstans

This filaria, believed by some to belong to the genus Dipetalonema (see following section), containing filariae of monkeys and other animals, is widely distributed in west and central Africa and also in northern South America and northern Argentina; it is limited to heavily forested, swampy regions in warm, moist climates. In some localities in Uganda and the Cameroons over 90 per cent of the population harbor the microfilariae in their blood. The adult worms are about as long as *Wuchereria bancrofti* but only about half as thick. They are usually found in connective tissue in the body cavities and pericardium, but Rodhain (1937) found a dozen adults under the capsules of a kidney. The microfilariae (see p. 443 and Fig. 150*D*) are present in the blood both day and night.

Fig. 155. Tails of females of *Acanthocheilonema perstans*, (*A*), and *Mansonella ozzardi* (*B*). Note split tail of former, without fleshy cores in the flaps, and the lappets of the latter, with fleshy cores. (After Leiper.)

The infection seems to produce no evident symptoms, at least in the majority of cases, but Enzer observed cases of persistent headache and drowsiness in individuals whose blood was teeming with the embryos and in whom there was no other evident cause for the symptoms. Others have observed continuous fever. Sharp (1928) showed that the intermediate hosts in the Cameroons are minute nocturnal midges, *Culicoides austeni* and *C. grahami* (see p. 627). The larvae develop in the breast muscles and emerge from the proboscis and head of the insect while it is biting. The insects bite only in darkness, and protection is obtained by sleeping in the presence of even a very feeble light.

Dipetalonema streptocerca

This parasite was long known only by the microfilariae (see p. 443), which resemble those of *A. perstans* but are usually longer and more slender and are found in the skin like those of Onchocerca. It occurs in nearly 50 per cent of natives in some parts of west and central Africa, but no symptoms can definitely be ascribed to it. Similar larvae were found in 6 of 11 chimpanzees in Belgium Congo; the adult worms, located in connective tissue, were assigned to the genus Dipetalonema, to which Acanthocheilonema is very closely related. The intermediate host is not known.

Mansonella ozzardi

This worm, related to *Acanthocheilonema perstans*, is common in parts of the West Indies, Yucatan, Panama, and neighboring coasts of

South America; it is also present in 25 to 30 per cent of the people in northern Argentina. The adults, found in the mesenteries or visceral fat, are about the size of *Wuchereria bancrofti;* the females are characterized by a pair of flaplike processes with fleshy cores at either side of the tail (Fig. 155*B*). Only a single incomplete male has ever been found. The microfilariae (see p. 444 and Fig. 150*E*) are much like those of *A. perstans* but differ in having pointed tails without nuclei. There is no evidence that the worm is pathogenic. Buckley (1934) showed that the intermediate host in St. Vincent, W. I., is *Culicoides furens* (see p. 627), the development being similar to that of *A. perstans;* it is completed in about 7 or 8 days.

Onchocerca

The members of the genus Onchocerca are long, threadlike filarial worms which live in the subcutaneous and connective tissues of their hosts, where they are usually imprisoned in tough fibrous cysts or nodules. The females are so extremely long and hopelessly tangled that it is very difficult to get entire specimens. In man the females sometimes reach a length of 500 to 700 mm. (over 2 ft.), and in cattle twice this length or even more, with the diameter of a coarse sewing thread (about 0.3 to 0.4 mm.). The males are very small by comparison, about 20 to 50 mm. long, with a diameter of 0.2 mm. The microfilariae (see p. 444 and Fig. 150*F*) are sharp-tailed and unsheathed, and differ from other human microfilariae in that they do not enter the blood stream but localize in the skin and eye tissues.

A number of species have been described from horses, cattle, antelopes, and man, but they are very difficult to distinguish, and some have been differentiated mainly on the basis of the usual location of the nodules in the host's body. All the species are recognizable by the presence of thickened ridgelike rings on the cuticle (Fig. 156*A*), much more conspicuous in females than in males. The male has a coiled tail bluntly rounded at the tip and provided with papillae but no alae (Fig. 156*B*); there are two unequal spicules. The females have the vulva near the end of the esophagus and have a bluntly rounded tail.

Some species, especially *Onchocerca gibsoni,* cause enormous financial loss by injuring the hides and carcasses of cattle by the hard nodules that form, especially on the brisket and flanks. Another, *O. reticulata,* inhabits the neck ligament of horses, causing " poll ill " and fistulous withers; the microfilariae cause papular, itching skin sores. This species occurs in the United States.

Human onchocerciasis is caused by *O. volvulus,* which occurs in southern Mexico, Guatemala, and northwest Venezuela in the Western

Hemisphere, and in central Africa in the Old World. The American parasite was once considered a distinct species, *O. caecutiens*, but there is no good basis for this. It was probably originally an African infection, introduced rather recently into Central America, where it was not discovered until 1915.

Life Cycle. The developing worms creep about in the subcutaneous tissue, but when they come to rest there is an inflammatory reaction which results in the formation of the characteristic fibrous cysts; in one instance a nodule was found in a child 2 months old, but usually

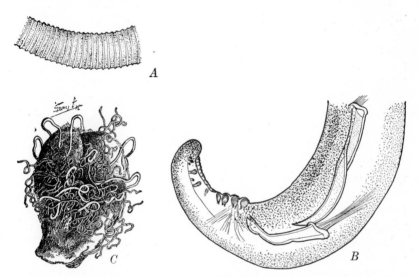

Fig. 156. *Onchocerca volvulus*. *A*, portion of body showing annular thickenings; *B*, tail of male, showing spicules and papillae; *C*, an opened Onchocerca nodule showing tangled worms inside. (*A* and *B* adapted from Fülleborn, *C* after Brumpt.)

a somewhat longer time is required for them to appear. They may grow to a diameter of 1 cm. in a year, but usually the growth is slower. Strong *et al.* in Guatemala usually found 3 or 4 worms in a nodule, but in Africa there are sometimes more than 100. The worms lie in tangles in the cysts (Fig. 156*C*), which vary from the size of a pea or smaller to that of a pigeon's egg; usually a swarm of microfilariae is present also. In most localities infected people have only from one to half a dozen nodules, but in some places in Africa 25 to 100 nodules are commonly seen, most of them only a few millimeters in diameter.

The uteri of the females are packed with coiled embryos enclosed in thin shells with polar extensions. When nodules are examined two kinds of microfilariae are usually seen: large ones, 250 to 360 μ long, similar to those seen in the skin, and smaller ones, 150 to 200 μ long, which Sandground believes have escaped from ruptured uteri. The embryos escape readily from the prisons which enclose their parents and make their way, not into the blood stream, but into the connective tissue just under the skin, where they accumulate in large numbers. Sometimes they emerge by hundreds when a bit of excised skin is placed in a saline solution for two or three hours.

The intermediate host in Africa was shown by Blacklock in 1926 to be a species of blackfly, *Simulium damnosum* (see p. 633); *S. neavei* is also a vector in the Congo and Kenya. In Guatemala and Mexico three species of Simulium that habitually bite man, *S. metallicum*, *S. ochraceum*, and *S. callidum*, serve as vectors. Vargas in 1942 found 100 per cent of *S. callidum* infected during September in certain parts of the Mexican state of Chiapas. Insects such as tsetse flies and mosquitoes that drill directly into the blood stream take up few or no embryos, whereas the blackflies, that take a minute or more to rasp a hole in the skin, may take up 100 to 200 embryos in a single meal, the salivary secretions attracting them from neighboring areas of skin. It is very likely that feeding preferences and other habits of the various species of Simulium are the principal factors in determining which species are important transmitters.

A species of Culicoides transmits *Onchocerca reticulata* of horses and perhaps also *O. gibsoni* of cattle in Africa, but it is unlikely that these midges play an important part, if any, in human infections.

Development takes place in the thoracic muscles in the orthodox manner, followed by invasion of the head and proboscis, the whole process requiring a week or more, according to temperature.

Epidemiology. In central Africa the infection has a wide distribution, but in America it is mostly limited to a narrow strip on the Pacific slope of the mountains of Guatemala and southwestern Mexico, between about 2000 and 4500 ft. elevation, where coffee is extensively grown and cultivated by a native Indian population. This region has a warm climate, abundant rainfall, luxurious vegetation, and numerous swift-flowing streams. In Mexico 20,000 people are affected in Chiapas and 11,000 in Oaxaca, but apparently the infection has not yet spread over all the areas where it could thrive. Dampf (1942) called attention to the danger of its spread along the Pan-American Highway, which passes through foci in both Mexico and Guatemala. The danger is greatest to natives since, as in the case of *Wuchereria bancrofti*, harmful effects develop only after continued exposure to infection.

Pathology. As already noted, the outstanding feature of onchocerciasis is the development of fibrous nodules enclosing the worms (Fig.

156C). In parts of Africa the nodules are largely confined to the trunk, especially just over the hips and on the knees, elbows, ribs, etc., but in some regions of the Belgian Congo, and especially in Central America, they are commonly found on the head. In Guatemala about 95 per cent are on the head, especially about the ears. The location of the nodules seems to be influenced by pressure on the skin, either by bones or by hats or clothing, which might temporarily make the going hard for the migrating worms and impede them long enough for the tissues to start the imprisoning process. The site of the bites of the intermediate hosts is certainly not the determining factor.

Ordinarily the nodules are not painful, and seldom suppurate, so usually give very little trouble. The microfilariae, however, which creep in the skin, especially in the general region of the nodules, sometimes cause other disturbances which may be very serious. An itching skin affection known as craw-craw is associated with the embryos in the skin, and sometimes the inflammation set up by the embryos leads to loss of pigmentation, degeneration of glands, and other complications. In Guatemala a condition known as " coastal erysipelas " has been attributed to onchocerciasis but is probably a secondary infection, though the skin may possibly be more susceptible as a result of filarial inflammation.

The most serious complication is interference with the eyes, often ending in blindness. This phase of the disease was for a time thought to be peculiar to America, but Hissette and Strong discovered places in the Belgian Congo where it is far worse than in Mexico or Guatemala. Strong found eye disturbances in about 5 per cent of cases in Guatemala, but in some localities in Mexico 10 to 20 per cent are thus afflicted. In northwest Congo Hissette found a village in which 68 of 156 persons had onchocercal disturbances of the eyes and 10 per cent were blind.

Strong (1934) carefully investigated this condition in Guatemala and found that the embryos escaping from nodules on the head had a tendency to invade the tissues of the eye — conjunctiva, cornea, iris, and other parts, sometimes even the optic nerve. Eye disturbances usually occur among adults with a history of nodules extending over 5 years or more. The lesions are chronic and progressive, beginning with injection of the conjunctiva, inflammation of conjunctiva and cornea, and development of opaque spots which run together. These lesions are probably due mainly to irritation set up by the continual passage of numerous embryos through the eye tissues, although the possibility of a toxic effect being involved cannot be ruled out entirely. The claim that there is prompt improvement in sight, or even its restoration, after removal of the nodules is unfortunately incorrect. The reported improvements are an interesting example of the power of suggestion and hope on the reactions of ignorant and trusting people. There is often a temporary amelioration of symptoms after removal of nodules, and the ocular lesions may be arrested in their progress, but anatomical changes cannot be corrected once they have occurred, and an individual blinded by an onchocercal infection can have little hope of any restoration of sight.

Diagnosis. Diagnosis can usually be made by puncturing and aspirating a nodule or by excising a small piece of near-by skin or conjunctiva with a razor (preferably not deep enough to draw blood) and examining for microfilariae by placing on a slide with a few drops of saline under a cover slip. Examination of fed blackflies, xenodiagnosis, may be an even better method when feasible. Precipitin and skin reactions to filarial antigens are unreliable, but a skin reaction following a single dose of hetrazan is of diagnostic value.

Treatment. The most effective treatment is excision of the nodules, which is usually possible. By systematically doing this, the amount of infection has been markedly reduced in Mexico. In Guatemala some success has been obtained with destruction of the adult parasites by injection of the cysts with various drugs (gentian violet, hexylresorcinol, mercuric chloride). The mercuric chloride is considered most effective. Culbertson (1947) got disappointing results from injections of an antimony compound, neostibosan, but promising results have been obtained from injections of Bayer 205, hitherto used principally in trypanosomiasis, and hetrazan (Burch, 1949). Both quickly kill the microfilariae and eventually injure the adults, but both produce such intense allergic reactions, probably from injured worms, that many patients refuse to continue the treatment; the symptoms consist of skin eruptions, burning of the feet and eyes, edema, and photophobia; some of these effects develop a few hours after the first dose is given.

Prevention. Among natives exposure to bites of blackflies is unavoidable. Systematically destroying the parasites or nodules in human beings in more or less circumscribed foci, as in Mexico and Guatemala, might be possible, but it is thought to be impracticable in Africa. Animals are not believed to constitute important reservoirs, since the parasites, though morphologically indistinguishable, seem to be biologically distinct.

A second alternative is elimination of breeding places of blackflies or treatment of them with larvicides (see p. 634), which has been done with remarkable success in Mexico and Guatemala, and also in areas in Africa where *Simulium neavei* is the vector. It might be impracticable where *S. damnosum* is the vector, since this species migrates for long distances. Another possibility is to reduce the contacts between man and the vectors. Clearing ground for a radius of 500 yd. around villages or local sources of infection is an effective barrier but is of no use in localities where the sources of infection are more scattered.

Other Filariae in Man

Scattered cases of a number of other adult or immature filariae which are of doubtful nature or unknown affinities are on record. One immature adult, *Filaria conjunctivae*, believed by Desportes (1939–1940) to belong to the genus Dirofilaria, has been found occasionally in cyst-like tumors of the eye, nose, arm, and mesentery in Europe and India. The females are 15 to 20 cm. long and 0.5 mm. broad. This worm causes a burning or itching sensation and localized edema. There are a few records of several other forms, most of them sexually immature, from the eye socket, lens, skin, or other places, most of which have not been definitely classified, and all of which are probably only accidental human parasites. One male of *Dirofilaria repens*, normally in the skin of dogs, was reported from a nodule in the eyelid of a woman in Russia. There is one record from Brazil of a filaria from the heart, *D. magalhaesi*, a worm closely related to the common heart filaria of the dog, and Faust in 1939 recorded a single male Dirofilaria from the inferior vena cava of an old Negress in New Orleans.

Filariae in Domestic Animals

Except for Onchocerca infections in cattle and horses (see p. 456) and occasional injury to horses from Onchocerca infections in the neck ligament, the larger domestic animals suffer relatively little from filarial infections. *Setaria equina* and *S. labiato-papillosa* are often found in the peritoneal cavities of horses and cattle, respectively, but do no appreciable damage except when, during an early period of wandering through the tissues, they occasionally blunder into the eye. Stomoxys transmits the cattle species. In the central and western states another species, *Stephanofilaria stilesi*, causes skin sores in cattle and sometimes in goats and pigs; in India *S. assamensis* causes " hump sore " in cattle, depreciating the value of the hides. It is a small worm, the females only 6 to 8 mm. and the males 2 to 3 mm. long, with cuticular spines behind the mouth.

In the Old World horses are afflicted by *Parafilaria multipapillosa*, and cattle in India by *P. bovicola;* the females are 40 to 70 mm. long and the males about 30 mm. As in the genus Filaria the vulva opens just beside the mouth. These worms live in subcutaneous tissue and pierce the skin to deposit their embryonated eggs, causing "summer bleeding" from small nodules and injuring the hides. Muscoid flies feeding on the blood suck up the eggs and serve as intermediate hosts. Sheep suffer from sores on the head caused by *Elaeophora schneideri*, the adult of which lives in the carotid and iliac arteries.

Heartworm of Dogs (Dirofilaria immitis). Dogs suffer severely from this worm, which usually inhabits the right ventricle of the heart and the adjacent parts of the pulmonary arteries. The females are 20 to 30 cm. long, the males about 12 to 18 cm. The microfilariae are unsheathed and show a partial periodicity. The infection is found in all warm climates and is very common in southern United States. Fleas serve as intermediate hosts and transmitters. Development takes place in the Malpighian tubules. Larval development also occurs in various species of Aëdes mosquitoes, but Summers (1943) doubts whether these are successful transmitters in nature.

When severely infected, dogs become unduly short of breath and show other signs of asphyxiation, occasionally falling dead. Some success in treatment with fuadin has been obtained, but not infrequently the dogs die, possibly because of fatal blocking of the pulmonary arteries by killed worms. Hetrazan by mouth or injection at frequent daily intervals for 3 weeks or longer is promising.

II. Spiruroids (Superfamily Spiruroidea)

Morphology. The superfamily Spiruroidea contains a large number of worms that are parasitic in all kinds of vertebrates. They vary enormously in form and include slender, filaria-like worms such as Thelazia and Gongylonema; large heavy-bodied forms superficially resembling ascarids, such as Physaloptera; short, thick forms such as Gnathostoma; and forms with bizarre females nearly spherical in shape, such as Tetrameres. Some have the head or body armed with spines or other cuticular embellishments. The mouth opens into a chitinized vestibule; in some, e.g., Thelazia (Fig. 157*B*), it has no lips, but in the majority there is either a single pair of lateral lips, e.g., Physaloptera and Gnathostoma (Fig. 169 *C*, *D*), or a pair of dorsoventral lips in addition to the lateral pair, but never three or six lips. The vulva usually opens in the middle region of the body. In the males the tail is spirally coiled; it usually has broad alae often ornamented with cuticular markings and provided with pedunculated papillae.

Important Species. The accompanying table gives a list of the forms that are of interest as parasites of domestic animals, including those that are accidental parasites of man. It will be seen that, though

SPIRUROIDS OF INTEREST AS PARASITES OF DOMESTIC
ANIMALS. ACCIDENTAL PARASITES OF MAN MARKED " * "

Name of Parasite	Definitive Hosts	Habitat	Intermediate Hosts
Ascarops (Arduenna) and Physocephalus	Pigs	Stomach	Dung beetles
Cheilospirura spp.*	Chickens and turkeys	Walls of gizzard	Grasshoppers, sow bugs (also beetles and sandhoppers)
Echinuria spp.	Ducks and geese	Stomach and small intestine	Daphnia, amphipods
Gnathostoma spinigerum*	Fish-eating carnivores	Stomach tumors	First host: Cyclops; second: fish, frogs, or snakes
Gongylonema spp.*	Ruminants, pigs, horses, rodents, fowls	Walls of esophagus or rumen	Dung beetles or roaches
Habronema microstoma, muscae and macrostoma	Horses	Mucosa or lumen of stomach	Maggots of Stomoxys or Musca (escape from proboscis of adults)
Hartertia gallinarum	Chicken (Africa)	Small intestine	Workers of termites
Physaloptera spp.*	Insectivorous and carnivorous mammals, birds, reptiles (common sp. in opossum)	Stomach or intestine	Cockroaches in two cases known
Protospirura spp.	Rodents, monkeys, etc.	Esophagus and stomach	Roaches, fleas?
Spirocerca sanguinolenta	Dogs	Tumors on esophagus, stomach, or aorta	Dung beetles
Tetrameres spp.	Poultry	Glands of proventriculus	Grasshoppers, roaches, amphipods, Daphnia
Thelazia callipaeda* and californiensis*	Dogs and man	Eye	Unknown
Thelazia mansoni	Chicken	Eye	Roaches

some of them live in the alimentary canal, most of them live in its walls or in more distant parts of the body.

Life Cycles. Except for specimens of Spirocerca that get misplaced in aortic cysts, the eggs of all these spiruroids get access to the alimentary canal and are voided with the feces. In all cases in which the life cycles have been worked out the thick-shelled, embryonated eggs are swallowed by coprohagous arthropods either in soil or in water,

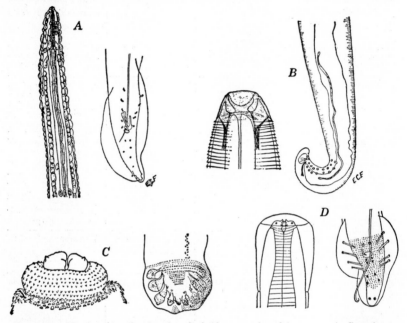

Fig. 157. Heads and tails of male spiruroid worms found in man. *A, Gongylonema pulchrum;* head, × 45 (after Ward); tail, × 48 (after Faust). *B, Thelazia callipaeda;* head, × 210; tail, × 33 (after Faust). *C, Gnathostoma spinigerum;* head and tail, × 39 (after Baylis and Lane). *D, Physaloptera caucasica;* head, × 22 (after Leiper); tail, × 16 (adapted from V. Linstow). (*A, B,* and *D* from *Human Helminthology* by Ernest Carroll Faust, Ph.D., Lea and Febiger, Publishers, Philadelphia; *C* from *Nematode Parasites of Vertebrates* by Yorke and Maplestone, J. and A. Churchill, Publishers, London.)

and in these the larvae develop. In most cases infection of the final host results from the swallowing of the intermediate host, but in at least some of the species accessory methods of transfer have been evolved. Although the species of Habronema of horses, which develop in maggots of stableflies or houseflies, may infect their hosts through the swallowing of infected adult flies, the larvae, after development in the Malpighian tubules or fat bodies, make their way to the head and voluntarily escape from the labium on warm wet surfaces as do filariae. They thus reach the lips, nose, or wounds, and finally infect via the mouth when licked off and swallowed. Although apparently unable to reach their destination by burrowing into the skin, it is obvious that their life cycle is a step toward the filarial type. Infective larvae if eaten by abnormal hosts may burrow into the tissues and become re-encapsulated. The writer found armadillos from hog lots with hundreds of cysts containing dead larval stomachworms of pigs (Ascarops and Physocephalus) obtained from eating infected grubs before the pigs got them. For Gnathostoma this seems to be routine procedure, for whereas cats are easily infected by feeding them gnathostome larvae encysted in second intermediate hosts (fish, frogs, snakes), attempts to infect them by feeding infected Cyclops have so far failed.

Since a considerable number of spiruroids are capable of partial and sometimes complete development in human beings, it is obvious that we owe our relative immunity to spiruroid infections to the fact that we are not for the most part voluntarily insectivorous. In the following paragraphs are considered briefly the principal forms recorded from man.

Gongylonema. These slender, filaria-like worms (Fig. 157A) live in the walls of the esophagus or mouth cavity. The females reach a length of 15 cm. and the males 6 cm., but the diameter is only 0.2 to 0.5 mm. Eight rows of wartlike bosses on the anterior end are a characteristic feature; the vulva of the female is not far from the anus, and the male has very unequal spicules and a coiled tail with asymmetrical alae.

Only seven human infections have been recorded, all of them with immature worms; although given the name *Gongylonema hominis,* they are probably identical with *G. pulchrum* of pigs and ruminants. Five of the cases occurred in white women in southern United States and two in Italy. All the patients were aware of the active migrations of the worms under the lips or cheeks and were much annoyed by them; the worms move so rapidly that considerable dexterity is required to remove them. Two of the patients also had nervous disorders which disappeared after they got rid of their parasites. Since dung beetles and roaches are the intermediate hosts it is obvious that human infection could not be common, for our appetites tend in other directions.

It is of interest to note that two species in rats, *G. neoplasticum* and *G. orientale,* frequently stimulate cancerous growths, but there is no evidence that other species do so.

Physaloptera. The genus Physaloptera contains numerous species parasitic in all sorts of carnivorous and insectivorous land vertebrates.

They are large worms (Fig. 157D), superficially resembling ascarids; they live most frequently in the stomach but may also live in the intestine and occasionally even the liver; they bury their heads in the mucous membranes and cause sores and ulcerations. The females are usually 3 to 10 cm. long by 1.2 to 2.8 mm. in diameter; the males about half this size. A characteristic feature is a collarette surrounding the head end and a pair of trilobed lips. The vulva is anterior in position. The male has a coiled tail with broad asymmetrical alae which meet in front of the anus and have very long papillae; the spicules are very unequal. One species, *P. caucasica*, normally parasitic in African monkeys, is said by Leiper (1911) to be fairly common in natives of tropical Africa; one case was found in the Caucasus in Europe.

Protospirura muricola. Though not yet recorded from man, this rodent parasite has been reported by Foster (1938) as causing an injurious and often fatal infection of captive monkeys. In general appearance it resembles a small Physaloptera but lacks the collarette. The parasites block the esophagus and irritate the stomach wall, sometimes perforating it. Cockroaches serve as intermediate hosts. It becomes more and more evident that eating roaches is a very bad habit for the animals that habitually indulge in it.

Gnathostoma spinigerum. This is a very robust worm, 25 to 50 mm. long, with a globular swelling at the head end which is armed with eight or more rows of thornlike hooks (Fig. 157C). The mouth is bounded by a pair of fleshy lateral lips. Behind the swollen head the body is clothed with overlapping rows of toothed scales, which gradually dwindle away posteriorly.

The natural hosts of this worm are wild and domestic cats, mink, and rarely dogs. The adults inhabit large tumors, sometimes an inch in diameter, in the stomach wall, opening into the stomach by one or more pores. They cause fatal peritonitis when they open into the body cavity, and the seasonal occurrence of the parasites in cats, as seen by the writer in Calcutta, suggests that they may be invariably fatal, for it seems impossible that the tumors could disappear completely soon after the worms had left.

The entire life cycle of this worm was not pieced together until 1936. In 1925 the writer found that almost every snake near Calcutta which he examined was infested with the larvae, which when fed to cats developed first in the liver and later invaded the stomach, but he was at a loss to see how cats and snakes managed to pass the infection back and forth between them in nature. Prommas and Daengsvang (1933) filled in one missing piece in the puzzle when they found that the eggs become embryonated and hatch in water, and develop in Cyclops. Both Africa *et al.* (1936) in the Philippines and Prommas and Daengsvang (1936–1937) in Siam finished the job when they showed that the larvae when eaten in Cyclops re-encyst in various fishes, amphibians, and snakes, and that carnivores become infected when they eat fish but not when fed Cyclops. Ninety-two per cent of the frogs, 80 per cent of the eels, and 30 to 37 per cent of certain other food fishes in the markets in Thailand were found to harbor larval gnathostomes.

Human infection with immature worms of this species, either wandering in the skin or in skin abscesses, has been recorded in a number of instances. Prommas and Daengsvang have found such infections to be fairly common in Thailand, and other cases have been recorded in various places in southeast Asia. Like many other parasites in a strange host, these worms, in the presumable absence of the usual guides on which they depend to reach their normal habitat, become lost and end up in places where they do not belong, and where, probably, they cannot mature, but the writer found eggs of the worm in presumably human feces on two occasions in Burma, so it seems likely that the worm sometimes finds its way to the proper destination in man. In view of the dangerousness of the infection in cats, eating of raw cold-blooded animals in places where this worm is endemic would seem a hazardous practice.

A single case has been recorded of human infection with another species of Gnathostoma, *G. hispidum*, normally found in pigs in the Old World. This worm, too, was hopelessly lost, wandering aimlessly under the skin.

Thelazia callipaeda and T. californiensis. These slender little worms, possibly more nearly related to the filariae than to the spiruroids, inhabit the conjunctival sac and lachrymal ducts of animals and occasionally man. At times they creep out over the eyeball, later returning to their nest in the inner corner of the eye. *T. callipaeda*, primarily a parasite of dogs in India, Burma, and China, has been reported from man four times in China. *T. californiensis*, reported by Stewart from sheep, deer, and dogs in brushy, mountainous places in California, has been found in man twice. Other species are important parasites of the eyes of cattle and horses in some places; altogether 19 species have been described from various mammals and birds.

The female worms are from 7 to 19 mm. long, the males somewhat smaller. The cuticle is pleated into well-defined striations with sharp edges; there are no lips, but there is a short vestibule (Fig. 157B). The vulva is anterior as in filariae, and the male has no caudal alae. The life cycle has not yet been elucidated, but roaches have been shown to serve as intermediate hosts for *T. mansoni* of chickens.

By their movements the worms irritate the eye considerably, causing a free flow of tears and injection of blood vessels, and sometimes severe pain and nervous symptoms. At first the eye is not seriously affected, but Faust (1928) observed that in the course of time the repeated scratching of the surface of the eyeball by the serrated cuticle of the worm causes the formation of scar tissue, and the eye gradually develops a cloudiness, progressing outward from the worm nest, which ultimately reduces the vision. African cattle are sometimes blinded by a Thelazia.

After the eye is desensitized with 1 per cent cocaine, the worms are easily removed with a forceps or swab if seen, but several examinations are usually necessary in order to get a complete catch.

Cheilospirurua sp. Africa and Garcia (1936) found a specimen belonging to this genus in a nodule on the conjunctiva of a Filipino. This is a case of a worm being not only in the wrong pew but also in the wrong church, for members of this genus, so far as known, normally live under the lung or the gizzard of birds. It is another example of abnormal behavior in an abnormal host.

III. The Guinea Worm, Dracunculus medinensis

(Superfamily Dracunculoidea)

The superfamily Dracunculoidea, placed by Chitwood in the suborder Camallanata, was formerly included with the filarial worms. It contains two genera of worms that are peculiar in the relatively enormous length of the female worms as compared with the midget males, and in the fact that during the course of their development the alimentary canal and vulva atrophy, leaving the body of the adult almost entirely occupied by the embryo-filled uterus. The embryos are liberated by the bursting of a loop of the uterus prolapsed through the mouth or through a rupture of the anterior end of the body. One genus, Philometra, contains parasites of the body cavity of fishes, and the other, Dracunculus, contains parasites of the connective tissues of mammals or reptiles.

Occurrence and Distribution. The guinea worm, *Dracunculus medinensis* (meaning the little dragon of Medina), has been known since remote antiquity, for one of its main strongholds is in the region of western Asia which cradled civilization. The " fiery serpents " which molested the Israelites by the Red Sea were probably guinea worms. It is still, as it was in ancient times, one of the important scourges of life from central India to Arabia, and it is locally important in the East Indies, Egypt, and central Africa. Stoll (1947) estimated that there are 48,000,000 human guinea-worm infections in the world. The disease is commonly associated with dry climates because of the concentration of water supplies in step-wells or reservoirs and the greater opportunity for Cyclops in the drinking-water supply to become contaminated from human skin. In innumerable villages in central and western India up to 25 per cent or more of the population suffer annually from guinea worm infections.

The human guinea worm became established in a few localities in tropical America but seems to have died out. Guinea worms have, however, been reported sporadically from raccoons, mink, dogs, etc., in various parts of the United States and in Brazil, and the writer (Chandler, 1942) found them to be very common in the hind feet of raccoons in eastern Texas. Except for their smaller size (up to 16 inches long) the adult female worms could not be distinguished from D. medinensis of the Old World. However, since in the Old World guinea-worm infections are very rare in animals in spite of their frequency in man, whereas in the New World animal infections are common and human infections are very rare if they occur at all, it seems best for the present to consider the New World guinea worm a separate species, D. insignis.

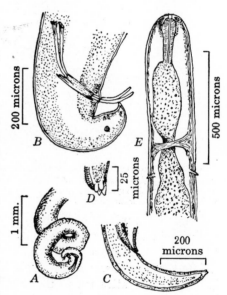

Fig. 158. Dracunculus medinensis. A, Tail end of male; B, same, more enlarged; C, tail end of female; D, tip of tail of female; E, head end of male, showing small, muscular, anterior portion of esophagus, and part of glandular, posterior part, constricted at nerve ring. (After Moorthy.)

Morphology. The gravid female worm, long the only form known, lives in the deeper layers of the subcutaneous tissues, where she usually can be seen lying in loose coils, like a small varicose vein, under the skin; sometimes she is more easily felt than seen until she produces a skin ulcer through which she gives birth to myriads of embryos. She reaches a length of 2.5 to 4 ft. with a diameter of 1 to 1.5 mm. The head end is bluntly rounded, and commonly ruptured in worms which have begun expelling embryos. The tail is attenuated and sharply hooked.

The males were practically unknown until Moorthy and Sweet (1936) obtained them in experimentally infected dogs. Mature specimens measured 20 to 29 mm. in length and were found 15 to 20 weeks after infection, but were not found when the gravid females were found in the skin at the end of 15 months. Males and young females of simliar size (Fig. 158) have the simple mouth surrounded by papillae and have an esophagus about 10 mm. long; in the females the vulva is a little

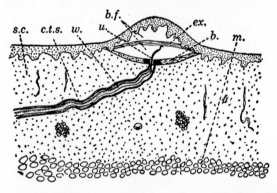

Fig. 159. Diagram of guinea worm in the skin at the time of blister formation; *b.*, base of ulcer; *b.f.*, blister fluid; *c.t.s.*, connective tissue sheath of worm; *ex.*, layer of exudate; *m.*, muscle layer; *s.c.*, subcutaneous tissue; *u.*, extruded uterus of worm; *w.*, worm. (Adapted from Fairley.)

anterior to the middle of the body. The males have a spirally coiled tail with 4 pairs of preanal and 6 of postanal papillae, but no alae, and two nearly equal spicules 0.5 to 0.7 mm. long.

Life Cycle. When ready to bring forth her young, the guinea worm is instinctively attracted to the skin, especially to such parts as are likely to, or frequently do, come in contact with cold water, such as the arms of women who wash clothes at a river's brink or the legs and backs of water carriers. The worm pierces the lower layers of the skin with the front end of her body and excretes a toxic substance that irritates the tissues and causes a blister to form over the injured spot (Fig. 159). The blister eventually breaks, revealing a shallow ulcer, about as large as a dime, with a tiny hole in the center. When the ulcer is douched with water a milky fluid is exuded directly from the hole or from a very delicate, transparent projected structure which is a portion of the worm's uterus. This fluid is found to contain hordes of tiny coiled larvae with a length of about 600 μ, one-third of which is occupied by the long filamentous tail (Fig. 160).

An hour or so later a new washing with cold water will bring forth a fresh ejection of larvae, and so on until the supply is exhausted, a little more of the uterus being extruded each time. After each ejection of the larvae the protruded portion of the uterus dries up, thus sealing in the unborn larvae and saving them for the next douching. This procedure, of course, increases the chances of some of the larvae finding Cyclops-inhabited water. The whole process is one of the neatest adaptations in behavior in all the realm of biology, enabling a blind, unmeditative,

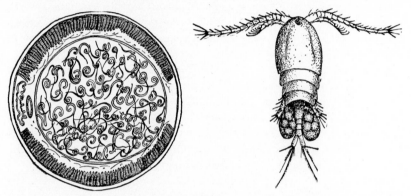

Fig. 160. Left, cross-section of guinea worm showing uterus filled with embryos. × about 30. (After Leuckart.) Right, a Cyclops, some species of which serve as intermediate hosts of guinea worms. × about 25.

burrowing worm to give her aquatic Cyclops-inhabiting offspring a fair chance in life even on a desert. She turns what would seem to be a hopeless handicap into an actual advantage.

When all the young have been deposited under the stimulus of contact with water the parent worm shrivels and dies and is soon absorbed by the tissues.

The embryo worms, safely deposited in water, unroll themselves and begin to swim about. They remain alive for several days but eventually perish unless swallowed by a Cyclops. When this happens they burrow into the body cavity of the surprised Cyclops, reaching that destination in from 1 to 6 hours. Moorthy never found a Cyclops with more than one larva in nature; when infected with more than four to five in the laboratory, development is interfered with. The writer never found more than two larvae of *Dracunculus insignis* to develop in experimentally infected Cyclops.

The larvae moult twice in the body cavity and reach the infective stage within 3 weeks. At this time they vary from 240 to 600 μ in length, the tail now being short. After feeding infected Cyclops to dogs the first specimens were found by Moorthy after about 10 weeks;

they were deep in the connective tissues and only 12 to 24 mm. long, although the vaginas of females 24 mm. long already contained a mucoid plug, indicating that they had already been fertilized. The worms appear to come to maturity in about 11 to 12 months after infection.

Epidemiology. In western India the infection is always associated with step-wells which, instead of being provided with buckets and ropes, are approached by steps, the people standing foot- or knee-deep in the water while filling containers. During this time the parent worm ejects her offspring, and at the same time previously infected Cyclops are withdrawn with the water. In African villages, ponds function in a similar manner.

In an epidemiological study in the Deccan, India, almost no infection was found in children under 4, but after that the incidence increased steadily to 85 per cent in the 30- to 35-year age group, then gradually fell off again. There may be from 1 to 50 worms per person but in most instances only 1 in a year. Few people suffer from infections for more than 4 years, after which immunity usually develops. The worms form their ulcers on the legs in about 90 per cent of cases.

Pathology. The first symptoms appear simultaneously with the beginning of the blister formation, and consists of urticaria, nausea and vomiting, diarrhea, asthma, giddiness, and fainting; some or all of these symptoms may be present. Fairley (1925) believes they are due to absorption of the toxin employed by the worm to form the blister. The symptoms strongly suggest an allergic reaction; injection of adrenalin brings about rapid improvement. Eosinophilia is marked.

Later symptoms result from secondary invasion of the ulcer by bacteria. The worms are usually mechanically extracted and, being elastic, are likely to break. The broken end of the worm draws back, carrying with it into its connective-tissue sheath various bacteria which produce abscesses. These may cause such severe infection as to necessitate amputation or may even lead to fatal blood poisoning. Joints are frequently involved, leading to permanent deformities. These occur with deplorable frequency in villages of the Deccan in India. There is some evidence that reinfections do not occur while an adult worm is still in the body. Most victims are incapacitated for several weeks; fortunately only a minority suffer permanent deformities or more serious consequences.

Treatment. Most drugs used against guinea worms have proved to be of little or no value, often, in fact, harmful, since local applications by natives after the ulcer has formed succeed only in causing secondary infections. Elliott (1942) reported excellent results from intramuscular injection of phenothiazine emulsified in olive oil into a number of places close to the worm. From 2 to 4 grams of phenothiazine can be injected at a sitting, with repetitions at weekly intervals; more than two courses are rarely needed. It takes 5 to 7 days for the drug to act; if a worm is being or is to be extracted, it is better to wait this long after injections.

Extraction of the worm by winding it out on a stick is a time-honored method which, with a few scientific refinements, is still widely used. Native medicine men extract the worm through the ulcer by repeatedly douching its head with water and then winding it out a little at a time. Care must be taken not to pull hard enough to rupture the worm; a safe extraction takes 10 to 14 days. If the ulcer is carefully treated with antiseptics, the worm can be withdrawn a little faster by exposing a loop and pulling it from both ends. Natives in India apply to the wound a green powder made of neem leaves, together with a choice assortment of contaminating bacteria, and the unfortunate patient has to fight his battle with the bacteria instead of the relatively innocent worm. If he loses his leg or his life it is the will of the gods and no fault of the doctor. Another native method is to apply a cone-shaped piece of metal over the exposed part of the worm and suck it vigorously until a negative pressure is created sufficient to draw the tissue up into the cylinder. The tongue is then applied and the finger quickly substituted, and after a few minutes the worm may be found in the tube.

By the use of local anesthetics and aseptic precautions, mechanical extraction is usually successful, and complete healing may follow in less than a week, as contrasted with the usual month.

Prevention. Prevention of the infection would be extremely simple if it were not for the scruples of the natives, often of religious nature, as to where and how they obtain and use their water. In India wherever step-wells are replaced by other types which keep the legs or arms out of the water, guinea worm disappears. If the water were strained through muslin to remove Cyclops, guinea worm would disappear, but even this is objected to. However, education and governmental pressure eventually bring results, and many areas in India that have suffered from guinea worm for centuries have been freed in recent years by altering the wells. Moorthy has had some success in destroying Cyclops by treating wells with dilute copper sulfate and " perchloron," and he reports that a fish, *Barbus puckelli*, feeds on them voraciously, but he emphasizes that abolition of step-wells is the only permanent and foolproof method of control.

REFERENCES

Filariae in General and Wuchereria

AUGUSTINE, D. L., Filariasis, *N. Y. State J. of Med.*, **45**, 495–499 (1945).

AUGUSTINE, D. L., and LHERISSON, C., Studies on the Specificity of Intradermal Tests in the Diagnosis of Filariasis, *Am. J. Hyg.*, **43**, 38–40 (1946).

BASU, C. C., and RAO, S. S., Studies on Filariasis Transmission, *Ind. J. Med. Research*, **27**, 233 (1939).

BROWN, H. W., The Treatment of Filariasis (*Wucheria bancrofti*) with Lithium Antimony Thiomalate, *J. Am. Med. Assoc.*, **125**, 952–958 (1944).

Current Problems in Filariasis, *Am. J. Pub. Health*, **35**, 607–613 (1945).

Recent Developments in the Chemotherapy of Helminthic Diseases, *Proc. 4th Intern. Congr. Trop. Med. and Malaria*, **2**, Sect. VI, 966–983 (1948).

BYRD, E. E., ST. AMANT, L., and BROMBERG, L., Studies on Filariasis in the Samoan Area, *U. S. Naval Med. Bull.*, **44**, 1–20 (1945).

CULBERTSON, J. T., Experimental Chemotherapy of Filariasis, *Trans. Roy. Soc. Trop. Med. Hyg.*, **41**, 18–54 (1947).

DICKSON, J. G., HUNTINGTON, R. W., JR., and EICHOLD, S., Filariasis in Defense Force, Samoan Group, *U. S. Naval Med. Bull.*, **41**, 1240–1251 (1943).

DIKMANS, G., Skin Lesions of Domestic Animals in the United States Due to Nematode Infections, *Cornell Veterinarian*, **38**, No. 1 (1948).

FRANCIS, E., Filariasis in Southern United States, *Hyg. Lab. Bull.*, **117** (1919).

FÜLLEBORN, F., Filariosen des Menschen, in *Handb. der path. Mikro-org.*, Kolle u. Wasserman, **6**, No. 28, 1093 (1929).

HINMAN, H., Filarial Periodicity, *J. Trop. Med. Hyg.*, **40**, 200 (1937).

HODGKIN, E. P., The Transmission of *Microfilaria malayi* in Malaya, *J. Malaya Branch Brit. Med. Assoc.*, **3**, 8 (1939).

HUNTINGTON, R. W., JR., Skin Reactions to *Dirofilaria immitis* Extract, *U. S. Naval Med. Bull.*, **44**, 707 (1945).

HUNTINGTON, R. W., JR., FOGEL, R. H., EICHOLD, A., and DICKSON, J. G., Filariasis Among American Troops in a South Pacific Island Group, *Yale J. Biol. Med.*, **16**, 529 (1944).

KNOTT, J., The Treatment of Filarial Elephantiasis of the Leg by Bandaging, *Trans. Roy. Soc. Trop. Med. Hyg.*, **32**, 243 (1938).

LANE, C., Filarial Periodicity, *J. Trop. Med. Hyg.*, **40**, 262 (1937).

Bancroftian Filariasis. Biological Mechanisms that Underlie its Periodicity and Other of its Clinical Manifestations, *Trans. Roy. Soc. Trop. Med. Hyg.*, **41**, 717–784 (1947). Discussion by Wilson, T., *ibid.*, **42**, 305–308 (1948).

MANSON-BAHR, P., The Nomenclature of the Filaria of the Pacific Producing Non-Periodic Embryos (*Wuchereria pacifica*), *Trop. Diseases Bull.*, **38**, 361 (1941).

NAPIER, L. E., Filariasis Due to *Wuchereria bancrofti*, *Medicine*, **23**, 149, 1944.

O'CONNER, F. W., and HULSE, C. R., Some Pathological Changes Associated with *W. bancrofti* Infection, *Trans. Roy. Soc. Trop. Med. Hyg.*, **25**, 445 (1932).

RAO, S. S., and MAPLESTONE, P. A., The Adult of *Microfilaria malayi* Brug, 1927, *Indian Med. Gaz.*, **75**, 159 (1940).

WARTMAN, W. B., Filariasis in American Armed Forces in World War II, *Medicine*, **26**, 333–394 (1947).

WEHR, E. E., A Revised Classification of the Nematode Superfamily Filarioidea, *Proc. Helminthol. Soc. Wash., D. C.*, **2**, 84–88 (1935).

Onchocerca

BURCH, T. A., Experimental Therapy of Onchocerciasis with Suramin and Hetrazan, *Bol. oficina sanit. panamer.*, **28**, 233–248 (1949).

DAMPF, A., La carretera panamericana y el problema de la oncocercosis, *Bol. oficina sanit. panamer.*, **21**, 753 (1943).

ORTLEPP, R. J., The Biology of Onchocerca in Man and Animals, *J. S. African Vet. Med. Assoc.*, **8**, 1 (1937).

STRONG, R. P., HISSETTE, J., SANDGROUND, J. H., and BEQUAERT, J. C., Onchocercosis in Africa and Central America; *Am. J. Trop. Med.*, **18**, No. 1. Supplement (1938).

STRONG, R. P., SANDGROUND, J. H., BEQUAERT, J. C., and OCHOA, M. M., *Onchocercosis*, Harvard University Press, 1934.

Other Filariae

BROWN, H. W., and SHELDON, A. J., Treatment of the Canine Heartworm (*Dirofilaria immitis*) with Fuadin and Sulfanilamide, *J. Am. Vet. Med. Assoc.*, **98**, 477 (1941).

BUCKLEY, J. J. S., On the Development in *Culicoides furens* Poey of *Filaria* (*Mansonella*) *ozzardi*, *J. Helminthol.*, **12**, 99 (1934).

CHANDLER, A. C., MILLIKEN, G., and SCHUHARDT, V. T., The Production of a Typical Calabar Swelling in a Loa Patient by Injection of a Dirofilaria Antigen, *Am. J. Trop. Med.*, **10**, 345 (1930).

CONNAL, A., and CONNAL, S. L. M., The Development of *Loa loa* in *Chrysops silacea* and in *Chrysops dimidiata*, *Trans. Roy. Soc. Trop. Med. Hyg.*, **16**, 64 (1922–1923).

DESPORTES, C., *Filaria conjunctivae* Addario, 1885, parasite accidentel de l'homme, est un Dirofilaria, *Ann. parasitol. humaine et comparée*, **17**, 380 (1939–1940).

FAIN, A., Répartition et étude anatomo-clinique des filarioses humaines dans le territoire de Banningville (Congo Belge), *Ann. soc. belge méd. trop.*, **27**, 25–63 (1947).

FAUST, E. C., Mammalian Heart Worms of the Genus Dirofilaria, *Festschrift Nocht*, 131, Hamburg, 1937.

IYENGAR, M. O. T., Studies on the Epidemiology of Filariasis in Travancore, *Indian Med. Research Mem.*, **30**, (1938).

McCOY, O. R., The Occurrence of *Microfilaria ozzardi* in Panama, *Am. J. Trop. Med.*, **13**, 297 (1933).

MACFIE, J. W. S., and CORSON, J. F. (*Microfilaria streptocerca*), *Ann. Trop. Med. and Parasitol.*, **16**, 465 (1922).

SHARP, N. A. D., *Filaria perstans:* its Development in *Culicoides austeni*, *Trans. Roy. Soc. Trop. Med. Hyg.*, **21**, 371 (1928).

SUMMERS, W. A., Experimental Studies on the Larval Development of *Dirofilaria immitis* in Certain Insects, *Am. J. Hyg.*, **37**, 173 (1943).

VOGEL, H., Zur Anatomie der *Microfilaria perstans*, *Arch. Schiffs- u. Tropen-Hyg.*, **32**, 291 (1928).

Spiruroidea

AFRICA, C. M., and GARCIA, E. Y., A New Nematode Parasite (*Cheilospirura* sp.) of the Eye of Man in the Philippines, *J. Philip. Isls. Med. Assoc.*, **16**, 603 (1936).

AFRICA, C. M., REFUERZO, P. G., and GARCIA, E. Y., Observations on the Life Cycle of *Gnathostoma spinigerum, Philip. J. Sci.,* **59**, 513; **61**, 221 (1936).

CHANDLER, A. C., A Contribution to the Life History of a Gnathostome, *Parasitol.,* **17**, 237 (1925); (Helminthic parasites of cats), *Indian J. Med. Research,* **13**, 219 (1925).

FAUST, E. C., Studies on *Thelazia callipaeda, J. Parasitol.,* **15**, 76 (1928).

FOSTER, A. O., and JOHNSON, C. M., Protospiruriasis, a New Nematode Disease of Captive Monkeys, *J. Parasitol.,* **24**, No. 6, Suppl., Abst. 75 (1938).

HIYEDA, K., and FAUST, E. C., Aortic Lesions in Dogs Caused by Infection with *Spirocerca sanguinolenta, Arch. Path.,* **7**, 253 (1929).

HOSFORD, G. N., STEWART, M. A., and SUGARMAN, E. I., Eye Worm (*Thelazia californiensis*) Infection in Man, *Arch. Ophthalmol. (Chicago),* **27**, 1165–1170 (1942).

LEIPER, R. T., On the Frequent Occurrence of *Physaloptera mordens* as an Internal Parasite of Man in Tropical Africa, *J. Trop. Med.,* **14**, 209 (1911).

LUCKER, J. T., Some Cross-transmission Experiments with Gongylonema of Ruminant Origin, *J. Parasitol.,* **19**, 134 (1932).

PROMMAS, C., and DAENGSVANG, S., (Life Cycle of *Gnathostoma spinigerum*), *J. Parasitol.,* **19**, 287 (1933); **22**, 180 (1936); **23**, 115 (1937).

STEWART, M. A., Ovine Thelaziasis, *J. Am. Vet. Med. Assoc.,* **96**, 486 (1940).

STILES, C. W., *Gonylonema hominis* in Man, *Health News, U. S. Pub. Health Service,* June, 1921.

Guinea Worms

CHANDLER, A. C., The Guinea Worm, *Dracunculus insignis* (Leidy, 1858), a Common Parasite of Raccoons in East Texas, *Am. J. Trop. Med.,* **22**, 153 (1942).

CHITWOOD, B. G., Does the Guinea Worm Occur in North America? *J. Am. Med. Assoc.,* **100**, 802 (1933).

ELLIOTT, M., A New Treatment for Dracontiasis, *Trans. Roy. Soc. Trop. Med. Hyg.,* **35**, 291 (1942).

FAIRLEY, N. H., and LISTON, W. G., *Studies on Guinea Worm Disease,* coll. papers from *Indian J. Med. Research* and *Indian Med. Gaz.,* Calcutta, 1925.

MOORTHY, V. N., An Epidemiological and Experimental Study of Dracontiasis in the Chitaldrug District, India, *Indian Med. Gaz.,* **67**, 498 (1932).

Observations on Development of *Dracunculus medinensis* Larvae in Cyclops, *Am. J. Hyg.,* **27**, 437 (1938).

A Redescription of *Dracunculus medinensis, J. Parasitol.,* **23**, 220 (1937).

MOORTHY, V. N., and SWEET, W. C., Experimental Infection of Dogs with Dracontiasis, *Indian Med. Gaz.,* **71**, 437; Biological Methods of Control, *ibid.,* 565; Natural Infection of Cyclops, *ibid.,* 568 (1936).

PART III—ARTHROPODS

CHAPTER 20
Introduction to Arthropods

To the average person it is astonishing to learn that the insects and their allies, constituting the phylum Arthropoda, include probably more than four times as many species as all other animals combined. It is even more startling for egotistical humanity to realize that this is not the age of man but the age of insects, and that man is only beginning to dispute with insects first place in the procession of animal life in the world.

Relationships. The Arthropoda are the most highly organized of invertebrate animals. Their nearest allies are the segmented worms or annelids, i.e., earthworms and leeches, but most of them show a great advance over their lowly cousins. Like the annelids they have a segmented type of body, though in some types, such as the mites, all the segments become secondarily confluent. Like the annelids, also, the arthropods are protected by an external skeleton which usually consists of a series of chitinous rings encircling the body. The most obvious distinguishing characteristic of the arthropods is the presence of jointed appendages in the form of legs, mouthparts, and antennae. Internally they are distinguished from other invertebrates in that the body cavity, so conspicuous in the annelids, has been entirely usurped by a great expansion and running together of blood vessels, so that a large blood-filled space called a hemocele occupies the space of the usual body cavity or celome. Within this space are blood vessels and a so-called heart, which retained their individuality while the other vessels fused. These vessels are not closed, however, but open into the hemocele at each end.

Classification of Arthropods. The phylum Arthropoda is divided by Comstock into thirteen classes, but only four of these concern us as human parasites or disease transmitters, namely, the Crustacea, the Arachnida, the Pentastomida, and the Hexapoda.

477

Crustacea. The Crustacea, including crayfish and water fleas, are primarily gill-breathing arthropods of the water. They are geologically of great antiquity, and among them are the most primitive of the typical arthropods. Their appendages are usually numerous and, taking the group as a whole, show a wonderful range of modifications for nearly every possible function. Although some are parasites of aquatic animals, none are parasites of man or other land animals. Small crustaceans of the order Copepoda serve as intermediate hosts of several worms parasitic in man, namely, certain species of Cyclops for the guinea worm and for *Gnathostoma spinigerum;* certain species of Cyclops and Diaptomus for tapeworms of the genus Dibothriocephalus and Spirometra; and Diaptomus for *Hymenolepis lanceolata.* Crabs and crayfish (members of the order Decapoda) serve as second intermediate hosts for the lung flukes.

Arachnida. The Arachnida, including spiders, scorpions, and mites, are for the most part highly developed arthropods, representing the terminus of a separate line of evolution. They probably had a common origin with the Crustacea, but they have become adapted to terrestrial life. The members of this class have four pairs of legs as adults, two pairs of mouthparts, and no antennae. The head and thorax, which usually form distinct sections of the body in insects, are grown together forming a cephalothorax, and in the ticks and many mites not even the abdomen remains as a distinct section. The Arachnida breathe by means of invaginations of the body which contain gills arranged like the leaves of a book, whence the name " book lungs." Some of the higher arachnids also have a system of branched air tubes or tracheae in the body similar to those found in the insects and myriapods. On the other hand, some of the small mites lack both book lungs and tracheae and respire through the cuticle. Only one of the eight orders of Arachnida, the Acarina (mites and ticks), contain parasitic species, but many of these are important disease vectors.

Pentastomida. The Pentastomida are degenerate wormlike creatures which in the adult stage have no appendages except two pairs of hooks near the mouth. If it were not for the larval forms, which have two pairs of short legs, their affinities with the arthropods might be doubted. They were formerly included with the mites for want of a better way of disposing of them. They are excellent examples of the degenerating effect of parasitic life. They have no circulatory or respiratory organs. Like many of the parasitic worms, they undergo their larval development in intermediate hosts.

Hexapoda. The Hexapoda, or insects, represent the zenith of invertebrate life. They are terrestrial arthropods which breathe by tracheae. Their appendages, however, are reduced to one pair of antennae (except in Protura, which have none), three pairs of mouth-parts (one pair more or less fused together), three pairs of legs, and usually two pairs of wings if not secondarily lost. All insects are readily divisible into three parts, the head, thorax, and abdomen.

Insect Morphology and Anatomy

The Cuticle. In the absence of any internal supporting skeleton in insects, the rigidity of the body is maintained by a cuticle more or less reinforced with a horny substance known as *chitin*. Since the chitin is

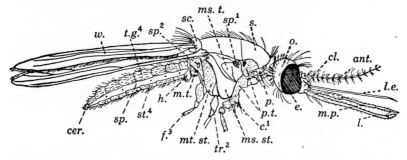

FIG. 161. Diagram of mosquito showing parts of body. The prothorax and meta-thorax with their respective legs are dotted, the mesothorax not dotted; *ant.*, antenna; $c.^1$, coxa of first leg; *cer.*, cerci; *cl.*, clypeus; *e.*, eye; $f.^3$, femur of third leg; *h.*, haltere; *l.*, labium; *l.e.*, labrum-epipharynx; *m.p.*, maxillary palpus; *ms. st.*, mesosternum; *ms. t.*, mesothorax; *mt. st.*, metasternum; *m.t.*, metathorax; *o.*, occiput; *p.*, patagium; *p.t.*, prothorax; *s.*, scutum; *sc.*, scutellum; *sp.*, abdominal spiracle; $sp.^1$, and $sp.^2$, first and second thoracic spiracles; $st.^4$, sternite of fourth abdominal segment; $tg.^4$, tergum of fourth abdominal segment; $tr.^2$, trochanter of second leg., *w.*, wing. (After Nuttall and Shipley, from Hindle.)

unaffected by caustic soda or potash, and since the characters used in the identification of insects are largely cuticular, it is often useful to soak or boil insects in caustic solutions to remove all the fleshy parts and leave the chitinous parts in a more readily examinable condition. The chitin is laid down in plates or rings, allowing movement and expansion of the parts of the body. Usually the parts of the head are entirely enclosed in chitin except the movable appendages, and the thorax is likewise enclosed, but some or all of the segments that make up the abdomen remain distinct and movable, with lightly chitinized areas between them. Even in each segment the chitin does not form complete rings; in the abdomen each segment has a dorsal plate or *tergite* and a ventral one or *sternite* (Fig. 161); in the thorax at least some of the segments also show a pair of lateral divisions, the *pleurites*. Each single chitinized plate is called a *sclerite;* the lines of separation between them are the *sutures*.

As arthropods grow they gradually become too large for their cuticles. The underlying hypodermis then lays down a new, thin, elastic cuticle under the old one. Certain cells produce a moulting fluid which partially dissolves the old cuticle, making it easier to shed after a split has been formed in it. After the moult the new cuticle hardens and then gradually thickens again by formation of more chitin.

Mouthparts of Insects. Incredible as it may seem, the mouthparts of all kinds of insects, from the simple chewing organs of a grasshopper

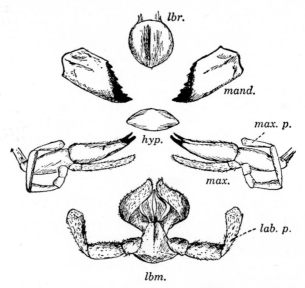

FIG. 162. Simple mouthparts of a chewing insect (Stenopalmatus); *lbr.*, labrum, or upper lip; *mand.*, mandible; *hyp.*, hypopharynx or tongue; *max.*, maxilla; *max. p.*, maxillary palpus; *lbm.*, labium or lower lip (really a second pair of maxillae fused together); *lab. p.*, labial palpus.

to the highly modified piercing organs of mosquitoes and the coiled sucking tube of butterflies and moths, are modifications of a single fundamental type which is represented in its simplest form in the chewing or biting type, as found in grasshoppers and beetles (Fig. 162). The mouthparts in these insects consist of an upper lip or *labrum;* a lower lip or *labium* bearing segmented appendages, the *labial palpi;* a pair of *mandibles* or jaws; a pair of *maxillae* lying ventral to the mandibles and bearing segmented appendages more or less like those on the labium, the *maxillary palpi;* and the *hypopharynx* on the floor of the mouth, through which the ducts of the salivary glands open. In addition the roof of the pharynx, under the labrum, has a chitinized *epipharynx;* this is often combined with the labrum to form a *labrum-epipharynx.*

Legs. The legs of insects (Fig. 163*A*) consist of five parts: the coxa, trochanter, femur, tibia, and tarsus. The *coxa* articulates the leg with the body and sometimes appears more like a portion of the body than a segment of the leg. The *trochanter* is a very short inconspicuous segment and sometimes appears like a portion of the femur. The *femur* and *tibia* are long segments. The *tarsus*, or foot, consists of a series of segments, most commonly five; often the first segment is much

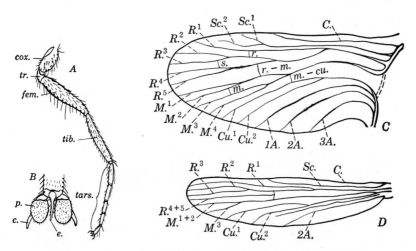

FIG. 163. Leg and wings of insects. *A*, leg; *cox.*, coxa; *fem.*, femur; *tars.*, tarsus; *tib.*, tibia; *tr.*, trochanter. *B*, foot, enlarged; *c.*, claw; *e.*, empodium; *p.*, pulvillus. *C*, diagram of primitive tracheae of wing from which veins are derived; *D*, venation of a mosquito wing showing a comparatively simple modification; *C.*, costa; *Sc.*[1 and 2], subcosta branches 1 and 2; *R.*[1 to 5], radius, branches 1 to 5; *M.*[1 to 4], media, branches 1 to 4; *Cu.*[1 and 2], cubitus, branches 1 and 2; *1A.*, *2A.*, and *3A.*, first to third anal; *r.*, radial cross vein; *s.*, sectorial cross vein; *r.-m.*, radio-medial cross vein; *m.*, medial cross vein; *m.-cu.*, medio-cubital cross vein (inadvertently omitted in mosquito wing). (*A* and *B* after Matheson, *C* after Comstock.)

the longest. Usually the tarsus is terminated by a pair of claws but sometimes only one. Often there are padlike structures, *pulvilli*, which have glandular hairs or pores through which an adhesive substance is excreted, permitting the insects to walk on the under side of objects. Sometimes there is a pulvillus at the base of each claw and also a similar median structure between them, called an *empodium* (Fig. 163*B*).

Wings and Venation. The structure of the wings of insects is often of great use in classification and identification. Only in the primitive subclass Apterygota are the wings primarily absent, although in many forms, especially parasitic ones, e.g., lice and fleas, they are secondarily lost. Typically there are two pairs of wings, borne by the second and third segments of the thorax.

The wings originate as saclike folds of the body wall, but the upper and lower surfaces become applied to each other and thus they appear as simple membranes. Where they flatten down against the tracheae the latter form hollow supports or *veins*. In most insects the majority of the veins are longitudinal but there are usually a few cross veins, which in some kinds of insects are very numerous. Figure 163*C* shows the hypothetical primitive arrangement of the venation of an insect wing but in many insects the modifications brought about by coalescence, anastomosis, atrophy, and addition of extra branches and cross veins often make it as bad as a Chinese puzzle to determine the true homologies of the resulting veins. The spaces between the veins are

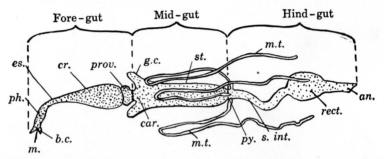

Fig. 164. Diagram of alimentary canal of an insect, showing portions pertaining to fore-gut, mid-gut and hind-gut, respectively; *an.*, anus; *b.c.*, buccal cavity; *car.*, cardium; *cr.*, crop; *es.*, esophagus; *g.c.*, gastric ceca; *m.*, mouth; *m.t.*, Malpighian tubules; *ph.*, pharynx; *prov.*, proventriculus; *py.*, pylorus; *rect.*, rectum; *s. int.*, small intestine; *st.*, stomach. (Adapted from Snodgrass.)

called *cells* and are named after the longitudinal veins behind which they occur. Figure 163*D* shows the wing of a mosquito as an example of a comparatively simple modification.

Internal Anatomy. The alimentary canal of insects (Fig. 164) has three primary divisions which may be of very unequal extent, namely, (1) the *fore-gut,* including pharynx, esophagus, crop, and proentriculus; (2) the *mid-gut,* including the stomach and sometimes a midintestine; and (3) the *hind-gut,* including the small intestine and rectum. The fore-gut and hind-gut are of ectodermal origin; the midgut is endodermal. The junction of the mid-gut and hind-gut is marked by the entrance of the *Malpighian tubules* (see second paragraph following).

The *pharynx* in bloodsucking insects is muscular and acts like a suction pump. The ducts of the *salivary glands,* which themselves lie in the thorax, may open into the floor of the pharynx or in bloodsucking forms may unite and continue to the tip of an elongated hypopharynx. The pharynx is followed by an *esophagus* which in some insects is expanded into a capacious *crop* and in some into a muscular *proventriculus* provided with chitinous teeth and serving the same function as the gizzard of a bird; in the mosquitoes three pouchlike *food reservoirs* are connected with the esophagus.

The true *stomach* follows the proventriculus and is sometimes provided with ceca that produce digestive juices; the stomach may constitute the entire mid-gut or it may be narrowed behind into a *mid-intestine*. A number of slender Malpighian tubules enter at the posterior end of the mid-gut. These function as excretory organs, corresponding to the kidneys of vertebrate animals; they extract waste products from the blood, convert them into insoluble form, and pass them into the hind-gut, to be voided through the anus along with the feces.

The *hind-gut* in some insects has a distinct *small intestine* followed by a more expanded *rectum,* but in others there is only a rectum, which is lined by chitin. Some insects have an expanded *anal pouch* at the posterior end.

The *tracheae* of insects constitute a ventilation system of air tubes ramifying all through the body even to the tips of the antennae and legs. They open by a series of pores along the sides known as *spiracles*.

The *nervous system* of insects is very highly developed. In some species the instincts simulate careful and accurate reasoning, and it is difficult not to fall into the error of looking upon them as animals endowed with a high degree of intelligence.

Sense Organs. *Sensory setae,* which serve as organs of touch like the whiskers of a cat, are widely distributed. Especially abundant are sensory organs for taste or smell; insects are not limited in the distribution of these organs as are mammals, for they can smell (or taste) with most of the surface of the body, the bases of the wings, the antennae, and the legs. Much has been written about the acute olfactory sense of such animals as dogs, but they are only crudely equipped compared with insects, which can detect extremely dilute odors over distances of probably a mile or more. Insects appear to depend more on the sense of smell than on any other type of sense perception.

The *compound eyes* of insects are not so efficient as the eyes of vertebrates; their power of accommodation is limited, and insects can see distinctly only for short distances. The image produced by the thousands of facets is a mosaic one, with no overlapping of the parts of the picture in eyes adapted to daylight, but with some overlapping in " night eyes." The latter consequently are capable of distinguishing objects and movements in very dim light, but they do not give sharp images. Many insects also have simple eyes or *ocelli*.

Many insects, at least those producing sounds, have organs of hearing, but in many instances they are hard to recognize as such. They may be on the legs, antennae, or abdominal segments.

Reproductive Organs. The reproductive organs (Fig. 165) consist of a pair of *ovaries* and *oviducts* in the females and of a pair of *testes* and *sperm ducts* in the males, with accessory glands and storage reservoirs for the seminal fluid in both the males and females. The external genital openings in both sexes are near the posterior end of the abdomen on the ventral side. The ovaries are usually compact, spindle-shaped bodies made up of a variable number of parallel *ovarian tubes,* all opening into a common oviduct. The germ cells gradually develop into mature eggs as they pass down the tubes; most insects also have nonproductive cells in the tubes which function as *nurse cells* for the nutrition of the eggs. In most insects the two oviducts unite into a common *vagina.* All female insects have a *spermatheca* or storage sac for sperms, since the pairing of the sexes occurs only once in insects, whereas the egg-laying period may extend over a long time.

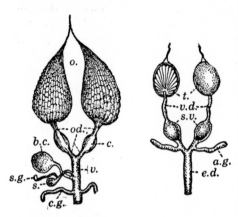

FIG. 165. Diagrams of ♀ (left) and ♂ (right) reproductive organs of an insect; *o.*, ovary; *od.*, oviducts; *c.*, egg-calyx; *b.c.*, copulatory bursa; *s.g.*, spermathecal gland; *s.*, spermatheca; *v.*, vagina; *c.g.*, collaterial gland; *t.*, testes; *v.d.*, vas deferens; *s.v.*, seminal vesicle; *a.g.*, accessory gland; *e.d.*, ejaculatory duct. (After Comstock.)

The *eggs* are fully formed with shells before being fertilized, but one or more minute pores, the *micropyles,* are left through which a sperm may enter, usually during the passage through the vagina. In some insects, e.g., the fleas, the shape of the spermatheca is one of the best identification characters in female specimens. Many insects have an *ovipositor* which may simulate a miniature saw, borer, or piercing organ for depositing the eggs; this versatile organ may be, in the Hymenoptera, modified into a *sting.*

The *testes,* like the ovaries, are made up of a group of tubules in which the sperms progressively develop. Each testis has a *vas deferens* which unites with its mate into an *ejaculatory duct* corresponding to the vagina of the female; its terminal portion may be chitinized and evaginated as an intromittent organ. Many male insects have highly developed *external genitalia* in the form of *claspers* and accessory parts fitted for holding the female at the time of pairing. In many instances, for example in mosquitoes and sandflies, the details of the structure of the external genitalia are of value in identification of closely related species. Some species of Culex cannot be differentiated with certainty in any other way. (See Figs. 218 and 242.)

Life History

Most insects hatch from eggs deposited by the mother, but in some instances free young are born; in the Pupipara the eggs not only hatch before birth but the young are retained in the body of the mother until they have reached the pupal stage. In this case only a few young are produced, but most insects lay large numbers of eggs, some all at once, some in batches at intervals, and others individually day after day.

Three principal types of life history can be recognized among insects. In the primitive subclass Apterygota alone there occurs *direct development*, in which the newly hatched insect is nearly a miniature of its parent and merely increases in size. This is also true of some of the higher insects that are secondarily wingless, such as lice. Among the higher insects, Pterygota, which are winged or secondarily wingless, the two common types of development are by *incomplete* and *complete metamorphosis*. Insects with an incomplete metamorphosis may differ more or less from their parents when hatched, but gradually assume the parental form with successive moults. The young or *nymphs* of such insects invariably lack wings and often have other characteristics different from their parents.

Insects with a complete metamorphosis are totally different from the parents when newly hatched and do *not* gradually assume the parental form. The early stages of such insects, usually wormlike, are called *larvae* in distinction from the nymphs of insects with an incomplete metamorphosis. Upon completion of their growth and development they go into a resting and more or less inactive stage and are then known as *pupae*. The pupa may have no special protection, as in mosquitoes and midges; it may retain the last larval skin as a protecting case called the *puparium*, as in muscid flies; or it may be encased in a *cocoon* of silk thread spun by the larva as a protection from the hostile world before going into its mummylike pupal state, as in fleas and many moths.

Although apparently inactive, the pupal stage is one of feverish activity from a physiological standpoint, for the entire body has to be practically made over. This transformation necessitates the degeneration of almost every organized structure in the body and a reformation of new organs out of a few undifferentiated cells left in the wreckage.

The time required for this wonderful reorganization is amazingly short. Many maggots transform into adult flies in less than a week, and some mosquito larvae transform into perfect mosquitoes in less than 24 hours.

The length of life of insects in the larval and adult stages varies greatly. The larval stage may occupy a small portion of the life, as in the case of many mosquitoes and flies, or it may constitute the greater part of it. Some may flies, for instance, live the greater part of two years as larvae, but they exist as adults not more than a few hours. As a rule male insects are shorter-lived than females; the length of life of the latter is determined by the laying of the eggs — when all the eggs have been laid the female insect has performed her duty in life and is eliminated by nature as a useless being. The result is the paradoxical fact that ideal environmental conditions *shorten* the life of these insects, since they facilitate the early deposition of the eggs.

Classification of Insects

The classification of insects is based mainly on three characteristics: the type of development, the modification of the mouthparts, and the number, texture, and venation of the wings. All bloodsucking insects have mouthparts adapted in some way for piercing and sucking, but the types vary greatly in different groups. Many of the more thoroughly parasitic insects, e.g., lice, bedbugs, and " sheep ticks," have secondarily lost their wings entirely or have them in a rudimentary condition. In the whole order of Diptera the second pair of wings is reduced to inconspicuous club-shaped appendages known as *halteres*.

Not all entomologists agree on the division of insects into subclasses and orders. According to Ross (1948) there are 28 orders, 26 of which fall into the subclass Euentoma. The other two contain primitive forms each falling into a separate subclass; they will not concern us here. In the Euentoma, which contains all the winged insects as well as two orders of primitive wingless ones, many of the orders comprise small or little-known groups. There are six " big " orders, members of which are known to everybody. These are (1) Orthoptera, the grasshoppers, crickets, etc.; (2) Hemiptera, the true bugs, aphids, etc.; (3) Coleoptera, the beetles; (4) Lepidoptera, the moths and butterflies; (5) Diptera, the flies, mosquitoes, etc.; (6) Hymenoptera, the bees, wasps, and ants. Important parasites and disease vectors of man and animals are found in two of these big orders, the Hemiptera and the Diptera, but others are found in three small orders, the Anoplura or sucking lice, the Mallophaga or chewing lice (bird lice), and the Siphonaptera or fleas. The characteristics of these five orders containing parasites are briefly as follows:

Hemiptera: metamorphosis incomplete; mouthparts fitted for piercing and sucking, the piercing organs being ensheathed in the jointed labium and folded under the head; first pair of wings, unless reduced, leathery at base and membranous at tip; second pair of wings, when present, membranous with relatively few veins. Parasites: bedbugs, conenoses, kissing bugs.

Anoplura: metamorphosis incomplete; mouthparts greatly reduced, fitted for piercing and sucking and retractile into a pouch under pharynx; wings secondarily lost. Parasites: sucking lice.

Mallophaga: metamorphosis incomplete; mouthparts reduced to a pair of mandibles fitted for chewing; wings secondarily lost. Parasites: "bird lice" or chewing lice of birds and mammals, none on man.

Siphonaptera: metamorphosis complete; mouthparts fitted for piercing and sucking, the piercing organs being ensheathed in the labial palpi and the maxillae modified as holding organs; wings secondarily lost. Parasites: fleas, chiggers.

Diptera: metamorphosis complete; mouthparts fitted for piercing and sucking, for sucking alone, or rudimentary; first pair of wings (absent in a few species) membranous with few veins; second pair of wings represented only by a pair of club-shaped organs, the halteres. Bloodsuckers: sandflies, mosquitoes, midges, blackflies, gadflies, tsetse flies, stableflies; parasites: Pupipara, maggots.

Arthropods as Parasites and Bloodsuckers

Degrees of Parasitism. All gradations exist between arthropods that are strictly parasitic throughout their lives, e.g., itch mites, hair follicle mites, and lice, and species that are purely predatory, existing entirely apart from their living restaurants except when actually feeding (e.g., mosquitoes, tabanids). Close to the strict parasite end of the series are the ixodid ticks and some adult fleas, which only intermittently leave their hosts. Somewhat farther removed are the bedbugs, triatomids, argasid ticks, and other adult fleas, which not only attend to their reproductive functions off the host but also leave to take their after-dinner naps; these forms, however, are normally inhabitants of the nests or habitations of their hosts and may be looked upon as parasites of the homes. Fleas are parasitic only as adults; certain mites and flies, only as larvae.

Effects of Bites. The effects produced by arthropod bites are brought about mainly by direct or indirect reactions to the salivary secretions. The usual effects are local redness and swelling with varying degrees of itching and sometimes pain. The restlessness and loss of sleep from the local irritation may lead to poor health or even downright illness in man or animals. Sometimes the local effects are very severe, but in bad attacks the effects are not merely local. Such symptoms as urticaria, fever, general body aches, severe headache, loss of appetite, nausea, extreme fatigue, and a rotten disposition have been reported in the literature or are personally known to the writer from attacks by blackflies, Culicoides, mosquitoes, bedbugs, lice, mites, and

ticks. The unthriftiness commonly seen in animals heavily infested
with ectoparasites is probably not entirely due to loss of blood or local
irritation, though both of these may have potent effects. In some
cases there are *special* toxic effects, such as the paralysis caused by
certain ticks (see p. 536) and the blue spots caused by crab lice.

Allergy and Immunity. The constitutional symptoms produced by
arthropod bites are highly suggestive of allergic reaction. The susceptibility of different individuals to the toxic effects of insect bites
varies widely and is certainly dependent to a considerable extent upon
sensitization. Herms (1939) cites reports of bites by the bug, *Triatoma
protracta,* causing within a few minutes nausea, flushing, palpitation,
rapid breathing, and rapid pulse, followed by profuse urticaria all over
the body. This suspiciously resembles the reactions of allergic individuals to stings of bees and wasps. The effects of itch mites and lice
become pronounced only after a preliminary period of sensitization
(see pp. 504 and **576**).

Immunity also plays a large part. The writer has seen innumerable
newcomers to Texas, including himself, who suffered intolerably from
redbug bites during the first season or two of exposure to them, but
who gradually became more and more immune to them. In New
Jersey it is a common experience for people from inland to suffer far
more severely from salt-marsh mosquitoes while vacationing on the
coast than do the residents, whereas people from the coast react similarly to the inland species of mosquitoes. Mellanby thinks that most
apparent cases of differences in individual attraction to insects are
really differences in reaction. In testing reactions of volunteers to
Aëdes aegypti bites, he found at first no immediate reaction but a
delayed reaction 24 hours later; after repeated bites for a month both
immediate and delayed reactions appeared; after further exposure
the delayed reaction diminished and disappeared; and eventually, in
some, the immediate reaction also disappeared, leaving complete immunity and apparent unattractiveness to the mosquitoes. Cherney,
Wheeler, and Reed (1939) called attention to the fact that California
fleas do not usually encroach on the comforts of the local population
but are a source of great misery to newcomers for several months to
several years.

Trager (1939) found that guinea pigs previously exposed to bites of
larval or nymphal ticks developed so much immunity that larval ticks
were incapable of feeding on them at all, and nymphs were unable to
feed to repletion, owing to such rapid cellular reaction to the bites that
the parasites were cut off from their food. Persons susceptible to flea

bites react positively to injection of flea extract, whereas immunes react negatively; most susceptible persons immunized by injections of the flea extract either become oblivious to fleas or are much less annoyed by them. Some retain their immunity several years, others for only a few weeks. McIvor and Cherney in 1943 showed that the immunized persons were not actually left in peace by the fleas, but were unaware of their bites.

Although acquired immunity plays a large part, there appear to be some true instances of distastefulness of individuals to insects, based on some difference in skin metabolism which is not yet understood. One instance has been recorded in which a man's skin was highly toxic to ticks.

Natural Repellence. Riley and Johannsen report a case of two brothers who volunteered to act as feeders for some experimental stock lice; the lice fed greedily on one but absolutely refused to feed on the other, even when hungry. The writer is relatively immune to nearly all arthropods and even to land leeches, but had to develop immunity to redbugs and was not immune to blackflies or Culicoides. He bathes with fair regularity and does not smoke, take drugs, or eat sulfur or garlic. This matter of natural repellence to arthropods needs further investigation.

Arthropods as Disease Transmitters

Important as arthropods sometimes are as parasites or bloodsuckers, it is in their capacity as carriers of germs or as intermediate hosts of other parasites that they have to be reckoned with as among the foremost of human foes. Since the beginning of the twentieth century many of the most important human and animal diseases have been shown not only to be transmitted by arthropods but to be *exclusively* transmitted by particular genera or species. In addition, there are a number of other diseases, such as yaws, pinkeye, virus encephalomyelitis, and anthrax, in which arthropods play an important but not exclusive role, and still others, such as many bacterial, protozoan, and helminthic infections of the digestive tract, in which they play a minor but not a negligible part.

Mechanical Transmission. The simplest method of disease transmission by arthropods is *indirect mechanical transmission,* in which the arthropods function as passive carriers of disease agents, picking them up on the bodies or in the excretions of man or animals and depositing them on food. The importance of any particular species of arthropod depends on the degree to which the structure of its body facilitates the carrying of germs and the extent to which its habits bring it in contact with sources of germs and later with food. Prominent among these indirect mechanical transmitters are houseflies and roaches.

Slightly more specialized is *direct mechanical transmission,* in which the insects pick up the germs from the body of a diseased individual and directly inoculate them into the skin sores, wounds, or blood of other animals. Biting flies, such as mosquitoes, Stomoxys, and tabanids, transmit blood diseases in this manner, e.g., anthrax, fowl pox, and virus encephalomyelitis. Flies that feed on sores or wounds, such as eye flies and many muscids, transmit skin or eye diseases, e.g., yaws, trachoma, and Oriental sore. In most of these cases the organisms do not live for more than a few minutes to a few days in the vectors.

Biological Transmission. When an arthropod plays some further part in the life of the parasite or germ than merely allowing it to hitchhike, and multiplication or cyclical changes or both take place within its body, the process is called *biological transmission.* Huff (1931) proposed a classification of different types of biological transmission as follows:

1. Propagative: the organisms undergo no cyclical changes but they multiply as in culture tubes. Example: plague.
2. Cyclopropagative: the organisms undergo cyclical changes and multiply in the process. Example: malaria.
3. Cyclodevelopmental: the organisms undergo developmental changes but do not multiply. Example: filariae.

To these we add:

4. Transporting (including vetebrates as well as arthropods): the organisms invade and often encyst in some host, specific or nonspecific, after developing elsewhere, and are transported by this host to the final host. Example: Syngamus.

Transovarial Transmission. Transmission of disease agents to offspring by invasion of the ovary and infection of the eggs, often loosely called " hereditary " transmission, is characteristic of arthropod infections where a state of almost perfect adaptation of parasite and host has been reached. It is especially frequent in mites and ticks, which transovarially transmit some Protozoa, tularemia bacilli, rickettsias, relapsing fever spirochetes, and some viruses. In Texas fever (see p. 217) and scrub typhus (see p. 511), transovarial transmission is a necessary part of the mechanism of transmission. Not many insect-borne infections are thus passed on from generation to generation though some viruses may be. *Trypanosoma cruzi* is sometimes passed by triatomids to their offspring by contamination after hatching, not by prenatal infection of the eggs.

Airplane Dissemination of Arthropods. Many domestic arthropods, or parasites on man, rats, or domestic animals, succeeded in making this " One World " for themselves in bygone days of slow boat travel. The airplane has made this a possibility for many more. Even if stowaway arthropods do not become established in their new surroundings, they may live long enough to pass diseases they may carry to local vectors or reservoirs.

Two unpleasant possibilities exist: (1) the introduction of more efficient vectors for diseases already in existence, e.g., *A. gambiae* to Brazil; (2) the introduction of new diseases with vectors or reservoir hosts. Ticks shipped from South Africa have arrived in this country harboring three different diseases not now known in America, and mosquitoes and ticks from Russia successfully carried with them an encephalitis virus. One shudders to think of the consequences if a yellow fever-infected mosquito were landed in India or China.

The only protection is very strict regulation of fumigation of airplanes from foreign countries. If the world is to be made safe from arthropod as well as human invaders in the future, these precautions will have to be used with the utmost care, for international air traffic is constantly expanding.

Insecticides and Repellents

Insecticides. Insects are killed by many chemicals that are injurious to vertebrates as well, such as hydrocyanic acid, sulfur dioxide, methyl bromide, arsenic, sodium fluoride, and nicotine sulfate, but fortunately are also highly susceptible to some chemicals that are only slightly poisonous to man and other warm-blooded vertebrates. The principal ones used before World War II were pyrethrum powder prepared from the flower heads of a species of Chrysanthemum, or oil-soluble pyrethrins extracted from it, and the powdered roots of Derris or Cubé plants, or an alkaloid, rotenone, extracted from these. During the war a number of synthetic insecticides relatively harmless to higher vertebrates came into use, particularly DDT (dichlorodiphenyltrichloroethane) and " 666 " or benzene hexachloride, of which only the γ isomer, constituting 5 to 12 per cent of the crude drug, is effective. More recently a relative of DDT, DDD, and chlordane or " 1068 " ($C_{10}H_6Cl_8$) have been developed and are even more effective against some arthropods. When pyrethrum was practically unobtainable during the war, synthetic thiocyanates (Lethane 384, Lethane 384 Special, and thanite) were used as substitutes; a 5 per cent solution of these is about equivalent to 0.08 per cent pyrethrum. All these chemicals except rotenone act primarily on the nervous system of the insects, causing paralysis. Pyrethrum knocks down almost immediately and, if in sufficient amount, kills in a few minutes. DDT, chlordane, and benzene hexachloride do not knock down so quickly, and they kill slowly, in from 30 minutes to several hours. Rotenone acts by inhibiting oxidation in tissues and may take 48 hours to kill; it is most effective against crawling or burrowing insects.

DDT is usually stated to have no repellent effect, which is an advantage, but mosquitoes and flies resting on a surface treated with it soon become excited and often leave a house or barn before they die.

Although all arthropods are affected by these various chemicals, the degree of susceptibility varies; e.g., DDT is considerably less effective and benzene hexachloride more effective against mites and ticks as compared with insects, and against roaches, bugs, and maggots as compared with mosquito larvae or adults; chlordane surpasses both against roaches. DDD compares favorably with DDT as a mosquito larvicide and is less toxic to fish, but it is less effective against flies and adult mosquitoes. Chlordane and benzene hexachloride have higher initial killing power against adult mosquitoes but less residual effect. Benzene hexachloride has a penetrating, disagreeable odor.

Insecticides fall into two general categories: stomach poisons and contact poisons. The former, of which sodium arsenite and Paris green are the best examples, are especially useful for plant-eating insects; only Paris green, extensively used as a finely divided powder for the surface-browsing Anopheles larvae to feed on, concerns us here.

Contact poisons include all the other insecticides mentioned above, as well as some others that are useful in special cases. They may be applied as fumigants (gas), dusts, sprays, ointments, or even as additions to food. The choice of an insecticide depends on the method of application, whether or not toxicity to a host is involved, the kind of arthropod, and speed of action required. The effectiveness of contact insecticides may be greatly influenced by their solvents, some of which permit penetration of the waxy surface layer of the cuticle much more readily than others (see Wigglesworth, 1945; Webb and Green, 1945). The activation of pyrethrins by addition of sesame oil is a good example.

Fumigants. For destruction of mites, argasid ticks, bedbugs, fleas, and rats in houses, barns, or animal pens, hydrocyanic acid gas (HCN) has been extensively used, but it is very toxic to all forms of life. A few deep breaths are fatal, and continued exposure to small amounts, as from inadequately ventilated mattresses or pillows, may be injurious; on the other hand the gas is not inflammable or explosive. The old method of generating HCN was by adding cyanide to sulfuric acid, but now it is generally released from cylinders of liquefied gas by scattering impregnated discs or by spreading calcium cyanide (Cyanogas) in thin layers on paper on the floors. HCN fumigation should be done by trained and experienced exterminators. With the advent of aerosols its use is largely outmoded except against rats.

Sulfur dioxide is another fumigant formerly widely used; it can be generated by burning sulfur in a humid atmosphere. It has the disadvantage of tarnishing metals and bleaching fabrics. In England during the war vaporization of heavy coal-tar naphtha distillate was extensively used in bomb shelters and crowded habitations. Special fumigants are the fumes from naphthalene flakes scattered on the floor to kill fleas; the fumes of nicotine sulfate painted on roosts to kill chicken lice; and p-dichlorobenzene to kill flies in deep latrines and garbage pits.

Sprays as Substitutes for Fumigants. For superficially located insects such as mosquitoes, flies, fleas, and to some extent bugs, mites, and ticks, pyrethrum sprays are very effective. Prior to the war they were dispensed from spray guns or atomizers and in some places reduced malaria by 90 per cent (see p. 210). The pyrethrum extract is usually dissolved in kerosene or similar oil; its effectiveness is increased considerably by addition of activators such as sesame oil. Mixed with DDT, the pyrethrum gives an immediate knock-down and then the DDT slowly kills. During the war " aerosol bombs " were developed which greatly improved indoor spraying. One bomb contained enough insecticide to treat 150,000 cu. ft. of space. The insecticide — usually pyrethrum with sesame oil and DDT — is dissolved in " Freon " liquefied under pressure. When released the " Freon " evaporates and releases the insecticide in very fine particles. A concentration of 15 per cent of nonvolatile substance is desirable in order to give particles about 2 to 10 μ in diameter; finer particles do not rest on flying insects. Atomizers give particles 50 to 150 μ in diameter. An aerosol containing 5 per cent DDT is about equal to 0.4 per cent pyrethrum and 8 per cent sesame oil.

Residual Sprays. The greatest value of DDT is the fact that when sprayed on surfaces as a 4 or 5 per cent solution in kerosene or as an emulsion, sufficient to leave a residue of about 200 mg. per sq. ft., it makes these surfaces deadly for 3 to 6 months to insects resting on them. Under some conditions residual effects have been observed for 3 years. Residual spraying has been extensively employed for the control of malaria with very good effects. DDT dissolves in kerosene to the extent of 5 per cent, in xylene 40 per cent, and in cyclohexanone 100 per cent. The latter concentrated solutions plus an emulsifying agent such as Triton-X100 are used in making emulsions.

Oils and Emulsions for Aquatic Insects. For mosquito larvae other than Mansonia oil films are very valuable, since they clog the tracheae when the larvae come to the surface to breathe. Oil entering the tracheae is ultimately fatal, but the action is greatly speeded by toxic impurities in the oil or by added insecticides such as pyrethrum extract or DDT. Other important attributes of a good mosquito oil are stability and spreading power (see Herms and Gray, 1944).

For subsurface insects such as the larvae of Mansonia, Culicoides, blackflies, and tabanids, as well as mosquitoes in general, emulsifying larvicides of the " Panama larvicide " type have been extensively used. They were mixtures of a soap or other emulsifying agent and oil with creosote, cresols, cresylic acid, pine oil, etc. These have now been replaced by DDT solution, emulsion, or suspension. Suspensions are made by mixing with water a 50-50 mixture of DDT powder and a dry wetting agent. A dose rate of 0.05 to 0.1 lb. of DDT per acre is sufficient except where there is dense vegetation. Airplane spraying of 0.1 to 0.2 lb. per acre, even where there is dense vegetation to penetrate, usually gives 98 to 99 per cent kills of mosquito larvae and reduces the adults to a like degree by killing them on the vegetation. In early experiments on some ponds it was a mystery why even untreated control ponds became free of mosquito larvae, until it was observed that ducks flying from pond to pond carried enough DDT on their feathers to extend the experiment! Some Pacific islands were so well disinsectized during the war that there were not enough insects left to pollinate the flowers on tomato plants.

When applied to streams, reservoirs, etc., other than by fine sprays, a dosage of 0.1 ppm. gives excellent results, but this is injurious to fish. Where the fish are more important than dead mosquitoes, 0.05 ppm. should be used or else a Paris green dust substituted. The latter is effective only against Anopheles larvae, however, and does not kill the eggs or pupae. It is harmless to other aquatic life.

DDT or benzene hexachloride dusts or sprays can also be used to destroy mites, ticks, rat fleas, flea larvae, blackfly larvae, tsetse flies, and maggots under outdoor conditions. These uses will be considered in sections dealing with these arthropods.

Insecticides on Man and Animals. DDT is now more extensively used to kill ectoparasites on hosts than any other substance. In powder form it is harmless; when dissolved in oil it penetrates the skin to some extent, but it takes large doses over a long period of time to produce toxic effects. Even breathing or swallowing reasonable amounts is not harmful. It has proved to be a godsend for treatment of lice on man and animals, and it is also highly effective for fleas, mites, and ticks, though benzene hexachloride is better for the arachnids, and repellents (see following section) are more often needed than insecticides for mites or ticks on man. Sulfur, which generates small amounts of hydrogen sulfide on the skin, has been the classical treatment for scabies and other mite infections, but benzyl benzoate has now largely replaced it. The latter is also an excellent repellent. The thiocyanates and benzyl or phenyl cellosolve in lotions or salves are also effective against human head lice or crab lice.

For animals, dips, sprays, or dusts containing DDT or benzene hexachloride are more effective and safer than the arsenic or sodium fluoride dips formerly used for lice, mites, and ticks. DDT or benzene hexachloride ointments or greases with sulfur are effective against warbles, Dermatobia, screwworms, etc. However, the best treatment for screwworms in animals is a diphenylamine smear, smear 62 (see p. 717).

Addition of insecticides to food has been tried chiefly with sulfur, which was supposed to render chickens unpalatable to lice, but it is not very effective. Some humans become repellent to redbugs (and also fellow beings) by eating sulfur, but there are wide individual differences in sulfur metabolism, and not all persons excrete sulfur derivatives through the skin in effective amounts. Benzene hexachloride fed to rabbits renders the droppings toxic to maggots and flea larvae. Knipling *et al.* (1948) obtained results against bloodsucking insects from drugs given by mouth which they considered sufficiently promising to warrant further investigation.

Repellents. These are substances that can be applied to the skin or clothing to keep insects, mites, or ticks from biting — they should be nontoxic, nonsensitizing, have no objectionable odor, and have lasting effect. Prior to World War II oil of citronella or other essential oils were most widely used, but the effect was too temporary. More recently, out of thousands of repellents tested, several good ones have been found, but no single one is equally effective against all kinds of arthropods, or even against different species of mosquitoes.

Widely used now are Indalone, particularly good against biting flies and some mosquitoes; Rutgers 612, best for most mosquitoes; and dimethyl phthalate, good against fleas and mites as well as many mosquitoes. A mixture of the three, the American GI repellent, is fairly effective against nearly all biting arthropods and land leeches also. Repellent action lasts from 2 to 8 hours according to conditions and kind of insect concerned. Dibutyl phthalate, less soluble than dimethyl phthalate, is very effective against redbugs and other mites; an ounce rubbed into the clothing is protective against redbugs even after 8 ordinary washings and is effective against schistosome cercariae also (see p. 281). Benzyl benzoate is an excellent mite repellent as well as one of the best miticides. No very good repellent against ticks has yet been found (see p. 550). Still newer repellents have been developed by the Naval Medical Research Institute, the best of which up to 1949 is NMRI-448, which protects longer than any of the others against most mosquitoes.

REFERENCES

ANDREWS, J. M., and SIMMONS, S. W., Developments in the Use of the Newer Organic Insecticides of Public Health Importance, *Am. J. Publ. Health,* **38,** 613–631 (1948).

CAMERON, T. W. M., Insecticides and Repellents in Modern Medicine, *McGill Med. J.,* **14,** No. 3 (1945).

CHERNEY, L. S., WHEELER, C. M., and REED, A. C., Flea Antigen in Prevention of Flea Bites, *Am. J. Trop. Med.,* **19,** 327 (1939).

COMSTOCK, J. H., *An Introduction to Entomology,* Ithaca, N. Y., 1925.

DUNNAHOO, G. L., Insect Control in Aircraft, *Soap Sanit. Chemicals,* **19,** 111 (1943).

ESSIG, E. O., *College Entomology,* New York, 1942.

EWING, H. E., *A Manual of External Parasites,* Springfield, Ill., 1929.

GOODHUE, L. D., Insecticidal Aerosol Production and Spraying Solutions in Liquefied Gases, *Ind. Eng. Chem.,* **34,** 1456 (1942).

GRAHAM-SMITH, G. S., *Flies in Relation to Disease (Non-Bloodsucking Flies),* Cambridge, 1913.

GRANETT, P., and HAYNES, H. L., Insect-Repellent Properties of 2-Ethylhexamediol-1,3 (Rutgers 612), *J. Econ. Entomol.,* **38,** 671 (1945).

HALL, M. C., Arthropods as Intermediate Hosts of Helminths, *Smithsonian Misc. Collections,* **81,** No. 15 (1929).

HERMS, W. B., *Medical Entomology,* New York, 1939.

HERMS, W. B., and GRAY, H. F., *Mosquito Control,* 2nd ed., Commonwealth Fund, New York, 1944.

HINDLE, E., *Flies and Disease (Bloodsucking Flies),* Cambridge, 1914.

HUFF, C. G., A Proposed Classification of Disease Transmission by Arthropods, *Science,* **74,** 456 (1931).

KARTMAN, L., New Developments in the Study of Ectoparasite Resistance, *J. Econ. Entomol.,* **36,** 372 (1943).

KNIPLING, E. F., The Development and Use of DDT for the Control of Mosquitoes, *J. Natl. Mal. Soc.,* **4,** 77–92 (1945).

KNIPLING, E. F., BUSHLAND, R. C., BABERS, F. H., CULPEPPER, G. H., and RAUN, E. S., Evaluation of Selected Insecticides and Drugs as Chemotherapeutic Agents against External Blood-sucking Parasites, *J. Parasitol.,* **34,** 55–70 (1948).

LEARY, J. C., FISHBEIN, W. J., and SALTER, L. C., *DDT and the Insect Problem,* New York, 1946.

LYLE, C., Achievements and Possibilities of Pest Eradication, *J. Econ. Entomol.,* **40,** 1–8 (1947).

MATHESON, R., *Medical Entomology,* Springfield, Ill., 1932.

METCALF, C. L., and FLINT, W. P., *Fundamentals of Insect Life*, New York, 1932.

MÖNNIG, H. O., *Veterinary Helminthology and Entomology*, London, 1934.

NEVEU-LEMAIRE, M., *Traité de zoologie médicale et vétérinaire, II Entomologie*, Paris, 1938.

PATTON, W. S., and CRAGG, F. W., *A Textbook of Medical Entomology*, London, 1913.

PATTON, W. S., and EVANS, A. M., *Insects, Ticks, Mites, and Venomous Animals of Medical and Veterinary Importance*, Pt. I, Medical; Pt. II, Public Health; London, 1929.

RILEY, W. A., and JOHANNSEN, O. A., *Medical Entomology*, 2nd ed., New York, 1938.

Ross, H. H., *A Textbook of Entomology*, New York, 1948.

STAGE, H. H., DDT to Control Insects Affecting Man and Animals in a Tropical Village, *J. Econ. Entomol.*, **40**, 759–762 (1947).

STEINHAUS, E. A., *Insect Microbiology*, Ithaca, N. Y., 1946.

STILES, C. W., and HASSALL, A., Key Catalogue of Insects of Importance in Public Health, *Hyg. Lab. Bull.*, **150**, 291 (1928).

TRAGER, W., Acquired Immunity to Ticks, *J. Parasitol.*, **25**, 37, 57 (1939).

WEBB, J. E., and GREEN, R. A., On the Penetration of Insecticides through the Insect Cuticle, *J. Exptl. Biol. Med.*, **22**, 8–20 (1945).

WIGGLESWORTH, V. B., Transpiration through the Cuticle of Insects, *J. Exptl. Biol. Med.*, **21**, 99–114 (1945).

CHAPTER 21

The Acarina. I. Mites

Acarina in General. The order Acarina of the class Arachnida includes a large number of species varying in size from some ticks which are half an inch or more in length to mites barely visible to the naked eye. The variety of body form is great, and some species when magnified appear grotesque. The majority of the species are more or less round or oval, with head, thorax, and abdomen all in one piece, but many have the cephalothorax (head and thorax fused together) distinctly marked off from the abdomen, while a few are quite worm-like in form. Some have the mouthparts attached to a basal piece articulated with the body and called a capitulum, but this is not a true head.

Many mites are free-living and prey upon decaying matter, vegetation, stored foods, and the like; some are predaceous and feed upon smaller animals; some are aquatic, even marine; and many are parasitic on other animals during all or part of their life cycle. Some of the parasitic forms are among the most important disease vectors, and the members of at least one group of free-living mites (Oribatoidea) serve as intermediate hosts for tapeworms (Anoplocephalidae).

Like other Arachnida (spiders, scorpions, etc.), the mites and ticks usually have two pairs of mouthparts and four pairs of legs, though the last pair of legs is not acquired until after the first moult. The legs have typically six or seven segments which, beginning next to the body, are named as follows: (1) coxa, (2) trochanter, (3) femur, (4) tibia, (5) protarsus, and (6) tarsus. The tarsus may be composed of several segments and is often terminated by one or more claws, and either bears the claws or lies between them. The first pair of mouthparts, the chelicerae, are sometimes needlelike, sometimes shaped like a grapnel hook, and often pincerlike, the pincers sometimes being at the tip of a long, exsertile, needlelike structure. The second pair of mouthparts, the pedipalps, are simple segmented palpi. In many kinds of Acarina the anterior end of the ventral side of the body is produced as a sort of chin or lower lip, the hypostome, which may be needlelike or barbed and rasplike (Fig. 179).

The digestive tract is well developed in most Acarina. The stomach

498

has pouches opening from it which act as food reservoirs, so that one meal may last for a long time. The intestine is usually short, and the excretory organs, Malpighian tubules, open into it not far from the anus. The reproductive organs, as in other Arachnida, open on the ventral surface of the abdomen but at different places in different species. Many mites possess tracheae and a pair of spiracles, while others, soft-skinned forms, simply absorb oxygen through the surface of the body.

Life History. There are usually four stages in the development of mites and ticks: the egg, the larva, the nymph, and the adult (see Fig. 188). The eggs are usually laid under the the surface of the soil or in crevices or, in some parasites, under the skin of the host. After a varying period of incubation the larva hatches in the form of a six-legged creature, often quite unlike the parent. After a single good feed the larva rests, sheds its skin, and appears with an additional pair of legs and a body form more closely resembling that of the parent but without developed sexual organs. The nymph thus produced feeds and moults once or several times and finally, after another period of rest during which the body is once more remodeled, moults again and comes forth as an adult male or female. There are many modifications in the development due to the slurring over of certain phases or interpolation of others, e.g., the moulting of some larval ticks and mites in the egg or just after hatching but before feeding, and the occurrence of additional intermediate stages in hydrachnids, trombiculids (p. 508), and tyroglyphids (p. 516).

Some mites have become adapted to live as internal parasites in the lungs and air sacs of snakes, birds, and mammals, and there are records of mites which are not normally parasitic at all living and multiplying in the human urinary bladder, but all the species normally infesting man are either external or subcutaneous in their operations.

Classification. The Acarina are usually divided into 8 or 10 superfamilies, each with several families. The accompanying key gives the principal characters for distinguishing the superfamilies and also the families that are of interest from a medical standpoint.

Key to the Superfamilies and Parasitic Families of Acarina

1*a*. Spiracles open on a pair of stigmal plates situated laterally behind or above third or fourth pairs of legs. (Figs. 181*A* and 170) ....2.

1*b*. Spiracles situated elsewhere or missing ....3.

2*a*. Hypostome conspicuous and barbed (Fig. 178); large, leathery forms; ticks (see Chap. 22) ....Superfam. **Ixodoidea.**

    (1) Dorsal shield present; capitulum anterior (Fig. 181*A*) ..Fam. *Ixodidae.*

    (2) No dorsal shield; capitulum ventral (Fig. 181*B*) ......Fam. *Argasidae.*

2b. Hypostome inconspicuous, without barbs; small forms with coriaceous shields on body ....Superfam. **Parasitoidea.**
    (1) A dorsal shield not quite covering back; chelicerae needlelike, or if pincerlike at tip, the tip not provided with teeth or setae (Fig. 170); chicken mites, tropical rat mites etc. (see p. 511) ..Fam. *Dermanyssidae.*

3a. Body vermiform; legs rudimentary (Fig 168); hair follicle mites of mammals (see p. 506) ....Superfam. **Demodicoidea,** Fam. *Demodicidae.*

3b. Body not vermiform; legs not rudimentary ....4.

4a. Body coriaceous with few hairs; a pair of specialized setae on posterior corners of cephalothorax, which is usually plainly distinct from abdomen; no eyes; very small mouthparts; body high; coxae all close together and tarsi without suckers; never parasitic ....Superfam. **Oribatoidea.**

4b. Body softer; no specialized setae on cephalothorax ....5.

5a. Aquatic, nearly spherical; no distinct cephalothorax; mouthparts usually ventral; water mites ....Superfam. **Hydrachnoidea**

5b. Not aquatic; mouth usually not concealed anteriorly ....6.

6a. Palpi small, 3-jointed; tarsi usually end in suckers; rodlike supports for legs visible under skin (Fig. 166) ....7.

6b. Palpi larger, 4- or 5-jointed; eyes usually present; tarsi never end in suckers; cephalothorax usually distinct ....9.

7a. Cuticle with fine "fingerprint" striations; cephalothorax not separate; tarsi with stalked suckers (Fig. 166) ....Superfam. **Sarcoptoidea.**
    (1) Vulva transverse; parasitic in skin; itch and mange mites ....
    ....Fam. *Sarcoptidae.*
    (2) Vulva longitudinal; parasitic in air passages or skin ..Fam. *Cytoleichidae.*

7b. No striations; no stalked suckers; cephalothorax usually distinct ....8.

8a. Abdomen more or less segmented; a pair of club-shaped setae between first and second pairs of legs; sucking mouthparts with needlelike chelicerae (Fig. 172); Pediculoides and Tarsonemus (see pp. 517 and 514) ....
    ....Superfam. **Tarsonematoidea,** Fam. *Tarsonematidae.*

8b. Abdomen not segmented; prominent pincerlike mandibles; no club-shaped setae as in 8a; no eyes; body elongate (Fig. 171); grain and cheese mites (see p. 515) ....Superfam. **Tyroglyphoidea,** Fam. *Tyroglyphidae.*

9a. Last joint of palpus forms thumb closing against claw of preceding joint, for grasping; body hairy ....Superfam. **Trombidioidea.**
    (1) Cephalothorax distinct, with median dorsal furrow; body clothed with feathered hairs; mandibles pincerlike at tip; adults free-living, larvae parasitic on vertebrates; redbugs (see p. 507) ......Fam. *Trombiculidae.*

9b. Last joint of palpus not thumblike; body with few hairs; (one species annoying to man, *Tydeus molestus*) Superfam. **Eupodoidea.** Fam. *Eupodidae.*

All the superfamilies except the **Oribatoidea** contain at least a few parasitic species. The **Oribatoidea** came into the limelight when Stunkard in 1937 showed that members of this group serve as intermediate hosts for Moniezia and other anoplocephalid tapeworms. They are small, hard-shelled mites that live about the roots of grass and have a superficial resemblance to tiny beetles. The *Hydrachnoidea* live either in fresh water or in the sea. Many of the former have larvae that parasitize mosquitoes in the larval stage after the manner of trombidiids, which they also resemble in having stages of development interpolated between the usual egg, larva, nymph, and adult stages.

Ixodoidea (ticks) are so conspicuous that they are popularly looked upon as quite distinct from other Acarina. Since they also overshadow the rest of the order in importance as disease transmitters they will have a separate chapter devoted to them. The **Parasitoidea** contain some free-living and some parasitic species, the latter including the chicken mites, rat mites, and one genus which infests the lungs of monkeys. The **Sarcoptoidea** (itch or mange mites) and the **Demodicoidea** (hair follicle mites) are the only mites that live their entire lives, generation after generation, as parasites; they are true internal parasites, the Demodicidae living in the hair follicles, the Sarcoptidae under the surface of the skin, and the Cytoleichidae in the lungs or air sacs of birds.

The **Tarsonematoidea** contain some species that attack insects (and man or other animals when the insects fail them) and other species which are injurious to plants. One injurious species is parasitic in the tracheae of honeybees. The **Tyroglyphoidea,** including the cheese and grain mites that cause grocer's itch, are mostly feeders on dead organic matter, but some attack plants and some, insects. The **Eupodoidea** are mainly fairly large, free-living, predaceous mites.

The **Trombidioidea** contain mites of variable habits. The Trombidiidae and Trombiculidae are free-living except in the larval stage, when the former are parasitic on insects and the latter on or in the skin of land vertebrates.

Itch and Mange Mites (Sarcoptidae)

Species. The minute rounded or oval, short-legged, flattened mites of the family Sarcoptidae are the cause of scabies or "itch" in man and of mange or scab in many kinds of animals. The species that attacks man, *Sarcoptes scabiei*, is so similar to forms of Sarcoptes causing mange in many other animals — dogs, foxes, cats, rabbits, ruminants, horses, and pigs — that all of these are considered mere biological varieties of one species. These varieties are so adapted to the hosts in which they have been living that it is difficult to transfer them to other hosts. Other genera attack various domestic animals. Following is a key to the most important genera:

1*a.* Posterior pairs of legs nearly or quite concealed under abdomen ....2.
1*b.* At least third pair of legs projecting ....3.
2*a.* Dorsum with spines and pointed scales (Fig. 166) ....***Sarcoptes.***

2b. Dorsum with spines and rounded scales ....*Notoëdres.*
2c. No dorsal spines or scales ....*Cnemidocoptes.*
3a. Pedicles of tarsal suckers very long ....*Psoroptes.*
3b. Pedicles short ....4.
4a. ♀ with suckers on legs 1, 2, 4; with posterior abdominal lobes .... **Chorioptes.**
4b. ♀ with suckers on legs 1, 2; abdomen without lobes ....*Otodectes.*

Notoëdres cati causes a very severe and sometimes fatal mange in cats; it temporarily infests man but soon dies out.   Psoroptes does not

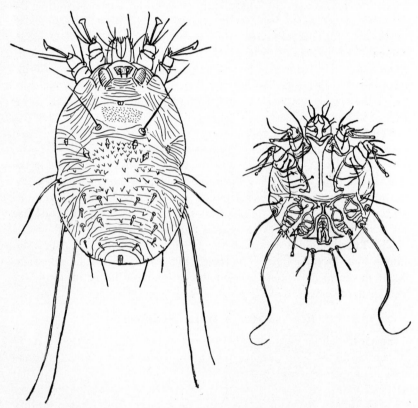

Fig. 166.   *Sarcoptes scabiei*, itch mite. Left ♀; right, ♂ × 150. (♀ After Buxton, ♂ after Monnig.)

burrow under the skin but causes " scab " in ruminants and horses; Chorioptes causes foot scab in horses, and Otodectes ear mange in carnivores; Cnemidocoptes has two species attacking chickens, one causing scaly leg, the other " depluming " mange.

Sarcoptes scabiei. The itch mites (Fig. 166) are minute whitish creatures, scarcely visible to the naked eye, of which the females burrow beneath the skin and lay eggs in the galleries which they make. They are nearly round, and the cuticle is delicately sculptured with numerous wavy parallel lines, pierced here and there by stiff projecting bristles or hairs. They have no eyes or tracheae. The mouthparts, consisting of a pair of minute chelicerae and a pair of three-jointed triangular pedipalps, are attached to a capitulum or head, as in ticks, this fitting into a groove in the front of the body. The legs are short and stumpy and are provided with suckerlike organs at the tips of long unjointed pedicels in the first two pairs of legs in the females, and in the first, second, and fourth pairs in the males; the other legs terminate in long bristles. The number of legs with pedicelled suckers, and whether or not the pedicels are jointed, are important characters in differentiating other

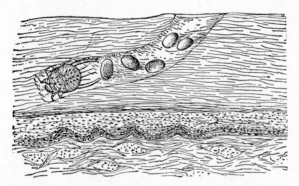

Fig. 167. Diagrammatic tunnel of itch mite in human skin, showing female depositing eggs. × about 30. (Adapted from Riley and Johannsen.)

genera in the family. In the human itch mite the male is less than 0.25 mm. in length and the female about 0.4 mm. in length.

The impregnated females excavate thin tortuous tunnels in the epidermis (Fig. 167), especially where the skin is delicate and thin. The tunnels measure from a few millimeters to over an inch in length and are usually gray from the eggs and excrement deposited by the female as she burrows; under a lens they look like a chain of minute grayish specks punctuated at intervals by a tiny, hard, yellow blister. The daily excavations of a mite amount to 2 or 3 millimeters.

Life Cycle. The eggs (Fig. 167), about 160 μ long, are laid in the burrows at the rate of 2 or 3 a day for more than 40 days. After they are all laid the female dies, usually at the end of a single tortuous burrow. The eggs hatch in a few days into larvae which resemble the adults except in minor details and in the absence of the fourth pair of legs. The larvae transform in 2 or 3 days into nymphs. The nymphs commonly build burrows for themselves and moult twice, the second time becoming adult male and female mites. The duration of the two nymphal periods is from $3\frac{1}{2}$ to 6 days, the entire development of the mites therefore requiring from 8 to 14 days.

The mites are not necessarily nocturnal as was formerly supposed, but wander about on the surface of the skin when it is warm, most frequently when the host is in bed. The males are usually stated to be short-lived and to remain on the surface of the skin, but Munro in 1919 questioned this. The males are not, however, very commonly found. The young impregnated females make fresh excavations of their own. Since there is a new generation about every 3 weeks, the rate of increase is potentially enormous, yet according to Mellanby (1943) the average number of adult females in an infested person is less than twelve, and not one person in ten has over thirty.

The Disease. The " itch " is a disease which has been known much longer than it has been understood; it was formerly attributed to " bad blood." In the past, itch swept over armies and populations in great epidemics, but it has decreased with civilization and cleanliness.

As shown by Mellanby (1943, 1944), the intense itching that characterizes the disease does not begin until a month or so after an initial infection, when the skin has become sensitized; prior to this there is very little discomfort. After 6 weeks there is enough irritation to disturb sleep, and after about 100 days the irritation may be continuous and unbearable. In previously uninfected persons the mites reach a peak population of 50 to 500 in 7 to 16 weeks, after which the number declines sharply to 10 or less. The lesions, however, get worse and often appear where there are no longer any mites, and secondary infections, such as impetigo, develop. In reinfections intense local irritation, redness, and edema begin in 24 hours, often causing the parasites to be removed by the fingernails or to leave voluntarily an environment that is unfavorable for them because of edema or septic infections. The itching may persist for days or weeks after the mites are removed or killed. In reinfections the average number of mites present is only 3 or 4. A few mites may, however, persist for a very long time.

The mites invade the skin of the hands and wrists most frequently. Mellanby found them there in 85 per cent of cases, but they also attack the groin and external genitals, breasts, feet, or other parts. The head is rarely attacked, although a severe " crusted " form of the disease called Norwegian itch occurs in Europe and attacks the head as well as other parts.

Although the burrows of the mites are often sufficiently characteristic to make a diagnosis possible, it should usually be confirmed by finding the mites, which are not in the vesicles but usually near them at the ends of the burrows. Scrapings from the blind ends of the burrows should be examined microscopically for adults or larvae; the latter are only about 0.15 mm. long.

Epidemiology. Infection can result only from the passage of male and female mites or of an impregnated female from an infected to a healthy individual. Normally this takes place by actual contact, rarely in the daytime on account of the secretive habits of the mites, but commonly at night, especially from one bedfellow to another. Mellanby found that transmission through bedding or clothing is relatively rare, except after contact with the small percentage of cases having a large number of mites. He was uniformly successful in establishing infections in previously uninfected volunteers by transfer of young impregnated mites but never younger stages. The adults can live apart from a host for 2 or 3 days under favorable conditions. It is possible for infection to be derived from mangy animals, though the mites, once adapted for several generations to a given host, do not often survive a transfer to a different species of host for more than a few days.

Treatment and Prevention. Since the mites and their eggs are situated beneath the skin, superficial treatments with home remedies seldom eliminate all the mites, although they may reduce their numbers. For many years the standard remedy was sulfur ointment (½ oz. of sulfur in 16 oz. of lard or lanolin) applied after softening the skin with soap and warm water. During World War II benzyl benzoate was found to be easier to apply and 100 per cent effective. Mellanby recommended a lotion consisting of equal parts of benzyl benzoate, soft soap, and isopropyl alcohol, but this often causes considerable skin irritation. Slepyan (1944) developed an effective treatment using a lotion consisting of 250 cc. of benzyl benzoate poured over a wetting agent (Duponal C, 20 grams) and then adding enough 2.5 per cent aqueous solution of bentonite, slowly without shaking, to make 1000 cc. The emulsion is then agitated until all the wetting agent is dissolved. After being bathed and scrubbed, the whole body below the head is painted with the lotion, which is allowed to dry on the skin. The body is repainted after 5 minutes. The patient is then put to bed under blankets for 4 hours, after which he takes a shower, is dried, and puts on clean clothing while his old clothing is laundered. This treatment also appears to be effective against crab lice. Another recommended treatment for scabies is 2.5 per cent benzene hexachloride in vanishing cream.

Prevention of this annoying infection consists merely in avoiding contact with infected individuals and of shunning public towels or soiled bed linen. When introduced among groups of previously uninfected individuals, scabies may cause extensive epidemics.

Hair Follicle Mites (Demodex)

The hair follicle or face mite, *Demodex folliculorum* (Fig. 168), of the family Demodicidae, is a wormlike creature, very unmitelike in general appearance, which lives in the hair follicles and sebaceous glands of various mammals. In man it occurs especially on the face and has been found in the ear wax. In dogs it has also been found in lymph glands. Numerous forms from various animals have been described as different species, but they are all strikingly alike and the extent of their specificity is questionable.

The wormlike appearance of the adult mites is due to the great elongation of the abdomen, which is marked by numerous fine lines

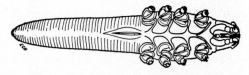

Fig. 168. Hair follicle mite, *Demodex folliculorum*. × 200. (After Mégnin.)

running around it. The head is short and broad, and the four pairs of legs, all similar, are short, stumpy, three-jointed appendages. The females are 0.35 to 0.40 mm. long, the males a little smaller.

The multiplication of these mites is slow. The eggs hatch into tiny six-legged larvae in which the legs are mere tubercles. It requires four moults to bring the larvae to sexual maturity.

The occurrence of these parasites in the hair follicles of man, particularly about the nose, is extremely common; in Germany Gmeiner (1908) found them in 97 of 100 random examinations of individuals with healthy skins. The presence of the mites rarely causes any symptoms whatever, and in man they should probably be considered entirely harmless parasites. Their occasional discovery in cases of acne, blackheads, and other skin conditions leads to suspicion that they are the cause of the condition. Actually, however, Gmeiner found them much less frequently in cases of acne and blackheads than he did in healthy skins and thought that the altered contents of the diseased follicles and skin glands was unfavorable for their development. In dogs, on the other hand, Demodex causes a severe and sometimes fatal form of mange. Some authors think the infection is extremely common in dogs, as it is in man, but that it produces symptoms only under conditions of poor health, vitamin deficiencies, etc. There is a scaly form of the disease in which the skin becomes red, wrinkled, and scaly, and loses its hair, and a pustular or abscessed form in which the skin is invaded by staphylococci, to which dogs are usually resistant. Similar forms occur in cattle, pigs, goats, and horses.

The method of transmission of the mites to another host is not definitely known, but it is probable that the adults wander on the surface of the skin at times and may then be transmitted by direct contact or by towels, as are itch mites. Since generation after generation may be produced on a single host the infection is potentially indefinite in its duration.

In dogs transmission takes place in a very irregular manner, and frequent instances are cited of infected dogs associating for a long time with uninfected ones without spreading the disease. Experiments with transmission of the canine follicle mite to man have invariably failed. No entirely satisfactory treatment is known, but promising results have been obtained on demodectic mange of cattle by rubbing in benzene hexachloride in lanolin ointment or brushing with a solution in linseed oil. Hog mange responds to a suspension of this drug containing 0.25 per cent of the γ isomer. Good food and hygienic conditions are important; not infrequently the disease disappears spontaneously. In 1946 good results were reported from treating mangy dogs with niacin, a vitamin in which dogs are frequently deficient.

Redbugs or "Chiggers" (Trombiculidae)

There is probably no creature on earth that can cause more torment for its size than a redbug, but in the Far East even this distinction is not enough, for in that area some species add injury to insult by transmitting a disease, scrub typhus, which during World War II caused more trouble in the Pacific area than any other insect-borne disease except malaria.

The redbugs (Fig. 169) are the six-legged larvae of mites of the family Trombiculidae, formerly considered a subfamily of Trombidiidae. The larvae of the latter are parasitic on insects, whereas the trombiculid larvae are always parasitic on vertebrates. This, as with the Hydrachnidae, is a biological trick for better dispersal. The nymphs and adults are velvety, scarlet-red mites that are free-living. It has been generally believed that they feed on various organic debris, but attempts to rear them on such materials have been only meagerly successful. Wharton (1946) reared one species very easily on insect eggs and later succeeded in rearing the common pest chigger, *Eutrom-*

bicula alfreddugési, on *Aëdes aegypti* eggs.   Other species, however, failed to thrive on such fare.

The parasitic larvae, called redbugs, rougets, chiggers, harvest mites, scrub mites, or various local names, are minute reddish or orange creatures barely visible to the naked eye (about 0.2 by 0.15 mm.) when unfed.   Just behind the capitulum is a small dorsal scutum ornamented with five (in some species six) feathered hairs and a pair of pseudostigmatic organs (Fig. 169) from which arise sensory hairs, long and slender in the human species, club-shaped in certain others.   There are also feathered hairs on other parts of the body and on the palpi

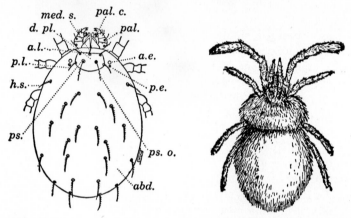

Fig. 169.   Left, common American redbug or chigger, *Eutrombicula alfreddugési,* × about 160.   (After Ewing.)   Right, an adult Trombicula, *T. akamushi,* × 40.   (After Nagayo *et al.*)

and legs.   Genera and species are distinguished by details of the dorsal scutum and of the hairs on the palpi and legs.

Life History.   The life cycle has been worked out completely in only a few species but is probably similar for all; it is peculiar in that extra cuticular coverings are produced between the usual stages, and that the fleshy parts of the legs are resorbed and totally new legs are formed in each successive stage.   The eggs, laid singly or in small groups, are deposited on the ground.   After the general body form is laid down in the egg a cystlike membrane develops around the embryo, which is exposed by the splitting of the egg shell.   This stage is called a deutovum and develops in about 6 days.   Six days later the fully developed larva hatches and attaches itself to a vertebrate host at the first opportunity and remains attached for from a few days to a month; Williams found that the larvae may pass the winter comfortably holed up in the ears of rabbits or squirrels.   After engorgement the larva drops off and moults; meanwhile the tissues of the appendages undergo lysis, and a thin chitinized shell is laid down under the old larval skin; this stage is called a protonymph or nymphochrysalis. In a few days an eight-legged nymph develops inside and emerges. After feeding and growing, the nymph changes to a preadult or imagochrysalis, from which an adult male or female emerges in about 6 days or more. The nymphs and adults (Fig. 169) are similar in appearance; the nymphs are about 0.5 mm. and the adults about 0.75 to 1 mm. long.

Important Species and their Habits. True redbugs anchor themselves to the surface of the skin, neither burrowing in or entering pores, although the larvae of Hannemania, in a closely related family, burrow into the skin of frogs. After attachment redbugs inject a salivary secretion which dissolves the skin tissue as it penetrates, forming a tubular structure in the skin called a stylostome, nearly as long as the body of the mite and filled with semidigested tissue debris on which the mite feeds. The mites do not feed on blood, although their red color when engorged gives that impression.

Some redbugs show marked host preferences, different species normally confining themselves to such hosts as rodents, bats, birds, or reptiles, respectively, but a few do not show much discrimination and are content to drool into the skin of almost anything they can get access to, whether it be a turtle, snake, robin, rabbit, mouse, or human being. Most species on mammals have a tendency to get into the ears. On man they run over the skin or through the meshes of clothing, most commonly coming to rest about the garters or belt.

Of the hundreds of species in over thirty genera which are found in all parts of the world, except possibly Africa, fortunately only a few are willing to engorge on man, and only one very small group of closely related species in the genus Trombicula, called the tsutsugamushi group after the Japanese name of the disease, seem to be concerned with transmission of scrub typhus to man.

The only species commonly attacking human beings in North America are *Eutrombicula alfreddugési*, widely distributed in southern United States and in the Mississippi valley; *E. splendens* (=*masoni*), common in wet localities in the southeastern states; and *E. batatas* (=*Acariscus hominis*), a pest species widely distributed in tropical America. In Europe *Neotrombicula autumnalis* is an annoying human pest. All parts of the Far East, New Guinea, and Australia have species which can make life miserable for man; two of the commonest in the area are *Trombicula hirsti* and *T. wichmanni*, which, according to Wharton, are very closely related to the pest species of the United

States. These, however, are not the transmitters of scrub typhus (see next section). In Queensland *T. sarcina* attacks man and also produces acute irritation and nasty sores on the legs of sheep. In Texas and the southeastern states a species of Euschöngastia is a pest of chickens and birds but leaves man alone.

The common pest redbug of the United States, *E. alfreddugési*, attacks principally turtles, snakes, ground birds, and rabbits and is content to feed on man and domestic animals, but unlike many species it does not often attack rodents. On snakes and lizards it may be so abundant as to form rusty red patches between the scales. This redbug is particularly abundant on loam or sandy soil covered by thickets but is seldom found in hardwood forests. Williams (1946) found them spottily distributed and especially abundant under blackberry bushes or at the base of trees. Before attachment they run about actively on or near the ground, eager to climb on a host, but they do not climb upon grass or brush. They can run about a foot in a minute — 1500 times their own length — but ordinarily do not travel far.

The irritation caused by redbugs, as in other arthropod attacks, is largely due to sensitization to the saliva injected. The reaction reaches its height of itching in from 12 to 24 hours, when the stylostome is well developed. Eventually the reaction becomes so rapid that very little saliva gets into the skin and the mites are unable to engorge; in some individuals almost complete immunity develops, except for a few reactive bites early in the season which act like a booster shot of a vaccine to revive immunity. Alcohol or camphor helps to allay the itching, and a bath with baking soda or ammonia in the water gives some relief, especially if taken soon after exposure. Dusting sulfur inside the stockings and on the legs is undoubtedly a helpful prophylactic if better repellents are not available (see below).

Transmission of Scrub Typhus. As mentioned previously, a small group of closely related species of the genus Trombicula in the Far East are transmitters of scrub typhus, a rickettsial disease (see p. 228). *T. akamushi* (= *T. fletcheri*) in Japan and New Guinea and *T. deliensis*, probably only a subspecies, in a wide area from India to southwest China, Malaya, the East Indies, New Guinea, and Australia are the only proved transmitters. They are primarily parasites of rats and other rodents. Other species of the group may spread infection among rodents, shrews, or bandicoots, which harbor the disease in nature.

The only member of the tsutsugamushi group so far found in America is *T. myotis* of bats. No suspicion of disease transmission was attached to American redbugs until Baker in 1946 made the startling discovery that meadow mice (*Microtus pennsylvanicus*) on an island in the St. Lawrence River were infected with a Rickettsia resembling *R. orientalis* of scrub typhus and probably transmitted by *Trombicula microti*. This species does not belong to the tsutsugamushi group but to a closely related group. Whether this is modified typhus, introduced scrub typhus, or a new but related disease is still in question.

Since the larval mites normally attack only one host and are not parasitic in the later stages, transovarial transmission is a necessary feature of the epidemiology of the disease. It is probable that vertebrate hosts of the Rickettsia are more incidental than true reservoir hosts.

Scrub typhus usually begins with a black sore or " eschar " at the site of the infective bite. Fever, insomnia, generalized inflammation of lymph glands, aches, and neuritis are the usual symptoms; often there is a rash also. The mortality varies from 3 to over 50 per cent in different places. The disease is differentiated from " shop typhus " (endemic or murine typhus) by the OXK Weil Felix reaction (see p. 228). Administration of *p*-aminobenzoic acid, as in other typhuslike diseases, greatly alleviates the symptoms. The antibiotics, aureomycin and chloromycetin, are effective in treatment.

Protection against Redbugs. During World War II it was found that practically complete protection against redbugs and scrub typhus could be obtained for weeks by rubbing dibutyl phthalate into the clothing. Later benzyl benzoate was adopted, but a 50-50 mixture of the two is equally as good. Spraying with DDT or, still better, with benzene hexachloride (see p. 491) eliminated redbugs from local areas used for encampments during World War II; 3 per cent benzene hexachloride in fuel oil at the rate of 6 lb. of drug per acre is effective for 2 weeks, and 10 lb. of dust per acre gives 90 per cent control for a month. In America a suspension applied at the rate of only 2 to 4 lb. per acre was found effective for a month. Griffiths (1946) found that removing grass and brush gave effective control as soon as the topsoil dried. Rat control is of little or no value.

Bloodsucking Mites (Dermanyssidae)

The family Dermanyssidae of the superfamily Parasitoidea (see p. 500) contains a number of species of mites that suck blood from mammals, principally rodents, and from birds or reptiles. One genus, Pneumonyssus, is parasitic in the lungs of monkeys, and another, Halarachne, in the lungs of seals and sea lions. Important species from the human standpoint are *Dermanyssus gallinae* of chickens and other birds, *Allodermanyssus sanguineus* of mice and sometimes rats,

and *Liponyssus bacoti* of rats.   The genus Dermanyssus has a large
dorsal shield rounded posteriorly and chelicerae that are needlelike in
females and pincerlike in males, while Liponyssus has a smaller dorsal
shield narrowed posteriorly and chelicerae pincerlike in both sexes.

Dermanyssus gallinae.   This, the " red mite " of poultry (Fig.
170*A*), along with one or two other species of poultry mites belonging
to the family Dermanyssidae, often causes irritation and annoyance to
people who work in chicken houses, live poultry markets, etc.

The mites live like bedbugs in cracks and crevices, nests, etc., feeding
on the chickens mainly at night and sometimes doing much damage
to them; they may actually bleed them to death.   The eggs are laid in

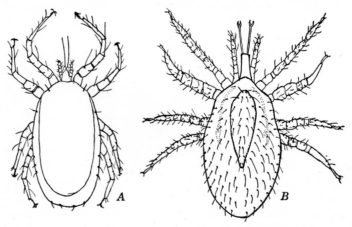

Fig. 170.   Dermanyssid mites;   *A*, *Dermanyssus gallinae*, chicken mite, × 50; *B*,
Liponyssus bacoti, tropical rat mite, × 42. (*A* adapted from Banks, *B* from Ewing.)

crevices and debris, and the larvae moult into eight-legged nymphs
before they begin sucking blood.   Although only able to live and
multiply on birds, they may remain on human skin for a day or two,
causing annoying bites.   There is a report of a London hospital which
was literally dusted with these mites originating from pigeon nests in
the roof.   Infested chicken houses, dovecotes, live poultry markets,
etc., sometimes remain infested for several weeks after the birds have
been removed.

This mite has been found to harbor and transovarially transmit the
encephalomyelitis viruses of the St. Louis and western equine types.
Many chickens develop antibodies, thus showing evidence of infection.
The mites, therefore, constitute an important reservoir of these viruses
between epidemics.   Experimentally this mite was found capable of
transmitting yellow fever to a monkey.

Spraying with carbolineum or creosote was the time-honored method of getting rid of these chicken mites until DDT and benzene hexachloride were developed; these chemicals have the advantage of not giving eggs flavors that did not come from the chickens.

Liponyssus. Members of this genus are important parasites of birds and rats and are concerned in transmission of certain rickettsial and virus diseases. *L. bacoti* (Fig. 170*B*), a common mite of rats in southern United States and throughout the tropics, is capable of transmitting endemic typhus (see p. 228) among rats and possibly occasionally to man, since it temporarily becomes an annoying human pest in rat-infested buildings when its normal hosts are killed or driven off. This mite is also able to transmit rickettsialpox (see next section) and Q fever (see p. 229). This mite should be distinguished from another common rat mite, *Echinolaelaps echidnius*, which has numerous conspicuous ventral plates and has not been incriminated as a disease carrier.

L. sylviarum is a frequent parasite of chickens and of many wild birds in North America and Europe, and *L. bursa* is an important chicken parasite in the tropics. *L. sylviarum* is a carrier of the St. Louis and western equine strains of encephalomyelitis and probably serves as a reservoir for these viruses by transovarial transmission just as *Dermanyssus gallinae* does. Unlike *D. gallinae*, *L. sylviarum* stays on the feathers of the birds instead of retiring to crevices in chicken houses or nests, so it cannot be controlled by the same methods; this and other feather mites, as well as bird lice, can be controlled by spraying with mixed DDT and lethane 72B as described on p. 588.

Mites and Rickettsialpox. In 1946 an outbreak of a previously unknown rickettsial disease which occurred in New York City was traced to an infection in mice, transmitted by a mouse mite of this family, *Allodermanyssus sanguineus*. Later *Liponyssus bacoti* (see preceding section) was shown to be a potential transmitter also. The disease begins like scrub typhus with a black eschar at the site of the bite, followed a week later by a sudden fever and a rash resembling chickenpox. The Rickettsia was named *R. akari* and is antigenically close to spotted fever.

Mites in the Lungs, Intestine, Urinary Passages, etc.

Lung Mites. A number of mites normally take up their residence in lungs or air sacs of various animals; e.g., *Cytodites nudus*, one of the Sarcoptoidea, lives in galliform birds, Pneumonyssus lives in monkeys, Halarachne in seals and sea lions, and Entonyssus in snakes. In Ceylon a number of cases of invasion of human lungs by normally free-living mites of the families Tarsonematidae and Tyroglyphidae have been reported; the infections have been accompanied by bronchial asthma and eosinophilia.

Mites in the Intestine.   There have been numerous reports of intestinal infections with mites.   The mites concerned have always been common household species of the families Tyroglyphidae (grain and cheese mites, see p. 515) and Tarsonematidae (p. 500), which also infest various vegetable products.   The eggs and the mites in all stages of development are frequently found in the feces of man, and of dogs and other animals fed on mite-infested food, but they are always dead. This pseudoparasitism with mites sometimes fills unsuspecting technicians with wonder and excitement when they discover the large eggs in the feces.

It is possible that ingestion of the mites in considerable numbers may occasionally cause gastro-intestinal disturbances.   Hase (1929) describes a famous German cheese, Altenburger " milbenkäse," that owes its piquant flavor to the presence of myriads of tyroglyphid mites, with which it is deliberately inoculated.   The mites and their feces make a moving grayish powder on the surface.   The ingestion of millions of mites and their excretions with this cheese often causes gastro-intestinal disturbances when the cheese is eaten for the first time, but those used to it suffer no ill effects.   Nevertheless, Hase observed that mite dust (dead mites, feces, cast skins, etc.) was so toxic to mice that 7 out of 12 fed with it died with dysenteric symptoms. The writer has seen dogs relieved of diarrhea when taken off mite-infested food.   There is no doubt, however, that any ordinary contamination of human food with mites would be of no consequence, and there is no sound evidence that they ever become established in the alimentary canal.

Urinary Infections.   Urinary infections with mites have frequently been reported, but in most of these cases it seems likely that the mites observed are really contaminations from containers or other sources. However, there are a number of apparently *bona fide* infestations of the urinary tract in which no source of contamination could be found. Mackenzie and Mekie in 1926 reported finding mites in the urine of patients with uncontrollable nocturnal enuresis; the urine contained abundant epithelial cells, parts of mites, and a black deposit.   The mites concerned were a tarsonematid, *Tarsonemus floricolus*, and tyroglyphids.   The latter are found in sugar, cereals, etc., but the Tarsonemus ordinarily lives on plants.   How they found their way into the urinary passages, if they actually did, is hard to understand.   Another case is reported of dead mites being found day after day in the urine of a

Japanese with cystitis. The mites, named *Nephrophages sanguinarius*, are believed to be tarsonemids.

In rare instances tyroglyphid mites establish residence in the canal of the outer ear and occasionally even penetrate to the middle ear and mastoid.

There have been a number of reports of tyroglyphid mites being found in cancers and other situations in the tissue of the body, but it is practically certain that these are cases of contamination.

Grocer's Itch and Allied Forms of Mite Dermatitis

Tyroglyphidae. Many mites, most of them belonging to the family Tyroglyphidae, are common pests of human dwellings, stores, and warehouses, where they attack all sorts of food materials, stored seeds, stuffing of furniture, etc.; when conditions are favorable they multiply until the infested materials are literally alive with them. They are especially commonly found in animal feeds, hay, grain, flour, sugar, dried fruits, copra, cottonseed, and cheese.

People who come into close association with infested goods develop symptoms which Hase (1929) thinks are of allergic nature. Though allergy undoubtedly plays a part, there is evidence that the bodies or excretions of the mites are toxic; this was shown by Hase's feeding of mite dust to mice (see previous section). The occurrence of purely allergic responses is not so common as to account for the appearance of dermatitis in whole groups of people working with infested materials, e.g., copra workers, or of all the people in a neighborhood acquiring dermatitis from dust from a grain elevator (see p. 547). It is true, however, that contact with living mites is unnecessary; symptoms are produced as readily, if not more so, by rubbing infested material on the skin, by having dust from it blow on the skin, or even by breathing the dust.

Both dermal and respiratory symptoms occur. The skin develops a typical itching urticaria, sometimes with large hives, sometimes eczematous. Asthma is common, and other frequent symptoms are quickened pulse, general aches, fever, and sometimes nausea, vomiting, and diarrhea. It is obvious that these symptoms are by no means peculiar to mite infections but are frequently observed in severe arthropod infections of other kinds. Few arthropods except mites develop in sufficiently prodigious numbers in human habitations to produce symptoms by their dust; in almost all other cases — bedbugs, fleas, mosquitoes, ticks, etc. — the production of symptoms depends upon the inoculation of saliva at the time of biting.

Some of the well-known examples of dermatitis from mites are grocer's or baker's itch, known all over the world; " copra itch " in copra mills in Ceylon; " miller's itch," familiar in most grain-raising countries; " vanillism " in handlers of vanilla pods; " cottonseed itch "; " barley itch "; etc. The affliction is not confined to man, for horses sometimes get dermatitis when provided with mite-infested hay.

The Tyroglyphidae, which are most frequently involved, are small white or yellowish, soft-bodied mites. They have prominent pincerlike chelicerae which are entirely unsuited for piercing the skin. The two commonest genera are Tyroglyphus (Fig. 171), which has an elongate body with a suture separating the cephalothorax from the

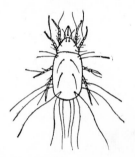 

Fig. 171.   Left, grain mite, *Tyrophagus putrescentiae* (= *Tyroglyphus longior*).   × 30. (After Fumouze and Robin.)   Right, Hypopus or traveling stage, ventral view.   Much enlarged.   (After Banks.)

abdomen and a few long simple hairs, and Glycyphagus, which is squattier and has a granular back, finely feathered hairs, and no suture separating the cephalothorax.

The life cycle of many species is remarkable in that, after reaching a nymphal stage in orthodox mite style, the mites change into a form called a hypopus (Fig. 171, *right*), which is a special adaptation for hitchhiking.   There are no mouthparts, the legs are short and stumpy, and there are ventral suckers on the abdomen.   In some species an encysted type of hypopus is produced to withstand desiccation.   Thus equipped for travel the mites attach themselves to insects or other objects and are transported to new localities.   They have frequently been mistaken for parasites, but they are no more parasitic than a man on horseback.   After dropping from their animated conveyances they moult into eight-legged nymphs, which after feeding become adults.

Infested substances are best burned or otherwise disposed of, and the containers, rooms, etc., then fumigated (see p. 492).   Carbon dioxide snow added to grain or feed in containers is often helpful in keeping down mites as well as mealworms and weevils.

Pediculoides ventricosus. This mite (Fig. 172) is a member of the family Tarsonematidae (see p. 500). The males and unencumbered females are only about 0.2 mm. long, barely visible to the naked eye. The pregnant females, however, retain their eggs and young in the abdomen until they are fully developed, the abdomen becoming a grotesquely enlarged brood sac, which may reach a diameter of 1.5 mm. The females retain their minute, slender form very briefly, for it may be only 6 days from brood to brood.

These mites are normally parasitic on grain-moth caterpillars and other insects in stubble, straw, stored grains, cottonseed, etc. In

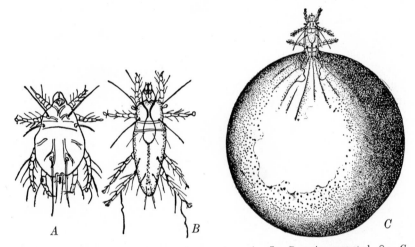

FIG. 172. *Pediculoides ventricosus*, louse mi . *A*, ♂; *B*, unimpregnated ♀; *C*, gravid ♀. Note clavate organs between first and second pairs of legs, characteristic of tarsonematid mites. (*A* and *B*, × 150, after Patton; *C*, × 75, after Brucker, from Webster.)

stored products the transformation and escape of their insect prey leave them with their normal food supply cut off, and the hungry mites then attack any flesh that comes their way. Serious infestations occur among grain thrashers, millers, etc., and sometimes new straw mattresses turn out to be veritable beds of fire.

An itching rash begins about 12 to 16 hours or sooner after exposure to the mites. The bites, at first red and inflamed, itch unbearably. Little blisters form and, when scratched and ruptured, develop into pustules or scabs; in bad attacks the usual constitutional symptoms of severe arthropod infestation develop — fever, rapid pulse, headache, nausea, etc. One case has been reported in which dust from a mite-infested grain elevator blew into the cottages in the neighborhood and produced dermatitis in all the inhabitants. Since the mites cannot thrive on human blood they soon withdraw, disillusioned, to try some other source of food, and consequently the symptoms usually subside within a week unless fresh detachments of mites are constantly being acquired.

The itching can be alleviated by alkaline baths or application of soda and soothing ointments. People exposed to infestation can get protection from bites by application of ointments or sulfur, followed by a change of clothes and a bath after exposure, but those who develop a dust dermatitis will get little relief from these measures.

Other Dermatitis-Producing Mites. A number of other mites may occasionally produce dermatitis. Brief mention should be made of members of the family Cheyletidae, belonging to the Sarcoptoidea, which are frequently found preying on truly parasitic mites in the fur or plumage of animals. One species, *Cheyletiella parasitivorax*, often found on rabbits and cats, occasionally attacks the mammalian host. This mite has been found responsible in a few cases of human eczema from handling cats.

Pentastomida: Tongue-worms and Their Allies

At one time this aberrant group of arthropods was classified with the Arachnida and was thought to be related to the mites, but it is now

Fig. 173. Left, head of *Armillifer armillatus*, × 3 (after Sambon). Right, head of nymph of *Linguatula serrata*, × 25. (After Faust.)

usually considered a separate class. The animals have become so modified by parasitic life that their affinity with the arthropods would be difficult to recognize if it were not for the form of the larvae, which are more or less mitelike and have either two or three pairs of legs. Even in life cycle they resemble parasitic worms in that they pass the immature stages in an intermediate host.

The adults have elongate bodies which are either flattened or cylindrical and divided into a series of unusually conspicuous rings which are not, however, true segments. There is no distinct division into head, thorax, or abdomen. On either side of the mouth at the anterior end there are two pairs of hollow, fanglike hooks, in some forms situated on fingerlike parapodia, which can be retracted into grooves like the claws of a cat (Fig. 173). These are believed to be vestiges of some of the appendages. At the bases of the retractile hooks there open a number of large glands, the secretion of which is believed to be hemolytic. The Pentastomida have a simple nervous system, a usually straight digestive tract, and a reproductive system. The anus is at the posterior end of the body. The females, which are larger than the males, have the genital opening either near the anterior or near the posterior end of the abdomen, but that of the males is anterior.

The life cycle involves two hosts. The adults usually live in the lungs or air passages of their hosts; the larvae live free or encysted in the viscera of some other host.

Classification. The classification of the Pentastomida according to Heymons and Vitzthum (1936) is as follows:

Order 1. **Cephalobaenida.** Hooks situated on fingerlike processes or at least swellings of the body behind mouth; genital opening anterior in both sexes. Fam. *Cephalobaenidae* in lungs of lizards and snakes; Fam. *Reighardiidae* in air sacs of gulls and terns.

Order 2. **Porocephalida.** Hooks not on prominences, arranged trapeze-like or in a curved line on either side of mouth; ♀ genital opening posterior.

Family 1. *Porocephalidae.* Body cylindrical. Adults in lungs of reptiles, young in great variety of vertebrates; young of the genus Armillifer usually in mammals, including man.

Family 2. *Linguatulidae.* Body flattened. Adults in nasal passages of dog and cat family, except one in crocodiles; young in all sorts of mammals, including man.

There is a single well-authenticated instance of human infection with an adult *Linguatula serrata* in the nasal passages, but visceral infection with immature stages of this species and of several species of Porocephalidae is surprisingly common.

Linguatula serrata. The adult worms are nearly colorless; the females are 100 to 130 mm. long with a maximum width of about 10 mm.; the males are only about 20 mm. long and 3 to 4 mm. wide. They occur in the nasal passages and frontal sinuses principally of dogs (Fig. 175) and occasionally other animals, where they suck blood. They sometimes cause severe catarrh, bleeding, and suppuration and may cause much sneezing and difficulty in breathing when they obstruct the nasal passages, but often they produce no symptoms at all.

The eggs (Fig. 174*B*), containing embryos with four rudimentary legs, are voided by the host with the catarrhal products of the respiratory system, the egg-laden mucus infecting water or vegetation. According to Hobmaier and Hobmaier (1940) eggs which are swal-

lowed hatch, and the larvae enter the body cavity but fail to develop
further in dogs or cats.   The eggs are resistant and live for a long time
outside the body.   When ingested by an intermediate host, e.g., sheep,

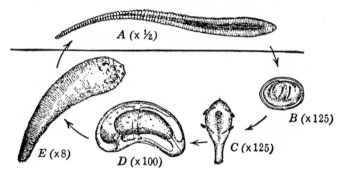

FIG. 174.   Life history of tongue-worm, *Linguatula serrata; A*, adult female from
nasal passage of dog; *B*, egg containing embryo; *C*, larva from sheep, man, or other
animals; *D*, encysted larva; *E*, second larval stage, from liver of sheep or man.   (*A* after
Neumann; *B*, *C*, and *D* after Leuckart; *E* after Railliet.)

rabbits, rats, man, etc., the embryos (Fig. 174*C*), 75 μ long, migrate
to the mesenteric ganglia and various other viscera and there become
encapsulated (Fig. 174*D*).   They moult twice and assume a pupalike
stage in which they are devoid of mouthparts, hooks, or segmentation,
and are 0.25 to 0.5 mm. long.   A number of other moults follow and

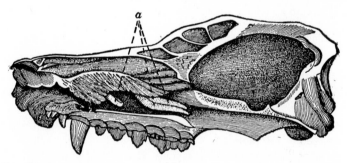

FIG. 175.   Head of a dog split in half to show three tongue-worms, *Linguatula serrata*,
(*a*) in the nasal cavity.   Reduced in size.   (After Colin, from Hall.)

after 5 or 6 months a nymphal stage is attained, in which the animal
possesses two pairs of hooks and has its body, 4 to 6 mm. in length,
divided into 80 to 90 rings, each bordered posteriorly by a row of closely
set spines (Fig. 173*B*).   These are shed when the nymph transforms
into an adult.   For a long time this nymph was looked upon as a distinct species.   The nymphs may remain alive in the intermediate host
for at least 2 to 3 years, but their capsules become thick so that they

are not easily liberated. This undoubtedly interferes with successful infection of a final host.

According to the Hobmaiers, contrary to the generally accepted belief, the nymphs do not leave their cysts during the life of the host but quickly liberate themselves after its death. Nor do swallowed nymphs succeed in migrating back to the pharynx from the stomach. To cause infection the nymphs must cling to the mucous membrane of the mouth before being swallowed or when vomited. The worms begin laying eggs about 6 months after infection and seem to live for about 2 years.

L. serrata is nowhere abundant, even in its normal hosts, though it has a wide geographic distribution; in some parts of Europe, however, adult parasites have been found in 10 per cent of dogs examined, and in some series of autopsies as high as 10 per cent of human beings have been found to harbor the nymphs. Usually they are dead and calcified and of no pathological importance. These infections are undoubtedly the result of too intimate contact with dogs. In the single human infection with the adult stage a frequent bleeding of the nose which had persisted for seven years ceased when an adult Linguatula was expelled in a violent fit of sneezing.

Armillifer. Man is frequently parasitized by the nymphs of at least two species of Armillifer, the adults of which live in the lungs of pythons and other snakes. The intermediate hosts include many kinds of mammals but particularly monkeys, which are important in the diet of pythons. Human infections with the encysted larvae of *A. armillatus* are common in Africa; Broden and Rodhain found 30 cases in 133 post-mortems of natives in Belgian Congo. Since some African natives esteem python for dinner, infection may result from handling them, as well as from contaminated water or vegetables. In the Oriental region this species is replaced by a closely related one, *A. moniliformis;* only a few human infections with this species have been seen — in Manila, Sumatra, and China.

These species of Armillifer have bright lemon-yellow cylindrical bodies, marked by braceletlike annulations which give then a screwlike appearance (Fig. 176*A*, *B*). The females are 90 to 130 mm. long, the males about 30 to 45 mm. In the intermediate hosts the nymphs (Fig. 177*D*) lie coiled up in cysts either embedded in or attached to the liver or other organs; they resemble miniatures of the adults. When ingested by pythons they are said to reach the lungs by burrowing through the stomach wall, but this may be incorrect, since both *Porocephalus crotali* and Linguatula reach the lungs via the throat and trachea (Penn, 1942). In the intermediate host development is

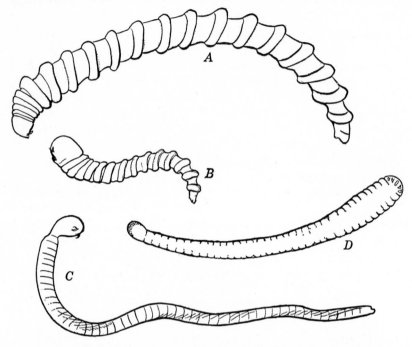

FIG. 176.   A, *Armillifer armillatus* ♀ ; B, same, ♂ ; C, *Kiricephalus coarctatus*, common in American colubrine snakes; D, *Porocephalus crotali*, in American rattlesnakes.   (A–C adapted from Sambon; D from Self and McMurray.)

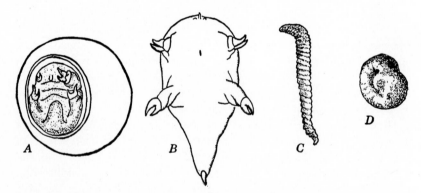

FIG. 177.   Stages in development of Porocephalids.   A, egg of Porocephalus with developed embryo, × 280; B, embryo of *Armillifer armillatus*, × about 500; C, nymph of Armillifer pressed out of cyst, × 3½; D, encysted nymph of same, × 3½.   (A and B after Sambon; C and D after Fülleborn.)

very slow, the nymphs requiring 1½ to 2 years to reach a length of 16 to 22 mm.

Two American cases of infection with porocephalid worms have been recorded. Since no American species of Armillifer are known, these worms may have been the young of *Porocephalus crotali* of rattlesnakes (Fig. 176*D*), or of *Kiricephalus coarctatus* of Colubridae (Fig. 176*C*). Both these genera although having annulated bodies lack the conspicuous rings of Armillifer. *P. crotali* nymphs are common in muskrats and other mammals.

Heavy experimental infections with immature worms produce injurious or even fatal effects, but there is no evidence that the light infections usually seen in man are pathogenic. One heavily loaded case reported by Cannon (1942) suffered from partial obstruction of the colon due to thickening of its parasite-studded walls. Since there are no characteristic symptoms, infections are recognized only at autopsies.

REFERENCES

AHLM, C. E., and LIPSHÜTZ, J., Tsutsugamushi Fever in the Southwest Pacific Theater, *J. Am. Med. Assoc.*, **124**, 1095 (1944).

BANKS, N., The Acarina of Mites, *U. S. Dept. Agr., Rep.*, **108**, 1915.

BUXTON, P. A., On the Sarcoptes of Man, *Parasitology*, **13**, 146 (1921).

CANNON, D. A., Linguatulid Infestation of Man, *Ann. Trop Med. Parasitol.*, **36**, 160 (1942).

DOVE, W. E., and SHELMIRE, B., Some Observations on Tropical Rat Mites and Endemic Typhus, *J. Parasitol.*, **18**, 159 (1932).

EWING, H. E., The Trombiculid Mites (Chigger Mites) and Their Relation to Disease, *J. Parasitol.*, **30**, 339–365 (1944).

FÜLLEBORN, F., Über die Entwicklung von Porozephalus und dessen pathogenen Bedeutung, *Arch. Schiffs-u. Tropen-Hyg.*, **23**, 1 (1919).

GMEINER, F., *Demodex folliculorum* des Menschen und der Tiere, *Arch. Dermatol. Syphilol.*, **92**, 25 (1908).

GREENBERG, M., PELLITTERI, O. J., and JELLISON, W. L., Rickettsialpox — A Newly Recognized Disease, III. Epidemiology, *Am. J. Publ. Health*, **37**, 860–868 (1947).

GRIFFITHS, J. T., A Scrub Typhus (Tsutsugamushi) Outbreak in Dutch New Guinea, *J. Parasitol.*, **31**, 341–350 (1945); A Further Account of Tsutsugamushi Fever at Sansapor, Dutch New Guinea, *J. Parasitol.*, **33**, 367–373 (1947).

HASE, A., Zur path.-parasit. und epid.-hyg. Bedeutung der Milben, insbesondere der Tyroglyphinae ———, *Z. Parasitenk.*, **1**, 765 (1929).

HEYMONS, R., and VITZTHUM, H. G., Beiträge zur Systematik der Pentastomiden, *Z. Parasitenk.*, **8**, 1 (1936).

HINMAN, E. H., and KAMPMEIER, R. H., Intestinal Acariasis Due to *Tyroglyphus longior* Gervais, *Am. J. Trop. Med.*, **14**, 355 (1934).

HIRST, S., *Species of Arachnida and Myriapoda Injurious to Man*, Brit. Mus., London, 1917.

The Genus Demodex Owen, Brit. Mus., 1919.

Mites Injurious to Domestic Animals, Brit. Mus., London, 1922.

HOBMAIER, A., and HOBMAIER, M., On the Life Cycle of *Linguatula rhinaria*, *Am. J. Trop. Med.*, **20**, 199 (1940).

JENKINS, D. W., Trombiculid Mites Affecting Man, I and II, *Am. J. Hyg.*, **48**, 22–44 (1948).

JOHNSON, C. G., and MELLANBY, K., The Parasitology of Human Scabies, *Parasitology*, **34**, 285 (1942).

KOHLS, G. M., Vectors of Rickettsial Diseases, *Ann. Internal Med.*, **26**, 713–719 (1947).

LOMBARDINI, G., Contributo alla conoscenza della morphologia dei Demodicidae. Chiave analitica de genere Demodex Owen, *Redia*, **28**, 89–102 (1942).

MACKIE, E. C., Parasitic Infection of the Urinary Tract, *Edinburgh Med. J.*, **33**, 708 (1926).

MELLANBY, K., *Scabies*, London, 1943.
The Development of Symptoms, Parasitic Infection and Immunity in Human Scabies, *Parasitology*, **35**, 197 (1944).

MICHENER, C. D., Observations on the Habits and Life History of a Chigger Mite, *Eutrombicula batatus*, *Ann. Entomol., Soc. Am.*, **49**, 101–118.

PENN, G. H., JR., The Life History of *Porocephalus crotali*, a Parasite of the Louisiana Muskrat, *J. Parasitol.*, **28**, 277 (1942).

PHILIP, C. B., Tsutsugamushi Disease (Scrub Typhus) in World War II, *J. Parasitol.*, **34**, 169–191 (1948).

ROGERS, G. K., Grain Itch, *J. Am. Med. Assoc.*, **123**, 887 (1943).

SLEPYAN, A. H., A Rapid Treatment for Scabies, *J. Am. Med. Assoc.*, **124**, 1127 (1944).

STILES, C. W., and HASSALL, A., Key Catalogue of the Crustacea and Arachnoids of Importance in Public Health, *Hyg. Lab. Bull.*, **148**, 197 (1927).

WHARTON, G. W., The Vectors of Tsutsugamushi Disease, *Proc. Entomol. Soc. Wash.*, **48**, 171–178 (1946).
Studies on North American Chiggers. 2. The Subfamilies, and *Womersia strandtmani* n.g., n.sp., *J. Parasitol.*, **33**, 380–384 (1947).

WILLIAMS, R. W., A Contribution to Our Knowledge of the Bionomics of the Common North American Chigger, *Eutrombicula alfreddugési* Oudemans, with a Description of a Rapid Collecting Method, *Am. J. Trop. Med.*, **26**, 243–250 (1946).

CHAPTER 22

Ticks

Although the ticks constitute only one of a dozen superfamilies of the order Acarina, they are popularly regarded as a quite distinct group because they are large and easy to recognize. They are not merely annoying pests but surpass all other arthropods in the number and variety of disease agents for which they are carriers. As carriers of human disease they rank next to mosquitoes, but as carriers of animal diseases they are pre-eminent.

General Anatomy. The body of a tick is covered by a leathery cuticle which is capable of great expansion in the females as they engorge themselves on their host's blood, filling the numerous complex pouches of the digestive tract. Unengorged ticks are flat, usually tapering to the anterior end (Fig. 181), but after engorgement they resemble beans or nuts (Fig. 182).

The cephalothorax is not marked off from the abdomen, but there is a small movable *capitulum* at the anterior end (Fig. 178). It is not a true head, although popularly so called; it consists of a *basis capituli* and the mouthparts. In the family Ixodidae the capitulum fits into a groove or *camerostome* at the anterior end of the body, whereas in the Argasidae it is ventral in position (Fig. 181).

The mouthparts consist of a *hypostome*, a pair of *palpi*, and a pair of mandibles or *chelicerae* (Figs. 178 and 179*I*). The hypostome is a prolongation of the ventral wall of the capitulum. It is a formidable piercing organ beset with row after row of recurved teeth (Fig. 179); these cause it to hold so firmly in the flesh into which it is inserted that forcible removal of the tick is liable to tear the body away from the capitulum, which remains embedded in the skin. The palpi are fairly rigid structures closely associated with the hypostome in most of the Ixodidae, but they are limber and leglike in the Argasidae (cf. Figs. 178, 179*I*).

In the Ixodidae there is a dorsal shield or *scutum;* this nearly covers the entire back in males, but in unengorged females it covers only about half the back or less, and in engorged ones becomes very inconspicuous. In the Argasidae there is no scutum, but the body is marked by numerous tubercles or little plaques. The spiracles are situated on characteristic stigmal plates located near the fourth coxae. The legs of all four pairs (three pairs in the larvae) are much alike and are terminated by a pair of claws on a stalk. The legs are long and

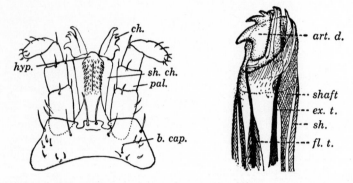

FIG. 178. Left, capitulum or "head" of argasid tick seen from ventral side; *ch.*, chelicera; *sh. ch.*, sheath of chelicera; *hyp.*, hypostome; *pal.*, palpus; *b. cap.*, basis capituli. (From Matheson.) Right, tip of chelicera; *art. d.*, articulated digit; *shaft*, shaft; *sh.*, sheath; *fl. t.*, tendon of flexor muscle; *ex. t.*, tendon of extensor muscle. (After Nuttall, Cooper, and Robinson.)

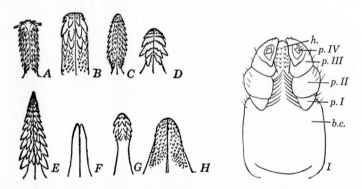

FIG. 179. *A–H*, hypostomes of various ticks; *A*, *Otobius mégnini*, nymph; *B*, *Argas persicus*, adult; *C*, *Ixodes ricinus*, female; *D*, same, male; *E*, *I. vespertilionis*, female; *F*, same, male; *G*, *Ornithodorus moubata*, nymph; *H*, *O. savigni*, adult. (*A* after Salmon and Stiles, others after Nuttall.) *I*, capitulum of Dermacentor, ventral view; *b.c.*, basis capituli; *h.*, hypostome; *p. I–IV*, articles I to IV of palpi; note small fourth article in pit on ventral side of third article; the chelicerae lie dorsal to hypostome, so do not show. (After Cooley.)

conspicuous when the body is empty but are hardly noticeable after engorgement. The genital pore and anus are on the ventral side, the former just behind the capitulum, and the anus some distance from the posterior end of the body (Fig. 181). The presence or absence and the arrangement of plates and grooves on the ventral side of the male body (Fig. 181) are of taxonomic value.

Habits and Life History. All ticks are parasitic during some part of their lives. The majority of them infest mammals, though many species attack birds and some are found on cold-blooded animals. A decided host preference is shown by some species, whereas others appear to be equally content with any warm-blooded animal that comes their way. In many species the hosts or parts of hosts selected by the adults are not the same as those selected by the immature forms.

FIG. 180. Texas fever tick, *Boöphilus annulatus*, laying eggs. (After Graybill.)

The life histories of all ticks are more or less similar. After several days of mating the female ticks engorge and soon drop to the ground and begin to lay their eggs (Fig. 180). These are deposited on or just under the surface of the ground. Some of the family Argasidae engorge several times, laying a batch of 20 to 50 eggs after each gluttonous repast. All the Ixodidae, on the other hand, lay their eggs after a single engorgement. The eggs number from a few hundred in some species to upwards of 10,000 in others and are laid in rather elongate masses in front of the female. The process of egg-laying by Ixodidae occupies several days.

The eggs develop after an incubation period which varies with the temperature from 2 or 3 weeks to several months. Eggs deposited in the fall do not hatch until the following spring. Newly hatched ticks are called larvae or " seed ticks " and are recognizable by having only six legs (Fig. 188*B*).

In the Ixodidae the seed ticks, soon after hatching, climb up on a blade of grass or bit of herbage and assume a policy of watchful waiting until some suitable host passes within reach. Seed ticks must be imbued with almost unlimited patience, since in many if not in the majority of cases long delays must fall to their lot before a suitable host comes their way, like a rescue ship to a stranded mariner. The jarring of a footstep or rustle of bushes causes the ticks instantly to stretch out to full length, feeling with their clawed front legs, eager with the excitemen of a life or death chance to be saved from starvation.

If success rewards their patience, even though it may be after many days or weeks, they feed for only a few days, becoming distended with blood and then dropping to the ground again. Retiring to a concealed place they rest for a week or more while they undergo internal reorganization. Finally they shed their skins and emerge as eight-legged but sexually immature ticks known as nymphs (Fig. 188*C*). The nymphs climb up on bushes or weeds and again there is a period of patient waiting, resulting either in starvation or a second period of feasting. Once more the ticks drop to the ground to rest, transform, and moult, this time becoming fully adult and sexually mature. In this condition a host is awaited for a third and last time, copulation takes place, sometimes even before a final host is reached, and the females begin their final gluttonous feeding which results in distending them out of all proportion. In some species, especially those that live on hosts which return to fixed lairs, copulation takes place away from the host. When this occurs, as it does in many species of Ixodes, the male is often not parasitic at all and may differ markedly from the female in the reduced structure of its hypostome (Fig. 179). In all species the males die shortly after copulation.

This, in general, is the life history of ixodid ticks, but it is subject to considerable variation in different species. In many species there are two nymphal periods instead of one. In some species, as in the cattle tick, *Boöphilus annulatus*, both moults take place directly on the host, thus doing away with the great risk of the tick's being unable to find a new host after each successive moult. In a few species the first moulting period is passed on the host, but the second is passed on the ground. According to the number of times ticks risk their future by leaving their hosts to moult and then seeking new hosts, they are called one-host, two-host, or three-host ticks. The majority of species have not yet discovered the advantage of moulting on the host. The most important asset of ticks to counterbalance the disadvantage of having to find new hosts is their extraordinary longevity. Larvae of ticks have been known to live more than 6 months without food, and adults have been kept alive in corked vials for 5 years.

The Argasidae differ in that they inhabit the nests or burrows of their hosts instead of the host itself. They usually drop off a host soon after a meal, which in different species takes from 10 minutes to several days, so they are seldom carried away from the abode of the host. This is in contrast to the Ixodidae, which inhabit the hosts rather than the homes and frequently remain attached for several days or even longer. Female Argasidae, except Otobius, lay batches of eggs at intervals of 2 to 4 months, the first laying beginning from a week to several months after mating and feeding. The eggs may number hundreds instead of thousands — a safe condition since the young argasids, reared in the home of the host, are in a much more advantageous position than the progeny of Ixodidae, which drop off and deposit their eggs anywhere in the wanderings of their host.

The Argasidae lead more regular and less precarious lives. Some species may feed several times between moults and may moult two to five times as nymphs. A few fail to feed in the larval stage at all, becoming nymphs about hatching time. Otobius does its last engorging as a second-stage nymph; the adults are not parasitic. The minimum time required to reach the adult stage varies from 3 to 12 months in different species. Adults may survive 5 to 11 years, including several years of starvation.

Classification. Both Argasidae and Ixodidae contain numerous disease transmitters and many others that are troublesome on account of the painfulness or subsequent effects of their bites. The family Argasidae contains four genera, Argas, Ornithodorus, Otobius, and Antricola, whereas in the Ixodidae there are about a dozen genera and about 400 species. The following table gives the principal distinguishing characters of the genera which are of interest as parasites of man or domestic animals. As will be seen, the important differentiating characters are the nature of the cuticle, presence or absence and number of anal plates in the male, details of the capitulum, and presence or absence of festoons and silvery ornamentation.

Argasidae. No dorsal shield; capitulum ventral.
1. Body oval and flattened, with sharply defined margins at sides; cuticle with small plaques (Figs. 181, 182, 186*B*) ....***Argas.***
2. Body usually somewhat pointed in front; no sharply defined margins at sides; cuticle warty (Figs. 184, 186*A*) ....***Ornithodorus.***
3. Same as *Ornithodorus* but body of nymphs spiny; adults not parasitic (Fig. 184, *6*) ....***Otobius.***

Ixodidae. Dorsal shield present; capitulum anterior; inhabits hosts, feeding once between moults.
1*a*. Anal groove in front of anus, horseshoe-like; scutum inornate; abdomen not festooned; no eyes; ♂ with many ventral plates (Fig. 183*C*); rostrum long, with club-shaped palpi (Fig. 183*D*) ....***Ixodes.***
1*b*. Anal grooves postanal if present ....2.
2*a*. Rostrum (mouthparts) longer than width of capitulum ....3.
2*b*. Rostrum shorter than width of capitulum ....4.
3*a*. Joints of palpi subequal; ♂ with adanal and a pair of accessory plates; festoons in young adults (Fig. 183*E*) ....***Hyalomma.***
3*b*. Second joints of palpi elongated; scutum ornate; abdomen festooned; ♂ without adanal plates (Fig. 183*F*, 190)..................***Amblyomma.***
4*a*. Anal grooves absent or very indistinct; no festoons; 2 pairs of ventral plates in ♂ (Fig. 183*A, B*) ....5.
4*b*. Anal grooves distinct (Fig. 181*A′*); festoons present ....6.
5*a*. Palpi with transverse ridges (Fig. 183*H*); first coxa forked (Fig. 183*B*) ....***Boöphilus.***
5*b*. Palpi without transverse ridges; first coxa not forked ....***Margaropus.***
6*a*. Ornate; no ventral plates in ♂; festoons present; first coxa deeply cleft (Fig. 202); basis capituli rectagonal (Fig. 183*J*); second joint of palpi much longer than third ....***Dermacentor.***

6*b*. Inornate ....7.

7*a*. Palpi conical, second joint flaring (Fig. 183*G*); basis capituli rectagonal; first coxa not deeply cleft; no ventral plates in ♂ ......*Haemaphysalis.*

7*b*. Palpi not conical, second and third joints of palpi about equal; basis capituli pointed at sides (Fig. 183*I*); first coxa deeply cleft; one well-developed pair of ventral plates in ♂ (Fig. 183*A*) ....*Rhipicephalus.*

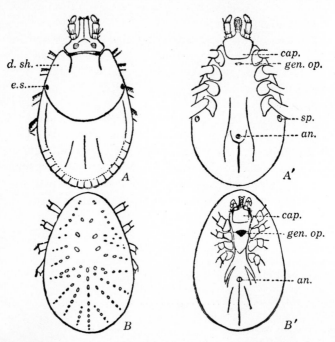

FIG. 181. Comparison of dorsal and ventral view of ixodid and argasid females; *A*, dorsal view of ixodid ♀; *A′*, ventral view of same; *B*, dorsal view of argasid ♀; *B′* ventral view of same; *an.*, anus; *cap.*, capitulum; *d. sh.*, dorsal shield; *e.s.*, eye spot; *gen. op.*, genital opening; *sp.*, spiracle.

FIG. 182. Argas (left) and Ornithodorus (right) as they appear when engorged. (After Brumpt.)

Important Species and Genera of Argasidae. In the family Argasidae the genus Argas is more common on birds than on mammals. Several species are important pests of poultry and transmit fowl relapsing fever and probably "range paralysis." All produce painful bites when human beings get in their way, and one, *A. mianensis* of Iran, sometimes lives and breeds in dirty human habitations.

The genus Otobius contains only two species, the ear tick, *O. mégnini*, found in southwestern United States and Mexico, and a rabbit tick

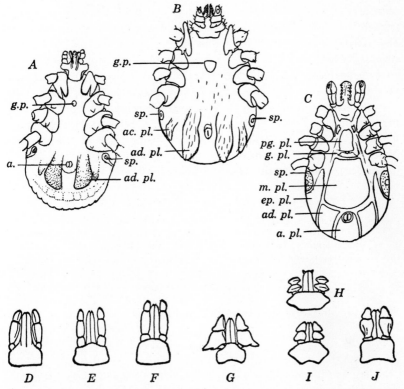

FIG. 183. *A*, *B*, and *C*, ventral views of male Rhipicephalus, Boöphilus, and Ixodes, respectively, to show ventral plates; *a.*, anus; *a. pl.*, anal plate; *ad. pl.*, adanal plate; *ac. pl.*, accessory plate; *ep. pl.*, epimeral plate; *g.p.*, genital pore; *g. pl.*, genital plate; *m. pl.*, medial plate; *pg. pl.*, pregenital plate; *sp.*, spiracle. *D* to *J*, capitula of various ixodid ticks; *D*, Ixodes; *E*, Hyalomma; *F*, Amblyomma; *G*, Haemaphysalis; *H*, Boöphilus; *I*, Rhipicephalus; *J*, Dermacentor.

in the northwest. *O. mégnini* has habits unlike other Argasid ticks in that the spiny nymphs often remain attached to the ears of horses and other domestic animals, and sometimes children, for months. The adults are not parasitic and do not feed.

The 46 members of the genus Ornithodorus attack mammals primarily, but only those associated with bats (11 of 25 species in the Americas) show marked host specificity. Some species, however, live almost entirely on rodents and other small mammals, whereas others commonly attack man and domestic animals; *O. moubata* habitually lives like the bedbug in human habitations, and a number of other species invade houses. The species occasionally found in houses in northern states is a bat tick, *O. kelleyi*.

Some species of Ornithodorus, e.g., *O. coriaceus* of California, cause painful and serious bites, but these ticks are particularly important as transmitters of relapsing fever (see p. 52). Ornithodorus ticks can also harbor a number of other diseases, e.g., spotted fever, tick-bite fever, Q fever, tularemia, and Russian encephalitis. Some species, e.g., *parkeri*, *nicollei*, and *rudis*, can transmit spotted fever by their bites, and different ones (*moubata* and *hermsi*) can transmit Q fever. The species of importance in connection with relapsing fever are discussed further under " Ticks and Relapsing Fever." Since these ticks are so important as potential transmitters of relapsing fever all over western North America, from Mexico to British Columbia, a key for the identification of important American species is given.

Key to Important American Species of Ornithodorus

1*a*. Two pairs of eyes present; first coxa distinctly separated from others (Fig. 184, *2*); large irregular depressed areas on back lacking tubercles; ♀ up to 9 mm. long; Southern California and Mexico ....*coriaceus.*

1*b*. No eyes; first coxa barely, if at all, separated from others; small disc-like or irregular areas without tubercles; length of ♀ from 5 to 7 mm. ....2.

2*a*. A pair of movable cheeks (Fig. 184, *3*) at sides of camerostome (*talaje* group) ....3.

2*b*. No movable cheeks (Fig. 184, *3*) at sides of camerostome ....4.

3*a*. Tubercles coarse; numerous irregular areas without tubercles (Fig. 184, *4*); no marked distal hump on tarsus 1; Mexico and Central and South America, sporadic all over U. S. ....*talaje.*

3*b*. Tubercles small; a few small disc-like areas without tubercles (Fig. 184, *5*); a distal hump on tarsus 1; Panama and northern South America; principal relapsing fever vector in those sections ....*rudis.*

4*a*. No cheeks; hood of capitulum projects beyond anterior end of body (Fig. 184, *1*) (*turicata* group) ....5.

4*b*. Cheeks are rounded nonmovable flaps at sides of camerostome; hypostome very small (145 μ long); tubercles very fine. High mountains west of Continental Divide, Arizona to Idaho, also in eastern Colorado; vector of relapsing fever ....*hermsi.*

5*a*. Tubercles in mid-dorsal region about 10 per linear mm.; hypostome over 600 μ long. Southwestern U. S. and Mexico north to Kansas, and Florida; vector of relapsing fever ....*turicata.*

5*b*. Tubercles in mid-dorsal region about 18 per linear mm.; hypostome 400 μ long or less; Wyoming and Washington; probably vector of relapsing fever ....*parkeri.*

Important Genera and Species of Ixodidae. Numerous species of the family Ixodidae occasionally attack man, but few habitually do so. Species belonging to a number of different genera are concerned with transmission of many important human and animal diseases and with the causation of tick paralysis. The important species involved in the various types of disease will be discussed under separate headings below.

Ixodes contains several important species. *I. ricinus*, the castor bean tick of Europe, transmits a piroplasmosis (*Babesia bovis*) of

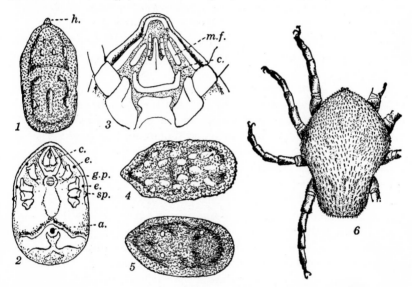

Fig. 184.   Details of species of Ornithodorus and Otobius to illustrate key.   *1*, dorsal view of *Ornithodorus turicata* (*h.*, hood);   *2*, ventral view of *O. coriaceus* (*a.*, anus;   *c.*, camerostome;   *e.*, eyes;   *g.p.*, genital pore;   *sp.*, spiracle);   *3*, camerostome of *O. talaje* (*c.*, camerostome;   *m.f.*, movable flap);   *4*, dorsal view of *O. talaje*;   *5*, dorsal view of *O. rudis*;   *6*, spiny nymph of *Otobius mégnini*, × 10 (*6* after Marx, from Banks.)

cattle in Europe and a virus disease of sheep, louping ill, in Great Britain. *I. persulcatus* is the principal transmitter of "spring-summer" encephalitis in Russia. *I. holocyclus* of Australia transmits a form of tick typhus in Queensland and also carries Q fever from bandicoots to cattle, making it accessible to man. Several species may cause tick paralysis (see p. 536). Several species occur in the United States, annoying dogs and occasionally man.

Amblyomma is a large genus of world-wide distribution. It is of great importance in the Americas in connection with the transmission of spotted fever and possibly other rickettsial diseases. *A. cajennense*, a common pest of domestic animals and man throughout tropical America, is the main transmitter of spotted fever in Brazil and Colombia. The lone-star tick, *A. americanum,* so called because of the single white spot on the scutum of the female (Fig. 190), is a transmitter of spotted fever in Texas and Oklahoma, where it is the commonest tick attacking man. It has also been found infected with Bullis fever. *A. maculatum,* the Gulf Coast tick, with fine silvery markings on the scutum, commonly attacks the ears of cattle as an adult; the immature stages have been found on meadow larks. Its bites often lead to screwworm infection; 50,000 cases were reported in 1935. This species has also been found to harbor a Rickettsia similar if not identical to that of boutonneuse fever in Europe. The closely related tick-bite fever of South Africa may also be transmitted by an Amblyomma, *A. hebraeum.*

Hyalomma contains several important Old World species. *H. aegyptium* causes bad wounds on the genitals and feet of domestic animals and carries a rickettsial disease similar to South African tick-bite fever. *H. savigni* has been found to harbor *Rickettsia burneti* of Q fever in Morocco. Various members of this genus are important vectors of Theileria infections (see p. 548) in cattle, sheep, camels, and horses in Africa and Asia.

Haemaphysalis contains a rabbit tick, *H. leporis-palustris,* that transmits spotted fever and tularemia among reservoir hosts in America (see p. 543), and another, *H. humerosa,* that transmits Q fever among bandicoots in Australia. *H. leachi* is a transmitter of tick-bite fever of man and piroplasmosis of dogs in South Africa. *H. concinna* is reported as a vector of tick typhus in the Soviet Far East.

Rhipicephalus contains several important transmitters of piroplasmosis in the Old World, particularly *R. bursa* among large domestic animals and *R. sanguineus* among dogs. The latter species, which has been imported and is becoming common in our southern states, is the principal carrier of boutonneuse fever in Europe and Africa. It harbors a mild rickettsial disease in Texas and has been found naturally infected with spotted fever in Mexico. It is also the carrier of canine piroplasmosis (see p. 548).

Böophilus, unlike most of the previously mentioned species, contains one-host ticks attacking cattle and other ruminants; they are the transmitters of *Babesia bigemina,* the cause of Texas fever. *B. annulatus* has been almost exterminated in the United States, except in a few places in Florida and along the Rio Grande, where it survives on deer. The closely related genus *Margaropus* contains the Argentine horse tick.

Dermacentor contains species of prime importance to man in the United States. *D. andersoni* and *D. variabilis* are important transmitters of spotted fever. *D. andersoni* has been referred to as a " veritable Pandora's box " of disease-producing agents, among which besides spotted fever are anaplasmosis, tularemia, brucellosis, *Salmonella enteritidis*, a bacterial " moose disease," Q fever, Colorado tick fever, and several forms of virus encephalomyelitis. Many of these can be transmitted by *D. variabilis* also, and both species can cause tick paralysis (see p. 536). *D. sylviarum* of Siberia transmits a rickettsial disease and a virus encephalitis.

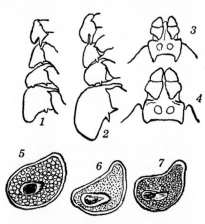

Fig. 185. Details of species of Dermacentor to illustrate key. *1*, coxae of *D. parumapterus;* *2*, coxae of *D. andersoni;* *3*, capitulum of *D. andersoni;* *5*, spiracular plate of *D. albipictus;* *6*, spiracular plate of *D. variabilis;* *7*, spiracular plate of *D. occidentalis.* (After Cooley.)

The species are largely confined to North America, Europe, and Asia. They are ornamented with silvery markings, abdominal festoons, well-developed eyes, and oval or comma-shaped spiracular plates. Several species (*andersoni, variabilis, occidentalis*) in their larval and nymphal stages attack rabbits and rodents, and in their adult stages attack rabbits and larger mammals, but *albipictus* is a one-host tick of large mammals. Following is a key to the North American adults according to Cooley (1938):

Key to Important Species of Dermacentor in North America

1*a*. Spurs on coxa I widely divergent (Fig. 185, *1*); southwestern U. S., mainly on rabbits; a possible transmitter of spotted fever among rabbits.. *parumapterus.*

1*b*. Spurs on coxa I with proximal edges parallel or a little divergent (Fig. 185, *2*) ....2.

2*a*. Spiracular plate oval, without dorsal prolongation and with goblets (bead-like structures under spiracular plate) few and large (Fig. 185, *5*); widely distributed in N. A., a one-host tick, mainly on deer, etc.; probably not concerned with spotted fever, though an experimental vector .....*albipictus.*

2*b*. Spiracular plate oval, with dorsal prolongation (Fig. 185, *6, 7*), and with goblets many or of moderate numbers ....3.

3*a*. Caudal projections from postero-lateral angles of dorsal side of basis capituli (cornua) long (Fig. 185, *3*); west coast, southern Oregon; larvae on rodents, adults on horse, deer, sheep, cow, dog, and man; a known carrier of tularemia and a suspected one of spotted fever ....*occidentalis.*

3b. Cornua short or of moderate length (Fig. 185, *4*) ....4.
4a. Spiracular plate with goblets very numerous and small (Fig. 185, *6*);
    eastern N. A., west to eastern Montana and central Texas, also western
    California; larvae on rodents, adults on many large animals but principally
    dogs; a transmitter of spotted fever and tularemia, experimental vector of
    anaplasmosis ....*variabilis.*
4b. Spiracular plate with goblets moderate in size and number (Fig. 185, *7*);
    northwestern N. A., south to northern New Mexico and Arizona, west to
    Sierras and Cascades, east to western Dakotas and western Nebraska, scat-
    tered records on west coast; larvae on small rodents, adults on all sorts of
    large mammals; vector of Rocky Mountain spotted fever and other
    diseases (see p. 543) ....*andersoni.*

Tick Bites.   The wounds made by ticks, especially if the capitulum
is torn off in a forcible removal, are very likely to become infected
and result in inflamed sores or extensive ulcers, not infrequently ending
in blood poisoning.   Some species seem more prone to do this than
others.   The writer was once nearly " done in " by the bite of a tick
in California, probably *Dermacentor occidentalis,* which has a bad
reputation.

Ticks may also be the cause of a serious or even fatal anemia when
present in large numbers.   Such anemias have been observed in horses,
moose, sheep, and rabbits.   Jellison and Kohls in **1938** found that 60
to 80 or more female *D. andersoni* feeding on rabbits would kill them
in 5 to 7 days.   According to Schuhardt in 1940, rats exposed to
Ornithodorus turicata in his " ticktorium " die after 3 hours' exposure.
Development of immunity to tick bites is discussed on p. 488.

Ticks can usually be removed successfully by gentle pulling, although
sometimes the mouthparts of species of Ixodes and Amblyomma, which
have long hypostomes with ugly barbs, may break off in the flesh.   If
the tick is *jerked* off, the whole capitulum may tear off.   A drop of
kerosene or a greasing with lard or vaseline to close up the spiracles
will cause a tick to loosen its hold in the course of a few minutes.
Application of a disinfectant should follow immediately.   Ticks can
be removed from ears by dropping a bland oil into them; pine tar oil
is used for ticks in the ears of animals.   Repellents and acaricides for
ticks are discussed on p. 550.

Tick Paralysis.   More serious than the painful wounds made by
ticks is a peculiar paralyzing effect of tick bites, known as tick paralysis.   This effect is produced only by rapidly engorging female ticks,
especially when attached on the back of the neck or at the base of the
skull.   There is no evidence of any infective organism being involved.
The cause of the paralysis is still obscure, but several investigators
have obtained evidence that the eggs of ticks contain a highly toxic

substance or that such a substance is formed during their development; it evidently makes its way to the salivary glands, since it is transmitted by the bites. Not all ticks produce the effect, but it is not limited to any one genus, nor does it extend to all the members of any one genus. In North America, *Dermacentor andersoni* and *D. variabilis* are responsible; in Australia, *Ixodes holocyclus;* in Crete, *Ixodes ricinus* and *Haemaphysalis punctata* (suspected); and in South Africa, *Ixodes pilosus*. *Rhipicephalus sanguineus* in Yugoslavia was found to contain the toxin. In one case in British Columbia *Haemaphysalis cinnabarina* was incriminated.

Since the paralysis is not invariably produced even by ticks situated at the base of the neck, it is possible that the bite must pierce or come in contact with a nerve or nerve ending. The paralysis usually begins in the legs and may result in complete loss of their use; it gradually ascends during the course of 2 or 3 days, affecting the arms and finally the thorax and throat. Unless the heart and respiration are affected, recovery follows in 1 to 6 or 8 days after removal of the engorging female ticks, even though other ticks remain. If the engorging ticks are not removed, the affection may result in death from failure of respiration or in spontaneous recovery after a few days or a week. The disease as observed in Australia differs from the North American type in that improvement is less immediate after removal of the offending tick.

Tick paralysis of man and animals, particularly cattle, sheep, dogs, and cats, is most frequent in northwestern United States and British Columbia, and in Australia, but has been reported from Crete and Yugoslavia in Europe and Somaliland in Africa. In South Africa sheep are paralyzed by *Ixodes pilosus*, but human cases are doubtful. It is by no means certain that all cases reported in animals are true tick paralysis, since symptoms that might be confused may be caused by tick-borne infections — Babesiidae, Anaplasma, rickettsias, viruses, or bacteria. A "moose disease" in northern Minnesota and Ontario suspected of being tick paralysis was seemingly due to a paralysis-causing bacillus, *Klebsiella paralytica*, harbored by the tick, *Dermacentor albipictus* (see Wallace, Cahn, and Thomas, 1933). Most human cases are in children and are most frequent in girls, whose long hair conceals attached ticks. Some of the cases are fatal.

Ticks and Disease

Ticks play an extremely important role as transmitters of disease to domestic animals and, fortunately to a somewhat less extent, to man. They are of outstanding importance in the transmission of organisms

of five principal types: (1) spirochetes of relapsing fever, (2) rickettsias of spotted fever and related diseases of man and animals, (3) Babesiidae and Anaplasma, causing many diseases of prime importance
to domestic animals, (4) *Pasteurella tularensis*, the bacterium of
tularemia, and (5) filtrable viruses of several types, including some
causing encephalomyelitis. The special relation of ticks to the diseases
caused by these five types of disease agents is considered in separate
sections below. *Rhipicephalus sanguineus* and probably others are
intermediate hosts for *Hepatozoon canis* (see p. 218), causing infection
when swallowed. *Dermacentor andersoni* and *Ornithodorus turicata*
have been found to harbor and transmit a bacillus, *Salmonella enteritidis*, which causes a paratyphoidlike disease in rodents and sometimes
gives trouble in experiments.

In addition to the species which serve as transmitters, others may
function as conservators, harboring the disease agents for long periods
of time, perhaps for life, without normally transmitting them. Certain
species of Ornithodorus, for instance, are conservators of rickettsias,
Trypanosoma cruzi, and *Pasteurella tularensis*.

Ticks and Relapsing Fever

Various species of Ornithodorus transmit relapsing fever to man and
among reservoir hosts in many parts of the world, including central
and north Africa, western Asia, Spain, Central and South America,
and the western half of the United States and Canada, where outbreaks have been recorded from Texas to British Columbia and from
Kansas to California. In all the proved cases of transmission of
mammalian relapsing fever by ticks, species of Ornithodorus have been
involved, but species of Argas (Fig. 186*B*) are the usual transmitters of
relapsing fever of fowls. In Iran the " miana bug," *A. mianensis*, is a
suspected vector of the human disease, and *Rhipicephalus sanguineus*
transmits *Borrelia theileri* among cattle, sheep, etc.

The spirochetes in various parts of the world and in different hosts
and vectors resemble each other very closely morphologically, but they
differ in immunological reactions. A discussion of relapsing fever and
of the relation of the spirochetes to ticks can be found in Chapter 4,
pp. 52–57.

Species Involved. *Ornithodorus moubata* of central Africa (Fig.
186*A*) is the only species of its genus which has become an uncondi-
tional human parasite, normally residing in human habitations.
O. savignyi of Ethiopia and southwest Asia seems to be dallying with
the idea of becoming domestic, for in addition to frequenting cattle,
pigpens, stables, etc., it sometimes overruns native bazaars and oc-

casionally houses, though this is not yet an established habit. It is only within the range of these two species that relapsing fever can be considered *primarily* a human disease.

O. rudis (Fig. 184, *5*) readily enters human habitations with rats in Panama and northern South America and is undoubtedly responsible for most of the relapsing fever in this area. *O. talaje* (Fig. 184, *3*), often confused with *O. rudis,* enjoys the blood of rats and pigs but shows a definite aversion to that of man, so if it enters houses it seldom makes its presence known. In California *O. hermsi* inhabits the nests

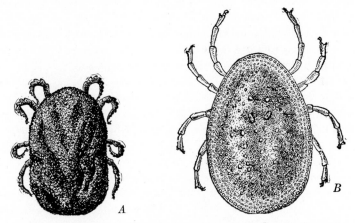

FIG. 186.   *A, Ornithodorus moubata,* × 3;   *B,* fowl tick, *Argas persicus,* × 5.
(After Braun.)

of chipmunks. The chipmunks move into mountain cabins in the Sierras during the winter and share their spirochete-infested ticks with vacationers in the summer.

With the exception of these instances in which the ticks invade human residences and there transmit their spirochetes, human relapsing fever results from intrusion upon the natural habitats of the ticks — in pigpens, caves, burrows, etc. It is possible that *all* species of Ornithodorus are capable of transmitting spirochetes, but some of the strains of the spirochetes may not be pathogenic for man. The important transmitters of sporadic human relapsing fever are as follows: North Africa and Spain, *O. erraticus;* western Asia, *O. tholozani* and *Argas mianensis;* south central United States and Mexican plateau, *O. turicata* (Fig. 184, *1*); California and other far western states, *O. hermsi;* and in the Northwest, *O. parkeri.* Apparently *O. coriaceus* (Fig. 184, *2*) of Southern California and Mexico is not a transmitter. A key to the important American species of Ornithodorous is given on p. 532.

Habits. The habits and life cycles of the various species of Ornithodorus differ only in details. The ticks are oval or elongated, usually somewhat pointed anteriorly, and have the leathery, mud-colored body covered with little shiny tubercles. They do not thrive in places where moisture is excessive but can stand a surprising amount of desiccation, whence their frequency in dry, dusty regions.

In the case of *O. moubata* and *O. savignyi* the larvae moult and become nymphs almost immediately after hatching, or even sooner, before partaking of their first meal. This is not true of the American species, however, which start looking for a place to drill almost at once. In some species, e.g., *talaje,* the larvae remain attached to a host for several days, but in others, e.g., *turicata,* they stay on only from 10 minutes to a few hours; this is always true with the nymphs and adults, which can become distended like berries in this time. The nymphs feed and moult a number of times, and the adults feed repeatedly between the laying of batches of eggs. During and just after feeding some species exude fluid from a pair of coxal glands opening just behind the first coxae, enough to bathe the ventral surface of the tick. Relapsing fever spirochetes are transmitted either by the coxal fluid or directly by the bite.

O. moubata lives in floors, crevices, thatch, etc., of native huts and rest houses along routes of travel, after the manner of bedbugs, and is sometimes a great pest. It is dispersed in bedding carried by caravans. *O. savignyi,* as already noted, is less of an indoor tick. *O. erraticus* is particularly associated with pigs and is common in the burrows of porcupines, which are probably its natural hosts.

In the Americas the habits of *O. rudis* and *O. hermsi* have already been mentioned. *O. parkeri* is abundant in burrows of ground squirrels and prairie dogs. *O. turicata* is a very indiscriminate feeder, taking its blood where it finds it; in Mexico it attacks pigs, in Kansas it has been found in burrows of rodents and sand holes of terrapins, and in Texas it haunts caves where it promptly transmits relapsing fever to anyone venturing into them. Since these ticks can live at least 7 years with food and 5 years without it and can pass the spirochetes to their offspring generation after generation, it is little wonder that spirochete infections are common among tick-bitten animals.

Control. Control methods vary with the species of Ornithodorus to be dealt with. *O. moubata* must be controlled as are bedbugs — by scrupulous cleanliness, elimination of hiding places, fumigation, or spraying with benzene hexachloride. *O. savignyi* usually conceals itself to a depth of an inch in dusty soil of camp sites, cattle stalls, etc., and can be reduced by harrowing the surface of the ground, strewing dry grass and brush over it, and burning it.   Locally, dusting with benzene hexachloride is effective.   Control of *O. rudis* may involve rat elimination, whereas getting rid of *O. hermsi* demands inhospitality to chipmunks.   The other species may need to be attacked in animal pens or shelters by the liberal use of turpentine, creosote, or benzene hexachloride, but in their natural wild habitats they need only to be left alone.

Ticks and Spotted Fever and Other Rickettsial Diseases

General Considerations.   Tick-borne rickettsial diseases (see p. 228), or tick typhus, as Megaw calls them collectively, occur in many parts of both the Old and New World.   A number of different strains, or species according to some, are recognized by their immunological reactions and sometimes by their pathogenicity.   Unlike the rickettsias of true typhus, the tick-borne varieties invade the nuclei as well as cytoplasm of the cells and so are sometimes placed in a separate genus, Dermacentroxenus.

In the ticks the organisms invade the entire body and are transovarially transmitted.   It is open to question whether a vertebrate reservoir host is actually needed, but epidemiological evidence suggests that it is.   Jellison in 1946 pointed out that the distribution of spotted fever in northwestern United States corresponds remarkably closely with the distribution of one species of cottontail rabbit, *Sylvilagus nuttalli*.   The distribution of *Dermacentor andersoni*, the only transmitter to man in the Northwest, also coincides with that of this rabbit; some other species of Dermacentor in North America, e.g., *D. variabilis* and *D. occidentalis*, have distributions corresponding with those of particular species of cottontails.   Jellison further pointed out that cottontails also occur in parts of Mexico, Colombia, and Brazil where spotted fever is endemic.   Since cottontails are the only animals that Dermacentor favors as a host in all its stages, suspicion attaches to them as reservoir hosts of spotted fever.   Yet it is a curious fact that, in spite of the readiness with which spotted fever can be inoculated into rodents, the rickettsia has not yet been isolated from any wild rodent.

In the Old World dogs have been found to serve as reservoirs for *Rickettsia conori* of boutonneuse fever, and it is possible that they may be reservoir hosts for spotted fever also.   Ground squirrels and gerbilles are also susceptible to *R. conori*.

Types of Tick-Borne Rickettsial Diseases.   The principal forms of tick-borne rickettsial disease are: (1) spotted fever in North and South America; (2) boutonneuse fever around the Mediterranean and probably the same disease in Kenya; (3) tick-bite fever in South Africa, possibly identical with boutonneuse fever; and sporadic cases of "tick typhus" of uncertain affinities in India, Malaya, eastern Siberia, and northern Australia. All these diseases are characterized by a severe rash or blotching of the skin, including face, palms, and soles; headache; body pains; fever; and a positive OX19 and OX2 Weil-Felix reaction (see p. 228). In the Old World forms there is usually a buttonlike black ulcer (eschar) at the site of the infective bite, hence the name boutonneuse, French for buttonlike. No entirely reliable treatment for rickettsial disease was available until 1948, when two antibiotics were found to be effective (see p. 229). *P*-aminobenzoic acid (PABA) has a very beneficial effect by inhibiting the growth of the organisms; experimentally treated animals that recover still harbor the organism and develop immunity.

A high degree of protection against spotted fever, as against other rickettsial diseases, is obtained by vaccination with killed rickettsia grown in the yolk sac of chick embryos as shown by Cox in 1938. Vaccines for some rickettsial diseases can also be prepared from the lungs of animals inoculated intranasally, but the Cox vaccine is still standard in the United States.

In addition to typhus-like tick-borne diseases there are two rickettsial infections of somewhat different nature that are transmitted by ticks — Bullis fever in Texas, and Q fever, which is probably cosmopolitan.

Spotted Fever and Its Vectors. This disease has long been known as a common and dangerous infection in the Rocky Mountain region of northwestern United States and Canada, especially Montana and Idaho. Since 1930 sporadic cases have become increasingly frequent in other parts of the United States, particularly on the middle Atlantic coast. The same disease, immunologically indistinguishable, occurs in parts of northern Mexico (where it is called "pinto fever"), in parts of Colombia, and in the São Paulo region of Brazil.

The disease is transmitted by the bites of ticks, but it takes about 2 hours of attachment before transmission is successful. The only tick known to be involved in transmission to man in the northwest is *Dermacentor andersoni*. In the eastern and southern states it is *D. variabilis;* in Texas and Oklahoma, *Amblyomma americanum;* in South America, *A. cajennense* and *A. striatum*. In Mexico the usual transmitter is not known with certainty, but strains of *R. rickettsi* have been isolated from *Rhipicephalus sanguineus* both in Texas and Mexico, and the Mexican *Ornithodorus nicollei* is a capable vector experimentally. In the northwest *O. parkeri* is an experimental vector, and a few cases of the disease have been found within the domain of *Dermacentor occidentalis* on the west coast.

The rabbit tick, *Haemaphysalis leporis-palustris*, although it never bites man, is a factor in keeping the disease alive among its reservoir hosts. The virus carried by the rabbit tick, as recovered in nature, is very mild in form as compared with the virulent strains obtained from *D. andersoni* and *D. variabilis;* when these species become numerous in a locality and begin transmitting the disease to other kinds of rodents and to man, virulent strains appear. It is not known whether the stepping-up of virulence is due to passage of the Rickettsia through

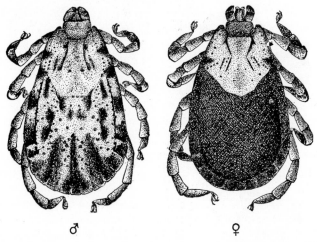

FIG. 187. Spotted fever tick, *Dermacentor andersoni*, male (♂) and female (♀). × 12.

other animals than rabbits or to development in Dermacentor instead of Haemaphysalis. Another species which may be an important transmitter among rabbits is *D. parumapterus*.

Dermacentor andersoni and other Dermacentors. *D. andersoni* (Fig. 187) is pre-eminent as a transmitter of spotted fever because during its immature stages it is a parasite of rodents, but as an adult it attacks a great variety of larger animals, willingly including man. It is a handsome reddish-brown tick, with the large dorsal shield of the male and the smaller one of the female conspicuously marked with silver. The six-legged larvae (Fig. 188*B*), of which there are about 5000 in a brood, attach themselves to rabbits or rodents, especially squirrels of various kinds. Usually the larvae, and the nymphs also, attach themselves about the head and ears of their host. After a few days the larvae drop, transform into nymphs (Fig. 188*C*), and again attack their rodent or rabbit hosts.

After dropping off these and transforming into adults they no longer pay attention to the smaller rodents but seek larger animals, especially

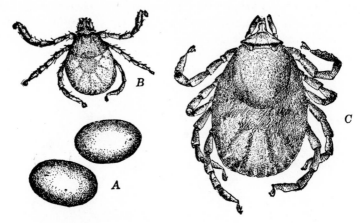

. 188.   Development of spotted fever tick, *Dermacentor andersoni;* *A*, eggs; *B*, larva; *C*, nymph.   × 30.

preferring horses and cattle, though they readily attack other wild and domestic animals and man.   Unlike most ticks, this species may take

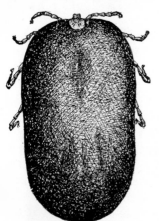

FIG. 189.   Spotted fever tick, *Dermacentor andersoni;* engorged female.   × 4.

2 or even 2½ years to complete its life cycle.   The winter is passed in either the nymphal or adult stage.

D. variabilis and *D. occidentalis* have similar life cycles.   *D. variabilis* seems to have a strong preference for meadow mice and white-footed mice in its immature stages and for dogs in the adult stage, but *D. occidentalis* has the same wide range of hosts as *D. andersoni* in both immature and adult stages.   A key for the differentiation of the important North American Dermacentors, with geographic distributions, is given on pp. 535–536.

Amblyomma americanum and A. cajennense.   *A. americanum,* the lone-star tick (Fig. 190), has a wide distribution in south central United States and is the commonest tick attacking man in Texas and Oklahoma; it is also abundant on deer, sheep, cattle, dogs, and rodents.   According to Parker, Kohls, and Steinhaus (1943) the

fact that this tick bites man in all its stages and that its nymphs sometimes occur in immense concentrations within small areas may account
for the multiple family infections occurring where it is the suspected
transmitter.

   A. cajennense is a common and widespread tick from the southern-
most tips of the United States to Argentina.   It can transmit spotted
fever experimentally, and the epi-
demiology suggests it as the principal transmitter in Brazil and
Colombia. Its preferred adult host
seems to be the horse, but men and
dogs are readily attacked.

   **Other Typhus-like Tick-borne
Infections.** Milder typhus-like diseases such as boutonneuse fever
around the Mediterranean, tick-bite
fever in South Africa, and tropical
typhus in Kenya are also carried
by ticks. These diseases are not
serologically identical to spotted
fever, though closely related. They
differ in that they cause the development of a little ulcer at the site of
the tick bite.

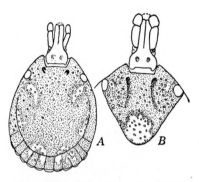

FIG. 190.   *Ambylomma americanum,*
lone-star tick.   *A*, male; *B*, dorsal shield
and capitulum of female.   (Adapted from
Cooley and Kohls.)

   The principal vector in the Mediterranean region and Kenya is the
brown dog tick, *Rhipicephalus sanguineus,* a species now distributed
all over the world and common in southern United States.   As noted
on p. 534, it has been found to harbor a relatively mild rickettsial
disease in Texas possibly identical with these Old World infections, and
it is susceptible to infection with spotted fever.   Dogs show no evidence
of rickettsial infections except a positive Weil-Felix reaction.
Rickettsial disease agents have been isolated by Anigstein and Bader
from *Amblyomma americanum* and *A. maculatum* collected from
cattle; those from *americanum* are virulent, those from *maculatum*
mild. The latter were previously isolated by Parker, Kohls, Cox,
and Davis in 1939 and called " maculatum fever."   The interrelations
of these various rickettsial infections are still very obscure, and much
is still to be learned about the extent to which they are modified by
passage through different vectors or development in relatively unsusceptible hosts such as dogs, pigs, and cattle.

   The principal vectors of tick-bite fever in South Africa are *Haemaphysalis leachi* and *A. hebraeum.* The latter also transmits " heart-
water " fever of ruminants, caused by *Rickettsia ruminantium.*   In

India and Malaya the vector of " tick typhus " is not definitely known; in eastern Siberia it is *Dermacentor sylviarum;* and in northern Queensland, *Ixodes holocyclus.*

Q Fever. This rickettsial disease, caused by *R. burneti,* an atypical rickettsia in that it passes certain filters, was first discovered in Australia, where it is transmitted among bandicoots by *Haemaphysalis humerosa* and from these animals to cattle and possibly occasionally to man by *Ixodes holocyclus.* Later an infection which proved to be identical was found in *Dermacentor andersoni* in Montana and Wyoming, *Amblyomma americanum* in Texas, and in several other ticks in the United States. The organism found in America was at first thought to be distinct and was named *R. diaporica.* During World War II the disease was observed in Panama, Italy, Greece, and North Africa, and is probably cosmopolitan. It is an influenza-like disease without a rash, causing fever, chest pains, and cough; in Europe it was called Balkan grippe or atypical pneumonia. Cattle and horses acquire light or inapparent infections, as do dogs and cats, but sheep and goats develop respiratory symptoms similar to those in man. In Greece natural infection in the latter animals was demonstrated by inoculation of milk into guinea pigs.

Unlike the typhus-like diseases, Q fever is not primarily dependent upon ticks for transmission to man; in fact, very few human cases have resulted from tick bites. Human outbreaks usually occur among stock handlers and people working in slaughterhouses and dairies. It spreads with remarkable facility among laboratory workers, apparently acquired by inhalation of droplets during preparation of rickettsial vaccines or possibly with dust. Handling of carcasses is dangerous, and it is suspected that the organisms can be inhaled with dust in stock pens and dairy barns. In an outbreak of 60 cases among stockyard and slaughterhouse workers in Texas in 1946 there was no evidence of tick transmission. Caminopetros in Greece considers milk the principal source of animal and human infection. The Rickettsia has been recovered from a number of dairies in southern California where human cases had been recognized. Raw milk was probably the cause of the outbreaks in Allied troops in Italy and Greece, where the method of transmission was not determined, although the disease was associated with barns and farm animals. In spite of its pneumonia-like character there is no evidence of its direct spread from person to person.

Bullis Fever. A previously unknown rickettsial disease first appeared in a few cases at Camp Bullis, Texas, in 1941 and seems now to be permanently established in central Texas. Rickettsias were isolated from cases and also from a naturally infected *Amblyomma americanum* by Anigstein and Bader. The Rickettsia involved is said not to be related to that of either Q fever or spotted fever. There are very few small rodents in the Bullis fever area; the principal hosts of *A. americanum* are deer, sheep, and goats.

Tularemia and Other Bacterial Diseases

Tularemia or rabbit fever is another disease of rabbits and rodents transmissible to man; human cases have been reported throughout the United States, Canada, and Alaska, and from Scandinavia to Japan in the Old World. The disease is characterized by a local ulcer at the site of inoculation, with enlarged and painful lymph glands in the vicinity and such generalized symptoms as fever, prostration, general aches, and localized pains. The fever lasts for several weeks, usually with an intermission between the third and sixth days. The disease rarely is fatal, but localized pains, weakness, and lassitude may last for several months, and a lasting immunity develops. Diagnosis is made by inoculating material from the ulcer or inflamed glands into laboratory animals or by an agglutination test.

The disease is caused by a bacillus, *Pasteurella tularensis* (see p. 233), closely related to the plague bacillus. It infects a large variety of mammals and even some birds, but rabbits and ground squirrels seem to be the preferred hosts. Philip and Jellison in 1935 reported a severe tick-borne outbreak among sheep in Montana. Great epizoötics sometimes affect jack rabbits, killing many of them.

Experimentally the disease can be transmitted by many different arthropods, including lice, fleas, deerflies, and ticks, but the last are probably the primary transmitters among natural hosts. It is trans-ovarially transmitted by *Dermacentor andersoni, D. variabilis,* and *Haemaphysalis leporis-palustris,* which are the commonest transmitters to rabbits in this country. The ticks transmit the disease either by their bites or by fecal contamination of skin abrasions; mere handling of an infected tick and subsequent rubbing of the eye may cause infection. The disease is also transmitted by contact and is frequently acquired by handling diseased animals, especially rabbits. In an epizoötic among beavers and muskrats in Montana and Wyoming, there were 38 known human cases from handling these animals. A remarkable feature, still not adequately explained, was the pollution of all the water and mud in rivers and tributaries over a large area for a period of 16 months. In spite of this, human infections from drinking or swimming in the water were few. In 1934 a water-borne epidemic was reported in Turkey.

Another bacterial disease that Tovar in 1947 found ticks able to transmit is undulant fever or brucellosis. Naturally infected ticks (*Amblyomma cajennense* and Boöphilus) are found on infected animals and may play an important role in the spread of the disease among animals and to man. Hitherto this disease was known to be transmitted by contaminated food or water or with the milk or meat of infected animals.

Ticks do not transmit other bacterial diseases to man, but some species transmit *Salmonella enteritidis* to laboratory animals (see p. 538), and *D. albipictus* has been found to harbor *Klebsiella paralytica,* associated with a " moose disease " (see p. 537).

Piroplasmosis, Anaplasmosis and Virus Diseases

The small blood protozoans belonging to the family Babesiidae (see p. 217) are the cause of numerous important diseases in domestic animals. To these the name " piroplasmosis " is generally applied, since the organisms were once named Piroplasma. Man is peculiarly exempt.

Texas Fever and Other Piroplasmoses. Texas fever or " redwater fever " (briefly described on p. 217) is of enormous economic importance in cattle-raising countries. It was formerly prevalent in southern United States but has now been wiped out. Smith and Kilbourne in 1893 set a milepost in history when they discovered its transmission by cattle ticks, *Boöphilus annulatus.* This is a one-host species, so it is obvious that a tick becoming infected on one animal would have no opportunity to infect another. It could not do so even if transplanted from one animal to another, for the organisms (*Babesia bigemina*) invade the eggs of the tick, and cyclical development takes place in the embryonic tissues of the developing offsprings (see p. 217). Many other species of Babesia are known to infect ruminants, horses, pigs, dogs, and even poultry. The life cycles of the various species are probably similar, since all of them are hereditarily transmitted in their tick vectors.

All the species of Boöphilus seem to be able to serve as intermediate hosts for the Babesiae of cattle, sheep, etc. In Europe *Ixodes ricinus* is an important transmitter of *B. bovis,* and species of Hyalomma and Rhipicephalus have been implicated in North Africa and elsewhere. *B. canis,* causing piroplasmosis in dogs, is transmitted by *R. sanguineus* in the tropics, by *Dermacentor reticulatus* in Europe (this species also transmits a Babesia of horses), and by *Haemaphysalis leachi* in South Africa. According to Shortt, *B. canis* can be transmitted by subsequent stages of an infected tick as well as by its offspring.

The Protozoa of the related genus Theileria (see p. 217), one of which causes the deadly East Coast fever of cattle in Africa, differ in their life cycles (worked out for *T. dispar* by Sergent *et al.*, 1936) since they are transmitted only by two-host or three-host ticks and never transovarially. Species of Rhipicephalus are the principal transmitters of East Coast fever, while *Hyalomma mauritanicum* transmits a milder North African Theileria infection.

Aegyptianella pullorum, a protozoan inhabiting the blood corpuscles of chickens, ducks, and geese and believed to belong to the Babesiidae, occurs in southern Europe and Africa and is transmitted by *Argas persicus.* A similar organism has been reported from fowls in New York and Philadelphia.

Anaplasmosis. This frequently fatal disease, which causes fever, jaundice, and a very severe destruction of blood corpuscles in cattle and other animals, is characterized by dotlike bodies in the blood corpuscles, called Anaplasma (see p. 218). The disease is very commonly associated with Babesia or Theileria infections, since the tick vectors often have double infections. It can be transmitted by at least seventeen species of ticks belonging to several different genera and also by the intermittent feeding of biting flies. It can also be transmitted by ticks to their offspring.

Virus Diseases. Ticks have been shown to harbor and in some cases to transmit a number of viruses infective for man and animals. *Dermacentor andersoni* can transmit the western form of equine encephalomyelitis, and *D. variabilis* has been shown to do the same for the St. Louis strain. "Spring-summer encephalitis," occurring in forested areas of Siberia and the Russian Far East, is transmitted principally by *Ixodes persulcatus,* in which the virus is transovarially transmitted. This virus has been found in the central nervous system of rabbits and hares, and the presence of antibodies against it indicates that inapparent infections are very common both in man and in animals. Birds, also, are carriers. *I. persulcatus* is also reported to be a vector of Japanese B virus. In Colorado and neighboring states a febrile disease called Colorado tick fever, caused by a filtrable virus, is carried and transovarially transmitted by *Dermacentor andersoni.* The same or a closely related virus has been isolated from *D. variabilis* on Long Island. The disease is strikingly like dengue (see p. 693) in most respects, including a very marked leucopenia.

In northern England and Scotland louping ill, a virus disease attacking the central nervous system, is transmitted among sheep by ticks, principally *Ixodes ricinus.* It has been reported from Russia also. In experimentally infected *Rhipicephalus appendiculatus* the virus was not congenitally transmitted. Man is believed to be sus-

ceptible.   In Kenya a virus disease with symptoms suggestive of yellow
fever, called Rift Valley fever, which is very fatal for sheep, less so for
cattle, and mild for man, is probably carried by ticks.   *R. appendiculatus* harbors the virus for 7 days after feeding on infected sheep.

Control of Ticks on Man and Animals

Ticks on domestic animals may be destroyed by hand treatment, by
dipping, or by skillful rotation of pastures.   The campaign against
Boöphilus annulatus in the United States by dipping, pasture rotation,
and federal quarantine was so effective that this tick has been eliminated from all but a few counties in Florida and the Rio Grande Valley,
where it still survives on deer.   In the past arsenical dips were considered most effective, but other acaricides are now preferred (see p.
495).   DDT is effective against newly hatched or newly moulted ticks
but has little effect on others.   However, 8 per cent DDT in grease
with 25 per cent sulfur added is effective against *Amblyomma maculatum* and *Otobius mégnini* in the ears of animals.   Thoroughly wetting
cattle with a 2.5 per cent DDT spray kills both body and ear ticks, and
protects them against mosquitoes, flies, and lice, as well, for periods
up to 45 days; two applications in a season will ordinarily suffice.   In
the writer's experience dogs keep nearly free of ticks if dusted with 10
per cent DDT or bathed with 2.5 per cent emulsion about once a
month.

Benzene hexachloride (see p. 491) is definitely superior to DDT for
ticks and mites.   A dip or spray of about 1:1700 emulsion can be used
without toxic effect and is highly effective.

No highly efficient repellent for ticks on man or animals has been
found which is sufficient to repel or kill the ticks before they can transmit disease.   The Naval Medical Research Institute tried to discover a
contact acaricide that could be relied on to protect man from spotted
fever when placed on clothes.   They tried to find something that would
inactivate *Dermacentor andersoni* within 2 hours after 30 minutes'
contact, on the assumption that ticks could cross treated clothing and
reach the skin in 30 minutes and would require a feeding period of 2
hours to transmit spotted fever.   Their best results were with benzene
hexachloride; 500 mg. on 3-inch squares of cloth inactivated ticks in
3 hours after 30 minutes' contact.   Brennan (1947) found various
repellents effective against *Amblyomma americanum* but less so against
Dermacentor andersoni; his preliminary results suggest phenyl cyclo-
hexanol as probably the best, giving 90 per cent protection against
D. andersoni for 2 weeks.   In the tests 2 cc. per sq. ft. was applied to
socks.

REFERENCES

ANIGSTEIN, L., and BADER, M. N., Investigations on Rickettsial Diseases in Texas, 1 and 2, *Tex. Repts. on Biol. Med.,* **1**, 105, 117, 298, 389–409 (1943).

BANKS, N. A., A Revision of the Ixodoidea or Ticks of the United States, *U. S. Bur. Entomol., Tech. Bull.,* **15**, 1908.

BEQUAERT, J. C., The Ticks or Ixodoidea of the Northeastern United States and Canada, *Entomologica Americana,* **25**, 73–120, 121–184, 185–232 (1945).

BISHOPP, F. C., and WOOD, H. P., The Biology of Some North American Ticks of the Genus Dermacentor, *Parasitology,* **6**, 153 (1913).

BRENNAN, J. M., Preliminary Report on Some Organic Materials as Tick Repellents and Toxic Agents, *Publ. Health Repts.,* **62**, 1162–1165 (1947).

BURROUGHS, A. L., HOLDENRIED, R., LONGANECKER, D. S., and MEYER, K. F., A Field Study of Latent Tularemia in Rodents with a List of All Known Naturally Infected Vertebrates, *J. Infectious Diseases,* **76**, 115–119 (1945).

COOLEY, R. A., The Genera Dermacentor and Otocentor in the United States, *Nat. Inst. Health Bull.,* **171**, 1938.

Determination of Ornithodorus Species, in Symposium on Relapsing Fever in The Americas, *Pub. Am. Assoc. Advancement Sci.,* **18**, 77–84 (1941).

The Genera Boöphilus, Rhipicephalus and Haemaphysalis (Ixodidae) of the New World, *Nat. Inst. Health Bull.,* **187**, 54 pp. (1946).

COOLEY, R. A., and KOHLS, G. M., The Genus Amblyomma (Ixodidae) in the United States, *J. Parasitol.,* **30**, 77–111 (1944).

The Genus Ixodes in North America, *Nat. Inst. Health Bull.,* **184** (1945).

The Argasidae of North America, Central America, and Cuba, *Am. Midland Naturalist,* Monogr. 1, 152 pp. (1944)

DAVIS, G. E., Ticks and Relapsing Fever in the United States, *Publ. Health Repts.,* **55**, 2347 (1940).

Tick Vectors and Life Cycles of Ticks, in Symposium on Relapsing Fever in the Americas, *Pub. Am. Assoc. Advancement Sci.,* **18**, 67–76 (1941).

DAVIS, G. E., COX, H. R., PARKER, R. R., and DYER, R. C., Studies of a Filter-Passing Agent Isolated from Ticks, *Publ. Health Repts.,* **53**, 2259 (1938).

FLORIO, L., and MILLER, M. S., Epidemiology of Colorado Tick Fever, *Am. J. Publ. Health,* **38**, 211–213 (1948).

FRANCIS, E., Arthropods in the Transmission of Tularemia, *Trans. 4th Intern. Congr. Ent.,* **2**, 929 (1929).

Longevity of the Tick, *Ornithodorus turicata,* and of *Spirochaeta recurrentis* within this Tick, *Publ. Health Repts.,* **53**, 2220 (1938).

HOOKER, W. A., BISHOPP, F. C., and WOOD, H. P., The Life History and Bionomics of Some North American Ticks, *U. S. Bur. Entomol., Bull.* **106**, 1912.

NUTTALL, G. H. F., WARBURTON, C., and ROBINSON, L. E., *Ticks, A Monograph of the Ixodoidea,* Pts. 1–4, London, 1908–1926.

PARKER, R. R., KOHLS, G. M., and STEINHAUS, E. A., Rocky Mountain Spotted Fever: Spontaneous Infection in the Tick *Amblyomma americanum, Publ. Health Repts.,* **58**, 721 (1943).

PARKER, R. R., and STEINHAUS, E. A., *Salmonella enteritidis:* Experimental Transmission by the Rocky Mountain Wood Tick, *Dermacentor andersoni* Stiles, *Publ. Health Repts.,* **58**, 1010–1012 (1943).

PARKER, R. R., PHILIP, C. B., DAVIS, G. E., and COOLEY, R. A., Ticks of the U. S. in Relation to Disease in Man, *J. Econ. Entomol.,* **30**, 51 (1937).

PHILIP, C. B., Ticks as Vectors of Animal Diseases, *Can. Entomologist,* **71,** 55 (1939).

STANBURY, J. B., and HUYCK, J. H., Tick Paralysis: A Critical Review, *Medicine,* **24,** 219–242 (1945).

WALLACE, G. J., CAHN, A. R., and THOMAS, L. J., *Klebsiella paralytica,* A New Pathogenic Bacterium from "Moose Disease," *J. Infectious Diseases,* **53,** 386–414 (1933).

CHAPTER 23

Bedbugs and Other Hemiptera

The Order Hemiptera. The order Hemiptera, comprising the true bugs, contains numerous species most of which are predaceous or feed on plant juices, but some of which habitually or occasionally suck blood. The most important of these are the bedbugs, which probably first became acquainted with man when he shared caves with bats and swallows during the Ice Age, and which have since become fully domestic, to the disgust of good housekeepers all over the world. Also important are the conenoses (Triatomidae); these are large, fierce bloodsuckers, some species of which have become habitual residents in human habitations and in tropical America are the transmitters of Chagas' disease. In addition, not only the wild bloodsuckers but also many forms which are predaceous on insects may inflict painful and even dangerous bites.

The Hemiptera have an incomplete metamorphosis, the adult condition being attained gradually by successive moults of the nymphs (see p. 485). The mouthparts (Fig. 193, *left*) are fitted for piercing and sucking. There is a short labrum covering the bases of the mouthparts. The labium is in the form of a 3- or 4-jointed beak bent back under the head and thorax and grooved on the

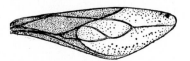

Fig. 191.   A hemipteran wing (Reduviid).

dorsal surface (ventral when bent under the head) to contain the stylet-like mandibles and maxillae. The mandibles are coarser and fit together to form two grooves — a large food channel and a small salivary duct. The hypopharynx and palpi are absent.

The wings, except in those forms, like the bedbugs, in which they are vestigial, are very characteristic; the first pair, called hemelytra, have the basal portion thickened and leathery while the terminal portion, which is sharply demarcated, is membranous (Fig. 191). The second pair of wings are membranous and fold under the others when at rest. Many bugs have " stink-glands " between the bases of the hind legs which secrete a clear volatile fluid by means of which they emit a strong offensive odor.

Bedbugs (Cimex)

General Account. The bedbugs belong to the family Cimicidae. They have broad, flat, reddish-brown bodies and are devoid of wings, except for a pair of bristly pads which represent the first pair of wings (Fig. 192). The eyes project prominently at the sides of the head, the antennae are four-jointed, and the beak is three-jointed (Fig. 193). The legs have the usual segments, the tarsi being three-jointed. The prothorax is large, indented in front for the head, and has flat lateral expansions. The mesonotum is small and triangular, bearing the wing pads, which nearly cover the metanotum. The abdomen is flat, its

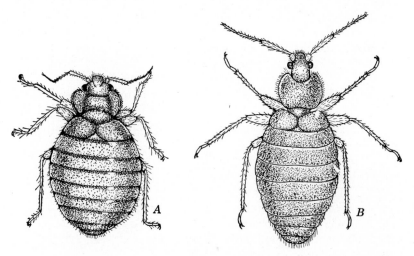

Fig. 192. Bedbugs. *A*, common bedbug, *Cimex lectularius; B*, Oriental or Indian bedbug, *C. hemipterus.* × 8. (Adapted from Castellani and Chalmers.)

contour an almost perfect circle in unfed bags, but elongated in full ones; it has eight visible segments, the first two (of nine) being fused. In males the abdomen is pointed at the tip, whereas in females it is evenly rounded. The greater part of the body is covered with bristles set in little cup-shaped depressions. These depressions are perforated at the bottom to allow for the passage of muscles which move the bristles. Murray describes having seen bugs raise the bristles upon meeting each other as cats raise their hairs or birds their feathers.

Bedbugs have a peculiar pungent odor known to all who have had to contend with these pests; the adults have the stink-glands situated in the last segment of the thorax, opening through a pair of ducts between the coxae of the hind legs. In the first four nymphal stages these glands are not present but are preceded by glands situated on the dorsal side of three of the anterior abdominal segments. The nasty odor of bedbugs has evidently inspired some faith in their medicinal value. Seven bugs ground up in water was said by Pliny to arouse one from a fainting spell, and one a day would render hens immune to snake bites. Even at the present time there are places in civilized countries where bedbugs are given as an antidote for fever and ague.

Species. The true bedbugs belong to the genus Cimex, but not all the species are human parasites; some confine their attentions, ordinarily at least, to birds and others, to bats. There are two widely distributed species that attack man; one is the common bedbug,

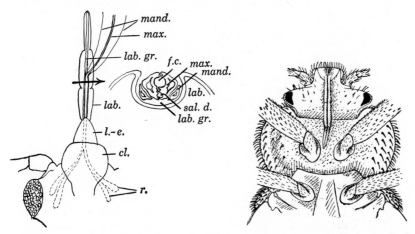

Fig. 193. Left, Mouthparts of bedbug, with cross section; *cl.*, clypeus; *f.c.*, food channel; *lab.*, labium; *lab. gr.*, labial groove; *l.-e.*, labrum-epipharynx; *mand.*, mandibles; *max.*, maxillae; *r.*, roots of mandibles and maxillae; *sal. d.*, salivary duct. Right, head and part of thorax of bedbug, ventral view.

C. lectularius, found in all temperate climates and sometimes also in tropical ones; the other is the tropical or Indian bedbug, *C. hemipterus* (formerly *rotundatus*) which is the prevalent species in the tropical parts of the world. It is distinguished by having less marked lateral expansions of the prothorax (Fig. 192). In west Africa another species, *Leptocimex boueti*, attacks man; it is a silky-haired, long-legged bug with small rectangular thorax.

Some other Cimicidae may become nuisances under special conditions. The proverbially superclean housekeepers of Holland villages, for instance, are sometimes greatly chagrined to find bugs in their spotless houses, the bugs being *C. columbarius* derived from pigeons nesting in the roofs. Similar temporary invasions by *C. pilosellus* of bats sometimes occur in dwelling houses, especially when the bats are driven away or migrate. The silky-haired bugs of the closely related genus

Oeciacus, which live in swallows' nests, also occasionally invade houses and cause much annoyance to the inhabitants, but the invasions are temporary; Myers in 1928 showed that this species requires bird blood before it will reproduce. The Mexican poultry bug, *Haematosiphon inodora*, is a related species resembling a bedbug but having longer legs, no odor, and a very long beak that reaches to the hind coxae. It is often a serious poultry pest in the dry parts of the southwest and sometimes invades houses and torments man. The Mexicans sometimes abandon or burn their huts to escape from them.

The interhostal traffic in bedbugs is not by any means a one-way affair, for the nests of sparrows and starlings, the burrows of rats, the attic roosts of bats, and also chicken houses and pigeon cotes are often invaded by hungry bugs that have been abandoned by their human sources of blood. The sparrows and starlings may frequently be a means of starting new colonies in other houses, but bats, contrary to popular opinion, probably rarely do, since they are not much given to visiting. Bugs found under bark and moss out of doors are not bedbugs but immature stages of other bugs that superficially resemble them.

Following is a key for the differentiation of the commoner Cimicidae likely to invade houses in America:

1*a*. Beak short, not extending behind first coxae (Fig. 193) ....2.
1*b*. Beak long, extending to hind coxae; legs long; no odor; on poultry in southwestern U. S. ....*Haematosiphon inodora.*
2*a*. Body hairs short, set in sockets only on dorsal side; pronotum deeply concave in front; third and fourth joints of antennae markedly slender (Cimex) ....3.
2*b*. Body hairs long and silky, set in sockets on ventral side also; pronotum not deeply concave; terminal joints of antennae only slightly more slender than basal joints; in nests of swallows; L. 4 mm. ....*Oeciacus vicarius.*
3*a*. Second and third joints of antennae about equal, third longer than fourth; L. 4 mm.; on bats ....*C. pilosellus.*
3*b*. Second joint of antennae shorter than third ....4.
4*a*. Lateral parts of pronotum with flat lateral expansions (Fig. 192*A*); in human houses in temperate climates; L. 5 to 6 mm. ....*C. lectularius.*
4*b*. Similar but smaller, rounder; shorter and coarser antennae; prothorax less concave in front; in pigeon houses (doubtful if a distinct species) .... *C. columbarius.*
4*c*. Pronotum rounded to margin on dorsal side (Fig. 192*B*); in human houses in tropics; L. 5 to 6 mm. ....*C. hemipterus.*

Habits. Bedbugs are normally night prowlers and exhibit a considerable degree of cleverness in hiding away in cracks and crevices during the daytime. When hungry they will frequently come forth in a lighted room at night and have even been known to feed in broad daylight. Favorite hiding places are in old-fashioned wooden bed-steads, in the crevices between boards, under wallpaper, and in similar places, for which their flat bodies are eminently adapted. They some-times go considerable distances to hide in the daytime and show re-markable resourcefulness in reaching sleepers at night. In the tropics newcomers often wonder why their heads itch under their sun helmets until they discover a thriving colony of bugs in the ventilator at the top.

When a bug is about to drill for blood the beak is bent forward and the piercing organs, gliding up and down past each other, are sunk into the flesh of the victim. Bugs seldom cling to the skin while suck-ing, preferring to remain on the clothing. Since a fresh meal appar-ently acts as a stimulus for emptying the contents of the rectum, the adherence to the clothing is a fortunate circumstance, inasmuch as it precludes to some extent the danger of bedbugs infecting their wounds with excrement, as do ticks.

In the course of 10 or 15 minutes a full meal is obtained and the dis-tended bug retreats to its hiding place, having first deposited a bit of excrement. According to Cragg, in the case of *Cimex hemipterus* a single full meal is not entirely assimilated for at least a week, although the bug is ready to feed again in a day or two, thus having parts of several meals in the stomach at once. Most bloodsucking insects com-pletely digest one meal before another is sought.

Bedbugs are able to endure long fasts; they have been kept alive without any food whatever for a year. Sometimes, however, bugs migrate from an empty house in search of an inhabited area. In cold weather they hibernate in a semitorpid condition and do not feed, but in warm climates they are active the year around. *C. lectularius*, according to Marlatt, succumbs at temperatures above 96° to 100° F. if the humidity is high. According to Bacot, unfed newly hatched bugs are able to withstand cold between 28° and 32° F. for as long as 18 days, though they are destroyed by exposure to damp cold after a full meal.

Hosts. Although man is undoubtedly the normal and preferred source of blood for *Cimex lectularius* and *C. hemipterus*, the bugs manage to get along surprisingly well on other kinds of blood when this source fails. Johnson in 1937 found experimentally that bedbugs thrive even better on mice than on men and about equally well on chickens. They sometimes multiply in great numbers in chicken houses, dovecotes, and white-rat cages. Dogs and cats are frequently bitten also.

Life History. The eggs of bedbugs (Fig. 194*A*) are pearly white oval objects, furnished at one end with a little cap which is bent to one

side.   The eggs are relatively large, about 1 mm. in length, and are
therefore laid singly or in small batches.   The total number of eggs
laid is about 100 to 250.   The bugs frequently return to the same places
to oviposit until sometimes as many as 40 eggs have been accumulated.

The eggs hatch in from 6 to 10 days during warm weather but are
retarded in their development by cold.   A week of freezing temperature reduces the hatching to 25 per cent.   The freshly hatched bugs
(Fig. 194B) are very small, delicate, and pale in color.   The skin is
normally moulted five times at intervals of about 8 days before the final
adult stage is reached, at least one gluttonous feed being necessary
before each moult in order to insure normal development and reproduction.   However, the bug may gorge itself several times between moults.
The several nymphal stages of the insect resemble each other quite

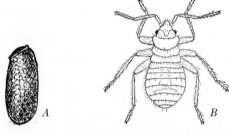

FIG. 194.   Egg (A) and newly hatched larva (B) of bedbug.   X 20.   (After Marlatt.)

closely except in the constantly increasing size and deepening color.
The wing pads appear only after the last moult.   The total time required for development to maturity under favorable conditions is
about 7 to 10 weeks, but starvation, low temperature, etc., may drag
out the period much longer.   There may, however, be three or four
generations in a year.

Effects of Bites.   The degree of irritation caused by bites of bedbugs undoubtedly depends to a large degree on development of
hypersensitivity or eventual immunity (see p. 488).   The irritation is
produced by the salivary secretion, but when an engorging bug is undisturbed much of the secretion is redrawn with the blood meal and the
irritation is lessened.   Continued excessive biting by bugs may cause
anemia, nervousness, insomnia, and general debility.   Titschack in
1930 found that the bites of 50 adults were enough to produce influenza-
like symptoms, whereas over 100 caused palpitation of the heart, headache, and eye disturbances.   Hase (1938) considered these eye disturbances to be a fairly common phenomenon when numerous bugs bite
day after day.

Bedbugs and Disease

General Considerations. The bedbug would appear at first sight to be eminently adapted for human disease transmission. Like an ex-criminal, it is under constant suspicion; with or without reason it has been on trial in connection with kala-azar and other forms of leish-maniasis, relapsing fever, infectious jaundice, South American trypano-somiasis, leprosy, plague, typhoid, infantile paralysis, some filaria infections, seven-day fever, typhus, tularemia, yellow fever, and even malaria and beri-beri. In spite of all this suspicion and some circum-stantial evidence there is still to be produced any single instance in which the bedbug has been shown to be more than a relatively un-important accessory in the transmission of any human disease.

Of the numerous pathogenic organisms mentioned above, none except infectious jaundice (from guinea pig to guinea pig) has been shown to be transmitted by the bites, although a number of them can be transmitted by inoculation of crushed bedbugs, or by the feces. One factor which limits the effectiveness of bedbugs as disease transmitters is their nonmigratory habit. Although frequently carried about in clothing they normally live in the homes and not on the persons of their hosts, and they would therefore usually be limited in the spread of a disease to the occupants of the infested place, except in the case of infested hotels, rooming houses, sleeping cars, boats, etc.

Patton's observation in India in 1907 that *Leishmania donovani* underwent multiplication and development in the alimentary canal of bugs fed on patients (see p. 145) led to years of fruitless efforts to establish the bedbug as a transmitter of kala-azar, but it finally had to be admitted that the bedbug plays no appreciable part in the epidemi-ology of either this disease or of Oriental sore. There seems to be no specificity in the relation between bedbugs and species of Leishmania or Leptomonas; even *L. ctenocephali* of fleas will develop in them.

The relation of bedbugs to the transmission of *Trypanosoma cruzi* is of the same nature. According to Brumpt these trypanosomes develop in about 80 per cent of bedbugs fed on infected mice but as a rule these bugs remain infected for a much shorter time than tri-atomids. There is no evidence that bedbugs play any appreciable role in the transmission of this disease in nature, although a related trypanosome of bats is claimed by Pringault to be transmitted by the bites of *Cimex pipistrelli*.

In a few instances relapsing fever has been transmitted to animals by bugs that had immediately before fed incompletely on infected animals, a method of transmission which is no more significant than the equally successful experiment of infecting an animal by pricking it with an injection needle that has just been inserted into an infected animal. Attempts to transmit relapsing fever experimentally by bites of bedbugs, except in this immediate mechanical manner, have invariably failed, although bugs have been shown to harbor the spirochetes for a number of weeks and may cause infection if their crushed bodies are injected. Both the louse-borne and tick-borne strains of the spirochetes will develop in bugs without being transmitted by them. The failure to transmit is definitely associated with the structure or habits of the bug and not with the viability of the parasite in this host. Further accusations against the bedbug as a primary factor in the dissemination of relapsing fever appear to be out of order.

Most attempts to transmit infectious jaundice by the bites of infected bedbugs have failed, but Blanchard and his colleagues claim to have accomplished this, between guinea pigs, by the bites of infected *Cimex lectularius*, some of which remained infective for over a month. The infection is easily transmitted by inoculating with crushed bugs.

Experiments in Brazil showed that the virus of yellow fever is present in the feces of bedbugs for several days after an infective feed and that these feces are infective when inoculated into monkeys, but there is nothing to suggest that bedbugs play any role in the transmission of yellow fever in nature.

Since the gut of bedbugs, as of many other insects, contains antibacterial substances, few bacteria succeed in establishing themselves in bugs. An exception is the bacillus of tularemia, *Pasteurella tularensis;* bugs fed on infected animals retain virulent organisms in the gut for life. The feces are infective, but the bugs do not transovarially transmit this bacillus. Bacot has shown that plague organisms, also, may develop in bugs though more slowly than in fleas and with a much higher mortality for the bugs. Bugs may possibly play a minor role in human plague.

Another bacterial disease shown by Tovar in 1947 to be transmitted by bedbugs as well as by fleas and ticks is undulant fever or brucellosis. Arthropods fed on infected animals transmitted the disease to other animals when biting, and they may play some part in spreading the disease among animals and from animals to man.

Bugs have also been " among those mentioned " in connection with leprosy, typhoid, infantile paralysis, and typhus, but the evidence is not sufficient to warrant much excitement over the danger. Probably they will be suspected of carrying many other diseases when other obvious transmitting agents are not discovered. In one epidemic of seven-day fever in the Sudan, for instance, since there was no evidence implicating other bloodsucking insects, the bedbugs, which were abundant in the barracks of the afflicted soldiers, were assumed to be responsible. Such evidence is, of course, entirely inadequate. Many epidemiologists would do well to read more detective stories and learn that the most obvious explanation is often not the correct one.

Remedies and Prevention

Prevention of " bugginess " consists chiefly in good housekeeping, but occasional temporary infestations are likely to occur in almost any inhabited building. In the past the only sure way of getting rid of bedbugs was fumigation with HCN or sulfur (see p. 492), but that method is now as obsolete as horse-and-buggy travel. The new insecticides, DDT, chlordane, and benzene hexachloride, provide the answer to the bedbug problem. One of these substances, preferably benzene hexachloride if one can stand the odor, applied as 1½ oz. of 10 per cent dust or 3 oz. of emulsion spray to each bed, gets rid of light infestations within 48 hours. It must be worked into all joints and crevices of the bed frame and applied lightly to the mattresses and pillows. The bugs, which, as mentioned previously, seek blood meals even when partly full, come in contact with the chemical when approaching a sleeper and die in a few minutes or hours. In very heavy infestations dusting or spraying into baseboard cracks, behind loose wallpaper, etc., will insure a speedy kill. The residual effect is good for 3 to 6 months.

Other Parasitic Bugs

Triatomidae. Most of the other true bugs which may be looked upon as normally human parasites belong to the family Triatomidae. This is a large family of bloodsucking bugs, many of them brightly colored; they are especially numerous in the tropics. Nearly all are active runners and good fliers. They have a small, narrow head with the long, filamentous, four-jointed antennae attached on its sides between the eyes and the apex. The beak is slender, straight, and three-jointed, and bent straight back under the head. The pronotum flares posteriorly and is usually fairly distinctly divided into an anterior and posterior lobe; the posterior angles of the latter may be round or pointed (see Fig. 195, *7* and *8*). Behind the pronotum is a triangular scutellum which may have a posterior spine. The abdomen has flattened lateral margins, the connexiva, not covered by the wings (Fig. 196). This and the leathery basal portion of the wing (corium) is usually marked with red or yellow, as is the pronotum.

Some workers, e.g., Usinger (1943), prefer to consider these bugs a subfamily of the Reduviidae or assassin bugs, which are predaceous on other insects and rarely bite vertebrates except in self-defense. However, they are readily distinguished from Reduviidae not only by their

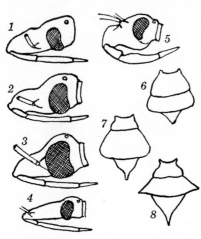

habits but also by their longer and more slender heads, slender straight beaks, and insertion of the antennae on the sides instead of the top of the head. (Fig. 195, *1, 5*.)

The bloodsucking habit of the Triatomidae is probably a recent experiment on the part of these bugs, evolutionarily speaking, for some of them still pursue bedbugs and are cannibals on each other, obtaining their blood second-hand by sucking it out of their brothers and sisters. The bites of tri-

FIG. 195. Heads and thoraces of various genera of triatomids and reduviids. *1* and *2*, Triatoma (*T. protracta* and *T. rubida*); *3*, Panstrongylus (*P. megista*); *4*, Rhodnius (*R. prolixus*); *5* and *6*, head and thorax of Melanolestes, a reduviid; *7*, thorax of Triatoma; *8*, thorax of Eratyrus. (*1–4, 7, 8* adapted from Pinto.)

atomids are usually not as painful as those of many nonbloodsucking Hemiptera, but in some individuals who are allergic they may cause local swelling, generalized itching, and headache. The bites of reduviids are usually more severe. The Triatomidae are of great importance because they are the natural and only important transmitters of *Trypanosoma cruzi.*

Genera and Species. According to Usinger (1943) there are 19 genera of triatomids in the Americas, but some of these contain species which are of no interest here. Used in separating genera are the place of insertion of the antennae, the shape and other characters of the prothorax and scutellum, and hairiness of the body.

The important genera of American Triatomidae, and of Reduviidae which occasionally cause painful bites, can be distinguished by the following key:

Reduviidae: Beak thick and curved; antennae inserted just in front of eyes on top of head; head relatively short (Fig. 195, *5*).

1*a*. A cogwheel-like ridge on pronotum ....*Arilus* (wheelbug).
1*b*. No cogwheel ridge ....2.
2*a*. Thorax constricted at or anterior to middle; color nearly uniformly dark brown ....*Reduvius.*
2*b*. Thorax constricted behind middle (Fig. 195, *6*) ....3.
3*a*. Wings and body all black or dark brown ....*Melanolestes.*
3*b*. A large yellow spot on wings ....*Rasahus.*

Triatomidae: Beak slender and straight; antennae inserted on sides of head; head elongated in front of eyes; thorax constricted anterior to middle; black or brown with red or yellow markings.

1*a*. Antennae inserted near apex of head, which is somewhat widened apically (Fig. 195, *4*, 196*B*) ....**Rhodnius.**

1*b*. Antennae inserted just in front of eyes (Fig. 195, *3*) ....2.

1*c*. Antennae inserted about midway between eyes and apex of head (Fig. 195, *2*) ....3.

2*a*. Body clothed in long curved hairs ....**Parastrongylus.**

2*b*. Body nearly naked ....**Panstrongylus.**

3*a*. Scutellum with a long pointed spine posteriorly and pronotum with pointed posterior angles (Fig. 195, *8*) ....**Eratyrus.**

3*b*. Scutellum without long spine; angles of pronotum rounded (Fig. 195, *7*) ....**Triatoma.**

About 70 species of Triatomidae inhabit nearly all the warm parts of the world, but they are especially abundant in America, where they are widely distributed from the southern half of the United States to Argentina. Many of them are partially predaceous, others almost entirely bloodsuckers. Though most of them will feed on a great variety of hosts, some are especially associated with certain animals. Most of the species inhabit the burrows or nests of wild mammals, but a few species habitually live in human habitations, in the daytime hiding like bedbugs in the cracks of walls, in thatched roofs, debris on the floor, etc., issuing forth at night to feed on their sleeping hosts. Most species are so active and hide so rapidly when a light is produced that they are hard to catch. It is probable that any of them would accept a human meal if the opportunity presented itself, but their habits and habitats render some species much more frequent human biters than others.

Life Cycle. The life cycle of triatomids is similar in general to that of bedbugs. The eggs are white oval objects when first laid, in some species turning yellowish or pinkish later; they are laid singly or in small batches by most species, but *Rhodnius prolixus* lays them in a mass joined together by a secretion. The total number laid by a female (not a *single* female as some writers say — they have to mate!) is usually from about 100 to 300. The eggs require from 2 to 3 weeks to hatch, the time depending on temperature. The wingless nymphs are light in color when they first hatch but soon darken. They moult a total of five times, always after a full blood meal, which is 6 to 12 times their own body weight! The later nymphal instars have the wings represented as rounded lobes (Fig. 197*B*). The whole development from egg to adult requires about a year in some species and 2 years in others.

Important Species.   Comparatively few species invade houses and become human pests.   In South America three species are of outstanding importance.   *Panstrongylus megistus* (Fig. 196*A*), the " barbeiro " of Brazil, a large, handsome red-trimmed black insect widely distributed in Brazil and neighboring countries, is one of the principal vectors of Chagas' disease.   It is thoroughly domestic in its habits and normally lives in the huts of natives.   *Triatoma infestans*, known in Argentina as the "vinchuca," replaces this species farther south and

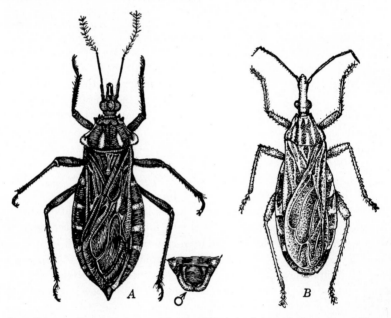

Fig. 196.   *A, Panstrongylus megista*, the " barbeiro," important vector of Chagas' disease in Brazil.   (Adapted from Chagas.)   *B, Rhodnius prolixus*, important vector in Venezuela.   (Adapted from Larrousse.)

west as a house-infesting pest.   This is the species whose habits were vividly described by Darwin in his *Voyage of a Naturalist*.   In northern South America *Rhodnius prolixus* (Fig. 196*B*) is the most annoying domestic species.   This bug is garbed in brown and yellow.   Although it is said by some writers to inhabit burrows of armadillos and pacas, Uribe failed to find it except in human habitations.

In the Old World a widespread tropical species, *Triatoma rubrofasciata*, is semidomestic in habits.   Most of the other triatomids pay attention primarily to rodents, armadillos, or other wild animals, but many of them frequently enter human habitations to bite if not to breed. Most of the species in the United States, eight of which have been found to harbor *Trypanosoma cruzi* (see p. 173), are commonly found associated with wood rats (Neotoma) or in nests of opossums or burrows of armadillos. The adults particularly are likely to invade barns, tents, or houses or to prowl about in the beds of outdoor sleepers. They are found throughout the southern half of the United States but are especially common in Texas, New Mexico, Arizona, and southern California. The species most often found invading houses are *T. gerstaeckeri* in Texas, which sometimes invades in great numbers; *T. rubida* (= *uhleri*), *T. protracta*, and *T. longipes*, found farther west and in Mexico; and *T. sanguisuga* throughout the South.

Reduviidae. Several reduviid bugs, which are not normally bloodsuckers, often bite man when interfered with, and their bites, as noted previously, are far more painful and toxic than those of the true bloodsuckers. In North and Central America there are a number of species of " kissing bugs " and " corsairs " of the genera Melanolestes, Reduvius, and Rasahus. The common kissing bug or black corsair, *Melanolestes picipes*, became very abundant in the United States at one time and gave opportunity for many startling newspaper stories. The wheelbug, *Arilus cristatus*, is another vicious biter.

Other Hemiptera. All Hemiptera have piercing mouthparts and many are capable of inflicting painful wounds, so it is safest not to handle any of them with the bare hands. Although the majority of the bad biters belong to the Reduviidae, the malodorous pito bug, *Dysodius lunatus*, of South America is worthy of mention. It is a broad, flat bug belonging to the family Aradidae; it frequents houses and bites severely. Among other species that bite when handled are various kinds of water bugs. The large " electric light bugs " are venomous enough to kill fish and even birds and to cause in man severe pain lasting for several days.

Triatomidae and Disease. Over 30 species of Triatomidae in South and Central America have been found to be capable of acting as intermediate hosts of *Trypanosoma cruzi* or a species which is morphologically indistinguishable from it. *Panstrongylus megistus, Triatoma infestans*, and *Rhodnius prolixus* are the most important natural transmitters of the disease to man. In Panama *T. dimidiata* is frequently found in houses, and it, as well as several other species, is known to harbor *Trypanosoma cruzi* in that country.

Panstrongylus megistus seems to be the species most frequently involved in human transmission in the greater part of Brazil. It is often accompanied by *T. sordida*, but naturally infected *megista* are much commoner than *sordida*. In other South American countries *T. infestans* is very commonly infected and is the principal transmitter, whereas in Venezuela and Colombia Rhodnius is the principal vector.

In the United States eight species: *gerstaeckeri, protracta, protracta woodi, rubida, longipes, heidemanni, sanguisuga,* and *ambigua,* have been found naturally infected. Packchanian in 1939 reported the

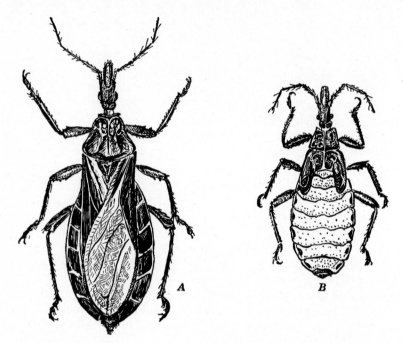

Fig. 197. *Triatoma protracta,* adult and nymph. (Adapted from Usinger.)

heaviest infections — 92 out of 100 *gerstaeckeri* collected in a house and barn in southern Texas and 65 per cent of *heidemanni* collected at Temple, Texas.

There are certain habits of Triatomidae that are of interest in connection with the transmission of trypanosomes. Cannibalism is a common habit among many of them. Young bugs, especially, often suck blood from the distended bodies of nest mates, and they sometimes suck blood from bedbugs. The robbed bugs seem quite untroubled and unharmed by it. Perhaps like the Romans of old they are glad to be rid of their meals in order to enjoy the ingestion of more. Rhodnius is said to feed upon the excreta of fellow bugs. In these ways and perhaps by contamination from feces, *Trypanosoma cruzi* can spread from bug to bug, but transovarial transmission does not occur. The percentage of infected bugs steadily increases with age up to the adult stage.

Since Chagas' disease is transmitted by contamination of bites by feces of the bugs or by rubbing the feces into the eye, species that are quick to defecate while feeding are the only important transmitters. The rare occurrence, if not complete absence, of Chagas' disease in the United States may be due to failure of species that are not habitually domestic, such as *T. protracta*, to defecate while feeding.

Besides transmission of *cruzi*-like trypanosomes, triatomids are also vectors of *Trypanosoma rangeli* (see p. 172), but *T. equinum* and *T. gambiense* survive in them for only a short time. In India and also in South America *Triatoma rubrofasciata* is a vector of a trypanosome of rodents, *T. conorrhinae*.

In Mauritius, *T. rubrofasciata* has been found to have *rickettsia*-like bodies which were transmissible to laboratory animals. Spirochetes of relapsing fever persist in triatomids for some time, and in Kansas the virus of western equine encephalomyelitis has been isolated from *T. sanguisuga*.

Control. Spraying houses with one of the newer insecticides is very effective in controlling the house-infesting species. According to Neghme in Chile, benzene hexachloride is more effective than DDT; spraying with a 5 per cent solution in kerosene controls the Triatoma population in houses for as long as 12 months.

REFERENCES
Bedbugs

BACK, E. A., Bedbugs, *U. S. Dept. Agr. Leaflet*, **146**, 1937.

DUNN, L. H., Life History of the Tropical Bedbug (*Cimex rotundatus*) in Panama, *Am. J. Trop. Med.*, **4**, 77 (1924).

HASE, A., Zur hygienischen Bedeutung der Parasitären Haus- und Vogel-wanzen, *Z. Parasitenk.*, **10**, 1 (1938).

Die Bettwanze, ihr Leben und ihre Bekämpfung, Berlin, 1917.

HERRICK, G. W., *Insects Injurious to the Household and Annoying to Man*, New York, 1924.

HORVATH, G., Revision of the American Cimicidae, *Ann. Mus. Hung.*, **10**, 257 (1912).

JOHNSON, C. G., The Ecology of the Bedbug, *Cimex lectularius* L. in Britain, *J. Hyg.*, **41**, 345–461 (1942).

MCKENNY-HUGHES, A. W., and JOHNSON, C. G., The Bedbug. Its Habits and Life History and How to Deal with It, *Brit. Mus. Nat. Hist., Econ. Ser.*, **5**, London, 1942.

MELLANBY, K., A Comparison of the Physiology of the Two Species of Bedbugs Attacking Man, *Parasitology*, **27**, 111 (1935).

Publ. Health Repts., The Bedbug, its Relation to Public Health, its Habits and Life History, and Methods of Control, Suppl., **129**, 1937.

Rep. Committee on Bedbug Infestation, 1935–1940, *Med. Research Council Special Rept. Ser.*, **245**, London, 1942.

Triatomidae

BUXTON, P. A., The Biology of a Bloodsucking Bug, *Rhodnius prolixus, Trans. Entomol. Soc. London,* **78**, Pt. 2, 227 (1930).

HASE, A., Beobachtungen an venezolanische Triatoma-Arten, sowie zur allgemeinen Kenntnis der Familie der Triatomidae, *Z. Parasitenk*, **4**, 585 (1932).

KOFOID, C. A., and WHITAKER, B. G., Natural Infection of American Human Trypanosomiasis in Two Species of Cone-nosed Bugs, *Triatoma protracta* and *T. uhleri* in the Western United States, *J. Parasitol.*, **22**, 259 (1936).

LARROUSSE, F., Étude biologique et systematique du genre Rhodnius Stal., *Ann. parasitol. humaine et comparée,* **5**, 63 (1927).

PACKCHANIAN, A., Reservoir Hosts of Chagas' Disease in the State of Texas, *Am. J. Trop. Med.*, **22**, 623–631 (1942).

READIO, P. A., Studies on the Biology of the Reduviidae of America North of Mexico, *Univ. Kansas Sci. Bull.,* **17**, 5 (1927).

USINGER, R. L., The Triatominae of North and Central America and the West Indies and Their Public Health Significance, *Publ. Health Bull.*, **288**, 83 pp. (1944).

WOOD, S. F., Notes on the Distribution and Habits of Reduviid Vectors of Chagas' Disease in the Southwestern United States, *Pan-Amer. Entomol.*, **17**, 85 (1941).

Observations on Vectors of Chagas' Disease in the United States, I, Calif., *Bull. Southern Calif. Acad. Sci.*, **41**, 61 (1942); II, Ariz., *Am. J. Trop. Med.*, **23**, 315 (1943).

See also References, Chapter **8.**

CHAPTER 24

Lice

ANOPLURA AND MALLOPHAGA

In former times human lice were looked upon with less disgust and loathing than they are in most civilized countries now. In days when a bath on Saturday nights (except in winter) was considered adequate and most laundering was done on river banks, lice intruded themselves in everyone's company, from the royal family to the lowest peasant. Even today, however, body lice are distressingly common in camps, jails, trenches, etc., where association with careless people cannot be avoided and facilities for cleanliness are not all that could be desired, especially in time of war. In some parts of the world lice are believed to be indicative of robust health and fertility.

Head lice are even more prevalent among the poorer classes in cities, particularly among children. A survey in England in 1939–1940 showed that in industrial cities 50 per cent of preschool children and of schoolgirls harbored them. In women the incidence never fell under 5 to 10 per cent, and in young women in industrial areas it was 30 to 50 per cent. Permanent waves tend to bring lice more peace and quiet in the heads of young women. The incidence was only 2 per cent in men, and relatively rare (under 5 per cent) in rural areas, where lousiness is considered a disgrace.

Comparison of Anoplura and Mallophaga. Lice are small wingless insects of which there are two quite distinct groups: the sucking lice, constituting the order Anoplura, and the chewing or bird lice, constituting the order Mallophaga. The former are exclusively mammalian parasites, while the latter are for the most part parasites of birds, although a number of them choose to infest mammals. The Mallophaga have nipperlike mandibles fitted for chewing instead of sucking, and they feed only on hair, feathers, and epidermal debris and not at all on blood, whereas the Anoplura have piercing mouthparts and nourish themselves on the blood of their hosts. In other respects these two groups of lice show many structural resemblances to each other and are now generally believed to be related, but it is impossible to determine how much the resemblances may be due to convergent evolution as a result of a parasitic form of life and how much to actual relationship.

Since the Mallophaga do not pierce the skins of their hosts they can have no part in the transmission of disease; they are nevertheless often injurious because of irritation of the skin surface and may be the cause of much unthriftiness by the annoyance and insomnia which their activities cause. The Anoplura, on the other hand, are important disease transmitters. The lice of these two orders are readily dis-

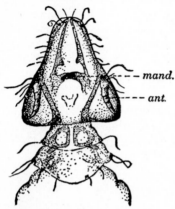
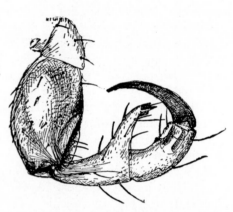

FIG. 198. Head of a species of Mallophaga (*Uchida* sp. from golden eagle). Note breadth of head compared with thorax, and pair of black-tipped mandibles; *ant.*, antenna; *mand.*, mandibles.

FIG. 199. Front leg of ♂ body louse, *Pediculus humanus*. Note huge claw and thumblike opposing process of next segment. × 100.

tinguishable by the presence in the Mallophaga and absence in the Anoplura of heavily chitinized mandibles which are brown or blackish. They can also be distinguished at once by the fact that the Mallophaga have very broad heads, always at least as broad as the thorax (Fig. 198), whereas in the Anoplura the head is always narrower than the thorax (Fig. 201). None of the Mallophaga are human parasites but some are annoying to domestic animals, particularly poultry. They are briefly considered on pp. 584–587.

Anoplura

Morphology and Physiology. The Anoplura have the body clearly divided into a narrow and often elongate head, a broad thorax, the segments of which are fused in nearly all species, and an abdomen that is more or less distinctly divided into segments (Fig. 201). There are primitively nine segments, but one or two of the anterior ones are fused or lost, so usually seven or eight are recognizable. In the crab louse, Phthirus, segments III to V are fused. Ordinarily segments III to VIII bear spiracles, and there is one pair of spiracles on the thorax also (two pairs in a family of lice on seals). The abdomen of lice is poorly chitinized except for the pleural plates at the sides in some genera, e.g., Pediculus. In the females the terminal segment of the abdomen is indented, whereas in the males it is rounded, with the large spikelike vaginal dilator often projecting from the dorsally situated sex opening just posterior to the anus.

The head has short three- or five-jointed antennae; eyes are absent in most species, but the human lice have small but prominent ones.

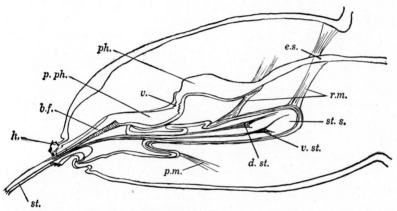

FIG. 200. Mouthparts of *Pediculus humanus;* *b.f.*, buccal funnel; *d. st.*, dorsal stylet; *es.*, esophagus; *h.*, haustellum (everted); *p. ph.*, prepharynx; *ph.*, pharynx; *p.m.*, protractor muscle; *r.m.*, retractor muscles; *st.*, stylets; *st. s.*, stylet sac; *v.*, valve; *v. st.*, ventral stylet. (Adapted from Sikora.)

The legs, except in one genus found on elephants, have each tarsus, consisting of one segment, armed with a large curved claw, quite grotesque in appearance in some species, which closes back like a finger against a thumblike projection of the tibia (Fig. 199). There are not even rudiments of wings.

The mouthparts (Fig. 200), fitted for piercing and sucking, are so highly modified that their homology is in doubt. There is a short tubular haustellum (*h.*) armed with teeth which can be everted so that the teeth are on the outside, as shown in the figure. Through this can be protruded three slender stylets or piercers, a dorsal and a ventral one forked at the base and toothed at the tip, and a very slender intermediate hypopharynx, not shown in the figure. The stylets are retractable into a blind sac (*st. s.*) lying under the pharynx and do not protrude except when in use. Blood is sucked through a channel formed when the dorsal and ventral stylets are applied to each other.

The stomach is provided with lateral pouches in order to increase the food capacity. Normally lice do not fill themselves to repletion and then wait until this food is digested before feeding again but enjoy more moderate meals several times a day.

All except the human body lice glue their eggs to hairs near the base. The eggs hatch in a few days, and the young nymphs closely resemble the adults except for their size and paler color. There are three nymphal instars; the third moult brings them to the adult stage in 3 weeks or less.

Most species of lice are quite closely limited to a single host, and sometimes even genera are thus limited. Kellogg has suggested that the evolutionary affinities of different birds and mammals may be demonstrated by the kinds of lice that infest them. Only about 200 species of Anoplura are known, but the species of Mallophaga are numerous. The Anoplura are divided into several families as follows:

1a. Nine pairs of spiracles; body robust and bristly; on seals, etc.
....Echinophthiridae.
1b. Seven pairs of spiracles; body flattened and spiny ....2.
2a. Eyes well-developed; head short anterior to antennae ....3.
2b. Eyes vestigial or absent; head long anterior to antennae ....4.
3a. Abdominal segments III and IV fused, with 3 pairs of spiracles; body crablike (Fig. 203); on man (crab lice) ....Phthiridae.
3b. Apparent abdominal segments 7; form slender (Fig. 201); on man and monkeys (body and head lice) ....Pediculidae.
4a. Antennae 3-segmented; on monkeys and rodents ......Haematopinoididae.
4b. Antennae 5-segmented; on many domestic and wild animals (Fig. 204)
....Haematopinidae.

Human Species. The lice infesting man belong to two genera, (1) Pediculus, including the head and body lice, and (2) Phthirus, with only a single species, the crab louse. Ferris (1935) recognized only three species of Pediculus, one on American monkeys, one on chimpanzees, and one, *P. humanus*, on man. The last species has two biological varieties, one inhabiting the head and known as *P. humanus humanus*, the other normally living on clothing and known as *P. humanus corporis*. During World War I, when lice enlarged their acquaintanceship extensively, the latter were called " cooties " or " graybacks."

No doubt both the head louse and body louse are the descendants of a species that roamed the hairy bodies of our forefathers in the days when we fought our struggle for existence with mammoths and cave bears instead of tax collectors and strike organizers. With the developing hairlessness of the host, the hunting grounds of human lice became more and more restricted. The crab louse adapted itself to the coarse residual body hair, but *P. humanus* solved the problem in two different ways: some retired to the fine hair of the head and became head lice, while others, more resourceful, adapted themselves to living on the clothing next to the skin and became body lice. With the differentiation of the principal races of man some slight differentiation of the head lice may also have occurred; Ewing recognizes four varieties, found on Caucasians, Negroes, Chinese, and American Indians, respectively, but other louse specialists do not recognize them.

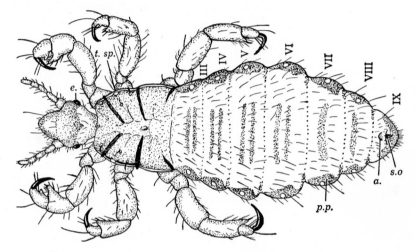

Fig. 201. *Pediculus humanus corporis*, body louse, ♂, × 40; *a.*, anus; *e.*, eye; *p.p.*, pleural plate; *s.o.*, sex opening; *t. sp.*, thoracic spiracle; III–IX, abdominal segments. (Adapted from Keilin and Nuttall.)

Even if such varieties once existed it would be almost impossible to find pure strains now, for the lice interbreed as do their hosts. Studies of ethnology of lice and of man are beset with the same difficulties.

Head and Body Lice (*Pediculus humanus*)

Morphology. The general appearance of *Pediculus humanus* can be seen from Fig. 201. The head has eyes and five-jointed antennae, the latter distinctly longer in the body than head lice. The thorax has a single pair of spiracles, situated between the first and second pairs of legs. The abdomen is composed of seven segments (III to IX), of which the first six bear spiracles. Pleural plates are well developed, but more so in head than in body lice, resulting in a more festooned appearance in the head lice. Females, somewhat larger than males, are usually from 2.4 to 3.3 mm. long in head lice and from 2.4 to 3.8

mm. in body lice. They can readily be distinguished from males by the indented posterior end of the abdomen and by the slenderer anterior legs with smaller grasping apparatus. In males the anus and sex openings are dorsal in position.

Biology. Head lice prefer to live in the fine hair of the head, though they sometimes wander to other parts of the body. They occur on all races of man in every part of the world. Buxton found that the majority of infested persons, however, harbor very few lice. In England a high percentage have only from 1 to 10, and less than 10 per cent have over 100, usually in girls 5 to 8 years old. Apparently brushing and combing keep them at a low level.

The body louse, on the other hand, lives on the clothing instead of the hair of its host; the German name " Kleiderlaus " is a very appropriate one. Possibly this louse developed independently from the ancestral ape-man louse, shifting its position from the waning hair to the clothes as nudism temporarily went out of style, but more likely it developed from the head louse. It is a true radical in its habits, for of all the lice in the world it alone lives elsewhere than in the hair of its host. A person infested with hundreds of body lice may remove his clothing and find not a single specimen on his body. An examination of the underwear will reveal them adhering to the inside surfaces. Here they live and lay their eggs, reaching across to the body to suck blood, holding to the clothing by their hind legs.

Life Cycle. The eggs of lice, commonly called " nits," are oval, whitish objects fitted with a little lid at the larger end through which the hatching takes place. The eggs of head lice are slightly less than 1 mm. in length, and are glued to the hairs by means of a cementlike excretion (Fig. 202A). The favorite " nests " are in the vicinity of the ears. The average number laid by each female, according to Bacot, is from 80 to 100.

Body lice lay slightly larger eggs and glue them to the fibers of the clothing (Fig. 202B), especially along the seams or creases. Under experimental conditions the body louse will sometimes lay eggs on hairs, but it nearly always selects the crossing point of two hairs and shows less skill than the head louse in attaching the eggs. The body louse shows a marked " homing " instinct in laying her eggs, and tends to cluster them until 50 or 75 have been collected. The total number of eggs may be from 200 to 300. The female begins production slowly but after a week of practice she reaches an output of about 8 or 10 per day, although there is never more than one developed egg in the body at a time. Unfertilized eggs are sometimes laid, but they do not develop. Egg-laying ceases at temperatures below 77° F., and a daily exposure to a temperature of 60° F. for only 2 or 3 hours causes a marked falling off in egg production.

At 80° to 85° F. the eggs hatch in about 8 to 10 days; at higher temperatures many die. No hatching occurs below 70° F., and eggs held below 60° F. for 7 to 9 days do not hatch even if warmed. Either excessive humidity or complete drying is fatal to the eggs. It is evident that in winter the laying off of the clothing at night in a cold room or the leaving of mattresses or bedclothes in the daytime is sufficient to prevent the laying or hatching of eggs.

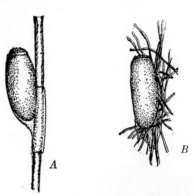

FIG. 202. *A*, egg of head louse attached to a hair; *B*, egg of body louse attached to fibers of clothing. × 25. (After Cholodkowsky.)

The young lice have an interesting way of escaping from the eggs. They suck air into the body and expel it from the anus until a cushion of compressed air is formed sufficient to pop open the lid of the egg. The newly hatched lice are almost perfect miniatures of the adults except that they have three-segmented antennae. They are ready to feed almost as soon as they emerge from the egg and will usually die in less than 24 hours if not allowed to feed. At a temperature of 95° F. and with as many daily feeds as would willingly be taken, namely 6, the lice pass through the first moult in 3 days, the second in 5 or 6 days, and the third, which brings them to maturity, in 8 or 9 days. With fewer feeds or lower temperatures the development is slower.

Egg-laying begins from 1 to 4 days after the final moult and continues at the rate previously described until the death of the insect. The average length of life for the females is about 35 or 40 days and probably a little less for the males.

Feeding Habits. Lice show less tendency to vacillate in their drilling operations than do fleas. They make a single puncture and then rely on the salivary secretion to dilate the capillaries by its irritation and thus facilitate the flow of blood; this sometimes requires several minutes. They may suck to repletion in a few minutes but often continue to pump blood into their stomachs intermittently for several hours, meanwhile voiding feces containing undigested blood corpuscles.

There seems to be some degree of specificity in the salivary secretion, since it is more efficient in aiding the lice to suck blood from man than from other animals. Rat blood seems to disagree with human lice.

Lice do not have the remarkable resistance to starvation displayed by ticks and bugs. At high temperatures they succumb in 2 or 3 days but at about 40° F. can live for 8 or 10 days without food. Adult lice stand exposure to moderate cold very well but are killed in a few hours at temperatures of 10° F. or below. They are highly susceptible to heat, especially when the humidity is high, and die in a few minutes at 122° to 126° F.

The maximum favorable temperature for the development and reproduction of lice is about 95° F. The absence of lice from hot countries — observable in Mexico, for instance, where they are abundant on the central plateau above 5000 to 6000 ft., but absent from the hot coastal strips — is apparently not due to the high temperature but probably to the disastrous effect of profuse perspiration and consequent excessive humidity between the clothes and skin. Head lice are found in hotter countries than body lice, especially in bareheaded people.

Effect of Bites. The effect of louse bites varies greatly with individuals and with the degree of sensitivity to them, for according to Peck, Wright, and Gant (1943) the principal symptoms appear to be allergic in nature. When persons previously unexposed to lice are experimentally bitten there is at first only a slight sting and little or no itching or redness. After about a week such a person becomes sensitized, and then the bites cause considerable irritation and inflamed red spots. When such persons are bitten by large numbers of lice there may be a general skin eruption, mild fever, and a marked feeling of tiredness and irritability. The bites themselves are only partially responsible; much of the reaction is due to contact of the bites with the feces of the lice, to which infested individuals also become sensitized.

Eventually the increased sensitivity gives way to immunity as with other insect bites (see p. 488), and people long infested become oblivious to them. During the stage of increased sensitivity the irritation leads to scratching, and sometimes the scratched bites become secondarily infected, causing pustules to form. Often areas around the bites turn brown, giving the skin a mottled appearance. In very negligent individuals badly infested with head lice the hair may become matted and form a sort of filthy carapace under which fungus growths develop, and the head may exude a fetid odor.

The interesting observation that white rats that have remained free

from lice for years promptly become lousy (probably from wild rats
or from a very few they previously harbored) when placed on a diet
deficient in riboflavin (one of the vitamin B complex), may possibly
have some bearing on the fact that some individuals seem to be
attacked more readily than others, and that lice become especially
prevalent under conditions of hardship and starvation. Diet may be

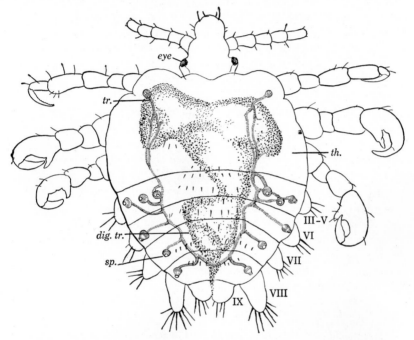

Fig. 203. *Phthirus pubis*, ♀, × 35; *dig. tr.*, digestive tract; *sp.*, spiracle; *th.*, thorax;
tr., trachea; III–IX, abdominal segments.

an important factor in louse-borne diseases, for riboflavin not only
protects rats against lice but it also increases their resistance to typhus,
though not to the extent that *p*-aminobenzoic acid does.

Crab Louse

The crab louse, *Phthirus pubis* (Fig. 203), is quite distinct from the
other two species of human lice. It has a very broad short body with
long, clawed legs, presenting the general appearance of a tiny crab,
from which it derives its name. The first pair of legs are smaller
than the others and do not possess a " thumb " in opposition to the
curved claw. The thorax is very broad with all the segments fused,
and the abdomen is greatly foreshortened. Its first three segments

(III to V) are fused into one, which bears three pairs of spiracles. The last four segments bear wartlike processes on the sides, the last pair of which is particularly large. This louse is grayish in color, with slightly reddish legs. The females are about 1.5 to 2 mm. in length, the males somewhat smaller. The favorite haunts are the pubic regions and other parts of the body where coarse hair grows, as in the armpits and in the beard, eyebrows, and eyelashes. Occasionally they infest almost the entire body except the head; the writer once saw a hairy individual who was covered with them from eyebrows to ankles. Unlike the other human lice this species is almost exclusively confined to the Caucasian race.

The females produce 25 or more eggs and glue them, one at a time, to the coarse hairs among which they live. A number of eggs may be glued to a single hair and often at some distance from the skin. The eggs hatch in 6 or 7 days, and the young become sexually mature in about 3 weeks. This species, even under favorable conditions, can live apart from its host only 10 or 12 hours. The eggs are said not to develop except at temperatures between 68° and 86° F., which are approximately the temperatures to which eggs attached to hairs beneath the clothing would be exposed in cool climates.

The bites of the louse usually cause extreme itching. The secretion of one of the pairs of salivary glands has a peculiar effect on hemoglobin, causing it to turn a violet color in the absence of air; in the body this often causes the formation of telltale pale blue spots up to a centimeter in diameter.

Lice and Disease

Louse-borne diseases have in the past ranked high among the minor horrors of war — higher, certainly, than they ever will again. In peacetime large louse-borne epidemics do not regularly occur since people and communities are rather sharply divided into those who tolerate lousiness and those who do not. The former are exposed to bites of lice from birth; they suffer from louse-borne diseases early in life, become immune, and are kept immune by repeated reinfection. The louse-free population suffers only sporadic cases since there is not sufficient louse traffic between the two components of a community to cause an epidemic except under disrupted conditions brought on by disaster, famine, or local conditions where facilities for keeping body and clothes clean are inadequate, as in construction camps, prisons, etc. Furthermore, there is ordinarily no opportunity for building up the virulence of the organisms concerned by a rapid sequence of human cases, as happens at the beginning of epidemics.

There are three diseases for which lice are the primary transmitters — epidemic typhus, trench fever, and relapsing fever. The first is caused by *Rickettsia prowazeki* (see p. 230), the second is believed to be caused by another rickettsia, *R. quintana,* and the third is caused by a spirochete, *Borrelia recurrentis* (see p. 52). Lice are certainly not the primary transmitters of either typhus or relapsing fever; epidemic typhus has undoubtedly been derived from flea-borne endemic typhus, and relapsing fever from tick-borne strains. The rat louse, *Polyplax spinulosa,* is capable of transmitting endemic typhus among rats. Typhus organisms are invariably fatal to lice, though unfortunately not quickly enough to prevent transmission, whereas fleas suffer no evident ill effects, and in mites and ticks the rickettsias are even transovarially transmitted. Relapsing-fever spirochetes have become better adapted to lice but are not transovarially transmitted. For a discussion of the interrelations of rickettsias and spirochetes with their various vectors, see pp. 228 and 52.

Epidemic Typhus. Louse-borne typhus, known in Europe for centuries, seldom makes itself evident except in extensive outbreaks during wars or other conditions when, as already noted, lice have an opportunity to extend their acquaintanceships widely and to transmit the organisms to many people who had no chance to develop immunity early in life. Zinsser says that typhus has killed more humans than any other disease. It was typhus that caused Napoleon to withdraw his armies from Russia. It is estimated that this disease killed 3,000,000 Russians during World War I. In former days the disease broke out on sailing ships or in prisons so frequently that it was sometimes called ship fever or jail fever. Hence the name epidemic typhus. In New York and Boston, however, and probably elsewhere, the disease exists in endemic form and is called Brill's disease. The majority of the cases occur among people who handle worn clothes, such as tailors and cleaners.

Body lice are the principal transmitters, perhaps because head lice are less frequently passed around. There is no evidence that crab lice are involved. Epidemics usually break out under crowded conditions and most frequently in winter, when people are closely huddled together and the lice nightly migrate from one pile of dirty clothing to another. The rickettsias multiply in the epithelial cells of the intestine and are voided with the feces. Transmission results from contamination of bites by the feces, or by the intestinal contents squeezed out when lice are crushed. The rickettsias live for weeks or possibly months in the dried feces or dead bodies of lice, which can cause infection by inhalation or contact long after the living lice are gone. This accounts for the Russian belief that a person who wears the clothes or boots of a victim of typhus will also die of it. There is no transovarial transmission. Although, as pointed out previously, the louse rickettsia, *R. prowazeki*, is probably derived from the flea strain, *R. typhi*, and is closely related to it, it is distinguishable in the laboratory by the fact that it fails to cause scrotal swelling and other scrotal reactions in guinea pigs, as does *R. typhi*.

In man epidemic typhus under epidemic conditions is much more severe than endemic typhus, sometimes causing the death of 70 per cent of its victims. This is doubtless due in part to exaltation of virulence by rapid passage through numbers of susceptible people and in part to lowered resistance under wartime conditions. Poor diet and undernourishment are big factors. The disease is marked by severe headache, prostration, high fever, and a rash caused by small skin hemorrhages. It can be prevented by vaccines and can be greatly reduced in virulence by administration of *p*-aminobenzoic acid (see p. 229) or of a new antibiotic, aureomycin. With DDT its prevention is now a relatively simple matter (see p. 582). In 1943 an outbreak in Naples was stopped short, the first time in history that such a thing had been done; it has since been accomplished in other outbreaks, e.g., in Mexico and Chile. It is unlikely that typhus will ever again cause devastating epidemics in civilized countries.

Trench Fever. It is generally believed that this disease is also caused by a rickettsia, *R. quintana* (see p. 230), which, like the non-pathogenic *R. pediculi*, lives in the lumen of the intestines of lice but not in the epithelial cells. Although unknown previously, this disease became so common during World War I that it caused more sickness than any other disease except scabies. After the war it fell into obscurity again, but a fresh outbreak occurred among people working in a typhus-vaccine laboratory in Warsaw just prior to World War II, and some small outbreaks occurred in the Balkans during that war. This exemplifies perfectly the influence of social conditions on louse-borne infections, when numerous people unaccustomed to lice are suddenly exposed to them. When lice are restricted to their homefolks, immunity to this mild disease probably develops early in life, and there is no opportunity for exaltation of virulence.

The infection is transmitted, like typhus, by louse feces, but since urine and feces of human cases are infective, it may not be spread exclusively by lice. It has a 10- to 30-day incubation period; the symptoms are headache, body pains, fever, albumin in the urine, and usually a rash.

Relapsing Fever. When lice ingest the blood of a relapsing-fever patient most of the spirochetes die in the alimentary canal within a very short time, but a few survive by penetrating into the body cavity. Although very sparse for a few days they become abundant after about a week. Neither the bites nor the feces of the lice are infective, and transmission occurs only by breaking or crushing lice and inoculating bites with the infective body fluid. For further information about relapsing fever see pp. 52–57.

Lice are involved in the transmission of a number of strains of relapsing-fever spirochetes in Europe, Iran, central and southern India, China, north Africa, Sudan, and west Africa north and west of the Cameroons. Although louse-borne strains were undoubtedly derived originally from tick-borne infections, lice seem not to be susceptible to some tick-borne strains (see p. 53).

Louse-borne relapsing fever shows the same peculiarities of occurrence as typhus; epidemics always rage fiercest in winter and usually break out during wartimes.

Lice and Other Diseases. Lice may also serve as mechanical transmitters of certain other diseases. The bacilli of bubonic plague have been found alive in both body lice and head lice taken from victims of the disease, and both species have been experimentally proved able to transmit plague from rodent to rodent in Java. Lice do not transmit plague by their bites, but they may transmit it when crushed, and possibly with their feces. Natives in Java kill lice by mashing them against the head of the host, which should make infection through the scratched sores on the head very easy. In Ecuador and Peru natives are said to kill lice by crushing them between the teeth; there is much more danger involved when man bites louse than when louse bites man.

Most bacterial diseases are not transmitted by lice except possibly immediately after an infective feed, for most bacteria are destroyed in the alimentary canal by an antibacterial substance. Lice have been suspected of transmitting various diseases just as bedbugs have, but no scientific evidence supports the suspicions.

Prevention and Remedies

Methods of Dispersal. The prevention of lousiness consists primarily in personal cleanliness. However, no amount of personal hygiene and cleanliness will prevent temporary lousiness if there is association with unclean and careless companions. Lousiness and human wretchedness and degradation have always been companions, but this does not imply that lice have any inherent abhorrence of a clean body if they can get access to it. From the nature of their habitats the common modes of infection of the three different species of human lice vary somewhat. The head louse depends for distribution largely on crowded cloakrooms, on promiscuous use of combs and brushes or borrowed hats and caps, and on the free-for-all trying on of headgear in haberdasheries and millinery shops. The body louse is dispersed by clothing and bed linen, usually at night, and finds fresh hunting grounds by nocturnal migrations from one pile of clothes to another. The crab louse sometimes utilizes public toilets for dissemination and is commonly spread by promiscuous sexual intercourse.

Where men are crowded together in prisons or war camps lousiness is almost sure to develop unless particularly guarded against, since some unclean persons are nearly always in the aggregation, and conditions are such that the infestation is given every opportunity to spread. Even under normal conditions there are many opportunities for dispersal. Buxton (1947) recalls seeing some men sitting on a wall in Iran, catching lice and dropping them into the street, with typhus and relapsing fever epidemic at the time. Of importance in connection with the spread of these diseases is the fact that lice desert a febrile patient and seek a new host. In Europe during World War II lice were mostly well controlled in military forces, but they spread extensively among civilians, especially in crowded bomb shelters and in crowded homes for evacuated children.

Elimination of Lice. Few preventive measures have given more spectacularly good results than the use of DDT in destroying body lice and protecting against them. During the latter part of World War II every American soldier and sailor was provided with a dusting powder consisting of 10 per cent DDT in pyrophyllite and was free of cooties for the first time in any war. The dust was applied by blow-guns to the head, skin, and clothing, without undressing. One pound of DDT powder was enough to dust 15 to 20 persons.

Though this method has now superseded all older ones for mass delousing, various other methods may be used for individuals. Since the lice live and deposit their eggs almost entirely on the underwear, they can be eliminated by a thorough bath and treatment of the clothing with hot water or dry heat at 160° F. for 1 minute, pressing with a hot iron, live steam, washing in any of many disinfectant solutions, or fumigation. Impregnation by dipping in a 5 per cent DDT solution or emulsion, enough to give a DDT dosage of 1 to 2 per cent of the weight of the garment, will render the clothes protective against lice through 6 to 8 washings. DDT does not kill the eggs of lice, but it persists long enough to kill the nymphs as soon as they hatch.   For head lice, too, about a level teaspoonful of 10 per cent DDT dust shaken from a jar with a perforated lid, rubbed into the hair, and not washed out for a week, was found by Cowan, McGregor, and Randolph (1947) to give 100 per cent control in school children with heavy infestations in south Texas.   No lice were found in children so treated, even after 4 weeks, and there were no injurious effects.   This is a tremendous improvement over the troublesome and messy procedures described in earlier editions of this book.

Crab lice have been easiest to eliminate in the past, by ointments containing various insecticides, but most of them had to be applied twice, since they did not kill the eggs.   A single application of 1 part

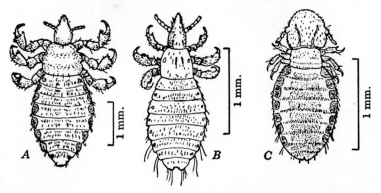

FIG. 204.   Cattle lice; *A* and *B*, Anoplura; *C*, Mallophaga.   *A*, *Haematopinus eurysternus; B, Linognathus vituli; C, Bovicola bovis.*

of 10 per cent DDT powder in 20 parts of cold cream rubbed over the hairy parts and followed by a soap bath 12 hours later is all that is necessary.   The itching stops and the lice die in 30 minutes.

Anoplura on Domestic Animals

As noted in the key on p. 572, the sucking lice that torment domestic animals belong to the family Haematopinidae, which differ from the Pediculidae mainly in the absence of eyes and in having longer snouts. Each of the common domestic animals has one or more of its own private species that it rarely shares with other kinds of animals.   The important genera can be distinguished as follows:

1*a*. Body with chitinized pleural plates (Fig. 204*A*) ....2.
1*b*. Body without chitinized pleural plates (Fig. 204*B*) ....3.
2*a*. All 3 pairs of legs about equally thick (Fig. 204*A*) ....***Haematopinus.***
 Important spp.: *H. suis* (very large) on pigs; *H. asini* on horses;

H. eurysternus (short-nosed louse) and *H. quadripertusis* (tail louse) on cattle.

2*b*. First pair of legs slenderer than others; on rats ....**Polyplax.**
Important sp.: *P. spinulosus,* a typhus transmitter on rats.

3*a*. Tergites and sternites of abdomen with only 1 row of hairs ....4.

3*b*. Tergites and sternites with 2 or 3 rows of hairs (Fig. 204*B*) .....**Linognathus.**
Important spp.: *L. vituli* (long-nosed or blue louse) on cattle; *L. stenopsis* on goat; *L. setosus* on dog and fox; *L. pedalis* on feet of sheep.

4*a*. Spiracles very small, not on tubercles ....**Haemadipsus.**

4*b*. Spiracles well-developed, on tubercles ....**Solenopotes.**
Important sp.: *S. capillatus* on cattle.

Like the Mallophaga (see p. 587) these lice stick closely to their hosts and are usually transmitted only by body contact, though horse lice are spread by blankets, saddles, etc.

The hosts are much more annoyed by these lice than they are by the Mallophaga. Their fur and skin are affected, and they become restless, lose their appetites, and become susceptible to other diseases. Constant licking by cattle produces hair balls in the stomach, and the foot louse of sheep may cause lameness.

Treatment for cattle, goats, and horses is best accomplished by spraying or dipping with 0.2 or 0.3 per cent DDT or benzene hexachloride emulsion or a similar dilution of 20 per cent DDT in pine oil; for cattle it takes about 1½ to 2 qt. per animal, leaving about 4 to 5 gm. of DDT. Dusting with 10 per cent DDT in pyrophyllite also gives good control, one dusting being effective for 6 weeks or more. The tail louse, *H. quadripertusis,* the most annoying species on cattle, is harder to control and requires a 1.5 per cent spray. Pigs can easily be deloused by application of 2 per cent DDT dust or emulsion or by adding waste crankcase oil to wallows.

Mallophaga

Morphology. Most Mallophaga are very small, less than 1 mm. in length, but a few are large. They have dorso-ventrally flattened bodies well adapted to gliding between feathers of birds, on which the great majority are parasitic. They have short inconspicuous antennae, which in the suborder Amblycera are tucked into grooves on the sides of the head as they are in fleas (Fig. 205*B*). There are no evident mouthparts except the strongly chitinized, pincerlike mandibles and, in the suborder Amblycera, a pair of short four-jointed maxillary palpi (Fig. 205*B*). In most species the thorax, which is narrower than the head, has two or three distinct segments which may make a continuous series, dorsally, with the eight abdominal segments. In most species the second to seventh segments bear spiracles. The legs are short and all much alike; except in a few species on mammals they are not fitted for clasping as are the legs of Anoplura.

The Mallophaga are divided into two suborders and a number of families. The families, genera, and species of interest as parasites of domestic animals are shown in the following keys:

Suborder **Amblycera.** Antennae club-shaped and mostly concealed in grooves; maxillary palpi 4-segmented (Fig. 205B). Only family important on domestic animals is Menoponidae, infesting poultry.

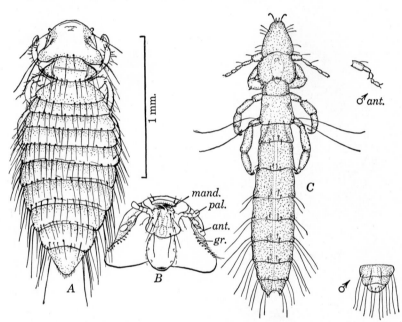

Fig. 205. Examples of two suborders of Mallophaga. *A, Menopon gallinae* of chickens, dorsal view; *B*, same, ventral view of head. (Adapted from Ferris.) *C, Columbicola columbae* of pigeons, ♀, and antenna and posterior end of abdomen of ♂. (After Martin.)

A. All tarsi with 2 claws, antennae 4-segmented; head evenly expanded behind and broadly triangular. **Menoponidae** ....1.

  1a. Thorax with 3 distinct segments (Fig. 206A) ....***Trinoton.***
      2 or 3 spp. on geese, ducks, and swans.

  1b. Thorax with 2 segments (Figs. 205A, 206B) ....2.

  2a. Abdominal segments with 2 rows of bristles ....***Eomenacanthus.***
      E. stramineus (body louse) of chickens.

  2b. Abdominal segments with 1 row of bristles ....3.

  3a. Eye lodged in a shallow sinus (Fig. 205A) ....***Menopon.***
      M. gallinae (shaft louse) of chickens.

  3b. Eye lodged in a deep sinus (Fig. 206B) ....***Colpocephalum.***
      C. turbinatum of pigeons and *C. pectiniventre* of geese.

Suborder **Ischnocera.** Antennae filiform and exposed; no maxillary palpi (Fig. 205*C*).

    1. Antennae 5-segmented; tarsi with 2 claws; infesting birds (Fig. 206*C–H*)
    ....**Philopteridae.**
    2. Antennae 3-segmented; tarsi with 1 claw (Fig. 204*C*); infesting mammals
    ....**Trichodectidae.**

A key to the principal genera of these two families, infesting birds and mammals respectively, is given below, with mention of the com-

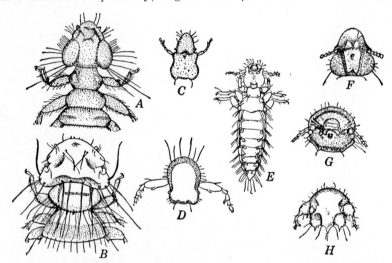

Fig. 206. Details of various Mallopnaga to illustrate key. *A, Trinoton querquedulae* of ducks; *B, Colpocephalum pectiniventre* of geese; *C, Esthiopterum crassicorne* of ducks; *D, Lipeuris caponis* of chickens; *E, Ornithobius cygni* of swans; *F, Philopterus dentatus* of ducks; *G, Goniocotes gigas* of chickens; *H, Goniodes pavonis* of peacock. (Adapted from various authors.)

moner and more important parasites of domestic animals in North America:

Ischnocera of Birds (Philopteridae)

A. Body long and slender.
    (1) **Lipeurus:** Head nearly hemispherical in front of antennae; in ♂ 1st segment of antenna much enlarged, third segment with prong (Fig. 206*D*).
    L. gallipavonis on turkey; *L. caponis* on chickens.
    (2) **Esthiopterum:** Head elongated in front of antennae; antennae as in (1); clypeus without dorsal spines (Fig. 206*C*).
    E. crassicorne on ducks.
    (3) **Columbicola:** Like (2) but clypeus with 2 pairs of spines dorsally.
    C. columbae on pigeons (Fig. 205*C*).
    (4) **Ornithobius:** ♂ antenna without prongs; abdomen with second chitinized band paralleling chitinized margin (Fig. 206*E*).
    O. cygni on swans.

B. Body broad, abdomen rounded.
(1) **Philopterus:** Antennae with 5 similar segments in both sexes; a horn-like process in front of insertion of antennae (Fig. 206F).
P. *dentatus* on ducks.
(2) **Goniocotes:** No prongs on segments of ♂ antenna; no spine in front of insertion of antennae (Fig. 206G).
G. *gigas* (3–4 mm. long) and G. *hologaster,* fluff louse, (0.8–1.3 mm. long) on chickens; G. *bidentatus* on pigeons.
(3) **Goniodes:** Antenna of ♂ with prong on third segment at least; no spine in front of insertion of antennae (Fig. 206H).
G. *dissimilis* on chickens; G. *damicornis* (2 mm. long) and G. *minor* (less than 2 mm. long) on pigeon; G. *parviceps* (2 mm. long) and G. *pavonis* (3 mm. long) on peacock; G. *meleagridis* on turkey.
Ischnocera of Mammals (Trichodectidae)
A. **Bovicola:** With pleural plates; antennae alike in both sexes (Fig. 205C).
B. *bovis* on cattle, B. *caprae* on goats, B. *equi* on horses, B. *ovis* on sheep.
B. **Trichodectes:** With pleural plates; antennae of ♂ with first segment of antenna enlarged.
T. *canis* on dogs.
C. **Felicola:** Without pleural plates; antennae alike in both sexes.
T. *subrostrata* on cats.

Life Cycle, Habits, etc. The Mallophaga live their entire lives, generation after generation, on their hosts. On birds they feed mainly if not exclusively on the barbules of feathers, and in mammals they live on epidermal scales, skin secretions, etc. The eggs are glued to feathers or hairs, sometimes in selected places, usually one a day. In the pigeon louse, *Columbicola columbae,* Martin in 1933 found the eggs to hatch in 4 days and the nymphs to pass through their three moults and reach maturity in about 3 weeks.

Except for occasional hitchhiking on the bodies of Hippoboscid flies, Mallophaga move from host to host only by direct body contact. For this reason they are usually kept in the family and pass from generation to generation of the same species. Thus isolated zoologically, many species and even genera have arisen which are closely confined to particular kinds of birds.

Although Mallophaga do not suck blood and can only exceptionally transmit disease, they frequently cause sufficient annoyance to their hosts to result in unthriftiness and, in chickens, a falling off in egg production.

Control. Control of Mallophaga on larger animals is the same as for Anoplura (see p. 584). Chickens can be freed of lice by dusting individual birds from a salt shaker with 6 gm. of 5 per cent DDT dust; by dipping birds in a 0.3 per cent emulsion; by spraying birds with 2.5 per cent emulsion; or by spraying floors, roosts, and nests with 2.5 per cent emulsion. The dipping is quickest and lasts longest; the house spraying is slowest. A mixture of DDT and Lethane (1 lb. of 50 per cent wettable DDT and ½ lb. Lethane 72B per 6 qt. of water, sprayed at the rate of 1 oz. per bird) gave perfect control of both lice and mites. Another method is to paint perches with 40 per cent nicotine sulfate in a partly closed building just before the birds go to roost; the fumes kill many but not all of the lice. Application of 5 to 10 lb. of sulfur to 100 sq. ft. soil in poultry yards gives good results for the birds dusting in it. Use of a weak DDT dust in dusting holes would probably be worth trying.

REFERENCES

BACOT, A. W., A Contribution to the Bionomics of *Pediculus humanus* (*vestimenti*) and *Pediculus capitis, Parasitology,* **9,** 229 (1917).

BUXTON, P. A., Studies on Populations of Head Lice (*P. humanus capitis*), *Parasitology,* **28,** 82 (1936); **30,** 85 (1938); **32,** 296 (1940); **33,** 224 (1941).
  The Louse, An Account of the Lice Which Infest Man, Their Medical Importance and Control, London, 2nd ed., 1947.

COWAN, F. A., McGREGOR, T., and RANDOLPH, N. M., DDT Dust for the Control of Head Lice, *Am. J. Trop. Med.,* **27,** 67–68 (1947).

DYER, R. E., RUMREICH, A., and BADGER, L. F., Typhus Fever, *Publ. Health Repts.,* **46,** 334 (1931).

EWING, H. E., A Revision of the American Lice of the Genus Pediculus, together with a Consideration of their Geographical and Host Distribution, *Proc. U. S. Nat. Mus.,* **68,** Art. 19 (1926).
  The Taxonomy of the Mallophagan Family Trichodectidae, with Special Reference to the New World Fauna, *J. Parasitol.,* **22,** 223 (1936).

FERRIS, G. F., Contributions toward a Monograph of the Sucking Lice, V, VI, and VIII, *Stanford Univ. Pubs. Biol. Sci.,* **2,** 1932–1935.

GRINNELL, M. C., and HAWES, I. L., Bibliography on Lice and Man, *U. S. Dept. Agr. Bibliographical Bull.,* **1** (1943).

KEILIN, D., and NUTTALL, G. H. F., Iconographic Studies on *Pediculus humanus, Parasitology,* **22,** 1 (1930).

NUTTALL, G. H. F., Biology of *Pediculus humanus, Parasitology,* **10,** 1, 80, 411; **11,** 201, 329; Biology of *Phthirus pubis, ibid.,* **10,** 375, 383; **11,** 329 (1917–1919).

PECK, S. M., WRIGHT, W. H., and GANT, J. Q., Cutaneous Reactions Due to the Body Louse, *J. Am. Med. Assoc.,* **123,** 821–825 (1943).

SIKORA, H., Beiträge zur Biologie von *Pediculus vestimenti, Centr. Bakt.,* 1, Orig., **76,** 523 (1915).

SOPER, F. L., DAVIS, W. A., MARKHAM, F. S., and RIEHL, L. A., Typhus Fever in Italy, 1943–1945, and Its Control with Louse Powder, *Am. J. Hyg.,* **45,** 305–334 (1947).

ZINSSER, H., *Rats, Lice, and History,* Boston, 1935.
  See also References of Chapters 4, 10, and 20.

CHAPTER 25

Fleas

SIPHONAPTERA

David Harum says, " A reasonable amount of fleas is good for a dog. They keep him from broodin' on bein' a dog." A goodly supply of fleas might likewise keep man from brooding over anything deeper than the presence of these fleas, but in some cases this in itself is a rather serious thing to brood over. Not only are fleas very annoying pests and a common cause of insomnia, but they may also serve as the disseminators of a number of important human diseases, among which bubonic plague stands foremost.

General Structure. Fleas, constituting the order Siphonaptera, are believed by most entomologists to be more or less distantly related to the Diptera or two-winged flies. Their bodies are much compressed to facilitate gliding between the hairs or feathers of their hosts. The head is broadly joined to the thorax, which is relatively small. The abdomen consists of ten segments, the first seven of which are simple rings, each protected by a pair of chitinous plates, a dorsal *tergum* and a ventral *sternum* (Fig. 207). The last three segments are modified differently in the male and female. In both sexes the tergum of the ninth segment has a pitted area covered with little bristles which is called the *pygidium;* it is probably sensory in function. The seventh abdominal tergite bears from one to four pairs of long antepygidial bristles.

All parts of the body are furnished with backward-projecting bristles and spines which aid the flea in forcing its way between dense hairs and prevent it from slipping backward. The efficiency of these spines is apparent when one attempts to hold a flea between his fingers. Many fleas have specially developed, thick, heavy spines arranged in rows suggestive of the teeth of combs and therefore known as *ctenidia* or " combs " (Fig. 210). There may be a *genal ctenidium* along the ventral margin of the head, or a *pronotal ctenidium* on the hind margin of the pronotum (the dorsal plate covering the first segment of the thorax), or in both places. The presence or absence of these combs and the number of teeth in them are of considerable use in identification of species.

The legs of fleas are very long and powerful and at first glance seem to possess one more segment than do the legs of other insects. They really consist of the usual number of segments with five-jointed tarsi, but are peculiar in the enormous development of the coxae, which in most insects are quite insignificant (Fig. 207). The shape of the

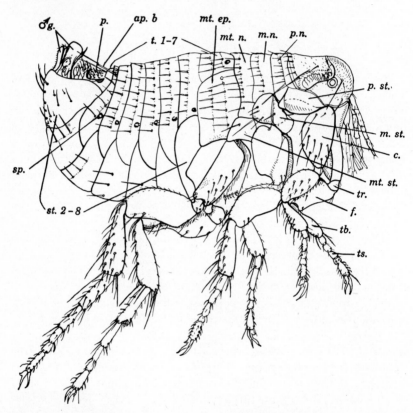

FIG. 207. *Xenopsylla cheopis*, rat flea, ♂; *ap. b.*, antepygidial bristles; *c.*, coxa; *f.*, femur; *m.n.*, mesonotum; *m. st.*, mesosternum; *mt. ep.*, metepimeron; *mt. n.*, metanotum; *mt. st.*, metasternum; *p.*, pygidium; *p.n.*, pronotum; *p. st.*, prosternum; *sp.*, spiracle; *st. 2–8*, abdominal sternites 2–8; *t. 1–7*, abdominal tergites 1–7; *tb.*, tibia; *tr.*, trochanter; *ts.*, tarsus; ♂*g.*, male genitalia. (Modified from Jordan and Rothschild.)

sternal plate to which the coxae are attached is suggestive of still another segment. The great development of the coxae as well as of the other segments of the leg gives unusual springiness and consequently enormous jumping power. The human flea, *Pulex irritans*, has been observed by Mitzmain to jump 13 in. horizontally and as much as 7¾ in. vertically; an equivalent jump for a man of average height would be over 450 ft. horizontally and over 275 ft. vertically! All the legs are furnished with rows of stout spines and are armed at the tip with a pair of large claws.

Simple eyes are present in some species of fleas but not in others. The antennae are short and club-shaped and consist of three segments, two small, the third large and laminated. When not in use they are folded back into special grooves for them on the sides of the head (Fig. 208, *ant. gr.*), but they can be rotated out or up over the head like a pair of horns. In many fleas there is a frontal notch or tubercle

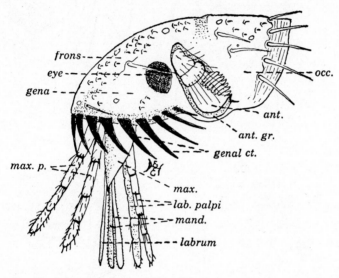

Fig. 208. Head of a flea, *Ctenocephalides felis* ♀; *ant.*, antenna; *ant. gr.*, antennal groove; *genal ct.*, genal ctenidium; *lab. palpi*, labial palpi; *mand.*, mandibles; *max.*, maxillae; *max. p.*, maxillary palpi; *occ.*, occiput. (After Ewing and Fox.)

on the front of the head. The region behind the antennal groove is called the *occiput;* the region in front of it is more or less divided into a forward *frons* and a lower *gena* (see Fig. 208).

The mouthparts are fitted for piercing and sucking. The labial palpi, usually with three to five segments, are grooved structures that fit together to form a sheath for the piercing organs, which consist of a pair of slender blade-like mandibles serrated at the tip, like little saws, and a bristle-like labrum. The maxillae are not developed as piercing organs but are large pyramidal structures with a spine at the tip, used for holding the head of the flea in position while feeding. They are provided with a pair of four-segmented palpi that might easily be mistaken for antennae. There is a muscular, sucking pharynx and a large, distensible stomach.

The male external genital organs consist of complicated claspers and other organs formed out of the ninth abdominal segment; the details of their structure are of much taxonomic value (Fig. 209C and D). The ninth tergite forms a *clasper* on each side provided with a dorsal

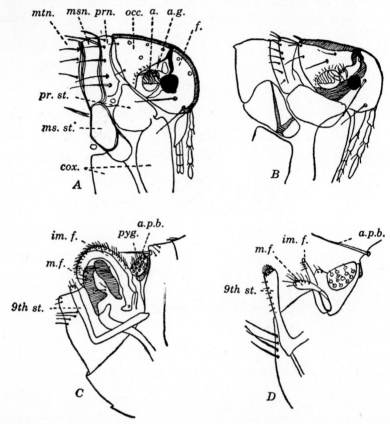

FIG. 209. Heads and posterior part of ♂ abdomen of *Pulex irritans* (A and C) and *Xenopsylla cheopis* (B and D); a., antenna; a.g., antennal groove; a.p.b., antepygidial bristle; cox., coxae; f., frons; im. f., immovable finger process of clasper; m.f., movable finger processes of clasper; msn., mesonotum; ms. st., mesosternum; mtn., metanotum; occ., occiput; prn., pronotum; pr. st., prosternum; pyg., pygidium; 9th st., ninth sternite. (After Fox.)

process or *immovable finger* and having hinged to it a *movable finger*. The ninth sternite is V-shaped, with an inward and upward projecting *vertical process* and a *distal lobe*. Between the ninth tergite and sternite is the *penis*, which is provided with a coiled *spring* inside the body. In the females the terminal segments of the abdomen are reduced and inconspicuous. In this sex a taxonomic character of great

importance is the form of the spermatheca (Fig. 213), which is chitinized and easily seen inside the abdomen in cleared specimens.

Classification.   Several hundred species of fleas have been described,
and more are constantly being discovered.   By some authors the
order Siphonaptera is divided into two suborders, the Fracticipita or
broken-headed fleas, which have a suture across the top of the head
between the bases of the antennae, and the Integricipita, which lack it
(cf. Figs. 210A, B, C), but Ewing and Fox (1943) do not accept this.
All the fleas of importance to man belong to the Integricipita except the
mouse flea, *Leptopsylla segnis* (Fig. 210B).   The division of fleas into

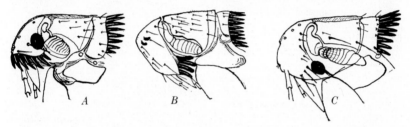

Fig. 210.   Heads of fleas, showing arrangement of ctenidia.   *A, Ctenocephalides canis;*
B, Leptopsylla segnis; C, Nosopsyllus fasciatus.   *A* and *C* belong to the Integricipita and
B belongs to the Fracticipita; note the joint over the head above the antennal groove.
(After Fox.)

families is a matter on which not all entomologists yet agree.   Ewing
and Fox recognize six families with eleven subfamilies; five families
are represented in North America.

The differentiation of genera of fleas is based largely on the presence
or absence of ctenidia on the head or on the pronotum, the number of
rows of bristles on the abdominal segments, the presence or absence of
eyes, the form of the antennae, the details of the genital organs, and
many minor characters concerning the bristles and the form of certain
plates of head or thorax.   The species are distinguished by very minute
characters in many cases, and even experts may disagree on identifica-
tions.   The following key will serve to identify the most important
families and genera of fleas so far as man and domestic animals are
concerned:

1a. Thorax much shortened, appearing telescoped; legs small; only 3 segments
 in feeble labial palpi (Fig. 214), **Hectopsyllidae**...........................2.
1b. Thorax not foreshortened; labial palpi with 4 or 5 segments ....3.
2a. Head with angular tubercle in front; hind coxa without patch of spinelets
 (Fig. 214A) ....***Tunga.***
 Important sp.: *T. penetrans* (chigger).
2b. Head almost round in front; hind coxa with patch of spinelets on inside

(Fig 215C) ....*Echidnophaga.*
Important sp.: *E. gallinacea,* sticktight flea of poultry, rats, etc.

3a. Abdominal tergites with only one row of bristles, **Pulicidae** ....4.

3b. Abdominal tergites with more than one row of bristles (Fig. 207) ....6.

4a. No combs ....5.

4b. Only pronotal comb ....*Hoplopsyllus.*
Important sp.: *H. anomalus,* plague vector on western ground squirrels.

4c. Pronotal and horizontal genal combs (Fig. 210A) ....*Ctenocephalides.*
Important spp.: *C. canis* and *C. felis* of dogs and cats; former has rounded forehead, latter low and flat forehead.

5a. Mesosternite without vertical chitinized bar (Fig. 209A) ....*Pulex.*
Important sp.: *P. irritans* of man and pigs.

5b. Mesosternite with vertical chitinized bar (Fig. 209B) ....*Xenopsylla.*
Important spp.: *X. cheopis, astia, braziliensis, hawaiiensis; X. cheopis* most important vector of plague from rats to man.

6a. Genal comb absent ....*Dolichopsyllidae.*
18 genera, mostly on rodents and birds; for important genera and species, see paragraph below.

6b. Short, usually vertical, genal comb; head with a break in chitin across top of head between eyes, allowing movement of two parts of head Fig. 210B). **Hystrichopsyllidae** ....7.

7a. Horizontal genal comb of 3 spines ....*Ctenophthalmus.*
Important sp.: *C. argyrtes* on rats and mice in Europe.

7b. Vertical genal comb of 4 spines; 2 small teeth near apex of head (Fig. 210B)
.... **Leptopsylla.**
Important sp.: *L. segnis,* common rat and mouse flea.

The family Dolichopsyllidae constitutes what was the genus Ceratophyllus until 1933 and is now split into about 18 genera. Most of these are parasites of rodents or rabbits, but the genus Ceratophyllus (in the strict sense) contains parasites of birds; two of these, *C. gallinae* in Europe and eastern United States and *C. niger* in western United States, are pests of poultry. They are distinguished by having 24 or more spines in the pronotal comb. Many of the rodent genera are fairly limited to particular kinds of rodent hosts; others show little specificity. *Nosopsyllus fasciatus* (Fig. 210C) is the commonest flea of domestic rats in temperate climates. It has 18 or 20 teeth in the pronotal comb. Some of the more important potential transmitters of sylvatic plague in this family are *Diamanus montanus, Oropsylla rupestris, Thrassis* spp., and *Opisocrostis bruneri* of ground squirrels; *Orchopaeus sexdentatus* of wood rats; species of *Oropsylla* and *Thrassis* on marmots; and *Opisocrostis hirsutus* on prairie dogs. Identification of the genera and species in this family is beyond the scope of this book, and students are referred to Ewing and Fox (1943) and Hubbard (1947).

Habits. Most fleas are neither as strictly host parasites as lice nor as strictly nest parasites as bedbugs. The nests or lairs of the host are the normal breeding places and are the homes of the eggs, larvae, and pupae; frequently adults are found in them too, but these are often either newly emerged fleas or fleas which have dropped off to deposit eggs. Some rodent and bird fleas are more frequently found in the nests than on the bodies of the hosts; in Russia fleas were found to move in and out of the burrows of ground squirrels at night. Some species, as already noted, seem to leave their hosts to deposit their eggs in the dens or lairs, whereas others lay the eggs at random in the fur of the host, whence they drop off when the animal shakes himself or prepares to sleep. The human flea drops its eggs in the dust and debris in cracks in floors, under carpets, etc.

Fleas leave the body of a dead host as soon as it becomes cold, and often show a preference for certain parts of the body. The nests or dens are the normal breeding places, and it is significant that those mammals which have no permanent habitations, such as monkeys and deer, are nearly free of fleas, although they seldom lack lice. Flea larvae thrive on blood, and some, e.g., *Nosopsyllus fasciatus*, are said to require it, yet they have no means of their own for obtaining it and the parents have to provide it in a semidigested condition in their feces. It is evident that the tendency of some fleas to leave their hosts for egg laying mainly in the nests is a wise provision of nature for the satisfactory nourishment of the larvae. Possibly the warmth generated by the host in its nest while sleeping or some odors connected with it indicate to the flea that the time and place are right for an excursion off the host.

Although most fleas show some degree of preference for particular hosts with which they are normally found associated, many species are not nearly so closely limited as lice are and may be found on a wide variety of hosts. When hungry they suck blood wherever they can find it, and it is because of this that rodent fleas are of importance to man as transmitters of such rodent diseases as plague and endemic typhus. Some species of rodent fleas, however, require less provocation than others to suck human blood.

The fleas found in human houses are mainly of three types: (1) human fleas (Pulex); (2) cat and dog fleas (Ctenocephalides); and (3) rat and mouse fleas. The last vary in kind in different parts of the world; in warm climates and in seaports elsewhere they are species of the genus Xenopsylla (Fig. 207), the foremost transmitters of plague, but in temperate climates they are mainly *Nosopsyllus fasciatus* (Fig. 210*C*) on rats, and *Leptopsylla segnis* (Fig. 210*B*) on mice. Wild rodents harbor numerous species of fleas; it usually takes an expert siphonapterologist to distinguish the genera, to say nothing of the species.

Life Cycle. The eggs of fleas are oval, pearly-white objects of relatively large size, sometimes one-third the length of the parent flea. Except in the case of the chiggers they are laid singly. The time required for the eggs to reach the hatching stage varies with the species and with climatic conditions from 2 or 3 days to over 2 weeks. Eggs of *N. fasciatus* will hatch at temperatures as low as 41° F., but those of Pulex and *Xenopsylla cheopis* require higher temperatures. The most favorable conditions for the development of most species are temperatures between 65° and 80° and a humidity of 70 per cent or more. The higher the temperature the greater the humidity required. In the nests and holes where fleas breed, however, favorable conditions of temperature and moisture may exist even when conditions in the open are highly unfavorable.

The larvae (Fig. 211) are tiny cylindrical maggotlike creatures with neither legs nor eyes. They have small brown heads and whitish

Fig. 211. Developmental stages of fleas. *Left*, larva of *Xenopsylla cheopis* (after Bacot and Ridewood); *right*, cocoon of *Pulex irritans*. × 12.

bodies composed of 13 visible segments and a hidden terminal one, all provided with rather sparse bristly hairs to aid in crawling. The last segment is terminated by a pair of tiny hooks.

The larvae avoid light and feed upon what bits of organic matter they can find, such as mouse " pills," crumbs, hairs, epidermal scales from their hosts, and the excrement of adult fleas. The larvae can be reared successfully in the laboratory when favorable temperature and humidity are constantly maintained and when they are fed on dried blood, fragments of dog biscuits, mouse " pills," etc. Some species, if not all, devour their shed skins after moulting.

The larvae crawl by alternately expanding and contracting the body like an earthworm. The duration of the larval stage varies with climatic conditions and food and to some extent also with the species. Under favorable conditions, i.e., at moderate temperatures and high humidity and with plenty of food, the larvae of some species pass through their two moults and enter the pupal stage in a week, whereas under unfavorable conditions the duration of the larval existence may be drawn out to over 3 months.

When ready to undergo their transformation into adults, the larvae spin little silken cocoons that are somewhat viscid, so that particles of dust and lint readily adhere to them and give them a dirty, dingy appearance (Fig. 211). Under favorable conditions it usually takes from 1 to 2 weeks before the adults emerge from the cocoons, but at low temperatures or in dry weather the insects may remain dormant in their cocoons for several months and thus tide over unfavorable seasons such as northern winters or dry seasons in the tropics. The complete life cycle takes a minimum of 3 weeks in the tropics and from 4 to 6 weeks in temperate climates.

The adult fleas do not become sexually mature or copulate for some days after they escape from the cocoon. Soon after copulation egg laying begins but no breeding takes place without blood meals.

The length of life of adult fleas depends largely on food supply, temperature, and humidity. At low temperatures (60° F.) well-fed fleas will live for at least 18 months. In the absence of a host they will survive for 1 to 2 years at low temperatures, but at ordinary temperatures starved fleas have much less power of endurance than ticks or even bugs. Some authors claim that Xenopsylla will survive for 2 or 3 months away from a host; others say they die in 8 or 10 days. Dog fleas certainly survive for several weeks, and rodent fleas survive for at least 4 months in the nests of hibernating ground squirrels. The optimum climatic conditions and normal length of life probably vary a great deal with different species. Most of the Ceratophyllus group and also *Pulex irritans* are fleas of temperate or cold climates, while the species of Xenopsylla are characteristic of hot climates.

Unlike most bloodsucking insects, fleas usually feed at frequent intervals, generally at least once a day and sometimes much oftener than this. Fleas frequently feed even when the digestive tract is already well filled, and may pass practically unaltered blood in their feces to be utilized, second-hand, by the larvae.

Fleas and Disease. Like most other bloodsucking parasites, fleas are intimately connected with the transmission of disease. The most serious charge against them is the dissemination of bubonic plague, which alone is sufficient to rank them among the most important insect enemies of man. Fleas are also the usual transmitters of the endemic or murine form of typhus; they are important transmitters of tularemia among rodents; they serve as intermediate hosts of certain tapeworms; and they have been suspected in connection with other diseases.

Fleas and Plague

Plague, although primarily a disease of rats and other rodents, ranks as a human scourge with such diseases as smallpox and leprosy. It is estimated that in the epidemic of the fourteenth century in Europe one-fourth of the population of that continent, or 25 million people, died of the disease, and superstition and unreasoning terror led to horrible persecution and torture. At present the disease is largely confined to tropical countries and is especially prevalent in India, where an average of over half a million deaths a year are caused by it.

With our new methods of control, however, Meyer (1947) thinks it unlikely that urban plague will henceforth be a major problem except in a few blighted areas. In the past it was often introduced from the tropics into other countries. In temperate climates it does not usually become epidemic but establishes itself in the local rat population where it may smolder on for a long time in an endemic condition, causing sporadic human cases or small outbreaks. During the present century it has been introduced into San Francisco and into a number of ports on the Gulf of Mexico. In the latter it was killed out, but from San Francisco it established itself permanently in sylvatic form (see p. 600). There is constant danger of fresh introductions in seaports wherever the strictest preventive regulations are not enforced. Once the disease has obtained a foothold the fight is a strenuous and expensive one.

Plague, caused by a small bacillus, *Pasteurella pestis* (see p. 233), exists in man in bubonic, septicemic, and pneumonic form. The bubonic form results from infection through the skin, usually by the bite of an infected and " blocked " flea. (See following section, " Mechanism of Transmission.") After a short incubation period, usually only 2 to 4 days, there is a sudden high fever, mental disturbance, and severe prostration, with characteristic large swollen lymph glands called buboes. The septicemic form is characterized by invasion of the general blood stream, and the pneumonic form by rapid multiplication of the bacilli in the lungs. The latter usually follows direct passage of the disease from man to man via the respiratory tract. There is some hope of recovery from bubonic plague, but the other forms are almost always rapidly fatal. A local outbreak of pneumonic plague frequently follows a bubonic case; in Oakland, Calif., in 1919, a man who became infected from a ground squirrel transmitted the disease to twelve other people, all of whom died.

Mechanism of Transmission. With few exceptions the great epidemics of plague follow epizoötics among house rats. As these animals succumb to the disease their orphaned fleas attack man and convey the infection to him. The usual mechanism of transmission was made clear by the work of Bacot and Martin in 1914. They observed that the Indian rat flea, *Xenopsylla cheopis,* after feeding on an infected animal, often had its digestive tract completely blocked by solid growths of plague organisms (Fig. 212). Such "blocked" fleas are unable to ingest more blood and in attempting to do so they regurgitate plague germs into their victims.

Fleas do not remain infective indefinitely; in hot weather they usually lose their infection in a week, though in cool weather it may last for 15 days. Many of them die as a result of the infection, especially in hot, dry weather, since they are unable to overcome the effects of desiccation by imbibing fresh blood. Since the infected fleas live such a short time in warm climates, epizoötics subside quickly, and with

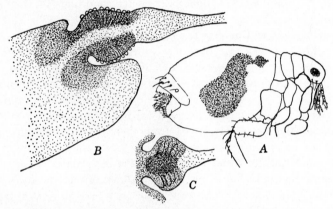

FIG. 212. Blocking of fleas by plague bacilli. *A*, position of proventriculus and stomach of flea as they appear when full of blood. *B*, proventriculus and fore part of stomach partially blocked (heavily shaded area). *C*, proventriculus completely blocked. (*B* and *C* adapted from Esky and Haas.)

them the human epidemics. The bites of fleas that do not become blocked are never infective, although the feces are. The feces may remain infective in dark, damp places for over a year and cause infections in rodent burrows long after the fleas have gone. This also might account for the continued occurrence of human cases after a rat epizoötic has died out, for human or dog fleas might infect bites with their feces even if not blocked. Such a situation was reported by Rotman in 1945 in Dakar, where DDT dusting of human clothing was resorted to.

Tropical Epidemic Plague. The species of Xenopsylla are the only fleas of domestic rats in which *Pasteurella pestis* thrives well enough to cause blockage regularly, and it is for this reason that human plague epidemics are almost universally associated with these fleas and quickly die out in their absence. Even all the different species of Xenopsylla are not equivalent. *X. cheopis* is more readily blocked and under a greater range of climatic conditions than others of its genus. It is further qualified as a plague vector by the fact that it needs less provocation to feed on man than do most rodent fleas. *X. braziliensis* is an almost equally good transmitter in parts of Africa where it is abundant. *X. astia,* on the other hand, which is widely distributed along with *cheopis* in India and Ceylon, is a much poorer vector and functions only under special climatic conditions. Under the hot, moist conditions of Colombo and Madras, where it frequently predominates, it is an inefficient transmitter, apparently because it quickly succumbs to a heavy infection, whereas experimentally it functions well under the cooler conditions of Bombay in the winter.

Imported Plague Epidemics. Plague is dispersed from one part of the world to another either by transportation of infected rats with their Xenopsyllas on ships or railway cars or by the transportation of the fleas alone, for example, in grain in which rats were formerly present. However, in view of the short time in which infected fleas either lose their infection or die, such fleas would not be likely to start an epidemic after more than two weeks apart from their hosts. Although in the past plague has been repeatedly introduced into the northern cities of America and Europe, it has never succeeded in becoming permanently established, and epidemics soon die out, although the epizoötics sometimes continue to smolder for a long while. In these places *Nosopsyllus fasciatus* and to a lesser extent *Leptopsylla segnis* and *Ctenophthalmus argyrtes* largely replace Xenopsylla on rats. These fleas rarely become blocked and so fail to transmit the infection by their bites. When cold weather comes, the temporary rat infestation with imported Xenopsylla tends to die out, and plague with it.

Sylvatic Plague. Although plague epidemics in cities outside the tropics soon die out and even the epizoötics among house rats quickly disappear, it does not necessarily mean that the infection has been exterminated. On the edges of cities where the domestic types of rats — black rats, roof rats, and Norway rats — come in contact with wild rodents such as ground squirrels, marmots, and wood rats, a certain amount of interchange of fleas invariably takes place. The result is that some of these wild rodents become infected with plague from fleas left behind by plague-killed rats. In a number of places in widely scattered parts of the world the disease has thus become permanently endemic in the wild rodent population, constituting what is known as sylvatic plague.

The disease is more often transmitted among rodents when fleas are bitten than when they bite; it may also be transmitted by scratching fleas or their feces into the bites or by cannibalism. Most rodent fleas do not become blocked as readily as does *X. cheopis*, and when blocked are likely to succumb more quickly. *Diamanus montanus*, however, one of the commonest fleas on western ground squirrels, is an exception. It is a better vector than *X. cheopis*, becoming blocked more frequently and more quickly and remaining infective longer.

It is doubtful whether fleas have much to do with the transmission of the sylvatic disease to man; this more often results from handling infected rodents. Possibly cats occasionally serve as intermediaries. Human cases are remarkably rare, and the disease may exist a long time before its presence becomes known, except for epizoötics among such gregarious rodents as ground squirrels, wood rats, prairie dogs, and marmots. As Meyer (1947) remarked, it is difficult to understand why human cases fail to develop in the midst of an epizoötic when fields and canyons are littered with carcasses of plague-killed rodents. But one human case acquired from a rodent may lead to a considerable outbreak as the result of pneumonic transmission, as already noted. Another danger is that as an epizoötic encroaches on a city the infection may reverse its procedure and jump back from wild rodents to domestic rats. Such an occurrence probably accounts for San Francisco's second city-wide outbreak in 1907–1908, four years after her first one died out. The second epidemic caused 159 cases and 77 deaths. Having sylvatic plague in your suburbs is like having rattlesnakes on your golf course or a Typhoid Mary in your kitchen. It is an unpleasant threat.

In the United States the disease escaped from San Francisco to ground squirrels on the outskirts after the outbreak in 1900–1904, and spread down the coast to Los Angeles. It is still there after nearly half a century of effort to exterminate it. In 1934 the disease was found to have jumped across California's central valleys to the foothills of the Sierras in the south and across the Sierras to Oregon's Great Basin in the north. Since then it has been discovered in 14 western states, from Washington to the Dakotas, from California to Texas and Oklahoma, and in Alberta and Saskatchewan in Canada. It had probably crossed the Sierras by 1929 and the eastern slope of the Rockies in Montana by 1933. Between 1936 and 1945 the U. S. Public Health Service examined nearly 600,000 rodents and over a million fleas in the western states, with 461 positive results, indicating infection in 38 species of wild rodents; on these over 50 species of fleas have been identified, at least 31 of which can transmit plague to guinea pigs.

Other important foci of sylvatic plague exist in central Asia and southeast Russia, where *Citellophilus tesquorum* is the chief vector among ground squirrels and marmots; in Manchuria, where *Oropsylla silantiewi* transmits among marmots and where in 1910–1911 an outbreak with 60,000 victims occurred among people hunting marmots for their skins; in South Africa, where *Xenopsylla eridos* transmits it among wild gerbilles and the semidomestic multimammate mouse, *Mastomys concha,* which comes into houses and passes on the disease to domestic rats which harbor *X. braziliensis;* and in the Argentine pampas, where a species of Rhopalopsyllus (one of the few combless fleas in the Dolichopsyllidae) transmits among small rodents (Graomys) and hares.

Sylvatic plague is comparable to typhus, relapsing fever, and yellow fever, all of which smolder silently and often unnoticed in their reservoir hosts, only flaring into epidemics when they come in contact with vectors that habitually or frequently bite human beings.

Control of plague will be considered along with that of endemic typhus, another disease transmitted from rodents to man by fleas, on p. 610.

Fleas and Typhus

In 1926 Maxcy pointed out that the epidemiology of sporadic cases of typhus occurring in southern United States was not suggestive of louse transmission but had the earmarks of a disease transmitted only occasionally to man from a rodent reservoir. Subsequent work by the U. S. Public Health Service showed that this was true and that this endemic type of typhus (see p. 228) existed among rats and was transmitted principally by fleas. The disease is associated with rat-infested localities such as granaries, markets, and restaurants. Fleas become infected with typhus more readily than lice and are not injured by the infection; they remain infective for life and for some time after death. Transovarial infection occurs. *Xenopsylla cheopis* (Fig. 207; 208*B*, *D*) seems to be the most important transmitter, but others, including the sticktight flea (Fig. 215) and *Leptopsylla segnis* (Fig. 210*B*), also harbor the rickettsia, *R. typhi* (see p. 230). In China, after initial cases from rodents, lice may spread the infection further among humans. In Mexico, too, intergradation between flea-borne and louse-borne typhus has been reported.

The disease in man is much milder than the epidemic louse-borne type and also differs from it in causing scrotal swellings in guinea pigs. In rats and mice it is usually symptomless; since the rats do not die from it their fleas are not forced by hunger to seek human blood. Besides, there is no mechanism like the blocking in plague to enable the fleas to transmit the disease by their bites; only their feces and crushed bodies are infective. Since this is much less likely to lead to human infection than the mechanism involved in epidemic plague transmission, human cases of this disease are sporadic, like sylvatic plague. Some cases may result from contamination of food by urine of infected rats or from handling the rats themselves. Endemic typhus exists in wild rodents and other small mammals as well as in house rats. In the United States the disease is endemic principally in the southern states, where *Xenopylla cheopis* is the commonest rat flea in seaports and (at least at certain seasons) for a considerable distance inland. Up to 1930 few cases of endemic typhus were reported in the United States, but after that time the disease became commoner year by year at an accelerating rate, until in 1945 over 5000 cases were reported, the largest numbers being in Texas and Georgia. In a survey in one Texas county 94 per cent of urban and 80 per cent of rural buildings harbored rats which by blood test were positive for typhus, and of 213 pools of the three commonest rat fleas (*Xenopsylla cheopis, Nosopsyllus fasciatus*, and *Leptopsylla segnis*), 53 harbored typhus. Some of these were found on kittens, puppies, and opossums.

The disease has repeatedly been introduced to more northern cities such as Washington, Cincinnati, and St. Louis along with *X. cheopis* which were presumably left behind in freight cars or trucks by frightened rats. Although *X. cheopis* has become established in many places in the interior and northern parts of the country and was reported by Becker in 1948 sometimes to be found in great numbers, thus far typhus does not appear to have become permanently endemic in these places. The gradual encroachment of this infection from the south and of plague from the west is not a pleasant outlook for midwestern cities.

Since 1945 the trend in number of typhus cases has turned back; in 1947 the reported cases had fallen to 2000. This is due to a vigorous antityphus campaign by the U. S. Public Health Service and the individual states through DDT dusting of rat runs (see p. 610), poisoning of rats with " 1080 " (fluoroacetate) and other raticides, and ratproofing of buildings.

Fleas and Other Diseases

Fleas occasionally become infected with tularemia (see p. 547), but they are probably not important transmitters. They also transmit Whitmore's bacillus, causing a glanders-like disease in rodents and man in southeastern Asia. Tovar in 1947 reported that fleas, as well as bedbugs and ticks, could transmit undulant fever or brucellosis (see p. 548). Fleas serve as intermediate hosts for the nonpathogenic rat trypanosome, *Trypanosoma lewisi,* and quite possibly for the related trypanosomes of other rodents also. *T. cruzi,* however, although it develops in such different arthropods as ticks and bugs, undergoes rapid degeneration in fleas. This is also true of relapsing-fever spirochetes. Fleas were long suspected of transmitting infantile and canine leishmaniasis (see p. 142) in the Mediterranean region. The occurrence of a natural Leptomonas in fleas provided considerable circumstantial evidence against them, but they were finally acquitted.

Fleas serve as intermediate hosts for certain tapeworms, among them *Dipylidium caninum* (see p. 344) of dogs, which is occasional in children, and *Hymenolepis diminuta* and *H. nana* of rats, mice, and man (see pp. 346 and 348). The eggs are ingested by larvae, but the cysticercoids finish their development in the adult fleas.

Notes on Important Species of Fleas

Human Flea. The only species of flea that is known to be a parasite of man primarily, with the exception of the chigger, is the appropriately named *Pulex irritans* (Fig. 209*A, C*), though in many places man is annoyed more by certain other species that are primarily parasites of his domestic animals. This flea is also a pest of pigs, and it has been found on dogs and other carnivores, on deer, and occasionally on rats and mice. It probably originated in Europe, whence it has been introduced to all parts of the world, but is relatively rare in the tropics, since it is killed by temperatures much over 85° F. This flea is the species that has made California as famous for its fleas as New Jersey is for its mosquitoes. A cool, humid summer climate combined with a mild, wet winter is ideal for this pest. Though more or less of a nuisance throughout the year in mild climates, this flea is less troublesome in winter, owing to relative inactivity, to slower reproduction, and to the fact that the flea more commonly attacks small mammals at this time of year.

The susceptibility of different individuals to flea bites is variable. The irritation that is normally produced, probably chiefly as a result of the injection of the insect's salivary secretions into the bite, causes the formation of a reddish pimple with some degree of swelling. Some people, however, are apparently entirely immune to flea bites and feel no pain from them. The writer on his first visit to California, warned to expect trouble from fleas, was pleasantly surprised to feel no discomfort other than tickling as the fleas promenaded, while a roommate spent many sleepless hours in pursuit of the wily fleas and in violent massaging of painful wounds. According to work by McIvor and Cherney immunity can be artificially induced in most people by injection of antigens made from pulverized fleas (see p. 489). The human flea is not an important plague transmitter because it seldom becomes " blocked," but it may cause some infections by its feces.

Dog and Cat Fleas. Next in frequence to the human flea as parasites of man are the dog and cat fleas, *Ctenocephalides canis* and *C. felis.* In the southeastern United States where the flea scourge competes very well with that of California, the dog flea is the species usually met with. During the moist, hot summers this species becomes exceedingly abundant. Although primarily a parasite of dogs and cats it willingly includes man in its bill of fare when its preferred hosts are not readily available. A case once came to the writer's attention in which the residents of a house were unmercifully bitten after disposing of a badly infested dog and two or three cats, although there had previously been no annoyance. Cat and dog fleas readily go from one of these hosts to the other. These fleas can easily be distinguished from any other common species by the presence of *two* well-developed ctenidia (Fig. 210*A*), each with numerous teeth.

The eggs are usually laid loosely in the fur, whence they fall out when the host shakes himself or is settling himself for a nap. They develop in the dust and dirt of kennels, woodsheds, house floors, or other places where infested animals are likely to go. Patton and Cragg found the inside of a hat in which a kitten had slept overnight so full of flea eggs that it looked as if it had had sugar sprinkled in it.

Dog and cat fleas, from their habits, are the species most frequently implicated in the transmission of the dog tapeworm (Dipylidium) to children. These species are even less frequently concerned with plague transmission than is *Pulex irritans.*

Rodent Fleas. The various species of fleas that infest rats, ground squirrels, and sometimes other rodents are only accidental parasites of man. If it were not for their importance in the spread of plague they would need no special consideration. For identification of the commoner species refer to the key on pp. 593–594.

The combless fleas of the genus Xenopsylla (Fig. 207), which are of the greatest importance in epidemic plague, are primarily residents of Asia and Africa. *X. cheopis,* however, probably originally from the upper Nile valley, has accompanied rats to all important seaports in the world and has not only established itself in them but has also become a permanent fixture in the fauna of rats far inland in some places. In the United States it is the dominant species in many parts of the southern states and has apparently established itself throughout the middle west and many places in the west. It attacks man more readily than most rodent fleas when deprived of its normal hosts.

There are a number of other species of Xenopsylla on rats, of which
X. astia has already been mentioned. *Xenopsylla cheopis* and *X. astia*
are readily distinguished by the form of the spermatheca in females
(Fig. 213) and by the ninth abdominal sternite in the males. *X. brasiliensis* is the prevalent rat flea in central Africa, but it also occurs
irregularly in hot parts of India, Brazil, and other tropical countries.

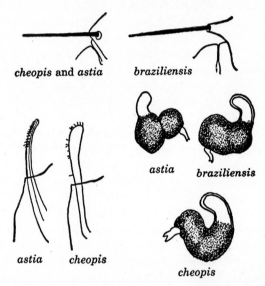

Fig. 213. Differential characters between common species of Xenopsylla. Above,
antepygidial bristle; at left below, ninth sternites; at right below, spermathecae. (From
Trop. Diseases Bull.)

X. eridos is a species found on veldt rodents in South Africa and is
associated with endemic plague there. *X. hawaiiensis* is common on
field rats in Hawaii but not on house rats.

In temperate climates the genus Xenopsylla is largely replaced on
rodents by fleas of the family Dolichopsyllidae and a few in the family
Histrichopsyllidae (see key, p. 594). The former constitute the
" Ceratophyllus group," characterized by having a well-developed
pronotal comb only, and two rows of bristles on each abdominal segment.

Nosopsyllus fasciatus (Fig. 210C) is the most prevalent flea on
domestic rats in temperate climates, and *Leptosylla segnis* (Fig. 210B)
is also very common on rats and mice in many places. It is interesting to note that all three of the commonest rat fleas, as well as the
domestic rats (Rattus spp.) and the house mouse are, like some of our
other worst pests (e.g., *Aëdes aegypti* and *Musca domestica*), imported

from the Old World. The most important of the many fleas found on wild rodents in North America are mentioned in the key on pp. 593 and 594. In addition to the Ceratophyllus group, the sticktight flea (see following section) is often found on rats and is a plague carrier.

Bird Fleas. There are three important fleas of poultry. One, the sticktight flea, *Echidnophaga gallinacea*, is related to the chigger, *Tunga penetrans*, and belongs to the family Hectopsyllidae (see key, p. 593); the other two are *Ceratophyllus gallinae* in Europe and eastern United States and *C. niger* in western United States. These last two have habits like those of rodent fleas, living primarily in the nests.

E. gallinacea (Fig. 215) sticks tight to its host, hence its name, sticktight flea. It is a very small flea commonly attacking chickens in warm and tropical countries, but it also attacks dogs, cats, rabbits, rats, man, and other animals. It is gregarious, collecting in clusters on the heads of poultry, in the ears of mammals, or other places. It burrows to some extent and probably deposits its eggs in the exudate that nearly covers the flea. Children are not infrequently attacked. Since this flea is susceptible to plague and attacks both birds and rodents, it may carry infection from wild to domestic rodents and when attached to such birds as vultures, hawks, or pheasants may even be a means of carrying it to distant places.

Chiggers. The chigger, chigoe, jigger, or sand flea, *Tunga penetrans* (Fig. 214), is the pest which inspired the sailor's oath, " I'll be jiggered." Originally found in tropical America, it was introduced to west Africa with some ballast sand in 1872. It spread rapidly over nearly the whole of Africa but has failed to establish itself in Europe or India. A closely related species, *T. caecigena*, has been found on the ears of rats in Shanghai. The chigger is a small flea, only about 1 mm. in length, of the family Hectosyllidae (see key, p. 593). The males and virgin females are similar to other fleas in habits, except that they attack a wide range of hosts. Man and pigs seem to be the principal hosts of this pest, but cats, dogs, and rats are also attacked.

The chigger breeds especially in regions with sandy soil shaded by heavy underbrush or in the earth floors of native houses. After emergence the fleas lie in waiting in debris on the ground and attack mainly the feet of animals or human beings which come their way. The particular importance of this flea lies in the fact that the impregnated females have the aggravating habit of burrowing into the skin, especially in such tender spots as under the toenails. Here, nourished by the blood of the host, the fleas produce eggs and retain them in the abdomen, causing it to swell into a great round ball as large as a pea. The head and legs appear as inconspicuous appendages (Fig. 214*B*). Only the two posterior segments of the abdomen do not enlarge; these act as a plug for the hole made in entering the skin. The eggs, up to a hundred in number, mature in about a week and are then expelled by the female through the protruding end of the abdomen. Sometimes the entire female is expelled with her eggs by the pressure of the inflamed tissue which surrounds her.

The eggs probably usually fall to the ground, where they undergo development in the orthodox siphonapteran manner; the larvae (Fig. 214C) feed on organic debris, grow to maturity after one instead of the

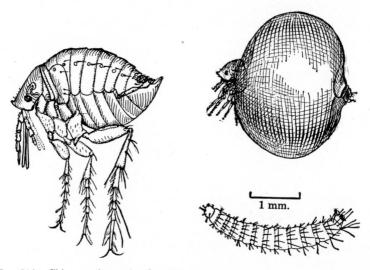

Fig. 214.   Chigger or burrowing flea, *Tunga penetrans.*   *Left,* male, × 40; *upper right,* gravid female, × 20; *lower right,* larva.   (Adults adapted from Patton and Evans; larva, from Faust and Maxwell.)

usual two moults, pupate in a cocoon, and finally emerge as adults after 17 days or more.   Faust and Maxwell, however, have observed an unusual case in which the thriving larvae were found in various stages of development in skin scrapings from the inguinal and pubic regions of a man who had been attacked in these parts by adult chiggers while sitting on some bales of sisal imported from Yucatan.

The wounds made by the burrowing female in the skin become much inflamed and very painful.   Frequently the distended abdomen of a flea is crushed and the eggs released in the wound.   In such cases the inflammation is greatly increased unless the crushed body and eggs are immediately expelled.   As soon as the eggs are laid, or even before, the skin surrounding the wound ulcerates and pus is formed. The empty female flea is expelled.   The sore which is left is very liable to infection by bacteria; this sometimes results in the loss of toes or even whole limbs through blood poisoning. In Central America deaths from tetanus and gas gangrene from chigger wounds are common.

Although usually only a few chiggers are present at a time, there are cases in which hundreds infest a person at once, literally honeycombing the skin and making the feet or other parts of the body so sore that the victim is rendered a complete invalid.

The treatment of chigger wounds formerly consisted in the destruction of the fleas while they were embedded in the wounds. This was done by applying insecticides or pricking with a needle, the dead insect being removed after ulceration. A better method is to enlarge the

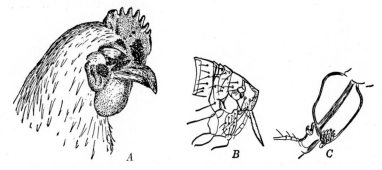

Fig. 215. *Echidnophaga gallinacea*, sticktight flea. *A*, clusters on head of chicken; *B*, head of flea; *C*, inner aspect of hind coxa. (*A* adapted from Bishopp; *B* and *C* from Fox.)

entrance hole of the flea with a clean needle and remove the parasite entire, then carefully dress the wound and protect it until healed.

Houses, yards, etc., in chigger regions should be kept as free as possible of dust, dirt, and debris. In Central America Quiros recommended a prohibition against driving hogs affected with chiggers through the streets, along with regulations for treating affected hogs where they are raised. Spraying premises with a 2.5 per cent DDT suspension quickly eliminates chiggers. Dusting the feet and socks with DDT is the best means of personal protection.

Flea Control

Strict cleanliness in private homes or public buildings prevents fleas from breeding in them. Uncared-for carpets and straw mattings afford excellent breeding grounds for the human flea, as do dusty cracks between floor boards, unswept corners under sinks, and any other place where the eggs and the young, undisturbed, may obtain enough moisture to keep them from drying up. Dusting with a small amount of 10 per cent DDT or spraying with a 2 to 5 per cent emulsion or kerosene solution quickly solves this problem.

Dogs can be cleared of fleas by dusting with 10 per cent DDT; a ring around the neck or abdomen or a line along the back is usually sufficient. In addition, the animals' usual resting and sleeping places should be dusted to kill the larvae. Cats lick off the DDT and are sickened by it, but lightly dusting the sleeping places soon controls the situation.

Control of Plague and Endemic Typhus. In controlling plague in the past reliance has been placed almost entirely on rat control, but this had its dangers, since the fleas, if not killed with the rats by fumigation with HCN, methyl bromide, or burning sulfur, were likely to turn their attention to man. This was especially true with typhus, since this disease does not kill the rats, and so only occasional human cases occur until the fleas are orphaned by poisoning, trapping, or driving off of their rat hosts. Often a rat campaign precipitates a number of human typhus cases.

Since the advent of DDT, it has become possible to control these diseases without this danger from orphaned fleas. The procedure is first to dust floors in rat-infested buildings and other places where rat fleas are likely to be. Rat runs are heavily dusted, and 1 to 2 oz. of dust are blown into each burrow opening. When properly done by trained workers the flea population on rats can be reduced 90 per cent or more. The rats pick up enough DDT on their feet and fur to kill fleas in their nests as well as on their bodies. In 10 counties having the highest typhus rates in the United States, dusting rat runs is believed chiefly responsible for a drop from 1074 cases of typhus in 1944 to 395 in 1946. Reduction of *Xenopsylla cheopis* averaged 84 per cent in treated areas. Even ordinary residual spraying in rat-infested buildings reduces rat ectoparasites very greatly in 6 to 12 days.

A day or two later the rats are destroyed by poisoning with one of two new and powerful raticides, " Antu " (*a*-naptha thiourea) or " 1080 " (sodium fluoroacetate). Antu is used in 1 to 2 per cent concentration in food baits; 1080 at the rate of 5 parts per 1000 with such baits as rolled oats, or in a 1 : 320 aqueous dilution (12 grams per gallon of water) set out in small containers such as bottle caps. Antu is more effective than 1080 against the brown or Norwegian rat and can be used more freely in residential areas, since 1080 is deadly to humans and pets as well as to rats. A dust containing 50 per cent Antu and 10 per cent DDT shows promise of being destructive to both rats and their ectoparasites.

In some situations Cyanogas fumigation (see p. 493) in burrows or
HCN fumigation in buildings is still the method of choice, particularly
where plague is present, in order to kill both rats and fleas at once.
After a rat campaign the rats can be kept off for the most part by
making food inaccessible to them and destroying their harboring places.

Both DDT dusting and rat poisoning are temporary measures. Permanent good comes only from ratproofing buildings where this is
possible, as it is in American cities. The cost is low compared with
loss from rats, even without considering their relation to disease, since
rats usually outnumber the human population three to two, and the
average cost of upkeep per rat for food and goods destroyed is estimated at ½¢ per day. That amounts to $1.80 per rat per year, or a
total of over $250,000 for a city of 100,000 population. DDT dusting,
followed by poisoning of rats with 1080, stopped a plague epidemic in a
Peruvian city 4 days after the first application of dust was finished
(Macchiavello, 1946). Additional protection is possible by the use of
vaccines, which are available for both typhus and plague.

In the control of sylvatic plague it is necessary to destroy ground
squirrels and other burrowing animals either by poisoning or by fumigation of the burrows. For the latter, carbon bisulfide is generally
used, being either evaporated or burned. The poison does not affect
the fleas, and fumigation with carbon bisulfide or even with hydrocyanic acid, seldom gets them all. Methyl bromide (10 cc. per burrow
opening) is more effective in destroying fleas as well as rodents, but it
is highly toxic to man and especially dangerous because it is colorless
and odorless.

REFERENCES

BACOT, A. W., (Bionomics of Common Rat Fleas, etc.), *J. Hyg.*, **4**, *Plague Suppl.*
III, 447, 1914.

BACOT, A. W., and MARTIN, J. C., Observations on the Mechanism of the Transmission of Plague by Fleas, *J. Hyg.*, **14**, *Plague Suppl.* III, 423, 1914.

BLANC, C. and BALTAZARD, M., Virulence des déjections de puces pesteuses, *Ann.
inst. Pasteur*, **72**, 486–489 (1946).

DYER, R. E., Endemic Typhus in the United States, *Proc. 6th Pacific Sci. Congr.*,
V, 731 (1942).

ELISHAWITZ, H., Epidemic Control with DDT, Antu, and 1080, *Soap Sanit.
Chemicals*, **23**, 127–129, 151, 153–159, 193 (1947).

ESKY, C. R., and HAAS, V. H., Plague in the Western Part of the United States,
Publ. Health Bull., **254**, 1940.

EWING, H. E., and FOX, L., The Fleas of North America, *U. S. Dept. Agr. Misc.
Pub.*, **500**, Washington, 1943.

FAUST, E. C., and MAXWELL, T. A., The Finding of the Larvae of the Chigoe,
Tunga penetrans, in Scrapings from Human Skin, *Arch. Dermatol. Syphilol.*,
22, 94 (1930).

HICKS, E. P., The Early Stages of the Jigger, *Tunga penetrans, Ann. Trop. Med. Parasitol.*, **24**, 575 (1930).

HIRST, L. F., Plague Fleas, *J. Hyg.*, **24**, 1 (1925).

JELLISON, W. L., and GOOD, N. E., Index to Literature of Siphonaptera of North America, *Natl. Inst. Health Bull.*, **178**, 1942.

MACCHIAVELLO, A., Plague Control with DDT and 1080. Results Achieved in a Plague Epidemic at Tumbes, Peru, 1945, *Am. J. Publ. Health*, **36**, 842–854 (1946).

MEYER, K. F., The Role of the Infected and the Infective Flea in the Spread of Sylvatic Plague, *Am. J. Publ. Health*, **28**, 1153 (1938).
The Prevalence of Plague in the Light of Newer Knowledge, *Ann. N. Y. Acad. Sci.*, **48**, 429–467 (1947).

PRINCE, F. M., and WAYSON, N. E., Plague — The Survival of the Infection in Fleas of Hibernating Ground Squirrels, *Publ. Health Repts.*, **62**, 463–467, 1167–1168 (1947).

STEWART, M. A., Present Knowledge of the Status of Vectors of Sylvatic Plague in North America, *Proc. 6th Pacific Sci. Congr.*, IV, 433 (1940).

STRICKLAND, C., The Biology of *Ceratophyllus fasciatus*......, *J. Hyg.*, **14**, 139 (1914).

WATERSTON, J., Fleas as a Menace to Man and Domestic Animals, *Brit. Mus. Econ. Ser.*, **3**, 5th ed., 1942.

WAYSON, N. E., Plague — Field Surveys in Western United States during 10 Years. (1936–1945), *Publ. Health Repts.*, **62**, 780–791 (1947).

CHAPTER 26
Diptera

I. BLOODSUCKING AND DISEASE-CARRYING FLIES OTHER THAN MOSQUITOES

Importance. From a medical point of view the Diptera are as important as all other arthropods put together, for in this order are included the normal transmitters of malaria, trypanosomiasis, leishmaniasis, yellow fever, dengue, papatasi fever, Oroya fever, encaphalomyelitis, and various types of filariasis. Without their dipteran transmitters these diseases would probably entirely disappear. Other diseases, such as anthrax, yaws and pinkeye, are mechanically conveyed by flies, and the housefly and other nonbiting flies are involved in the mechanical transmission of all kinds of filth diseases. Besides all this, the Diptera include also all the insects which infect wounds, skin, nasal passages, or digestive tract as maggots.

General Structure of Diptera. To understand the relations of these numerous important insects and their classification, we must make a brief survey of the characteristics and classification of the order Diptera. The whole order can usually be distinguished readily from other insects by the fact that there is only one pair of membranous wings, the second pair of wings being represented only by an insignificant pair of knobbed rodlike appendages known as halteres (see Fig. 161*H*). Even in those forms in which the wings are secondarily absent the halteres are usually present. These are vibrated with great speed during flight (300 times per second) and act as balancers. In many of the Cyclorrhapha there are membranous expansions posteriorly at the base of the wings, which are folded under the wings when at rest. These are called alulae, calypteres, or squamae, and are sometimes quite conspicuous, as in the houseflies and their allies (see Fig. 260).

The legs consist of the usual segments (see p. 481), generally with long coxae. The tarsi are usually terminated by two claws with padlike " pulvilli " under them, and often a third appendage, the " empodium," between them, either bristlelike or resembling a third pulvillus. The head is joined to the thorax by a very slender, flexible neck. The thorax has its three component parts fused. The abdomen

usually consists of from four to nine visible segments and is terminated
by the ovipositors or egg-laying organs in the female and by the
copulatory organs in the male.

The antennae and also the palpi are of considerable use in classification; the extent of the variations in the antennae may be gathered from
Fig. 216. In the more generalized families, e.g., the Nematocera, the
antennae consist of many segments which, except the basal two, are
similar in form (Fig. 216A, B) and often bear whorls of hairs which
in the males give a plumose effect, e.g., in male mosquitoes. In more
specialized families the terminal segments tend to coalesce more or

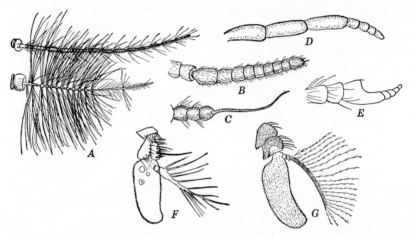

Fig. 216. Types of antennae of Diptera; A, ♀ and ♂ mosquito (Culex); B, Simulium,
blackfly; C, Chrysopila, a leptid; D, *Chrysops dissimilis;* E, Tabanus; F, Musca, housefly; G, Glossina, tsetse fly.

less (Fig. 216C, D, E), as in the tabanids and other Brachycera, or
the segments beyond the third are reduced to a simple or plumose
bristle or arista which appears as an appendage of the enlarged third
segment (Fig. 216F, G), as in nearly all of the Cyclorrhapha (fleshflies, houseflies, tsetse flies, etc.).

The mouthparts are profoundly modified in accordance with the
habits of the flies. In the botflies, in which the adults live only long
enough to reproduce their kind, the mouthparts and even the mouth
are much degenerated; in the nonbloodsucking forms, such as the
common housefly, the mouthparts are developed as a fleshy proboscis
which is used for lapping up dissolved foods; in the bloodsuckers,
which are the forms that particularly interest us here, the mouthparts
are developed into an efficient sucking and piercing apparatus. In
some, e.g., mosquitoes (Fig. 241), sandflies, blackflies, and horseflies

(Fig. 227), the lower lip acts as a sheath for the other parts which are fitted for piercing and sucking; in others, e.g., the stablefly, Stomoxys (Fig. 231), and the tsetse flies, Glossina (Fig. 232), the lower lip itself forms a piercing organ, and the epipharynx and hypopharynx form a sucking tube, the mandibles and maxillae being absent. The evolution of this type of proboscis is discussed and illustrated on p. 640.

Life Histories. All the Diptera have a complete metamorphosis, but beyond that fact the life history varies within wide limits. Most flies lay eggs, some of which require several days of incubation; others hatch within a few minutes. Others, e.g., the sheep nasal fly, *Oestrus ovis*, deposit newly hatched larvae, and still others, e.g., the tsetse flies and the Pupipara, do not deposit their offspring until they have undergone their whole larval development and are ready to pupate.

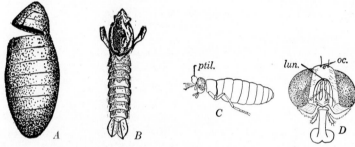

Fig. 217. *A* and *B*, types of pupal cases, showing manner of emergence of adults. *A*, empty puparium of blowfly, typical coarctate pupa of Cyclorrhapha; *B*, empty case of mosquito, typical obtected pupa of Orthorrhapha; *C*, newly emerged fly showing bladder-like ptilinium (*ptil.*) by which the end of the pupal case is pushed off; *D*, face of fly showing crescent-shaped scar or lunule (*lun.*) left by drying up of ptilinium; *oc.*, ocelli. (After Alcock.)

The larvae of Diptera may be simple maggots without distinct heads or appendages and capable of only limited squirming movements, e.g., the screwworms, or they may be highly developed, active creatures, e.g., the larvae of mosquitoes and midges. Many are aquatic, many others terrestrial; usually the eggs are laid where the larvae will find conditions suitable for their development, and the flies often show such highly developed instincts in this respect that it is hard not to credit them with actual forethought.

The pupae of the Diptera also vary widely. In one suborder, Orthorrhapha, the pupa is protected only by its own hardened cuticle, or, as in the blackflies, a spun cocoon, and is often capable of considerable activity; from this " obtected " type of pupa (Fig. 217*B*) the adult insect emerges through a longitudinal slit along the back. In the other suborder, Cyclorrhapha, the pupa retains the hardened skin

of the larva as a cocoonlike covering or " puparium " and is usually
capable of very slight movement; from this " coarctate " type of pupa
(Fig. 217A) the adult escapes by pushing off the anterior end of the
puparium; except in a few families (suborder Aschiza) this is done
by means of a hernialike outgrowth on the front of the head.   This
outgrowth, called the " ptilinium " (Fig. 217C), shrinks after the fly
has emerged, but leaves a permanent crescent-shaped mark on the head
known as the " frontal lunule " (Fig. 217D), which embraces the
bases of the antennae.

Adult flies are usually not long-lived, and often live only a few days,
just long enough to copulate and lay their eggs.   Some species, however, e.g., mosquitoes, may live for several months.

The classification of the Diptera into major divisions and the characteristics which distinguish the forms that are of medical or veterinary importance are shown in the following key:

Suborder Orthorrhapha.   Pupa not encased in old larval skin and often active;
  adults emerge through longitudinal dorsal slit (Fig. 217B); larvae usually
  with well-developed or somewhat reduced head; wing venation usually
  fairly simple.

  1a. Antennae of at least 6 similar joints, and usually long (Fig. 216A, B);
       larvae with well-developed head; series **Nematocera** ....2.
  1b. Antennae short, with 3 segments, of which the third may show some
       annulation (Fig. 216E); series **Brachycera** ....5.
  2a. Antennae much longer than head, with distinct whorls of hairs at joints,
       plumose in males ....3.
  2b. Antennae not much longer than head, with no long hairs (Fig. 216B);
       body stout and " humped "; wings broad, with only anterior veins well-
       developed (Fig. 224); (blackflies) ....***Simuliidae.***
  3a. Body clothed with scales; scales on wing veins and fringe (Fig. 250);
       (mosquitoes) ....***Culicidae.***
  3b. Body and wings without scales ....4.
  4a. Wings with 9 to 11 more or less parallel and equal veins, with no cross
       veins except at base (Fig. 218); body often hairy and mothlike........
       .... ***Psychodidae.***
  4b. Wing veins not all nearly parallel; body not very hairy; small and short,
       with broad wings folding flat over abdomen, often mottled and with the
       anterior veins thickened (Fig. 223) ....***Ceratopogonidae.***
  5a. Third antennal segment annulated, never with a bristle (Fig. 216D, E);
       a forked vein near tip of wing (Fig. 226A); mouthparts fitted for pierc-
       ing; wings held apart when at rest; large robust flies..........***Tabanidae.***
  5b. Antennae short, with a bristle or style (Fig. 216C); abdomen long and
       tapering; snipe flies ....***Leptidae.***

Suborder Cyclorrhapha.   Pupa encased in old larval skin (puparium) and
  usually inactive; adults escape through circular split at one end (Fig.
  217A); larvae maggotlike, without distinct head; wing venation highly
  modified.

1*a*. No frontal lunule (Fig. 217*D*) ....suborder **Aschiza**.
No bloodsuckers, but includes a few myiasis-producers, *Eristalis* of family **Syrphidae**, and *Aphiochaeta* of family **Phoridae**.

1*b*. Frontal lunule present; suborder **Schizophora** ....2.

2*a*. Opposite legs of each pair close together; abdomen distinctly segmented (Fig. 266); larval development outside uterus except in tsetse flies; section **Myiodaria** ....4.

2*b*. Opposite legs of each pair widely separated; larval development in uterus; parasitic; section **Pupipara** ....3.

3*a*. Thorax distinct from abdomen; palpi slender and elongate, forming sheath for proboscis (Fig. 238*B*); wings often absent; if present, with stronger veins crowded along costal margin; head and body usually flattened ....***Hippoboscidae.***
(1) Wingless; pupae glued to wool; on sheep (sheep tick, Fig. 238*C*)....
.... *Melophagus.*
(2) Winged (Fig. 238*A*); pupae develop off host; on horses, camels, dogs, *Hippobosca;* on birds, *Pseudolynchia,* etc.

3*b*. Palpi broader than long; wing veins not crowded; on bats .... **Streblidae.**

4*a*. Alulae (or calypteres) rudimentary or absent; subsection *Acalyptratae*...5.

4*b*. Alulae well developed; subsection *Calyptratae* ....6.

5*a*. Mouthparts vestigial; horse botflies ....***Gastrophilidae.***

5*b*. Mouthparts normal; wing without subcostal or anal veins, and no closed cells (Fig. 237) (eye flies) ....***Oscinidae.***

6*a*. Proboscis well developed; wings about as in Fig. 231*A*, **(Muscoidea)** .....7.

6*b*. Mouthparts vestigial; no palpi; hairy, beelike flies (botflies); (for key to genera, see p. 709) ....***Oestridae.***

7*a*. Proboscis fleshy, fitted for lapping or at most for scratching (Fig. 230, I and II): arista with lateral hairs, or, rarely, bare; houseflies, fleshflies, blowflies, screwworm flies. See key on pp. 708–709.

7*b*. Proboscis fitted for piercing ....8.

8*a*. Palpi short, not forming sheath for proboscis (Fig. 230, III) (Stable-flies) ....*Stomoxys.*

8*b*. Palpi long, capable of sheathing proboscis (Fig. 230, IV) ....9.

9*a*. Arista with long feathered hairs on upper surface; wings folded on top of each other (tsetse flies) ....*Glossina.*

9*b*. Arista with simple hairs on upper surface; wings diverge when folded (hornfly) ....*Siphona.*

SUBORDER ORTHORRHAPHA
Phlebotomus or Sandflies (Psychodidae)

General Account. Phlebotomus flies, commonly known as sandflies, are minute hairy midges found in nearly all warm and tropical climates of the world, with the exception of Australia and the East Indian Islands. They belong to the family Psychodidae, most of which resemble tiny moths on account of their very hairy bodies and moth-like pose. They are easily recognized by the characteristic wing venation, with nine longitudinal veins reaching the edge of the wing and with no cross veins except near the base.   The characteristic venation in Phlebotomus is shown in Fig. 218*B*.

Phlebotomus is the only genus in the family (except Pericoma, a vicious biter in Australia) which has a long proboscis and sucks blood. Phlebotomus holds its wings erect over the body when in repose and does not have the usual mothlike appearance.

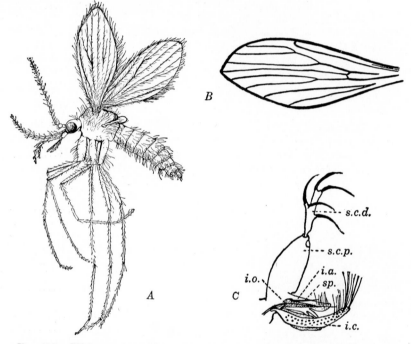

FIG. 218.   *Phlebotomus argentipes.*   *A*, adult ♀ ; *B*, venation of wing; *C*, male genitalia; *s.c.d.*, distal segment of superior clasper; *s.c.p.*, proximal segment of superior clasper; *i.a.*, intermediate appendage, with spine (*sp.*); *i.o.*, intromittent organ; *i.c.*, inferior clasper.   (Adapted from Sinton.)

Morphology.   The sandflies (Fig. 218*A*) are small dull-colored insects, usually yellowish or buff, slender in build, with hairy body, very long and lanky legs, and narrow hairy-veined wings.   They have long slender antennae, long maxillary palpi, and a proboscis longer than the head.   The proboscis consists of a fleshy labium containing dagger-like mandibles and maxillae, both with sawlike teeth at the tips; a bladelike hypopharynx containing the salivary duct; and a flat dagger-like labrum-epipharynx which is provided with sensory hairs and spines and is probably not used as a piercing organ.   The piercing organs project beyond the tip of the labium when at rest, and the labium does not bow back when the other parts are in action, as it does in mosquitoes. The male genitalia consist of three appendages (Fig. 218C), the details of which are of great value in identification. Other characters useful in classification are details of the palpi, form of the spermatheca, and nature of the pharyngeal teeth. Identification, especially of females, is difficult.

Habits. The females feed exclusively on blood. Their bites are very annoying, causing an amount of irritation which seems quite out of proportion to the size of the insect. The preferred hosts vary with the different species; *Phlebotomus minutus* feeds practically entirely on cold-blooded animals, particularly geckos; *P. argentipes* feeds by preference on cattle and then on man; *P. papatasi, sergenti,* and *perniciosus* seem to take particular delight in human blood. One Texas species, *P. anthophorus,* has only been found feeding on rabbits, but another, *P. diabolicus,* is an annoying human pest in south central Texas. The males of at least some species appear not to feed at all, subsisting on the remnants of the last larval food. One African species, however, is said to have biting males. Sandflies are very short-lived and seldom survive more than a fortnight. Most sandflies are nocturnal; in some places they seem to forage for only an hour or so after sundown. During the day they hide in dark corners, cellars, crevices of rocks, etc. Their powers of flight are very limited; their range is rarely over 50 yd. When disturbed on walls they usually fly only a few inches, appearing to hop rather than fly. Their breeding places are nearly always within a few hundred feet of their feeding places.

Life History (Fig. 219). Most species of Phlebotomus lay their eggs in crevices in rocks, masonry, or crumbling buildings, between boards in privies or cesspools, in rubbish or damp, loose soil, etc. The eggs are usually deposited within a few days after emergence and the first blood meal, and vary from 40 to 60 in number; some individuals lay second batches of similar size after a subsequent feed. When deposited, the eggs are literally shot out by the female to a distance several times the length of the abdomen. The eggs are viscid and adhere to the surfaces with which they come in contact; it would seem that the peculiar method of ejecting the eggs is a protective adaptation, facilitating their deposition in the farthest reach of a crevice where even the tiny insect itself could not penetrate. The eggs are elongate and of a dark, shiny brown color, with fine surface markings which vary in different species (Fig. 219A).

The incubation of the common Old World *Phlebotomus papatasi* requires from 6 to 9 days under favorable conditions, but the eggs are very susceptible to external conditions and die quickly if exposed to sunlight or if not kept damp. *P. argentipes* eggs may hatch in 4 days. The larvae (Fig. 219*B*) are tiny caterpillarlike creatures with a relatively large head and heavy jaws (Fig. 220) and with two pairs of long bristles on the last segment of the abdomen which are held erect and spread out fanwise; in the newly hatched larvae there is only one pair of bristles. The body is provided with numerous toothed spines which give it a rough appearance (Fig. 220). These spines differ in different species and, together with the relative length of the

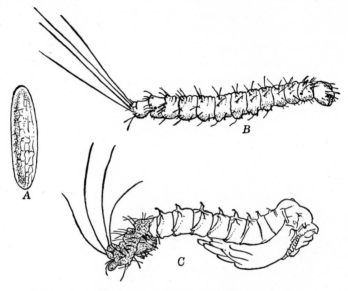

FIG. 219. Life history of *Phlebotomus papatasi*. *A*, egg; *B*, larva; *C*, pupa. (Adapted from Patton.)

caudal bristles, form good identification marks. The larva of *P. papatasi* when full grown is less than 5 mm. long and it is therefore not so large as an ordinary rice grain.

The larvae feed on decaying vegetable matter, fecal particles, and other organic debris. Phlebotomus larvae often " play 'possum " and feign death. For all species a high degree of humidity is required, and in the case of *P. argentipes* the wet-bulb temperature must not exceed 80° F. Hibernation probably occurs always in the larval state.

The full development of the larvae requires from 2 weeks to 2 months or more, depending almost entirely on the temperature. Larvae which hatch at the beginning of cold weather do not pupate until the following spring. The pupa (Fig. 219*C*) is characterized by a very rough cuticle over the thorax but can be identified best by the last larval skin, which adheres to its posterior end. It is colored much like its surroundings and looks like a tiny bit of amorphous matter. The pupae are less susceptible to drying than the larvae. In warm weather the adult insect emerges after 6 to 10 days, but this is much delayed by low temperatures. The entire life cycle from the laying of the eggs to the emergence of the adults may be passed through in a

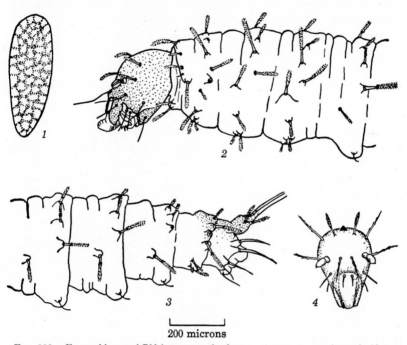

200 microns

FIG. 220. Egg and larva of *Phlebotomus anthophorus*. *1*, egg; *2*, anterior end of larva; *3*, posterior end of larva (only bases of caudal bristles shown); *4*, front view of head of *P. minutus*. (*1–3* after Addis; *4* after Howlett.)

month in hot weather, though it takes 2 months or more in cool weather. In Malta, according to Newstead, the cycle takes about 3 months.

Sandflies and Disease

Sandflies are of great importance as the transmitters of the various types of leishmaniasis and of a filtrable virus disease called three-day fever, or more commonly sandfly, Phlebotomus, or papatasi fever, after its vectors. Sandflies are also the transmitters of Oroya fever (see p. 623).

Sandfly Fever. This relatively mild virus disease (see p. 232) in many respects resembles dengue and may be confused with influenza. It comes on suddenly with fever, headache, pain in the eyes, stiffness of neck and back, and rheumatic pains. As in dengue, a reduction in white blood cells (leucopenia) is a prominent feature. It is often followed by a prolonged period of malaise and depression. It was experimentally shown by Doerr in 1908 to be transmitted by *Phlebotomus papatasi*. The insects become infective about 6 or 7 days after feeding on a patient in the first or second day of the fever. Since sandflies are so short-lived and frequently suck blood only once, whereas the disease can be transmitted by apparently unfed flies, it had long been suspected that the infection was transmitted to the offspring; Whittingham (1922) proved this to be true by producing sandfly fever by the bites of flies bred from infected parents in England. There is no evidence as yet that any species but *P. papatasi* is able to transmit sandfly fever; this species has been found in all places where the disease occurs except at Aden. A disease reported as sandfly fever was reported from south Texas in 1924, but its identity is questionable. Since the infection is of very short duration in man, it presumably is conserved from one season to another in the sandflies. No animal except man is susceptible to the virus.

P. papatasi is of medium size, reaching about 2.5 mm. in length. It is pale yellowish gray with a dull red-brown stripe down the middle of the thorax and a spot of the same color at either side. It is found in many parts of southern Europe, north Africa, and in southwestern Asia. The adult flies choose caves, cellars, catacombs, and similar locations as hiding places. In northwest India they have been observed to hide in large numbers in cracks in the soil, in which they undoubtedly breed, protected from excessive heat or dryness. Sandbags used for raising the sides of tents may supply ideal hiding places. On still, warm nights they emerge to feed on human beings who are close at hand, but they avoid even light breezes and can be kept away by ceiling fans. Some houses are found to be much more infested than others, possibly owing to the proximity of suitable breeding places and to the lack of breezes. Dark rooms on the sheltered side of the ground floor of houses are most likely to be infested. The distance traveled by the adults is very short, but they may be carried long distances by public conveyances.

Leishmaniasis. The baffling problem of transmission of the various forms of leishmaniasis (see pp. 145–146) was not finally solved until 1941, but there is no longer any doubt that sandflies are the principal transmitters of all forms of the disease. The species involved in the different forms of leishmaniasis are not the same. The principal transmitters of Oriental sore are *P. papatasi* (see p. 152) and *P. sergenti*, the females of which are almost indistinguishable. *P. sergenti* is undoubtedly the most important transmitter in Mesopotamia and India, though *papatasi* appears to play the leading role in north Africa. On the east coast of Italy *P. perfiliewi* appears to be a vector. It breeds in dung heaps; if these are over 250 to 300 ft. from houses there is little or no Oriental sore.

The species primarily concerned in transmission of the American form of dermal leishmaniasis, caused by *L. brasiliensis*, are not well known. Aragão in 1922 succeeded in getting leptomonad infections in *P. intermedius* fed on espundia sores and in one instance produced a sore on the nose of a dog by inoculation of macerated flies. In 1940–1941 Pessôa *et al.* found naturally infected specimens of several species, especially *migonei* and *pessoai*, and succeeded in transmitting the disease by their bites.

Most of the species concerned with kala-azar in the Old World belong to the *P. major* group. In India it is *P. argentipes*, a species which is about 2.5 mm. long and is grayish with silvery white tarsi. The adults seem to feed by preference on cattle but attack man when cattle are not readily available. The fly is very local in distribution, being found especially in masonry or thick mud-walled houses and rarely in thin-walled bamboo-and-plaster huts. It breeds in earthen floors and in damp sheltered earth contaminated by the droppings of animals. The adults live only 3 days without food and usually die after the first oviposition, when about 50 to 60 eggs are laid. The adults fly only a few yards, are strictly nocturnal, and never rise to the second floor of a building.

In China *P. chinensis* becomes infected readily after feeding on infected hamsters (*Cricetulus griseus*) and is probably the natural vector. This species seems to have but one brood a year.

Adler and Theodor and others have shown that *P. perniciosus* and *P. major* are the probable natural transmitters of the Mediterranean infantile and canine types of kala-azar. Proboscis infections, however, are rare and occur only late in the season, a fact which may have some bearing on the epidemiology of the disease (see p. 147). *P. perniciosus* is much less frequently found in houses than is *P. papatasi*.

In South America the parasites of visceral leishmaniasis develop readily in both *P. intermedius* and *P. longipalpis* when these flies are fed on infected dogs.

Oroya Fever. Oroya fever or Carrion's disease is an acute febrile disease caused by a very minute organism, *Bartonella bacilliformis* (see p. 229), occurring in valleys on the slopes of the Andes in Peru, Chile, Ecuador, and Bolivia. In 1938 it appeared in epidemic form in the province of Nariño in Colombia, causing 1800 deaths in 9 months in a population of perhaps 200,000. The acute stage of the disease is characterized by high fever, severe anemia, aches, and albuminuria, and is often fatal. In more chronic cases it is followed by an eruption of nodules called verruga peruviana. In mild cases the eruption may be the only manifestation, and it is considered a good sign when it appears. Some cases seem to be symptomless. Geiman developed good culture media for the organism, making possible an agglutination test for diagnosis.

The probable relation of sandflies to this disease was pointed out by Townsend in 1913. In the Peruvian Andes the disease is limited to a comparatively small zone and is contracted exclusively at night. Townsend obtained some positive experimental evidence incriminating a species which he named *Phlebotomus verrucarum*. Fifteen years later Noguchi and his colleagues amply confirmed Townsend's conclusions. They incriminated both *Phlebotomus verrucarum* and *P. noguchii*, but Hertig (1942) thinks that *P. noguchii* was erroneously identified.

P. verrucarum is found in the deep-cut canyons of the west slope of the Peruvian Andes at elevations between 2800 and 8000 ft. Within this zone it would be extremely dangerous to be caught at night, for no ordinary screening would afford adequate protection. At lower elevations the valley is too arid for sandflies to breed, and at higher elevations the cold nights inhibit their activity. In the verruga zone there is a favorable combination of cool summers, warm sunny winters, moderate rainfall, and mild nights — a zone of perpetual spring. *P. verrucarum* is a strictly nocturnal species which enters houses readily and bites man freely. *P. noguchii* and *P. peruensis* do not seek man and probably play no part in the transmission of human disease.

Control. Because of their short flight range, which is seldom over 75 to 100 yd., and their tendency to stay close to the ground, sandflies are very easily controlled locally by DDT sprays. Spraying the inside and outside of houses, rock walls, etc., eliminates them for months. The long life cycle results in a very slow comeback of a depleted population. Hertig and Fairchild (1948) obtained some remarkable results in sandfly control in a Bartonella zone in Peru. When venturing beyond the protected area after sundown it is necessary to use protective clothing and repellents, of which dimethyl phthalate is probably best.

Biting Midges or No-see-ums (Ceratopogonidae)

Morphology. The tiny flies belonging to this family (Fig. 221) go by various names: midges, gnats, punkies, or sandflies, and, in the west, " no-see-ums " because of their minute size, which is seldom over 1 to 2 mm. in length. They can usually be distinguished from allied insects by the peculiar venation of the wings (Fig. 223), the first two veins being very heavy whereas the others are more or less indistinct. The scales so characteristic of mosquitoes are absent. The proboscis

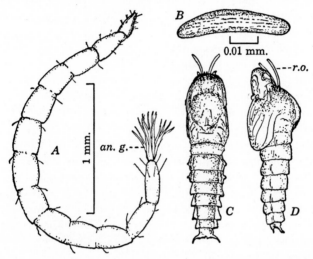

Fig. 221. Immature stages of Culicoides. *A*, larva; the anal gills (*an. g.*) are retractile, there is no proleg, and the anal segment has three pairs of hairs; *B*, egg, much enlarged; *C* and *D*, dorsal and lateral views of a pupa; note slender respiratory organs (*r.o.*) on thorax.

is never long, even in the bloodsuckers, and one marvels at the irritation which can be inflicted by such a small insect with such a small organ. As in mosquitoes the males are distinguishable by the more plumose antennae. In many ways they closely resemble the non-bloodsucking midges of the family Chironomidae, in which they were long included as a subfamily, but they are distinguished by the failure of the thorax to project like a hood over the head or to have a longitudinal dorsal groove. They are easily distinguishable from the simuliids by the longer antennae and more slender bodies, as well as by the wing venation. Most species have characteristically mottled wings (Figs. 222, 223). The great majority of the species that attack man and animals belong to the genus Culicoides, but there are annoying pests in the genera Leptoconops, Ceratopogon, and Forcipomyia also.

Habits and Life Cycle.   Only the females are bloodsuckers.   Nearly all the members of the family become active at dusk, but if disturbed many of them will bite in the shade, even on bright days.   Both sexes are attracted by lights.   They are much more active fliers than Phlebotomus and are said to go as far as half a mile in search of a host, but only when the air is still.   Most of the species appear to prefer cattle, camels, or other animals as food, but some species readily attack man.

The eggs of Culicoides, several hundreds in number, are deposited in gelatinous masses like miniature masses of frog eggs and are usually moored to some object under water in swamps or ponds; many species favor brackish or salt water.   After a few days the eggs hatch and give rise to minute, slender wormlike larvae (Fig. 221*A*) which burrow in wet mud or sand either in or out of water; their movements suggest giant spirochetes.   Culicoides larvae, unlike chironomid larvae, do not have pseudopods on the first or last segments of the abdomen.   At the posterior end there are gill-like structures that can be protruded (Fig. 223); the larvae do not need air as do mosquito larvae.   The food probably consists of microscopic plant and animal life or organic debris.   The pupa (Fig. 221*D*) rather resembles that of a mosquito, except that the abdomen is kept extended instead of curled under and the pupa hangs from the surface in a vertical position, breathing through a pair of trumpetlike tubes as do mosquitoes.   Both larvae and pupae are hard to find, and the presence of a breeding place is more frequently discovered by finding the floating pupal cases from which the adults have emerged.   The entire life cycle probably occupies 2 weeks or more, according to temperature.

Annoyance.   The bites of Culicoides produce nettlelike pricks which are sometimes followed by burning sensations and intolerable itching. Some species are so minute as to be individually overlooked, but they may be so abundant as to give a gray tinge to the skin and to cause extreme irritation.   A certain degree of immunity to the effects of their bites is acquired, at least by some individuals, after years of exposure to them.   Dove, Hall, and Hull (1932) think the flies are attracted by the heat emanating from warm bodies, but the writer believes they are attracted largely by animal odors, since he has been attacked by great swarms upon opening a rabbit carcass.   The flies usually attack exposed parts of the body but will bite through thin clothing.   Salt-marsh breeders (*C. dovei* and others) are intolerable pests along the southern Atlantic seaboard of the United States, so much so as to have retarded development of these areas.   Other annoying species occur in Maryland, the Cascade Mountains of Oregon, and in many places in the tropics. They seriously interfere with romance on moonlit beaches in the West Indies and Central America.

Midges as Disease Carriers

Bloodsucking midges have been accused of transmitting a Peruvian form of dermal leishmaniasis, and they serve as intermediate hosts for two human filarial worms, *Acanthocheilonema perstans* and *Mansonella ozzardi*. A species of Culicoides has also been shown to be the transmitter of *Onchocerca reticulata* in horses (p. 456).

Two species of land-breeding midges, *Forcipomyia utae* and *F. townsendi*, have been incriminated by Townsend as the carriers and intermediate hosts of the parasite causing uta, a form of leishmaniasis occurring on the western face of the Andes in Peru. According to Townsend, sores resembling uta and containing a few leishman bodies were produced in laboratory animals by inoculation of ground-up midges, and two cases are cited in which uta sores developed after the bites of midges. The case against these insects cannot be considered proved, but the evidence is suggestive.

Culicoides and Filarial Infections. Sharp (1928) proved two species of Culicoides, *C. grahami* and *C. austeni* (Fig. 222), to be the intermediate hosts of the filarial worm *Acanthocheilonema perstans* (see p. 455) in British Cameroons, where about 92 per cent of the natives are infected. The ingested larvae go through the usual course of development in the thoracic muscles and are ready to emerge from the proboscis or head on the seventh or eighth day. Usually from 4 to 7 worms develop from a feeding. The female flies feed only in darkness; such dim light as a ¼-candlepower lamp in a 7-ft. tent gives full protection, and even a full moon keeps the flies from biting. The white residents are protected by the use of nets and lights and by the preference of the flies for black skin.

Fig. 222.   *Culicoides austeni,* vector of *Acanthocheilonema perstans.* × 20. (After Sharp, from Fülleborn.)

Buckley (1934), working on the island of St. Vincent, W. I., showed that a Culicoides, *C. furens* (Fig. 223), serves as an intermediate host for another filarial worm, *Mansonella ozzardi* (see p. 455). The development in Culicoides is similar to that of *Acanthocheilonema perstans*. *C. furens,* a notorious biter, is a brackish-water breeder widely distributed in the West Indies and tropical America south to Brazil.

Steward in 1933 showed that *Onchocerca reticulata*, the cause of fistula of the withers or head (poll-evil) in horses, is transmitted by *C. nubeculosis* in England. This species breeds in liquid manure and other foul stagnant water. There is a suspicion that Culicoides may

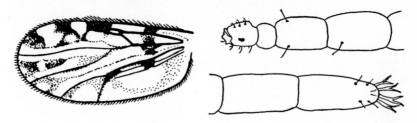

Fig. 223.   *Left*, wing of *Culicoides furens* (after Hoffman); *right*, anterior and posterior ends of larva of *C. furens* (after Painter).

also be involved in the transmission of Onchocerca in cattle in South Africa, although at present only blackflies are known to transmit human and bovine onchocerciasis.

Control. The control of Culicoides presents a difficult problem, since they breed over such extensive areas of marshes. Dove, Hall, and Hull think that drainage ditches which allow in-and-out flow of tidewater would be effective in dispersing Culicoides larvae, whereas stagnant ditches favor their accumulation. Some reduction can also be obtained by drainage and elimination of shade at the edges of marshes. DDT emulsions have some effect, but DDT is quickly detoxicated by mud, and so it is not as effective as it is against mosquito larvae. Dorsey (1947) used 12 to 15 lb. of DDT per acre to control Culicoides breeding in tidal mangrove swamps on Palau in the Pacific. Benzene hexachloride or phenothiazine emulsions might give better results. Protection from adults can be obtained by spraying screens with DDT and using repellents (see p. 495).

Blackflies or Buffalo Gnats (Simuliidae)

The blackflies, as annoyers of domestic animals and man, are among the most important of insect pests, since they often appear in overwhelming hordes. The females are most vicious bloodsuckers, and in especially bad outbreaks they may kill large numbers of animals. A famous migratory European species, *Simulium columbaczense*, killed 16,000 domestic animals in 1923 and about 14,000 in 1934 in the Balkans. Unlike most small biting flies, blackflies are diurnal. They have a world-wide distribution, being found from the arctics to the tropics and up to perpetual snow on mountains, wherever there is running water.

Morphology. These small insects, which constitute the family Simuliidae, are quite unlike the other flies of the group (Nematocera) to which they belong. Instead of the usual slender, long-legged, midge-like flies of this group, we have in the blackflies small, robust, hump-backed creatures with short legs and broad wings (Fig. 224). The antennae are composed of 11 segments, but they are short and stocky and have no hairs at the joints. The proboscis in the female is short

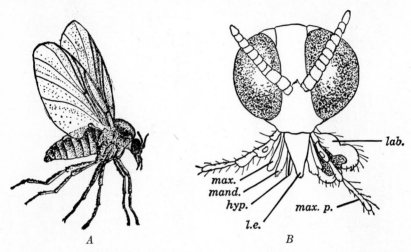

Fig. 224. *A*, Blackfly, *Simulium pecuarum*, × 7 (after Riley). *B*, Mouthparts of Simulium; *hyp.*, hypopharynx; *lab.*, labium; *l.e.*, labrum-epipharynx; *mand.*, mandible; *max.*, maxilla; *max. p.*, maxillary palpus. (After Alcock.)

but heavy and powerful; in the males, which are not bloodsuckers, it is poorly developed. The mouthparts (Fig. 224, *right*), consisting of toothed daggerlike mandibles and maxillae, and also a hypopharynx and labrum-epipharynx, resemble in general those of Phlebotomus.

Most of the northern species are black, whence their name, but some of the species are reddish brown or yellowish, and they may be variously striped and marked. The wings are either clear or of a grayish or yellowish color, with the few heavy veins near the anterior margin often distinctively colored. Some of the species are not more than 1 mm. in length, and the largest of them scarcely exceed 4 mm.

Life History. Unlike the mosquitoes and midges, blackflies breed in running water, and few streams flow too swiftly for them. The eggs (Fig. 225*A*), which have a peculiar slimy coating, are laid in large masses, up to many thousands, by a number of females. They are deposited by some species on leaves or blades of grass which are occasionally licked by running water, the weight of the eggs sufficing to submerge them; other species dart into the water and oviposit directly on the slimy surfaces of submerged stones or twigs.

The famous Columbacz fly of the Balkans (see following section), *Simulium columbaczense*, has two races, one of which breeds on sub-

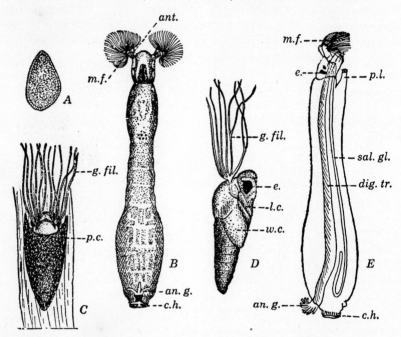

Fig. 225. Developmental stages of Simulium. *A*, egg of *S. venustum*; *B*, larva of *S. bracteatum*; *C*, pupa, in pupal case, of *S. venustum*; *D*, free pupa of *S. jenningsi*; *E*, side view of a larva showing some of its anatomy; *an. g.*, anal gills; *ant.*, antenna; *c.h.*, posterior circlet of hooks; *dig. tr.*, digestive tract; *e.*, eye; *g. fil.*, gill filaments; *l.c.*, leg cases; *m.f.*, mouth fans; *p.c.*, wall-pocket-like pupal case; *p.l.*, proleg; *sal. gl.*, salivary and spinning gland; *w.c.*, wing case. (From Jobbins-Pomeroy.)

merged vegetation in shallow water along the sides of the Danube, the other on stones on the river bottom down to a depth of 65 ft. In some places in Ontario the slimy boards of old lumber chutes are favorite breeding places. Some species are suspected of laying their eggs above the water during the summer, in places where they will later be submerged.

The eggs require 4 to 5 days or longer to hatch. The larva (Fig. 225*B*) attaches itself to a stone or other submerged object by means of concentric circles of minute hooklets at the blunt posterior end of the body. The hooks hold fast to glutinous silken threads spun by the larvae. As expressed by Alcock, " one of the most characteristic attitudes of the larva is to sit upright on the end of its tail — to use the language of the poets of the daily press — with its mouth fans standing out from its head like a pair of shaggy ears." The mouth fans, which are very delicate and elegant, are used for sweeping microscopic particles into the mouth as they are brought by the running water. The stump of a leg on the first segment (Fig. 225, *p.l.*) is used in conjunction with the posterior sucker for creeping, the larva looping along like a " measuring worm "; it is also of use in constructing the silken cocoon from the secretions of the salivary glands. This little proleg has a crown of tiny hooklets that make it possible for the larva to hold its ground even in a torrent of water.

The salivary glands extend back to the posterior end of the body (Fig. 225, *sal. gl.*). The fluid secreted hardens to silk at once on exposure to water and is used not only in spinning the cocoon but also in spinning anchoring threads and life lines. According to Malloch, the larva when disturbed releases its hold and floats downstream, holding by the stumpy leg to a silken thread which is being spun out and by means of which the insect later regains its former position. The larvae breathe by means of tiny gills that can be projected through a slit in the last segment of the abdomen (Fig. 225, *an. g.*). The larvae are always found in colonies, sometimes forming veritable carpets on boards or stones.

After 2 or 3 weeks or longer, the larvae spin for themselves a partial cocoon which is variously shaped like a jelly glass, slipper, wall pocket, etc., open at the upper end for the extrusion of the branching gill filaments which are used as breathing organs (Fig. 225C). Some species simply spin a snarl of threads, the work of a whole community, in the meshes of which the pupae exist in a fair state of protection. The general form of the pupae can be seen in Fig. 225D. The breathing filaments vary greatly in different species and may have from four to sixty branches.

The adults emerge in from 3 days to a week or more and are carried to the surface by a bubble of air which has been collected inside the old pupal skin. The adults are short-lived and lay their eggs soon after emergence. The whole life of a generation from egg to egg may be passed in 6 weeks to 2 months or more. Some species produce only a single generation in a year, but others produce two, and still others three or more; the number also varies with the climate. *S. venustum*, for instance, has two generations a year in Canada, the mature larvae of the second generation hibernating and producing the first brood of adults in the spring, but this same species is said to have five or six generations in South Carolina. Probably all species hibernate as larvae.

Migrations. The adults of many species travel a mile or more and possibly a number of miles. Some species have a tendency to settle in the ears of horses or cattle and are thus passively dispersed. The European Columbacz fly, breeding in incredible numbers in about 60 miles of the Danube River in Yugoslavia, is peculiar in being truly migratory. Swarms are said to rise high into the air, where they are passively carried by air currents for 100 miles or more, after which they come down and begin an active migration, covering 3 to 6 miles per day. Their depredations in exceptionally bad years were mentioned in the opening paragraph of this chapter.

Species and Food Habits. The species of blackflies are numerous, but all are included in the single genus Simulium, with several subgenera which some workers elevate to the rank of true genera. Some species largely confine their attacks to birds, and some to domestic animals; some have never been observed to feed on either man or domestic animals but may feed on wild birds or cold-blooded vertebrates. Comparatively few species commonly attack man. Bequaert in 1938 said that of 57 species known in Africa only 5 have been reported as biting people. One of the most troublesome species in the United States is *S. pecuarum*, the famous buffalo gnat of the south central portion of the country. This species was formerly more abundant than now and was a terrible scourge to mules and cattle. *S. venustum* is one of the most important molesters of man. It occurs over the greater part of the eastern portion of North America.

Annoyance. In the estimation of the writer, no insect scourge is more terrible than an attack of blackflies. In parts of Sudan (Dongola) a species known as the nimetti, *Simulium griseicollis*, renders life a burden during the winter months. In the Balkans there are instances of children as well as animals being killed by attacks of the Columbacz fly. The writer's experience occurred in the woods of northern Ontario early in June. The flies were at the height of their short season and made the lives of man and animals almost unbearable. It was with some impatience (having been reared among the mosquitoes of New Jersey) that he submitted, on first arrival, to the precautions recommended to keep the flies from being able to bite, and his carelessness resulted in many individuals of the fearful swarms getting through his armor. The resulting bites, which bled at first, were only slightly painful to begin with but became progressively more swollen and more agonizingly itchy for three days, when the bites became oozing pimples.

Accompanying this there was a feeling of general ennui and despondence with some fever. Subsequent attacks, though far from pleasant, were not so severe in their effects, a certain amount of immunity apparently having been built up. On account of the slow development of the symptoms it seemed possible that they were due to the injection of a virus. Stokes, however, showed that the effects of blackfly bites, essentially as described above, can be reproduced by the injection of material from preserved flies.

Simulium and Disease

Onchocerciasis. Blacklock (1926) showed that in Sierra Leone *Simulium damnosum*, a widely distributed species annoying to man, serves as an intermediate host for the filarial worm, *Onchocerca volvulus*. Subsequently *S. neavei*, another man-biter, was found to be a transmitter in central Africa. In 1930 Hoffman in Mexico and in 1931 Strong and Bequaert in Guatemala showed that three species of Simulium serve as intermediate hosts and transmitters in those countries, namely, *S. metallicum* (=*avidum*), *S. ochraceum*, and *S. callidum* (=*mooseri*). These blackflies appear to exert a chemotactic attraction on the microfilariae in the skin which results in an astonishing concentration of them in the stomachs of the engorged insects.

Bequaert thinks that food preference is the principal factor in determining which species of Simulium transmit Onchocerca infections; he believes that any species habitually biting man in an endemic region should be looked upon with suspicion. The same is probably true in the case of onchocerciasis of cattle. Further details about onchocerciasis will be found on pp. 456–460.

Simulium damnosum is a species that is widely distributed in equatorial Africa. It is uniform black, with golden hairs on the thorax. It breeds in large flowing rivers and is very abundant along their banks where there is high grass or dense vegetation to protect it from wind.

All the Central American vectors breed in small, rapidly flowing streams of clear water above 3000 ft. elevation. Other species breed in larger or more sluggish lowland streams but are not involved in the transmission of Onchocerca. *S. metallicum* is a small black species, 1.5 to 2 mm. long, which breeds in fair-sized streams; *S. ochraceum* is about the same size, with yellowish-red thorax, black legs, and yellow and black abdomen, and breeds in small seepage streams; *S. callidum* is 2 to 3 mm. long and is yellowish, with a few black spots on the abdomen. All three species readily attack man and animals outdoors but do not enter houses.

Leucocytozoön Infections of Birds. O'Roke (1934) found *Simulium venustum* to be the intermediate host of *Leucocytozoön simondi* (see p. 217), which causes a malaria-like disease of ducks in northern United States serious enough to prevent the raising of them in some localities and undoubtedly very injurious to wild ducks. *S. nigroparvum* transmits a similar destructive disease of turkeys caused by *L. smithi.* This disease and its transmission by blackflies have been observed in Nebraska and in Virginia.

Control

DDT has proved a very effective insecticide for destruction of blackfly larvae. An isolated area of 65 square miles in Africa was successfully freed of *S. neavei* by treatment of two rivers with a 10 per cent emulsion applied by dripping from tins at the rate of 5 ppm. for 30 minutes at a time, at intervals of 10 to 14 days or longer over a period of about 5 months, long enough to include oviposition by all adult flies. The difficulties were the large amounts needed for large rivers, the killing of fish, and difficulty of application to slow-moving streams.

In Guatemala, Fairchild and Herera in 1945 found that only 0.1 ppm. was needed and that it did not have to be applied in the rather expensive standard emulsion with xylene and Triton but could be applied as a simple dilution in turpentine and kerosene or as a suspension by mixing with any wetting agent. In small seepage streams, placing a small piece of quick-dissolving soap containing DDT would suffice. DDT is soluble in water to the extent of 1 part in 10 to 15 million, which apparently is enough to knock out blackfly larvae. In some streams the treatment was effective for distances up to about 5 miles or more. By using Dampf's suggestion of treating all streams in an area during dry seasons, blackflies could probably be exterminated over considerable areas.

For protection against adults, repellents (see p. 495) are a tremendous boon, but the crawling habits of the flies must be taken into account, and other parts of the body than those which are directly exposed must be treated. Few blackflies habitually enter houses, and once in they usually endeavor to escape, so fumigation is seldom necessary. In camp life and for the protection of animals in pastures smudges are indispensable. The flies will not tolerate the smoke, and domestic animals soon learn to take advantage of its protection. During the blackfly plague in Bulgaria mentioned previously, smudges were used also for the protection of animals while working in the daytime. Cheap repellents made of emulsions of kerosene or various resinous oils with soap and water have also been recommended for spraying animals.

Horseflies (Tabanidae)

The tabanids are the only Brachycera which suck blood except some species of the family Leptidae, but as yet no suspicion of disease transmission has fallen on that family.   The Leptidae are easily distinguished by the long tapering abdomen and the form of the antennae (Fig. 216C).   The tabanids, known as gadflies, horseflies, etc., are

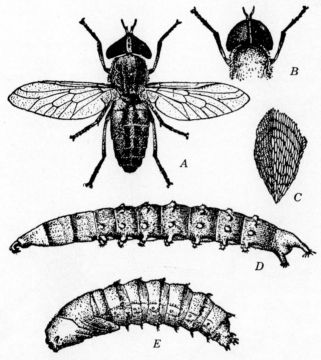

FIG. 226.   Life history of a tabanid, *Tabanus kingi*, a " seroot " of Sudan.   *A*, adult female, × 3; *B*, head of adult male, × 3; *C*, egg mass, laid in crevices of rock, × 5; *D*, larva, × 2½; *E*, pupa, × 2½.   (After King.)

mainly animal pests, but many species attack man also, inflicting painful bites.   They are also implicated in the spread of certain diseases of man and animals.   The females alone are bloodsuckers, the males living chiefly on plant juices; even the females in some genera feed on flowers.   These flies, of which over 2500 species have been recorded, occur in every part of the world, but the species are most abundant in warm climates.

Morphology.   The tabanids are of large size and heavy build (Fig. 226A).   They are often beautifully colored in black, brown, and orange tones, sometimes with brilliant green or green-marked eyes, though in most species of temperate climates the huge eyes are brown

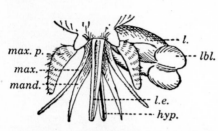

or black. The head is large and in the male is almost entirely occupied by the eyes, which meet across the crown of the head (Fig. 226*B*); in the females a narrow space is left between them. The antennae are of characteristic shape (Fig. 216*D, E*), varying somewhat in the different genera. The mouthparts (Fig. 227) are almost exactly like those of the blackflies on a large

FIG. 227. Mouthparts of a tabanid; *hyp.*, hypopharynx; *l.*, labium; *lbl.*, labellum; *l.e.*, labrum-epipharynx; *mand.*, mandible; *max.*, maxilla; *max. p.*, maxillary palpus.

scale. The stabbing and cutting parts are usually short, heavy, and powerful, though in one genus, Pangonia, the proboscis is very long, enabling the fly to pierce even through thick clothing.

The thorax is relatively long, and the wings are large and expansive and usually held at a broad angle to the body, as shown in Fig. 228.

FIG. 228. Left, a long-beaked tabanid, *Pangonia ruppellii*, of eastern Africa, × 2. (Adapted from Castellani and Chalmers.) Right, a deerfly, *Chrysops callidus*, × 4.

The markings of the wings usually give the easiest means of identification of the genera. Of the four genera most important as human pests, Tabanus (Fig. 226) is large and has clear or smoky wings, with no spots or a few small scattered ones; Pangonia (Fig. 228) also has clear or smoky wings but can be distinguished by the long proboscis; Haematopota is of moderate size and has wings with profuse scroll-like markings; and Chrysops, the species of which are often small, even smaller than a housefly, has conspicuous black bands and spots on the wing (Figs. 228 and 229).

Life History and Habits. All the tabanids breed in water or in damp places. The eggs (Fig. 226C), several hundred in number, are laid in definitely shaped masses on the leaves of marsh or water plants, on the leaves or twigs of trees overhanging water, or in crevices of rocks along the sides of streams. When deposited the eggs are covered by a gluey waterproof secretion that binds them together; they are white at first but soon turn dark. They are deposited during the summer and under favorable circumstances hatch in 4 to 7 days. Many are attacked by small hymenopteran parasites.

The newly hatched larvae fall into the water or to wet ground. The larvae (Fig. 226D) are cylindrical legless creatures, tapering at each end. The body has eleven segments exclusive of the very small and often retracted head. Each segment has a row of wartlike processes provided with spines or hairs. The larvae are voracious feeders; most species prey upon soft-bodied animals such as earthworms and insect larvae and are not averse to cannibalism if food is scarce, but most species of Chrysops feed on dead organic matter. The larvae grow rapidly during the summer but remain inactive and with little or no growth during the winter. In the spring they complete their development and creep out to drier ground to pupate. The pupa (Fig. 226E) often resembles the chrysalis of a butterfly in form. The pupal period is relatively brief; according to Cameron (1926) it seldom extends beyond 2 weeks and may be as short as 5 days. The whole life history of species of temperate climates therefore occupies about a year, sometimes more, but it may be shorter in tropical species, in which there are probably several broods a year.

The adult flies are strictly diurnal and are often active in the clear sunlight of a summer day, though many forest-dwelling forms, e.g., the deerflies, Chrysops, prefer shade. They do not go in swarms as do many other biting insects but are usually solitary in habit. They are strong flies and may be found at considerable distances from the breeding places. Most of the species are very deliberate and persistent in their feeding and are not easily disturbed when they have begun to suck blood. Gadflies collect near pools and skim over the surface of the water, the underside of the body often touching the water. Knowledge of this habit led Portchinsky in Russia to devise a means of trapping the flies on oil-covered pools.

Tabanids and Disease

Trypanosomes. Tabanids are of importance in connection with the transmission of some of the trypanosomes of animals. *Trypanosoma evansi*, causing surra in horses, cattle, camels, dogs, etc., is undoubtedly commonly transmitted by tabanids. Many investigators have proved that the disease can be transmitted in a mechanical manner by the soiled proboscis of flies that have had interrupted feeds, i.e., began their meal on one animal and finished it on another. El debab of camels in North Africa, caused by the closely related *T. soudanense*, is apparently transmitted in a similar manner. In French Indo-China the closely related *T. annamense* is believed to be transmitted from wild buffaloes to cattle by forest tabanids and then to be transmitted among domestic animals mainly by the stablefly, Stomoxys.

In many parts of the world cattle are infected with apparently harmless trypanosomes, *T. theileri* or closely related forms, which are not only mechanically transmitted by tabanids but also undergo a developmental cycle in the fly. Nöller succeeded in producing infection in cattle by inoculating cultures made from tabanids infected with "*Crithidia subulata*," thus proving that this really is identical with the trypanosome; whether such a cycle of development can occur in the case of surra remains to be proved. It has also been shown that *T. brucei*, causing nagana in animals, *T. equinum*, causing mal-de-caderas, and *T. equiperdum*, causing dourine, can be mechanically transmitted by interrupted feeding of tabanids. There is, therefore, little doubt that the trypanosomes of human sleeping sickness may also occasionally be transmitted in this manner, though the danger cannot be considered very great. The frequency with which tabanids, annoyed by a swishing tail, fly to other animals to continue a feeding makes them especially good mechanical transmitters.

Tabanids have been suspected of causing sporadic cases of dermal leishmaniasis by inoculation of the leptomonads or crithidias commonly found in them, but there is no conclusive evidence of this. As already noted, the crithidias, in some cases at least, are the developmental stages of *T. theileri*.

Transmission of Other Diseases by Interrupted Feeding. Tabanids may be of importance in transmitting a number of other infectious blood diseases by means of a soiled proboscis during interrupted feeding on herds of animals, just as in the case of some of the trypanosomes mentioned above. Anaplasmosis (see p. 218) can be transmitted within 5 minutes after feeding on an infected animal. Anthrax can also be transmitted in this manner by either tabanids or Stomoxys. This is a very destructive bacterial disease affecting domestic animals and transmissible to man. It may enter the body through skin abrasions, aerial spores, or contaminated food. Since ticks, fleas, and bedbugs have been found capable of transmitting undulant fever or brucellosis, it will not be surprising if tabanids are incriminated also. Tabanids can also transmit swamp fever of horses.

Tularemia. Species of Chrysops, particularly *C. discalis*, have been found to be important transmitters of tularemia (see p. 547) in Utah and other places in western United States. The flies were found to be infective for at least 14 days after biting an infected rabbit.

Loa loa. Certain species of Chrysops, locally known as mangrove flies, are the intermediate hosts of a human filarial worm, *Loa loa* (see p. 453), in the tropical jungles of Africa. The microfilariae of this worm, unlike those of *Wuchereria bancrofti*, swarm in the blood in the daytime. Development of the larvae takes place in the abdomen of the fly, but the infective larvae subsequently invade the proboscis as is usual with filariae. The species of Chrysops known to be involved are *C. dimidiata* (Fig. **229**), *C. silacea*, and *C. distinctipennis*.

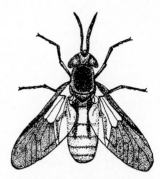

Fig. 229. *Chrysops dimidiatus,* vector of *Loa loa.* (After Grünberg, from Fülleborn.)

Control

Prevention of bites from tabanids, especially during an epidemic of anthrax or where diseases which may be transmitted by tabanids are prevalent, is important. Practically the only means that can be employed is the use of repellents, as for other insect pests (see p. 495). Owing to their habit of burrowing in mud, it is difficult to exterminate tabanids in their early stages. DDT emulsions may have some effect, but the detoxicating effect of mud on this chemical would certainly lower its efficiency, as in the case of Culicoides. Benzene hexachloride, chlordane, or phenothiazine may prove to be better. However, spraying large animals with DDT to combat other flies (see p. 642) greatly reduces the number of tabanids on ranches and farms. Philip reported a marked reduction in numbers in northern Minnesota by drainage of swamps.

SUBORDER CYCLORRHAPHA

We pass now from the suborder Orthorrhapha to the other suborder of Diptera, the Cyclorrhapha, which are distinguished by having larvae without distinct heads and by the fact that the adults escape from the pupal case by a circular opening in the head end.   This suborder includes some important bloodsuckers (stableflies, hornflies, tsetse flies, Pupipara) and many nonbloodsuckers which are nevertheless important to man and animals either as mechanical carriers of disease germs (houseflies, blowflies, eyeflies) or as parasites in the larval stage (bots, warbles, etc.).

Superfamily Muscoidea

This group of flies, characterized by having well-developed squamae, normal mouthparts, and with the legs of opposite sides attached close

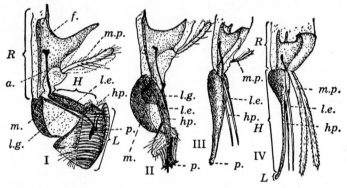

Fig. 230.   Evolution of bloodsucking proboscides in muscoid flies.   I, *Musca domestica*, for lapping only; II, *Musca crassirostris*, for scratching and tearing skin; III, Stomoxys, and IV, Glossina, for tearing and piercing skin.   Note progressive shortening of rostrum, reduction of labellum, and elongation of haustellum; strengthening of haustellum by development of mentum and labial gutter; freeing of hypostome from labial gutter; and development of prestomal armature.   *R*, rostrum, retractile into head; *H*, haustellum, which can be bent at right angles to rostrum; *L*, labellum, highly developed with pseudotracheal grooves in Musca, reduced to a mere tooth-bearing tip to proboscis in Stomoxys and Glossina; *f.*, fulcrum, supporting rostrum; *a.*, apodeme; *m.*, mentum, much more highly developed in scratching and piercing forms; *l.g.*, labial gutter, poorly developed in *M. domestica*, better developed in *M. crassirostris*, in which it has a deep keel, and very well developed in piercing forms; *l.e.*, labrum-epipharynx, reduced in piercing forms; *hp.*, hypopharynx, largely fixed to labial gutter in Musca, free in piercing forms; *m.p.*, maxillary palpi, developed as sheaths for proboscis in Glossina.   (Adapted from figures by Patton, and Patton and Cragg.)

together, include the houseflies (Muscidae), stableflies and hornflies (Stomoxyidae), tsetse flies (Glossinidae), and the blowflies, fleshflies, and screwworm flies (Sarcophagidae and Calliphoridae).   All were once included in the single family Muscidae.

The majority of the members of this superfamily have fleshy proboscides fitted for lapping up liquid foods.   Some have acquired the habit of devoting nearly all their time to the skins of animals, flitting from spot to spot in search of blood or exudations.   Such, according to Patton (1932), are *M. bezzii* and *M. lusoria*, which are therefore potential mechanical transmitters of blood infections. From these scavengers Patton has traced an interesting evolutionary development of the proboscis into a scratching and tearing and finally a piercing organ (see Fig. 230). *M. crassirostris* (Fig. 230, II) is able to rasp and tear a hole through the skin of cattle and suck the exuding fluid. A much higher development is reached in Stomoxys and Siphona (Fig. 230, III), in which the elongated, strengthened, and styletlike proboscis acts as a piercing organ after a hole has been rasped and torn. The proboscis of the tsetse flies (Fig. 230, IV) is the culmination in this line of evolution. The tsetse flies and a number of the blood-feeding species of Musca have become viviparous; most of these deposit their larvae at the beginning of the second stage, but one, *M. planiceps*, a bloodsucker, deposits its larvae one at a time at the beginning of the third stage, as do the tsetses.

All the blood-feeding members of the genus Musca, all the tsetse flies, and most of the Stomoxyidae are Old World species. Our houseflies, stableflies, and hornflies are probably all importations from across the seas.

Hornflies and Stableflies (Stomoxyidae)

Hornfly (Siphona irritans). This small blackish fly, about half the size of a housefly, causes endless misery to cattle; no other pest except possibly screwworms are as inimical to the contentment of cows. The fly sometimes attacks other domestic animals but rarely man. On ranches in the southwest an average of 4000 flies per animal is frequent. They stay on the animals most of the time, night and day, stabbing them and sucking blood usually twice a day. The loss of blood from a herd of 500 cattle with 4000 flies apiece is estimated at 7 quarts a day. The irritated animals become restless, cease to graze, and lose vitality not only from loss of blood but also from loss of food. The resulting heavy loss of meat and milk is inevitable. In 1945 hornflies were estimated to have caused a loss of 86 million pounds of meat. Fortunately, since they stick fairly closely to one animal, hornflies do not transmit diseases as frequently as stableflies and tabanids.

Hornflies usually leave the animals only to lay eggs. They swarm to a fresh dropping, crawl under it and lay their eggs, and return to the animal in 5 to 10 minutes. The larvae develop in the dropping in about 10 to 12 days; they are about 7 mm. long and have large black stigmal plates (see p. 706) very close together. They pupate in soil under the dropping; the flat and wingless adults that emerge crawl off to rest for an hour, distending the abdomen and unfolding the wings. The flies live for 6 or 7 weeks and lay about 400 eggs.

Hornflies, because of their habit of staying on animals, are easily controlled by spraying animals with DDT (1 pint of 2 per cent emulsion per animal, followed by ½ pint per animal 3 weeks later). Even much lighter applications may be effective. Gains up to 40 lb. or more (in one case 80 lb.) occur within a week following treatment. Laake

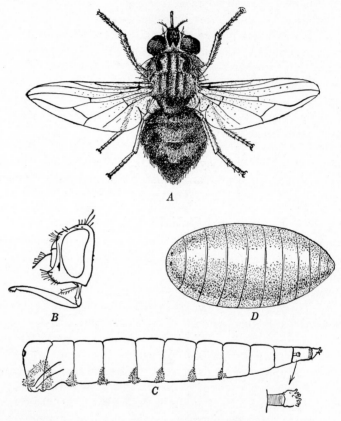

FIG. 231. Stablefly, *Stomoxys calcitrans*. *A*, adult; *B*, head, side view; *C*, larva, with enlargement of anterior spiracle; *D*, pupa. (Adult, × 5; larva and pupa, × 7.)

estimated that a pound of DDT caused a gain of 2360 lb. of animals. Complete extermination of hornflies would not be extremely difficult. DDT control is so effective that the animals have no further use for their tails. As one stockman said, "Might as well use them for oxtail soup!"

Stableflies (Stomoxys). The genus Stomoxys contains a number of Old World species, but one, *S. calcitrans*, the stablefly or dogfly (Fig. 231), is an annoying pest of animals and man all over the world. In some outbreaks the stablefly may cause as much loss in beef and milk as the hornfly. The stablefly resembles the housefly so closely that it is often mistaken for it, whence the common belief that houseflies can bite. It is easily distinguished by its narrow, pointed, shiny-black proboscis (Figs. 230, III, and 231*B*).

Stableflies breed by preference in decaying straw or rotting vegetable matter or straw mixed with manure, particularly of horses. An unusual scourge of them, sufficient to harass cattle severely and to denude the beaches of bathers, occurs on part of the Florida coast where washed-up piles of seaweed, trapped in lakes behind sand dunes, afford ideal breeding places, especially in September. Later, in December, extensive breeding occurs in piles of peanut litter and celery strippings farther inland.

The eggs are deposited in small batches; in a few days they hatch into white, semitransparent, footless maggots (Fig. 231*C*) distinguishable by the form and position of the stigmal plates at the posterior end (see Fig. 261). The larvae mature in 10 days to a month or more and pupate in drier parts of the breeding material. The chestnut-colored pupae (Fig. 231*D*), 6 to 7 mm. long, hatch in a week or more in warm weather.

Stableflies frequently begin a meal on one animal and finish it on another, so they may mechanically transmit Oriental sore and such blood infections as trypanosomiasis and anthrax. They are particularly important as transmitters of *Trypanosoma evansi*, the cause of surra. Stomoxys and Musca also serve as intermediate hosts for spiruroid nematodes of the genus Habronema (see p. 464), parasites in the stomach of horses. Habronema larvae may cause human conjunctivitis when liberated by flies in the sore eyes of children. Stomoxys is also an intermediate host for the filaria, *Setaria cervi*, or deer, and for a tapeworm of chickens, *Hymenolepis carioca*.

In 1912 and 1913 Rosenau and others adduced the theory that the stablefly was responsible for the transmission of infantile paralysis, and the theory was apparently supported by some facts in the epidemiology of the disease (though contradicted by others), and by carefully conducted experiments. In subsequent experiments, however, the results have been uniformly negative. The virus causing the disease is present in abundance in human feces and can be found in sewage. The role of some arthropod is suggested by the epidemiology, but there is little circumstantial evidence against Stomoxys.

Control of stableflies is easily accomplished by spraying animals with 2 per cent DDT emulsion and spraying barns or other favorite insect resting places with a 5 per cent emulsion. One spraying is usually adequate for 3 to 6 weeks. Along the west Florida coast, where marine vegetation washed up on shore breeds enough of these flies to make life miserable, application of 2 gallons of 0.5 per cent DDT emulsion per 100 sq. ft. gave excellent results; about 100 to 600 gallons per mile of shore was needed.

Housefly (Musca domestica), etc.

The ubiquitous housefly suffered a serious setback when automobiles replaced horses in cities, and in this country it is now facing the possibility of extermination since the advent of DDT sprays. Two states (Idaho and Iowa) have actually embarked on extermination campaigns, which a few years ago would have seemed a fantastic dream. In a number of cities anyone seeing a fly is asked to report it, so that the source can be hunted and treated. In Moscow, Idaho, a university student who needed some flies for experimental work sought for them in vain for two weeks and finally caught a few in a farm house. However, the outlook for extermination has become somewhat clouded by the discovery that some races of flies are naturally immune to DDT and others can acquire immunity. Other insecticides will have to be called on to help.

The housefly is still too well known to require detailed description, but one may be necessary in a future edition of this book. This fly is a particularly important transmitter of filth germs, especially those of intestinal diseases, because it frequents privies and feces for egg laying, and dining tables and kitchens for food. It harbors vast numbers of germs on its sticky feet; vomits them from its food reservoirs with liquid to melt sugar or cake so that these delicacies will pass through the pores of its labellum; and deposits germs in its feces (flyspecks). It is probably the greatest single factor in the epidemiology of bacillary dysentery and is an important one in typhoid, cholera, food poisoning, etc. Poultry can become infected with fowl cholera (Pasteurella) by feeding on flies that have had access to blood from infected animals. In addition houseflies have been found to pick up and harbor the virus of poliomyelitis, though there is still no evidence that they are an important factor in the disease; their possible role is discussed on p. 231.

About 99 per cent of flies in houses are *Musca domestica*, except sometimes in fall and winter when houses may be invaded by large numbers of the cluster fly, *Pollenia rudis*, a calliphorid fly parasitic on earthworms in its larval stage. The housefly lays its eggs by preference in horse manure but will also use manure of chickens, pigs, or man, and sometimes other decaying animal or vegetable substances, such as that in garbage dumps.   The eggs hatch in 12 to 24 hours, and the maggots, recognizable by their stigmal plates (see Fig. 261), are full grown in a few days.   They then move to drier places, pupate, and emerge as flies in about 2 to 3 weeks.   In her lifetime, averaging about 6 or 8 weeks, a female deposits about 2000 eggs.

Flies are usually easily destroyed by DDT, benzene hexachloride, or chlordane spraying of houses, screens, barns, privies, and other insect resting places.   During World War II large areas were cleared of all kinds of flies by airplane spraying of DDT at the rate of 8 oz. per gallon of fuel oil, 2 qt. per acre, repeated at 7-day intervals for 21 days, when all immature stages would have become adults.   In buildings it is seldom necessary to spray everywhere; spot treatments of favorite resting places with strong dusts or sprays will suffice.   However, as Hall pointed out in 1948, residual spraying of inside walls of food-handling establishments is undesirable since the flies do not die until they have staggered, stumbled, and bumbled about, often into food.

A city can, if it wishes, eliminate flies to the point where swatters, flytraps, and flypaper are as outmoded as hitching racks and spinning wheels, and screens can be left open by day.   The cost is from 5 to 30 cents per person.

Some fly control can be obtained by treatment of contents of latrines, etc., with rather large quantities of insecticides to kill maggots, but, since maggots are not as susceptible as most insects and are difficult to reach, attacks on the adults usually work out better.   As a preliminary to all-out campaigns, treatment of walls and pits of latrines, where flies get access to pathogenic germs, is helpful in reducing fly-borne diseases.

Blowflies

Although the housefly is the most important mechanical carrier of pathogenic organisms, many other flies may also serve in the same capacity.   Attention should be called to the blowflies (Calliphoridae), some of which breed in dung but most of which breed in carcasses. They may carry not only germs of enteric diseases but also those of plague, anthrax, undulant fever, and tularemia.   An unsolved enigma, but one that may have significance, is the fact that a high percentage of blowflies (principally *Phoenicia sericata* and *Phormia regina*) collected in the vicinity of poliomyelitis cases were found to harbor the virus.   They probably did not get it from human feces; where, then, did they acquire it?   The answer might help to solve the problem of polio transmission.

Tsetse Flies (Glossina)

The bites of tsetse flies are less painful than those of tabanids or Stomoxys; it is in the role of carriers of trypanosome diseases that they gain their importance. Not only human sleeping sickness but also trypanosome diseases highly fatal to many domestic animals are transmitted by these insects (see p. 179). The abundant and varied wild game of Africa, particularly the numerous species of antelopes, are the chief natural source of food for tsetse flies, and since the flies serve as intermediate hosts for the trypanosomes harbored by the wild game,

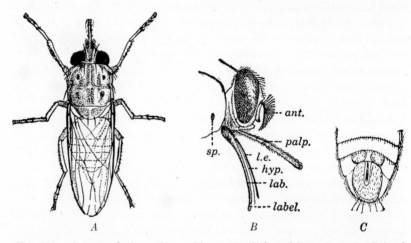

A   *B*   *C*

Fig. 232.   *A*, tsetse fly in resting position, × 4. (Adapted from Austen).   *B*, head and mouthparts of tsetse fly; *ant.*, antenna; *hyp.*, hypopharynx; *lab.*, labium; *label.*, labellum; *l.e.*, labrum-epipharynx; *palp.*, labial palpus; *sp.*, spiracle. (After Alcock.) *C*, hypopygium of male tsetse fly.   (After Alcock.)

it is obvious that when man or domestic animals are bitten by these flies they are in great danger of being inoculated with one or more species of trypanosomes.

The tsetse flies (Fig. 232), are elongated dark brown or yellowish-brown flies, some species no larger than ordinary houseflies, others larger than blowflies. They constitute the genus Glossina, which is now usually put into a separate family Glossinidae but is sometimes still included, as are Stomoxys and the hornflies, in the Muscidae. There are about 15 species, all confined to Africa except one species that enters southwestern Arabia.

Tsetses when at rest (Fig. 232) have their wings folded flat, one directly over the other, like the blades of a pair of scissors; the proboscis projects horizontally in front of the head. They are more difficult

to identify on the wing, although the darting manner of flight and
buzzing sound are said to be quite diagnostic to one who is familiar
with them. The appearance of the mouthparts and antennae is characteristic (Fig. 232*B*). The proboscis consists of a piercing labium
with a bulblike base and special structures at its tip for rasping and
tearing. In its anterior groove are a delicate labrum-epipharynx forming a food trough and a fine hypopharynx containing the salivary duct.

The elongated maxillary palpi, each
grooved on its inner face, close
together to form a sheath (see p.
640 and Fig. 230, *IV*).

The thorax is relatively large
and quadrangular with a characteristic pattern which is, however, inconspicuous in some species. The
abdomen may be nearly uniform
dark brown or pale brown banded
with a dusky color. The male has
a large oval swelling on the underside of the last segment of the
abdomen, the " hypopygium " (Fig.
232*C*), which forms a good distinguishing mark between the sexes.

Fig. 233. Approximate ranges of tsetse
flies. (Compiled from Austen.)
≡ . . . range of entire genus Glossina
\\\ . . . range of *G. palpalis*
/// . . . range of *G. morsitans*

Tsetse flies are fortunately limited to central Africa, except the
one species in southwestern Arabia,
from south of the Sahara Desert to the northern parts of the Union of
South Africa (Fig. 233). They are not evenly distributed over this
great area, but are limited locally to " fly belts." Not all the factors
causing the " patchy " distribution of tsetses are known; there are cases
where close limitation to certain areas cannot be explained by any
known requirements of the flies.

Tsetses are diurnal in habits, but *G. pallidipes* will bite on moonlit
nights. *G. palpalis* and probably other species seldom rise more than
a few feet above the ground. All of them seem to be guided to shelter-
ing trees and food animals by sight and can be attracted by dummy
animals standing in conspicuous places. Moving objects also attract
them.

Tsetses show marked preference for certain colors, being especially
attracted to blacks or browns and repelled by white. The dark skin
of Negroes is selected in preference to pale skin to such an extent that
a white man is seldom troubled when accompanied by natives. Black

or dark clothes are preferred to light ones; khaki color, however, appears to be particularly attractive to them.

Food Habits. Both sexes of tsetse flies are bloodsuckers, but they also suck plant juices. Different species have different tastes. *Glossina morsitans* and *G. pallidipes* are much more dependent on mammalian blood than is *G. palpalis* or *G. tachinoides* and under normal conditions seldom take other blood, and then apparently only avian blood. For this reason *G. morsitans* is very dependent on large game or domestic animals and rapidly falls off in numbers and shows evidences of starvation when deprived of such food. Although there is then an increase in the percentage feeding on human blood, it seems that the food deficiency cannot be made up entirely at human expense. Small mammals cannot be utilized on account of their retiring and nocturnal habits.

G. palpalis and *tachinoides* are much less discriminating than *morsitans* and feed freely even on reptiles and amphibians; in fact, *palpalis* often subsists largely on crocodiles and large lizards. Nevertheless these species, too, decrease in numbers with the elimination of big game, but there is much less evidence of starvation, and there is little reason to believe that they would cease to exist even where the fauna is reduced to the possible minimum; *tachinoides* seems to make ends meet even where man is the only available host. The habit many species have of frequenting places where game animals come to drink or browse and of feeding early in the morning or at evening seems to be an adaptation to the habits of these large mammals.

Life History. Tsetse flies differ from most related flies in their remarkable manner of reproduction. They do not lay eggs, and the single developing larva is retained within the body, being nourished by special " milk glands " on the walls of the uterus while lying with its stigmal plates, containing the spiracles, close to the genital opening of the mother. The larva passes through its moults and is full grown and ready to pupate before it is born occupying practically all of the swollen abdomen of the mother. As soon as one is born another begins its development, and new larvae are born about every 10 or 12 days, provided the temperature is around 75° or 80° F. and food is abundant. There are few data on the total number of young produced, but in one captive fly eight larvae were produced in 13 weeks, and only one egg was found left in the body. Pregnant flies often abort when disturbed, and cases are known in which the larvae pupated within the abdomen of the mother, to the destruction of both of them.

The larva (Fig. 234*C*) is a yellowish-white creature about 8 to 10 mm. in length with a pair of dark knoblike protuberances at the posterior end of the body between which are the stigmal plates. Immediately after birth it hides itself at a depth of 1 to 2 cm. in loose soil or under dead leaves and transforms to a pupa (Fig. 234D). This turns a dark purplish-brown color. It is shaped like a small olive and has at the tip of the body the blackish knobs which are so characteristic of the larval stage also. The shape and size of the knobs and of the notch between them are good distinguishing marks between species.

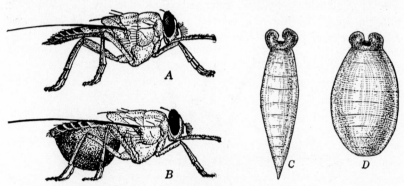

FIG. 234. *A* and *B*, *Glossina morsitans* before and after feeding, × 4. (Adapted from Austen.) *C*, newly born larva of *G. palpalis*. *D*, pupa of *G. palpalis*.

The duration of the pupal stage may be from 17 days to nearly 3 months. Few adults emerge at temperatures below 70° or above 86° F.

All species select dry, loose soil in shaded, protected spots for deposition of the grown larvae. The maternity spots seem to be selected more for the safety and convenience of the mother while giving birth than for the suitability of the place for pupal development. The length of life of tsetses is probably less than a year.

Tsetse Flies and Trypanosomiasis. As remarked before, the enormous importance of tsetse flies lies in their role as carriers of trypanosomes (see Chapter 8). The principal transmitters of *Trypanosoma gambiense* are *Glossina palpalis* and *G. tachinoides;* in northern Nigeria and northern Cameroons *G. tachinoides* is the primary transmitter. The principal transmitter of *T. rhodesiense,* which is probably only a variety of the much more widespread *T. brucei,* is *G. morsitans,* although in Tanganyika the closely related, darker-colored *G. swynnertoni* was shown by Swynnerton to be the probable transmitter. This species attacks man more readily than any other. In an epidemic in Uganda in 1940–1943 *G. pallidipes* was the principal transmitter.

Although *Glossina palpalis* and *G. tachinoides* are undoubtedly the normal transmitters of Gambian sleeping sickness, and *G. morsitans,* *G. swynnertoni,* and *G. pallidipes,* of Rhodesian sleeping sickness, they are not the only species capable of transmitting these diseases, at least under laboratory conditions. *G. morsitans* has been found experimentally to be an even more efficient transmitter of *T. gambiense* than *G. palpalis*. *G. brevipalpis* is also an experimental vector. Even in natural carriers of a particular trypanosome, a very small percentage of flies are found naturally infected, and not more than a few per cent can be infected experimentally. Moreover, it is evident that a single species of fly shows marked differences in receptivity to infection in different parts of the range. The refractory nature of some west African races of *G. palpalis* possibly accounts for the absence of sleep-

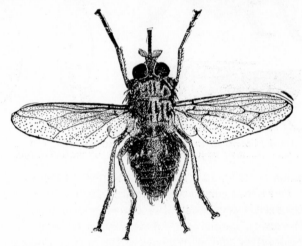

FIG. 235. *Glossina palpalis*, carrier of Gambian and Nigerian sleeping sickness. × 4. (After Austen.)

ing sickness in Dahomey and neighboring states. It is probable that climatic conditions and food habits play a leading part in determining susceptibility of flies to trypanosome infections.

G. palpalis and G. tachinoides. *Glossina palpalis* (Fig. 235) is a large dark species with blackish-brown abdomen and with gray thorax having indistinct brown markings. It is found over the whole of west Africa from the Senegal River to Angola and east to the upper valley of the Nile and the eastern shores of the central lakes (Fig. 233,\\\). Its range is thus nearly coincident with that of Gambian sleeping sickness. This species, more than any other except *G. tachinoides,* which occurs around the southern border of the Sahara Desert, is dependent on the presence of water. In the rainy season the flies extend their range to headwaters which are dry during the remainder of the year, and they retreat again with the drying up of the water. They are seldom found more than 30 yd. from the edge of a river or lake where vegetation overhanging the water is abundant, although they follow man or animals for a few hundred yards from such positions. This species and *G. tachinoides* are found only in shady and fairly humid places. In the Gold Coast in the dry season these species retire to well-defined foci consisting of definite plant associations. It is feared that *G. palpalis* may sometime bridge the short gap between the head-waters of the Congo and the Zambesi and become established along the latter river and its tributaries, carrying sleeping sickness with it.

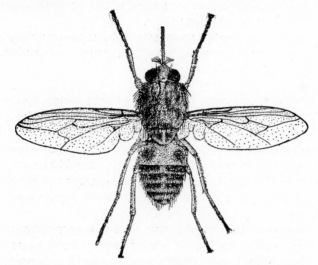

Fig. 236. *Glossina morsitans*, carrier of Rhodesian sleeping sickness. × 4.
(After Austen.)

It is strictly limited to forest areas in which trees or shrubs with permanent foliage predominate; it is found neither in deep impenetrable forests nor in grasslands.

G. tachinoides is one of the smallest tsetse flies, being about the size of a housefly. Its habitats are practically the same as those of *G. palpalis*, but it is satisfied with thickets more sparsely shaded by mixtures of deciduous and evergreen trees and it can withstand higher temperatures. It is seldom found near villages but rather in sparsely settled areas where game and river animals are abundant.

G. morsitans and G. swynnertoni. *Glossina morsitans* (Fig. 236), carrier of many trypanosome infections of animals and of *T. rhodesiense,* is the most widely distributed species of tsetse fly (Fig. 223,///) and is also the best known, having attracted to itself the attention of big-game hunters in Africa for many years. It is slightly smaller and much lighter colored than *G. palpalis*. *G. morsitans* is not confined to the immediate vicinity of water but prefers hot dry savannahs with bush or scattered trees where there is a moderate amount of shade for cover. It is not found in either the dense forest or open grassland. It seldom feeds on anything but mammalian blood. Baboons are said to be relished by the fly in some parts of Africa, and wild and domestic pigs are often fed upon.

The habit of following moving objects is especially marked in this species, and some observers state that flies have followed them several miles, frequently alighting on the ground to rest or on the person pursued, often without attempting to bite.

G. swynnertoni is also a dry-area fly and has habits closely similar to those of *morsitans* but is much more limited in its distribution.

Control

Attacks of tsetse flies can be avoided to some extent by the use of the usual insect repellents (see p. 495), by flyproof clothing or veils, and by wearing white clothes. When it is necessary to travel through fly-infested places where sleeping sickness occurs, all such measures should be adopted, or, better still, the fly belts should be passed through in the darkness of night when the insects are inactive. Railroad trains and steamboats passing through fly belts should be protected by flyproof screens.

Extermination of tsetses on a large scale is a very difficult matter, but locally it is quite feasible. Clearing away of brush along streams infested by such species as *Glossina palpalis* and *G. tachinoides* is the most valuable measure in connection with their local destruction. In Gold Coast over 1000 square miles were freed of these species by this method between 1940 and 1945. If brush is cleared for a distance of 30 yd. from the edge of water in proximity to fords, villages, washing places, etc., the flies quickly disappear and do not reappear as long as the cleared area is *kept* clear. Grass burning is sometimes resorted to, but this impoverishes the soil and is advocated only under exceptional conditions. In Rhodesia *exclusion* of fire operates against *morsitans* and *swynnertoni*, presumably by favoring predators that feed on the pupae.

G. morsitans is more difficult to eradicate than *G. palpalis*, since its habitats, though sharply confined to belts, are not so closely limited to the edge of water and are therefore more difficult to clear. Since, however, the areas occupied are usually not over a few square miles at the most, complete deforestation of such areas when near villages or highways is sometimes feasible. In southern Rhodesia 6000 square miles have been freed of tsetses by controlled game reduction, brush clearing, and fencing. In Zululand, where *G. pallidipes* predominates, eradication from 40 square miles of brush country was effected by spraying DDT from planes on the vegetation. Five applications at 2-week intervals almost entirely eliminated the flies. In other places DDT spraying of vegetation at about 2-week intervals reduced the flies 97 per cent in 11 weeks, after which no flies were seen for 8 weeks. Local eradication was accomplished in one area by driving cattle sprayed with DDT through the woods a number of times.

The destruction of pupae by natural enemies undoubtedly aids in limiting their numbers. The pupae are attacked by parasitic insects but apparently not to a sufficient extent to reduce their numbers seriously.

The control of tsetse flies by the wholesale destruction of wild game is a subject over which there has been much flowing of ink. The extent to which such destruction, even if possible, would actually control the flies is questionable. Lloyd fenced off a large area in Nigeria to exclude game animals and studied the effect on the tsetse flies. There were fewer of all species of tsetses and an indication that destruction of game would ultimately exterminate *G. morsitans*, but *G. palpalis* and *tachinoides*, though reduced in numbers, showed no evidence of starvation.

Tsetses tend to disappear with the encroachment of civilization, as demonstrated near Elisabethville, Belgian Congo. In east Africa, on the other hand, there is good reason to believe that the appearance of Rhodesian sleeping sickness was the direct result of more frequent association of tsetses with domestic animals and man following the reduction in wild game. It seems at least possible that wholesale destruction of large wild animals would result in the development of races of flies adapted to feeding on domestic animals and breeding under conditions existing where domestic animals are kept. It would have been most unfortunate if the rich, varied, and unique wild life of Africa had had to be destroyed to make that continent habitable.

Eye Flies (Oscinidae)

The eye flies (Fig. 237) are small, nearly hairless flies, about 1.5 to 2.5 mm. long, of the family Oscinidae (or Chloropidae), belonging to the acalyptrate division of the Cyclorrhapha. The larvae of some species are pests of growing wheat, etc., but most of those annoying to man breed in excrement or decaying organic matter. *Hippelates pusio* was found by Hall to breed in almost any substance in an advanced state of decay but when artificially bred did best in human excrement.

The entire development from egg to adult required 11 days or more, averaging about 18 days. Although the eye flies do not have mouthparts that enable them to pierce the skin and so are not bloodsuckers in the ordinary sense, many of them are habitually attracted by the skin and natural orifices of man and animals, lapping up perspiration, excretions, exudations of sores and wounds, or blood from scratches or insect bites. Some species appear to be especially attracted to the eyes and lachrymal secretions of man, whence their name. The proboscis is fitted for lapping, as in the housefly, but is capable of being

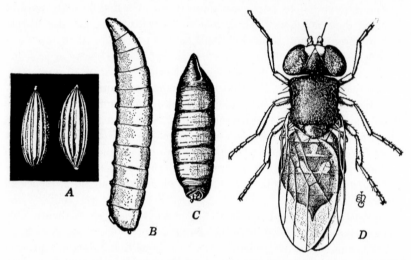

Fig. 237.   Stages in life cycle of American eye fly, *Hippelates pusio*.   *A*, eggs, in dorsal and lateral views; *B*, mature larva; *C*, pupa; *D*, adult ♀.   *A*, × about 45; *B*, *C*, and *D*. × about 18.   (After D. G. Hall.)

used as a rasping instrument to cause minute scarifications on the delicate conjunctival epithelium or on granulation tissue of sores, thus assisting pathogenic organisms in gaining entrance. The habits of these insects, therefore, render them particularly dangerous mechanical carriers of eye infections and of various diseases of the skin and mucous membranes as well. Graham-Smith (1930) gives a review of the principal species concerned in disease transmission.

Relation to Eye Diseases. In the Coachella Valley of California and in parts of Florida *Hippelates pusio* (Fig. 237) is a sufficient nuisance to be a limiting factor in the development of the country. It is a small fly, 2 mm. in length, which is active throughout the day for 9 or 10 months of the year but particularly in spring and fall. It persistently buzzes around the heads of men and animals, frequently darting at the eyes or into the ears or feeding on sores or mucous membranes. In one high school 1500 children were reported as suffering from " pinkeye " in 1929; 50 per cent of the young children of the region had some conjunctivitis, and 10 per cent had chronic trachoma.

In India and the East Indies another member of the family, *Siphunculina funicola*, with similar habits, is responsible for spreading conjunctivitis and probably skin infections also. In Egypt, where eye infections are particularly common, houseflies and related species are usually considered to be the principal transmitting agents, but oscinid flies are very common in some places and should be investigated in connection with the ophthalmia that is so prevalent.

Eye Flies and Yaws. Members of the family Oscinidae are an important, perhaps one of the most important, factors in the transmission of yaws (see p. 73). Nichols in 1912 was convinced that eye flies, *Hippelates flavipes*, were responsible for the majority of cases of yaws in the West Indies, and similar views have been expressed by a number of other writers in the West Indies and Brazil. In Trinidad this species is called the " yaws fly."

Kumm and Turner (1936) found that the spirochetes of yaws remain motile in the pharynx and esophageal diverticula of *H. flavipes* for at least 7 hours but lose their motility in the mid-gut and do not undergo development in the fly as do the spirochetes of relapsing fever in lice. The flies commonly regurgitate drops of fluid after feeding; these drops contain viable spirochetes. Kumm and Turner experimentally transmitted the disease to rabbits both by bites of the flies and by inoculation of esophageal diverticula. There is a close correlation between the distribution of this fly and that of yaws in the West Indies. It was possible to catch over 1500 flies feeding on yaws sores within 15 minutes, so the opportunities for transmission are obvious.

In Assam, Fox in 1921 showed that epidemics of another spirochetal infection, Naga sore (see p. 76), are associated with plagues of *Siphunculina funicola*, which swarm on the sores and mechanically transmit the infective material.

Control. Control of these flies is difficult, but the suppression or treatment of decaying organic matter and improved sanitation to prevent breeding in human excrement would be of some value. Parman in 1932 advocated the use of box traps baited with odoriferous decaying infusions. DDT spraying of animals for other flies, and of buildings, etc., for houseflies, will certainly reduce the number of eye flies.

Pupipara

This peculiar group of Diptera, sometimes called louse flies, ectoparasites of birds and mammals, have leathery, saclike abdomens and have the opposite legs inserted wide apart. The mouthparts are similar to those of a tsetse fly but with the piercing proboscis partly retractile into a pouch in the ventral part of the head, the projecting part then sheathed by the labial palpi. In the winged forms the eyes are large and the antennae exposed, but in the wingless "sheep tick," *Melophagus ovinus*, the eyes are small and the reduced antennae sunken in pits on top of the head. As the name Pupipara implies, they give birth, one at a time, to larvae which almost immediately bury themselves and pupate, like tsetse flies. There are four families, of which

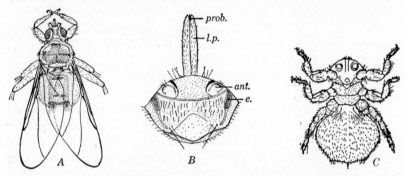

FIG. 238. *A, Pseudolynchia canariensis;* note large eyes and exposed antennae; *B* and *C, Melophagus ovinus*, the ked or " sheep tick." In *B*, note small eyes, antennae sunk in pits, and long palpi sheathing mouthparts, as in tsetse flies. (*A* and *B* adapted from Massonat; *C* from Metcalf and Metcalf.)

two are exclusively parasitic on bats — the so-called bat ticks, which are most unflylike in appearance; one on bees; and one, the Hippoboscidae, on birds and various mammals.

The genus Hippobosca includes winged forms, various species of which attack horses, cattle, camels, dogs, etc., in the Old World. The cattle species transmit the nonpathogenic *Trypanosoma theileri* of these animals, and the species attacking dogs have been suspected of transmitting canine leishmaniasis. Pseudolynchia, also winged, attacks nestling birds; one species, *P. canariensis* (=*maura*) (Fig. 238*A*), is the intermediate host of the very common pigeon parasite, *Haemoproteus columbae* (see p. 216). *Lynchia fusca* transmits *H. lophortyx* among California quail.

Lipoptena includes deer-infesting species whose wings break off after a host has been reached. *Melophagus ovinus* (Fig. 238*B*, *C*), the sheep tick or ked, is a wingless form that glues its pupae to the wool of its hosts, where they remain for about 3 weeks before hatching. The gestation period is about 7 days. These parasites may be a source of great annoyance to sheep; they also serve as the intermediate host of nonpathogenic *Trypanosoma melophagium*, and a Rickettsia, *R. melophaga*. Although sometimes severe pests of domestic animals, these highly specialized Diptera only exceptionally bite man but produce painful bites when they do so.

REFERENCES
General

CURRAN, C. H., *The Families and Genera of North American Diptera*, Ballou, N. Y., 1934.

HAYES, W. P., A Bibliography of Keys for the Identification of Immature Insects, Pt. I., Diptera, *Entomol. News*, **49**, 246–251 (1938); **50**, 5–10 (1939).

SNODGRASS, R. E., The Feeding Apparatus of Biting and Disease-Carrying Flies, *Smithsonian Misc. Collections*, **104**, No. 1, (1943).

Psychodidae (Phlebotomus, etc.)

ADDIS, C. J., JR., Collection and Preservation of Sandflies (Phlebotomus) with Keys to U. S. Species, *Trans. Am. Microscop. Soc.*, **64**, 328–332 (1945).

ADLER, S., and THEODOR, O., Investigations on Mediterranean Kala-azar, Pts. I–IX, *Proc. Roy. Soc. (London)*, **108**, B, No. 759, 447 (1931); **110**, B, No. 768, 402 (1932); **116**, B, No. 801, 494 (1935).

DOERR, R., FRANZ, K., and TAUSSIG, S., *Das Pappatacifieber*, Leipzig, 1909.

HERTIG, M., Phlebotomus and Carrion's Disease, I–IV, *Am. J. Trop. Med.*, **22**, Suppl. 75 (1942).

HERTIG, M., and FAIRCHILD, G. B., The Control of Phlebotomus in Peru with DDT, *Am. J. Trop. Med.*, **28**, 207–230 (1948).

LARROUSSE, F., Étude systématique et médicale des Phlebotomes, *Trav. lab. parasitol.*, Paris, 1921.

MARETT, P. G., The Life History of Phlebotomus, *J. Roy. Army Med. Corps*, **17**, 13 (1911).

SABIN, A. B., PHILIP, C. B., and PAUL, J. R., Phlebotomus (Pappataci or Sandfly) Fever, A Disease of Military Importance, *J. Am. Med. Assoc.*, **125**, 603–606, 693–699 (1944).

SMITH, R. O. A., HALDER, K. C., and AHMED, I., Further Investigations on the Transmission of Kala-azar, I–VI, *Indian J. Med. Research*, **28**, 575, 481, 585 (1940); **29**, 783, 789, 799 (1941).

TOWNSEND, C. H. T., Progress in the Study of Verruga Transmission by Bloodsuckers, *Bull. Entomol. Research*, **4**, 125 (1913).

WHITTINGHAM, H. E., and ROOK, A. F., Observations on the Life History and Bionomics of *Phlebotomus papatasii*, *Brit. Med. J.*, No. 3285, 1144 (1923).

YOUNG, T. C. M., RICHMOND, A. E., and BRENDISH, G. R., Sandflies and Sandfly Fever in the Peshawar District, *Indian J. Med. Research*, **13**, 961 (1925–1926).
See also References, Chapter 7.

Ceratopogonidae (Culicoides, etc.)

BUCKLEY, J. J. C., On the Development in *Culicoides furens* Poey of *Filaria* (*Mansonella*) *ozzardi*, *J. Helminthol.*, **12**, 99 (1934).

DOVE, W. E., HALL, D. G., and HULL, J. B., The Salt Marsh Sandfly Problem (Culicoides), *Ann. Entomol. Soc. Am.*, **25**, 505 (1932).

PAINTER, R. H., The Biology, etc., of Sandflies in Honduras, *15th Rept., Med. Dept. United Fruit Co.*, 245 (1927).

ROOT, F. M., and HOFFMAN, W. A., The North American Species of Culicoides *Am. J. Hyg.*, **25**, 150 (1937).

SHARP, N. A. D., *Filaria perstans;* its Development in *Culicoides austeni, Trans. Roy. Soc. Trop. Med. Hyg.*, **21**, 371 (1928).

THOMSEN, L. C., Aquatic Diptera, Pt. V, Ceratopogonidae, *Cornell Univ. Agr. Expt. Sta. Mem.*, **210**, 57–80 (1937).

Simuliidae (Blackflies)

BARANOV, N., Stand der Kolumbatscher Mückenforschung in Jugoslawien, *Z. Parasitenk.*, **11**, 215 (1939).

BEQUAERT, J. C., Notes on the Blackflies or Simuliidae, with Special Reference to Those of the Onchocerca Region of Guatemala. Part III of " Onchocerciasis," Contrib. No. 4, Harvard Univ. Dept. of Trop. Med., 1934.

BLACKLOCK, D. B., The Development of *Onchocerca volvulus* in *Simulium damnosum, Ann. Trop. Med. Parasitol.*, **20**, 1, 203 (1926).

DYAR, H. G., and SHANNON, R. C., The North American Two-winged Flies of the Family Simuliidae, *Proc. U. S. Nat. Mus.*, **69**, Art. 10 (1927).

FAIRCHILD, G. B., and BARREDA, E. A., DDT as a Larvicide against Simulium, *J. Econ. Entomol.*, **38**, 694–699 (1945).

JOBBINS-POMEROY, A. W., Notes on Five North American Buffalo Gnats of the Genus Simulium, *U. S. Dept. Agr. Bull.* **329**, 1916.

O'KANE, W. C., Blackflies in New Hampshire, *N. H. Agr. Expt. Sta. Tech. Bull.* **32**, 1926.

O'ROKE, E. C., A Malaria-like Disease of Ducks Caused by *Leucocytozoön anatis, Univ. Mich. School Forestry Bull.* **4**, 1934.

TWINN, C. R., The Blackflies of Eastern Canada, *Can. J. Research,* **14**, 97 (1936). See also References on Onchocerca, p. 475.

Tabanidae

CAMERON, A. E., Bionomics of the Tabanidae of the Canadian Prairies, *Bull. Entomol. Research,* **17**, 1 (1926).

CONNAL, A., and CONNAL, S., The Development of *Loa loa* in *Chrysops silacea* and *Chrysops dimidiata, Trans. Roy. Soc. Trop. Med. Hyg.*, **16**, 64 (1922).

FRANCIS, E., Sources of Infection and Seasonal Incidence of Tularemia in Man, *Publ. Health Repts.*, **52**, 103 (1937).

MARCHAND, W., The Early Stages of Tabanidae (Horse Flies), *Rock. Inst. Med. Research Monogr.* **13**, 1920.

MITZMAIN, M. B., Tabanids and Surra, *Philippine J. Sci.*, B, **8**, 197, 223 (1913).

PHILIP, C. B., The Tabanidae (Horseflies) of Minnesota, *Minn. Agr. Expt. Sta. Tech. Bull.* **80**, 32 pp. (1931).

SCHWADT, H. H., Horseflies of Arkansas, *Univ. Ark. Expt. Sta. Bull.* **332**, 1936.

STONE, A., The Bionomics of Some Tabanidae, *Ann. Entomol. Soc. Am.*, **23**, 261 (1930), Horseflies or Tabanidae of the Nearctic Region, *U. S. Dept. Agr. Misc. Pub.* **305**, 1938.

Muscoidea

AUSTEN, E. E., and HEGH, E., *Tsetse Flies,* Imp. Bur. Entomol., London, 1922.

BISHOPP, F. C., The Stable Fly . . . , *U. S. Dept. Agr. Farmers' Bull.* **1097,** 1931.

BLAKESLEE, E. B., Surface Sprays for Control of Stablefly Breeding in Shore Deposits of Marine Grass, *J. Econ. Entomol.,* **38,** 548–552 (1945).

BRUCE, W. G., and BLAKESLEY, E. B., DDT to Control Pests Affecting Livestock, *J. Econ. Entomol.,* **39,** 367–374 (1946).

ENDERLEIN, G., Ueber die Klassifikation der Stomoxinae und neue Arten aus Europa und Afrika, *Z. angew. Entomol.,* **14,** 356 (1928).

FISKE, W. W., Investigations into the Bionomics of *Glossina palpalis, Bull. Entomol. Research,* **10,** 347 (1910).

GRAHAM-SMITH, G. S., Flies in Relation to Disease. *Non-Bloodsucking Flies,* Cambridge, England, 1914.

KING, W. V., and LENERT, L. G., Outbreaks of *Stomoxys calcitrans* along Florida's Northwest Coast, *Florida Entomologist,* **19,** 33 (1936).

MITZMAIN, M. B., The Bionomics of *Stomoxys calcitrans, Philippine J. Sci.,* B, **8,** 29 (1913).

NASH, T. A. M., Climate, the Vital Factor in the Ecology of Glossina, *Bull. Entomol. Research,* **28,** 75 (1937).

Tsetse Flies in British West Africa, Colonial Office, London, 1948.

NEWSTEAD, R., EVANS, A. M., and POTTS, W. H., Guide to the Study of the Tsetse Flies, *Liverpool Sch. Trop. Med. Mem.,* n. s., No. 1 (1924).

PATTON, W. S., A Revision of the Species of the Genus Musca, etc., *Ann. Trop. Med. Parasitol.,* **26,** 347 (1932).

SÉGUY, E., Diptera, Fam. Muscidae, *Gen. Insectorum,* Fasc. 205, 1–600 (1937).

SIMMONS, S. W., and DOVE, W. E., Breeding Places of the Stable Fly or " Dog Fly," *Stomoxys calcitrans* (L.), in Northwestern Florida, *J. Econ. Entomol.,* **34,** 457 (1941). See also *ibid.,* **35,** 582, 589, 709 (1942).

SWYNNERTON, C. F. M., The Tsetse Flies of East Africa, *Trans. Roy. Entomol. Soc. (London),* **84,** 1936.

TOOMEY, J. A., TOKACS, W. S., and TISCHER, L. A., Poliomyelitis Virus from Flies, *Proc. Soc. Exptl. Biol. Med.,* **48,** 637 (1941).

Oscinidae

GRAHAM-SMITH, G. S., The Oscinidae (Diptera) as Vectors of Conjunctivitis, and The Anatomy of Their Mouth Parts, *Parasitology,* **22,** 457 (1930).

HERMS, W. B., The Coachella Valley (Calif.) Hippelates Fly Project, *J. Econ. Entomol.,* **21,** 690 (1931).

KUMM, H. W., and TURNER, T. B., The Transmission of Yaws from Man to Rabbits by an Insect Vector, *Hippelates pallipes, Am. J. Trop. Med.,* **16,** 245 (1936).

Pupipara

BEQUAERT, J., A Monograph of the Melophaginae, or Ked-Flies, of Sheep, Goats, Deer and Antelopes (Diptera, Hippoboscidae), *Entomol. Americana,* **22,** 1–64 (1942).

CHAPTER 27

Diptera

II. MOSQUITOES

Importançe. Of all existing insect pests mosquitoes are Public Enemy No. 1. The mere annoyance which the enormous numbers of them cause by their bites is sufficient to have made some parts of the world practically uninhabitable. Rich pieces of country have remained unsettled and some of the choicest hunting and camping grounds in North America are practically closed to the camper by the countless millions of mosquitoes that transform a camper's paradise into an intolerable hell. When travelling through such places repellents are essential, and even then the unceasing " zangs " of threatening mosquitoes are hardly less trying on the nerves than the actual attacks.

Unlike most insect pests the mosquitoes of cold northern countries are if anything more abundant than they are in the tropics. The far northern mosquitoes do not, however, act as carriers of disease; terrible as they are, they wage clean warfare, whereas many tropical mosquitoes have their spears poisoned with death-dealing disease germs. No less than four important human diseases are normally transmitted by mosquitoes exclusively — malaria, yellow fever, dengue, and filariasis. In addition various forms of encephalomyelitis (see p. 232) are primarily transmitted by mosquitoes, and a South American fly, Dermatobia, usually depends on mosquitoes for transportation of its eggs to the skin of man or animals, where they hatch and cause myiasis. Fowlpox of poultry and numerous forms of bird malaria are also frequently transmitted by mosquitoes.

General Structure. Mosquitoes, comprising the family Culicidae (see key, p. 616), can easily be distinguished from all other Diptera, some of which superficially resemble them, by the presence of scales along the wing veins and a conspicuous fringe of scales along the hind margin of the wings. The venation (see Figs. 163 and 247) is very similar in all the species, but the coloration produced by the scales, especially in Anopheles, is useful in identification of species in that genus. Most of the Culicidae have a long prominent proboscis containing needlelike organs for piercing and sucking, but in one subfamily there is no long proboscis.

660

Figures 239, 240, 241, and 51 illustrate the main features of a mosquito. The sexes can be distinguished most readily by the antennae (Fig. 240); in the female they are long and slender with a whorl of a few short hairs at each joint, whereas in the male they have a feathery appearance due to tufts of long and numerous hairs at the joints. In many mosquitoes the palpi also furnish a means of distinguishing the

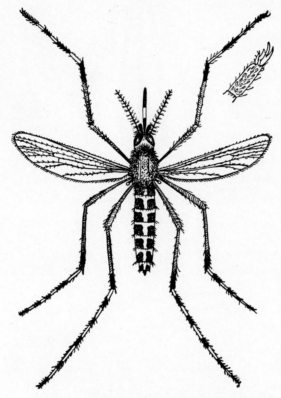

Fig. 239. Adult ♀ mosquito (*Aëdes sollicitans*).

sexes; they are usually long in the males but short in the females (Fig. 240), but in Anopheles they are long in both sexes, and in some mosquitoes, e.g., Uranotaenia, they are short in both.

The proboscis also differs in the sexes and fortunately is so constructed in the male that a mosquito of this sex could not pierce flesh if he wished. At first glance the proboscis appears to be a simple bristle, sometimes curved, but when dissected and examined with a microscope it is found to consist of a number of needlelike organs lying in a groove in the fleshy labium which was the only part visible

before dissection.   In the female mosquito there are six of these needlelike organs, the nature and names of which are shown in Fig. 241.   The
labrum-epipharynx and hypopharynx act together to form a tube for

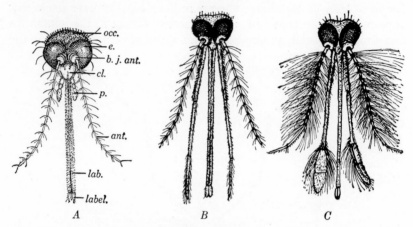

Fig. 240.   Heads of mosquitoes.   *A*, ♀ Culex; *B*, ♀ Anopheles; *C*, ♂ Anopheles;
ant. antenna; *b. j. ant.*, basal joint of antenna; *cl.*, clypeus; *e.*, eye; *lab.*, labium; *label.*,
labellum; *p.*, palpus; *occ.*, occiput.   (*A* adapted from Matheson; *B* and *C* original.)

drawing up blood into the mouth.   A tiny tube runs down through the
hypopharynx, opening at its tip, through which saliva is poured into the
wound as through a hypodermic needle to prevent blood from coagulating.   The maxillae and mandibles are needlelike piercing organs,

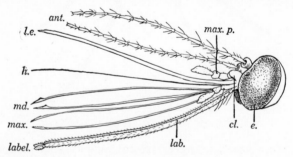

Fig. 241.   Head and mouthparts of ♀ Anopheles; *ant.*, antenna; *cl.*, clypeus; *e.*, eye;
h., hypopharynx; *lab.*, labium; *label.*, labellum; *l.e.*, labrum-epipharynx; *max.*, maxilla;
max. p., maxillary palpus; *md.*, mandible.   (After Matheson.)

the former recognizable by their sawtooth tips.   The ensheathing
labium bows back as the mosquito bites, the flexible tip or labellum
acting as a guide for the piercing organs as they are sunk into the
flesh.   In male mosquitoes the piercing organs are much degenerated,
only the suctorial part of the apparatus being well developed.

Besides the variations of the parts mentioned already, adult mosquitoes vary in the form, distribution, and color of the scales that clothe much of the body and the edges and veins of the wings; the distribution of bristles on the thoracic sclerites (Fig. 247); the details of the male reproductive organs at the tip of the abdomen (Fig. 242); the details of the female hypopygium; the relative length of parts of the leg; and in other respects. Mosquitoes have three food reservoirs connected with the esophagus, in addition to a large stomach (Fig. 51). These reservoirs are used for storage of " aspirated " foods such as fruit juices, but not for blood, which passes directly to the stomach. This practically precludes the possibility of *direct* transmission of disease germs immediately after an infective feed. Connected with the

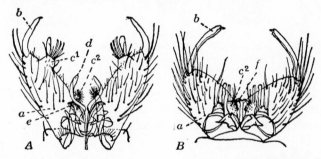

Fig. 242. Male genitalia of mosquitoes; *A, Culex quinquefasciatus, B, Anopheles quadrimaculatus;* a, side piece; b, clasper filament; c^1, lower lobe of side piece; d, harpago; e, harpe; f, uncus. (After Howard, Dyar, and Knab.)

proboscis is a pair of salivary glands consisting of three lobes each, lying in the anterior part of the thorax. It is in these that the malaria parasites collect after development; from here they are poured with the secretions of the glands into the wounds.

Life History

In a general way the life histories of all mosquitoes are much alike, but they differ in details.

Eggs. The eggs of mosquitoes (Fig. 243) are usually oval with various surface markings and, in Anopheles, with a peculiar " float " of air cells. The number of eggs laid by one female mosquito varies from 40 or 50 to several hundred. Species of Aëdes and Psorophora lay their eggs singly out of water; Anopheles lays them singly in loose clusters on water (Fig. 244A); Culex, Theobaldia, and Uranotaenia lay them in little boat-shaped rafts called egg-boats, the individual eggs standing upright (Fig. 244B); and Mansonia lays them in irregular clusters on the underside of floating leaves.

Most of the common mosquitoes of temperate climates lay their eggs on the open surface of water or attach them to some partially sub-

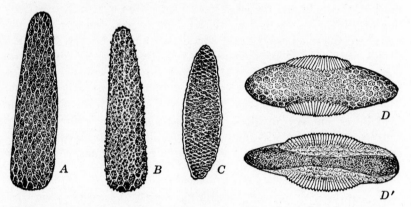

Fig. 243.   Eggs of mosquitoes;   A, *Theobaldia inornatus;*   B, *Mansonia perturbans;*   C, *Aëdes aegypti;*   D, *Anopheles punctipennis,* dorsal view;   D', same, ventral view.   × 75. (After Howard, Dyar, and Knab.)

merged object; a few species lay eggs that sink.   Species of Aëdes lay their eggs in dry places that are likely to be submerged later, or just at or above the water line in tree holes or containers — a useful bio-

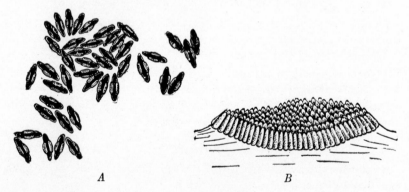

Fig. 244.   Eggs of mosquitoes.   A, eggs of Anopheles on surface of water.   × 13. (After Howard.)   B, egg-boat of Culex floating on water.   × about 8.

logical adaptation to make an adequate supply of water likely when the eggs hatch.

In most mosquitoes of temperate climates the eggs hatch in a few days or even within 24 hours.   In the species of the far north the eggs probably never hatch until the following spring, being laid in depressions on the ground that are usually not immersed until the melting of the winter snows.   Such hibernating eggs are said not to hatch unless they have been exposed to freezing temperatures. Mosquitoes of dry, hot countries lay eggs that are highly resistant to desiccation and do not lose their vitality during months of dryness. Such species must almost " live while the rain falls " and must be prepared to utilize the most transitory pools for the completion of their aquatic immature stages. In such cases the embryo within the egg shell develops to the hatching point, so that it is ready to begin the larval existence almost with the first drop of rain. Eggs of some species of Aëdes (*vexans* and *lateralis*) may remain viable in the soil for several years.

Such mosquitoes further fortify their race against the unkind environment by laying their eggs in a number of small batches instead of in a single mass, as is the habit of mosquitoes where water is plentiful. Just as a man runs less risk of ruin if he deposits his money in a number of insecure banks rather than in a single uncertain one, so it is with mosquitoes and the places where they deposit their eggs. Another remarkable adaptation of dry-climate mosquitoes is the variation in the hatching periods of the eggs in the same batch; not all hatch with the first drops of moisture, but some lie over until subsequent immersions, thus insuring a much better chance that some of them, at least, will not waste their life on the desert air with too little water to enable them to reach maturity.

The vagaries of different species in selecting breeding places are discussed on the following pages. The only feature common to all is the fact that the eggs do not hatch except in the presence of water.

Larvae. The larvae, which are always aquatic, are well known as wrigglers or wiggle-tails (Fig. 245). When first hatched they are almost microscopic, but they grow rapidly to a length of 8 to 15 or 20 mm. The bunches of long bristly hairs on the body take the place of legs and aid the larva in maintaining a position in the water. There is a rotary mouth brush of stiff hairs used to sweep small objects toward the mouth; in predaceous species these are sometimes modified into rakelike structures or into strong grasping hooks for holding prey (Fig. 249, 8).

A trumpet-shaped siphon or breathing tube (Fig. 245, s.) is present on all mosquito larvae except Anopheles, in which it is undeveloped. It is used to pierce the surface film of the water to draw air into the tracheae for, although aquatic, mosquito larvae are air breathers and make frequent trips to the surface to replenish their air supply. The leaflike anal gills (Fig. 245, *an. g.*) on the last segment of the abdomen differ from true gills in that air tubes or tracheae instead of blood vessels ramify in them. They may function primarily as osmotic regulators rather than respiratory organs since they are always larger in mosquitoes living in saline water. In well-aerated water larvae can live for a long time, but they die within a few hours if shut in water without dissolved air. In one genus, Mansonia, the larvae absorb air from the air-carrying tissues in the roots of certain aquatic

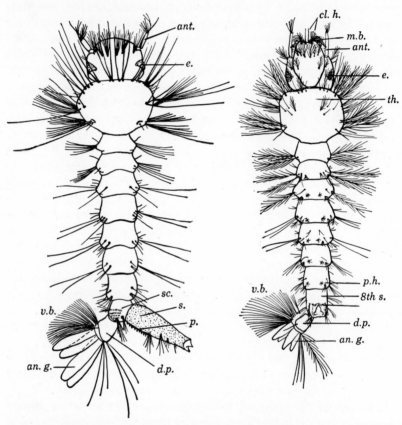

FIG. 245. A, Larva of *Culex quinquefasciatus* (after Soper); B, larva of *Anopheles punctipennis* (after Matheson); *an. g.*, anal gills; *ant.*, antenna; *cl. h.*, clypeal hairs; *d.p.*, dorsal plate of 9th segment; *8th s.*, 8th segement of abdomen; *e.*, eye; *m.b.*, mouth brush; *p.*, pecten; *p.h.*, palmate hair; *s.*, siphon or breathing tube; *sc.*, patch of scales on 8th segment; *th.*, thorax; *v.b.*, ventral brush.

plants, piercing them with the apex of the breathing tube (Fig. 249, *11*) and thus avoiding the necessity of rising to the surface of the water.

Mosquito larvae, unless suspended from the surface film by means of the breathing tube, have a tendency to sink, and they rise again only by an active jerking of the abdomen, using it as a sculling organ. Some species are habitual bottom feeders; others feed at the surface; some live on microscopic organisms, others on dead organic matter;

and still others attack and devour other aquatic animals, including young mosquito larvae of their own and other species. Soluble and colloidal substances in water can also be utilized.

The larvae shed their skins four times and then go into the pupal stage. Mosquitoes of temperate climates usually take from five days to two weeks to complete the larval existence, depending almost entirely on temperature and abundance of food. In the mosquitoes adapted to take advantage of transitory rain pools the larvae may transform into pupae within two days. On the other hand, some mosquitoes habitu-

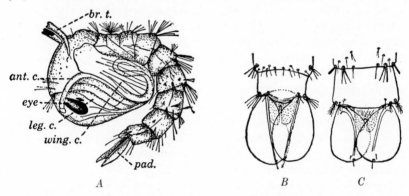

FIG. 246. *A*, pupa of *Culex pipiens; ant. c.*, antennal case; *br. t.*, breathing tubes; *leg c.*, leg cases; *pad.*, paddles; *wing c.*, wing case. × 10. (After Howard, Dyer, and Knab.) *B* and *C*, end of abdomen of pupae of *Aëdes vexans* and of *Anopheles occidentalis*, respectively. Anopheles has peglike spines at apical angles of all but last segment, and culicines have single tuft of branched fine hairs anterior to angle. (Adapted from Matheson.)

ally pass the winter as larvae. Larvae of most mosquitoes can live for several days on a wet surface but do not succeed in pupating except in water.

A key for the identification of the larvae of different genera, and of important American species, is given on pp. 675–677.

Pupae. The general form of the pupa can be seen in Fig. 246; it resembles a tiny lobster deprived of appendages and carrying its tail bent. The pair of earlike breathing tubes on the cephalothorax takes the place of the trumpetlike tube of the larva and is used in the same manner. Unlike the larva, the pupa is lighter than water and requires muscular effort to sink instead of to rise. The pupae of Mansonia, like the larvae, do not come to the surface for air but pierce the air channels in the roots of aquatic plants with their pointed breathing tubes.

The transformation into the adult during the pupal stage may be a matter of a few hours in the case of the dry-climate mosquitoes, but in most species it requires from two days to a week, depending on the temperature. The adult mosquitoes emerge head first through a longitudinal slit along the back of the thorax. After their exit they rest a few moments on the old pupal skin, stretch and dry their wings, and then take flight. They may suck blood within 24 hours, but several days to a week or more elapse before they lay eggs.

Adult mosquitoes vary to a remarkable degree in habitats, feeding habits, mode of hibernation, choice of breeding grounds, and other habits. Knowledge of the habits and habitats of particular species is of great economic importance, since it does away with useless expenditure in combating harmless or relatively harmless species and aids in the fight against particularly noxious ones. The measures that would be required to control a yellow fever or dengue epidemic would have little or no effect on malaria, and vice versa. Cutting down jungle to admit sunlight to water would eliminate malaria in some places but would be the best way in the world to increase it in others. In dealing with mosquito-borne diseases or mosquito plagues it is obvious, therefore, that the particular species involved should be determined and their habits thoroughly understood.

Ecological Groups. Because of their variable breeding habits and choice of breeding places, their different tastes in blood, and the different extent of their travels, the various species of mosquitoes have very different relations to human beings. The majority that are annoying to man can conveniently be divided into a number of general groups.

The most universally annoying are the *house mosquitoes* that breed in and about houses in cities as well as on farms, seldom traveling more than a few hundred yards. In the United States these species are mainly *Culex pipiens* in the north and the closely related *C. quinquefasciatus*, accompanied by the yellow fever mosquito, *Aëdes aegypti*, in the south. In suburban and rural areas they are joined by *Anopheles quadrimaculatus*. Some countries are so unfortunate as to have anopheles as urban house mosquitoes, e.g., *A. stephensi* in India and *A. gambiae* in most parts of Africa. In the Orient two or three other species of Aëdes, *A. albopictus*, *A. scutellaris*, and *A. pseudoscutellaris*, are household pests. These house mosquitoes are controlled by eliminating small local breeding places; when these species are involved people at 2100 Main Street may complain bitterly of mosquitoes while those of 2500 Main Street may rarely see one.

The *salt-marsh mosquitoes* are another important group; they lay their eggs in dry depressions in marshes or fields and hatch after rains, floods, or high tides. The salt-marsh forms are particularly annoying, since they migrate 30 or 40 miles from their breeding grounds. **The** advent of a heavy rain after a dry spell may cause the egg production of weeks to hatch, and billions of mosquitoes are produced simultaneously. Marshes on the east coast of Florida may average 30 to 50 million larvae per acre. Under favorable conditions of temperature, humidity, and breeze they migrate inland and literally blanket the country for miles. Towns in their path have a veritable plague of mosquitoes, but it seldom lasts more than a few days. Only large-scale, pre-invasion attacks have any effect on the salt-marsh mosquitoes. The principal members of this group are two species of Aëdes (*sollicitans* and *taeniorhynchus*) distinguishable from other common species in the United States, except for some of the large, metallic-colored Psorophoras, by a white band on the proboscis and striped legs. *Sollicitans* has a median dorsal white stripe on the abdomen, *taeniorhynchus* only black and white crossbands. *A. dorsalis* is a small brown mosquito without a band on the proboscis but with the tarsal segments banded at both ends; it is a salt-marsh species on the northwest coast but breeds in fresh water in the northern interior. The Psorophoras breed in temporary rain pools in meadows and often become very abundant 4 or 5 days after a heavy rain. A few species of these are predaceous on other mosquito larvae.

The *swamp mosquitoes* constitute a third group. These produce brood after brood in stagnant water, e.g., in low pastures, swamps, rice fields, ditches, irrigation ditch overflows or seepage, and floodwaters. In North America all the Anopheles fall into this group, and also several species of Culex (*territans* and *salinarius* in the east and *tarsalis* in the west), one widely distributed species of Aëdes (*vexans*), and *Theobaldia incidens* in the west. These species travel moderate distances, sometimes up to several miles, but are usually amenable to control by drainage or spraying. The Mansonias also belong in this group but cannot be controlled by the same methods.

A fourth group consist of *prairie and woodland mosquitoes*, including most of the species of Aëdes, which lay their eggs on the dry ground in summer to hatch in snow pools or rain puddles the following spring. They are the scourge of picnickers, campers, hunters, and fishermen, especially in mountains and in the far north. For these mosquitoes there is no method of control except large-area spraying from planes.

A fifth group are forest species breeding in tree holes or aerial plants, including the malaria-carrying *Anopheles bellator* of Trinidad and species of *Haemagogus*, vectors of jungle yellow fever in South America.

Breeding Places. The breeding places of mosquitoes include practically any kind of water except the open sea; some species show very little preference, whereas others seem to be unreasonably choosy. There are species which breed in reedy swamps, woodland pools, eddies of rivers, slow-flowing streams, holes in trees, pools of melted snow, salt marshes, tide pools, crab holes, pitcher plants and other water-bearing plants, or in broken bamboo stems filled with water. The species of Mansonia breed only in pools in which certain water plants grow, especially water lettuce (Pistia) or water hyacinths. *Aëdes aegypti* and a few other species have become domesticated and have altered their ancestral tree-hole-breeding habits to utilize artificial containers (see p. 690).

Some species breed only in pure clear water, others prefer filthy water; some breed only in sunlit water, others only in the shade; some demand quiet water, others breed only in flowing streams. Sometimes, of apparently similar pools, some will produce vast numbers of mosquitoes whereas others are left uninhabited; for the most part nobody knows why. Attempts have been made to correlate the preferences shown by mosquitoes with food, acidity or alkalinity, oxygen concentration, dissolved solids, etc., but with little success. The complexity of the problem is great, for odors may attract or repel the females searching for places to lay eggs; substances in the water may be directly injurious to the larvae; or, what is probably usually the dominant factor, the quantity or quality of the food may or may not be suitable. Most mosquito larvae, however, are able to use a considerable variety of foods, though living organisms are usually preferred. Barber successfully reared certain larvae on algae, bacteria, or ciliates alone. Biological control of mosquitoes may eventually be possible, but so far only the surface has been scratched.

Migration. As already noted, the distance mosquitoes travel from their breeding places varies greatly with the species; knowledge of this is of great importance in connection with control. *Aëdes aegypti* is seldom abundant more than a city block away from its breeding place, and the house-frequenting species of Culex seldom more than a few hundred yards. The writer has repeatedly been impressed with the fact that when mosquitoes are continuously complained of in cities, a breeding place can almost invariably be found within a block and often in the immediate vicinity. Most Anopheles make nightly migrations but seldom appear in appreciable numbers more than half a mile to a mile from their breeding places; a few species are known to migrate up to ten miles. Aëdes on northern prairies are attracted by moving herds of animals and may follow them for many miles. Salt-marsh mosquitoes, however, are the only really migratory species, sometimes going 30 to 40 miles from home (see p. 668). *A. aegypti* is annually carried inland from the Gulf Coast by trains and busses and to northern ports on ships. Hawaii originally had no mosquitoes, but three species, *Culex quinquefasciatus, Aëdes aegypti*, and *A. albopictus*, have been introduced with sailing vessels. In 1930 the deadly African malaria transmitter, *Anopheles gambiae*, was introduced and established in Brazil, as it was some years earlier in Mauritius and the Seychelles and later in Egypt.

Time of Activity. Although mosquitoes are usually thought to be nocturnal, and though this is true of most of the common species of temperate climates, it is by no means characteristic of the whole group. Many species, including most Anopheles and *Aëdes scutellaris*, are active chiefly at twilight in the evening or early morning. Knab found that the mosquitoes of northern prairies, where the nights are too cold for them, are active throughout the day only: A large proportion of forest-living tropical species, at least in America, are diurnal. Some of the mosquitoes of the northern woods are apparently always ready to bite when a victim approaches, whether it be day or night. *Aëdes aegypti* feeds by preference in the early morning or late afternoon. Here again a knowledge of the habits of particular species is important, since it may aid in the intelligent avoidance of disease-carrying forms.

Food Habits. Heretical as it may sound, mosquitoes feed mainly on plant juices, honey, etc. Philip found flowers, e.g., goldenrod, to be good collecting places for all but Anopheles mosquitoes. All adult males are strictly vegetarians and some females are also, e.g., *Megarhinus*, which, interestingly enough, is strictly cannibalistic on other mosquito larvae in its larval stage. Most females, however, although also feeding on nectar, etc., are voracious bloodsuckers, and some species, e.g., *Aëdes aegypti*, and probably most others, require a blood meal before they can lay fertile eggs. Huff, however, found that dining on blood is not always a necessary prelude to maternity, at least for *Culex pipiens*. Roubaud bred twenty generations of this species without ever allowing the adults to feed at all. Some species indiscriminately attack any warm-blooded or even cold-blooded animal, but others show strong preferences. *Aëdes spencerii* of our northern prairies flies towards any large object which its instinct leads it to suspect as a source of food. The importance of various species of Anopheles as malaria transmitters (see pp. 202, 678) depends largely on the extent to which they choose man as food. This is why *A. gambiae* is more dangerous than *quadrimaculatus*, and *quadrimaculatus* than *punctipennis*. *Anopheles gambiae* is one of the few species showing a strong preference for human blood. *Aëdes aegypti* shows no distaste for man but readily bites other mammals, birds, and even cold-blooded animals, and matures more eggs on some of these bloods than it does on human blood.

Hibernation. The method employed by mosquitoes for passing the cold or dry seasons varies with the species. Many mosquitoes of temperate or tropical climates hibernate or pass the dry season as adults, the females stowing themselves away in hollows in trees, caves, crevices in rocks, cellars, barns, etc., to come forth and lay their eggs in the spring. A few species hibernate in the larval stage; *Wyeomyia smithii* larvae become enclosed in solid ice in the leaves of the pitcher plant in which they live. Most hibernating larvae retire to the bottom of their breeding pools during cold weather and do not survive freezing. Many temperate- and warm-climate mosquitoes and all the northern ones pass the unfavorable season in the egg state, which may be looked upon as the *common* method of hibernation. Most Anopheles survive the cold season either as adults or as larvae but usually not as eggs.

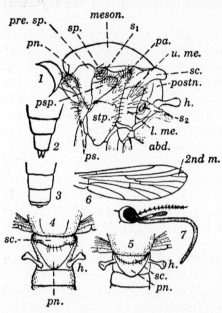

Fig. 247. Details of mosquito morphology to illustrate key to adults. *1*, side view of thorax of mosquito (Psorophora) showing plates and groups of bristles useful in distinguishing genera; *p.a.*, pre-alar bristles; *pn.*, prothoracic bristles; *pre. sp.*, prespiracular bristles (missing in Psorophora); *ps.*, prosternal bristles; *sp*, spiracular bristles; *psp.*, postspiracular bristles; *stp.*, sternopleural bristles; *u. me.* and *l. me.*, upper and lower mesepimeral bristles; *sc.*, scutellum; *s₁*, 1st spiracle; *s₂*, second spiracle; *h.*, haltere; *meson.*, mesonotum; *postn.*, postnotum; *abd.*, abdomen. *2*, shape of end of abdomen of Aëdes ♀. *3*, shape of end of abdomen of Culex ♀. *4*, trilobed scutellum of Culicini; *h.*, haltere; *sc.*, scutellum; *pn.*, postnotum. *5*, scutellum of Anophelini, without lobes; *pn.*, postnotum. *6*, wing of Uranotaenia, with short second marginal cell. *7*, head of Megarhinus, with curved proboscis.

Length of Life. The length of life of mosquitoes varies with the species and the sex. Male mosquitoes seldom live more than 1 to 3 weeks; their duty in life is done when they have fertilized the females. Paradoxically, the more favorable the conditions the shorter the lives of the females. They die soon after all their eggs are laid; with plenty of blood meals and readily available breeding places this may be only 3 or 4 weeks, whereas under less favorable conditions it may be several months. The species which lay all their eggs in a mass at one time are short-lived and have several generations a year, whereas those in which the eggs are laid in small lots at intervals live for several months. Species in which the females hibernate are still longer-lived, but since they are not active in winter their *effective* life may be short.

Classification. More than 2000 species of Culicidae have been described, the majority of which belong in the tropics, although the north is richer in individuals; 123 species have been described in the United States and Canada. There are two subfamilies, the Corethrinae, with a short nonpiercing proboscis, and the Culicinae, including all the true mosquitoes. The further divisions into tribes and genera are shown in the following key, which is provided for the identification of the genera found in North America and of the more common or important species:

Key to Adults of North American Genera of Mosquitoes, with Notes on Commonest Species

I. **Tribe Sabethini.** Postnotum (Fig. 247, *postn.*) with tuft of setae; tropical, nonbloodsucking species, breeding in water-holding plants, two widespread species in North America....*Wyeomyia smithii* and *W. haynei*. (Palpi short in both sexes; very small; color metallic, with underside of abdomen, tips of middle legs, and spot on top of head silvery white; breeds in pitcher plants.)

II. **Tribe Anophelini.** Postnotum without setae; scutellum not lobed (Fig. 247, *5*); palpi long in both sexes (Fig. 240); wings usually spotted or mottled; resting position usually not humpbacked; proboscis nearly parallel with axis of body (Fig. 251, *bottom*); only 1 genus....*Anopheles.*

III. **Tribe Culicini.** Postnotum without setae; scutellum trilobed (Fig. 247, *4*); palpi short in females; wings rarely spotted, never mottled; resting position humpbacked (Fig. 251, *bottom*).

   1*a*. Proboscis rigid, down-curved (Fig. 247, *7*) ....*Megarhinus.* (Large, brilliantly colored, nonbloodsucking species, mostly tropical; 1 species in east and south, breeding in tree holes.)

   1*b*. Proboscis flexible, not curved ....**2.**

   2*a*. Second marginal cell ("2nd m" in Fig. 247, *6*) less than half as long as petiole; palpi short in both sexes ....*Uranotaenia.* (Small, tropical, nonbiting, pool-breeding mosquitoes.)

   2*b*. Second marginal cell over half as long as petiole (Fig. 163*B*) ....**3.**

   3*a*. Spiracular bristles present (Fig. 247, *1*); size large; metallic colors present or absent ....**4.**

   3*b*. Spiracular bristles absent; size medium or small; no metallic colors..**5.**

   4*a*. No postspiracular bristles (Fig. 247, *1*); size large; color not metallic ....*Theobaldia.* (1 common species on west coast, *T. incidens*, which has dark spots on wings, banded abdomen, and unstriped legs.)

4*b*. Postspiracular bristles present; size usually large; metallic colors present ....*Psorophora.*
(One species, *P. ciliata,* is largest mosquito in United States.)

5*a*. Fourth joint of front tarsi very short ....*Orthopodomyia.*
(Tree-hole breeders, mostly in tropics. The one species in the United States has thorax with 6 narrow white lines and striped legs.)

5*b*. Fourth joint of front tarsi normal ....6.

6*a*. Female with tip of abdomen truncated or blunt (Fig. 247, *3*) ....7.

6*b*. Abdomen of female pointed, with exserted cerci (Fig. 247, *2*); eggs laid singly above water ....*Aëdes.*
(Three main ecological groups: (1) tree-hole breeders *(Stegomyia),* from which *A. aegypti* was derived; (2) salt- or freshwater-marsh species with successive broods; (3) single-brood species breeding in spring pools from eggs laid previous summer.)
Common North American species:

(*a*) *aegypti;* black with white striped legs and abdomen; black proboscis; lyre-shaped mark on back of thorax.

(*b*) *salt-marsh mosquitoes; sollicitans* (Fig. 239) and *taeniorhynchus* with white band on proboscis, *sollicitans* brown with median stripe on abdomen, *taeniorhynchus* darker, abdomen barred black and white; *cantator* with less prominent leg bands and no stripe on proboscis, confined to Atlantic coast.

(*c*) *vexans;* freshwater-marsh and floodwater breeder, favoring filthy water; thorax bronze, abdomen black with white stripes; tarsi with very narrow white rings; widespread in United States and Canada.

(*d*) *dorsalis;* in salt marshes and on western plains; tarsi white-ringed on both ends of joints; abdomen white-scaled, with two black patches on each segment; northern United States and Canada.

(*e*) *spring pool-breeders;* numerous species, without the combination of characters of above species.

7*a*. Female abdomen truncated; palpi of female usually ¼ as long as proboscis or longer; wing scales large and broad ....*Mansonia.*
(1 species in North America, *M. perturbans;* has white-striped abdomen and legs; yellow band on proboscis.)

7*b*. Female abdomen blunt (Fig. 247, *3*); palpi less than ⅕ as long as proboscis; wing scales narrow ....*Culex.*

(*a*) Brown species with proboscis and legs unstriped; abdomen with distinct white bands; common in and about houses........
......*pipiens* and *territans* in north, *quinquefasciatus* in south.

(*b*) Similar, with very narrow or no bands on abdomen; breeds in marshes; less domestic; in eastern United States........*salinarius.*

(*c*) Proboscis with white band; abdomen and legs white-striped; breeds in ground pools, seldom enters houses...........*tarsalis.*

Identification of Larvae of Common or Important
North American Species

Anopheles Larvae. No breathing siphon (Fig. 245*B*); lie parallel with surface.

1a. Both pairs of anterior clypeal bristles (Fig. 248, *4, 5*) simple or slightly feathered ....2.

1b. Outer pair of anterior clypeal bristles profusely branched (Fig. 248, *1, 3*); leaflets of palmate hairs notched at tip (Fig. 248, *7, 8*) ....3.

2a. Both pairs of anterior clypeal bristles slightly feathered (Fig. 248, *5*); leaflets of palmate hairs narrow, pointed (Fig. 248, *6*); palmate hairs on all of first 7 abdominal segments, those on first small ....*albimanus.*

2b. Both pairs of anterior clypeal bristles simple (Fig. 248, *4*); leaflets of palmate hairs narrowed to slender point at tip (Fig. 248, *8*); palmate hairs rudimentary on first and second segments, all about same size on other segments ....*pseudopunctipennis.*

3a. Fourth and fifth abdominal segments with two pairs of branched dorsal hairs; palmate hairs on 5 segments, smaller on segments 3 and 7 ....*crucians.*

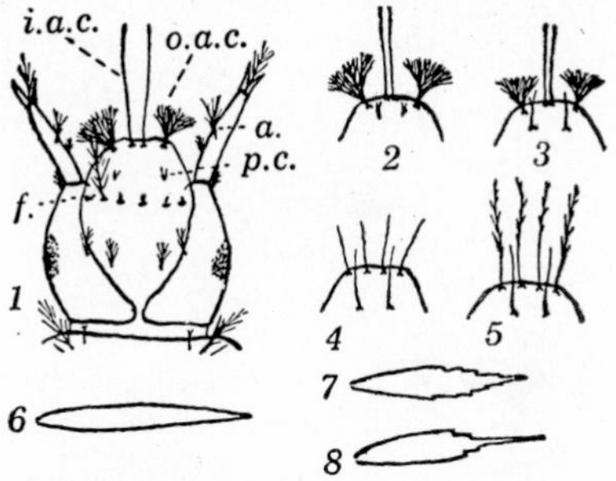

Fig. 248. Details of structure of Anopheles fourth-stage larvae for use in identification. *1*, Head of *A. quadrimaculatus;* a., antennal hair; f., frontal hair (one of six); *i.a.c.*, inner anterior clypeal hair; *o.a.c.*, outer anterior clypeal hair; *p.c.*, postclypeal hair; *2*, clypeal region of *A. punctipennis. 3*, clypeal region of *A. crucians. 4*, clypeal region of *A. pseudopunctipennis. 5*, clypeal region of *A. albimanus. 6*, element from palmate hair of *A. albimanus. 7*, same, from *A. quadrimaculatus, punctipennis* or *crucians. 8*, same from *A. pseudopunctipennis.* (Adapted from figures by Russell and by Root.)

3b. Fourth and fifth abdominal segments with one pair of simple or 2-branched dorsal hairs; palmate hairs rudimentary on first segment, small on second ....4.

4a. Anterior internal clypeal hairs close together at base (Fig. 248, *2*); palmate hairs on second abdominal segment less well developed, not pigmented, and usually not seen under low magnification ......*freeborni, punctipennis.*

4b. Anterior internal clypeal hairs separated at base (Fig. 248, *1*); palmate hairs on second abdominal segment better developed, pigmented, visible under low magnification........
....*quadrimaculatus.*

Culicine Larvae. Breathing siphon present (Fig. 245*A*).

1a. Breathing siphon spinelike at tip, used to pierce air channels in roots of aquatic plants (Fig. 249, *11*); larvae do not come to surface....**Mansonia.**

1b. Breathing siphon normal ....2.

2a. Anal segment with no ventral brush (Fig. 249, *2*) ....**Wyeomyia.**

2b. Anal segment with ventral brush ....3.

3a. Siphon without pecten; anal segment ringed by chitinous band; chitinous plate on eighth segment also (Fig. 249, *9, 10*) ....4.

3b. Siphon with pecten ....5.

4a. Mouth brushes modified into coarse prehensile lamellae, hooked for seizing prey (Fig. 249, *8*); plate on eighth segment with 2 spiny hairs (Fig. 249, *9*); in tree holes ....**Megarhinus.**

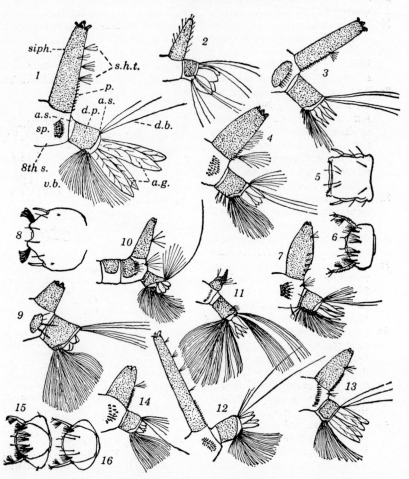

Fig. 249. Details of structure of culicine larvae to illustrate key (from Dyar). 1, posterior portion of larva of *Culex quinquefasciatus;* *a.s.,* anal segment; *8th s.,* eighth segment; *a.g.,* anal gills; *d.b.,* dorsal brush; *d.p.,* dorsal plate (a complete ring in this and many other species); *p.,* pecten or comb; *siph.,* siphon; *sp.,* patch of spines on eighth segment; *s.h.t.,* siphonal hair tufts. 2, *Wyeomyia smithii,* posterior end. 3, *Uranotaenia sapphirinus,* posterior end. 4, *Theobaldia incidens,* posterior end. 5, *Psorophora ciliata,* head. 6, *Psorophora (Janthinosoma) columbiae,* head. 7, *Psorophora (Janthinosoma) columbiae,* posterior end. 8, *Megarhinus septentrionalis,* head. 9, *Megarhinus septentrionalis,* posterior end. 10, *Orthopodomyia signifera,* posterior end. 11, *Mansonia perturbans,* posterior end. 12, *Culex salinarius,* posterior end. 13, *Aëdes aegypti,* posterior end. 14, *Aëdes taeniorhynchus,* posterior end. 15, *Aëdes canadensis,* head. 16, *Aëdes dorsalis,* head.

4b. Mouth brushes normal; double row of stout spines on eighth segment
(Fig. 249, *10*); in water-holding plants or tree holes......**Orthopodomyia.**

5a. Siphon with several pairs of ventral tufts (Fig. 249, *1*); anal segment
ringed (Fig. 249, *1*); siphon usually at least 4 or 5 times as long as wide
.... **Culex.**

   a' Antenna with tuft at or before middle; all but one of ventral tufts of
siphon represented by single hairs ....*territans.*

   a'' Antenna with tuft well beyond middle; several tufts on siphon......*b.*

   b' Siphon 7 × 1 (Fig. 249, *12*) ....*salinarius.*

   b'' Siphon 5 × 1 or less ....*c.*

   c' Siphon with 5 hair tufts, all in line ....*tarsalis.*

   c'' Siphon with 4 hair tufts, third out of line (Fig. 249, *1*) ....
.... *pipiens* and *quinquefasciatus.*

5b. Siphon with a single pair of ventral tufts ....6.

6a. Anal segment ringed; spines of eighth segment attached to posterior
margin of a chitinous plate (Fig. 249, *3*) ....**Uranotaenia.**

6b. Spines of eighth segment not attached to a chitinous plate ....7.

7a. Spines of distal part of pecten produced into long hairs; hair tuft at base
of siphon (Fig. 249, *4*) ....**Theobaldia.**

7b. Pecten of short spines; hair tuft near middle of siphon or beyond.......8.

8a. Anal segment ringed by chitinous plate, and ventral brush partly inserted
into it (Fig. 249, *7*); in temporary rain pools ....**Psorophora.**

   (*a*) Mouth brushes prehensile; antennae not projecting anterior to head
(Fig. 249, *5*); predaceous; very large ....subgenus **Psorophora.**
In North America two spp., *ciliata* and *howardi.*

   (*b*) Mouth brushes normal, and antennae large (Fig. 249, *6*); size smaller;
several common United States species; subgenus ...... **Janthinosoma.**

8b. Anal segment not ringed, or if ringed, ventral brush posterior to it (Fig.
249, *13, 14*) ....**Aëdes.**

   a' Pecten with teeth detached outwardly; antenna spined all over;
siphon 3 × 1 ....*vexans.*
siphon 2½ × 1, on northern prairies ....*spencerii.*

   a'' Pecten without detached teeth ....*b.*

   b' Comb scales 8 to 12, in a single row; anal segment not quite ringed
(Fig. 249, *13*); head hairs all single; anal segment short ....*aegypti.*

   b'' Comb scales in triangular patch ....*c.*

   c' Anal segment ringed ....*d.*

   c'' Anal segment not ringed ....*e.*

   d' Siphon about 2 × 1 ....*sollicitans.*

   d'' Siphon less than 2 × 1 (Fig. 249, *14*) ....*taeniorhynchus.*

   e' Anal segment nearly twice as long as wide; head hairs single or double
(Fig. 249, *16*); anal gills large, *stimulans;* anal gills very small, *dorsalis.*

   e'' Anal segment about 1½ times as long as wide; head hairs multiple
(Fig. 249, *15*) ....*canadensis.*

Mosquitoes and Malaria

As was shown in Chapter 9, malaria is one of the most important
and one of the most deadly of human diseases. This being true, the
mosquitoes, which are the sole means of transmitting the disease, must

be looked upon as among the most important and most deadly enemies of the human race. The role of mosquitoes in causing disease, especially malaria, has been suspected by various peoples as far back as any records go. The steps which led to the *proof* of the relation of mosquitoes to malaria are briefly outlined on pp. 185–186.

Fortunately not all mosquitoes are malaria carriers; in fact, only one genus, Anopheles, comprising a number of more or less well-defined subgenera which have been considered genera by some workers, is known to be able to transmit human malaria, and not even all the species of this genus are incriminated. The majority of the species can be experimentally infected with malaria parasites, but some much more readily than others. There is also a difference in the facility with which certain species can be infected with different malarial species and strains (see p. 203). The malaria parasites of birds are transmitted, primarily at least, by species of Culex or Aëdes.

As repeatedly pointed out elsewhere, mere experimental infection of an insect with a disease germ or even successful transmission by it under experimental conditions means very little with respect to its role in nature. Many other factors come into play which cannot be studied in the laboratory and the combined effect of which can be learned only by extensive and carefully studied epidemiological evidence. *A. punctipennis*, for example, though a proved transmitter of malaria in the laboratory, is eliminated in nature by its habits. It is a " wild " species which seldom enters occupied houses and which shows a strong preference for animal over human blood.

In Europe the common and widespread *A. maculipennis* is not a uniform species but consists of a number of biologically distinct races, now sometimes considered species, some of which are dangerous malaria vectors whereas others are in most places practically harmless. Two members of this group occur in the United States, *freeborni* throughout the west and *occidentalis* on the Pacific slope and in the north, but only *freeborni* is an important vector. The races differ in coloration of eggs and other minor morphological characters and in such biological ones as breeding in fresh or brackish water, hibernation, and — most important — in willingness to feed on man instead of cattle. Freshwater races of *maculipennis* with barred eggs are primarily cattle feeders and are harmless except when they are faced with the alternative between starvation and a distasteful human meal. Such conditions exist in backward regions where animal husbandry is poorly developed. On the other hand, the varieties with unbarred eggs that breed in either fresh or brackish water are naturally man-eaters and will transmit malaria regardless of the number of animals available to divert their appetites.

A. maculipennis is not alone in being composed of races differing in their feeding and breeding habits. Several of the " big shots " in the transmission of malaria, including *A. sinensis, maculatus, aquasalis, pseudopunctipennis,* and perhaps *gambiae* and *funestus,* behave differently in one place than in another. In the United States *pseudopunctipennis* is an apparently harmless species, but in mountainous regions from Mexico to Argentina it is Public Enemy No. 1 among the anophelines. But as Hackett remarks, it is not to be supposed that nature has been kind enough to help us distinguish the races everywhere by painting identification marks on the eggs. The races differ not only in food habits but also in susceptibility to malarial infection (see p. 196).

Much valuable information on food preferences of Anopheles has been obtained by precipitin tests of the blood obtained from their stomachs. King and Bull tested the three common Anopheles of southeastern United States, only one of which, *A. quadrimaculatus,* is an important carrier in nature, with the results shown in the table.

Species	No. Ex'd	Per Cent Fed on Man	Cattle	Pigs	Horses	Dogs	Birds
A. *quadrimaculatus*	272	32.4	48.1	5.1	2.5	1.5	0.8
A. *crucians*	236	1.3	66.5	14.1	12.8	4.2	0.9
A. *punctipennis*	10	0.0 — all fed on animals					

Of 652 *A. pseudopunctipennis* in northern Argentina, where this species is an important vector, Davis found that 50 per cent had fed on man, 21.8 per cent on dogs, and only 23 per cent on all the large domestic animals combined. The United States strain of this species would undoubtedly give very different results.

Identification of Anopheles. The Anopheles mosquitoes, fortunately, are fairly easy to identify in all stages of their development except as pupae. They represent a primitive group of mosquitoes and in many respects are less specialized than other members of the family. The different species of the genus vary a great deal in choice of breeding places, habits, and appearance, so that it is necessary in any malarial district to determine which species are malaria carriers, how they may be identified, where they breed, and what their habits are. The majority of the species have mottled or spotted wings, and the arrangement of the markings is usually a good means of identification (Fig. 250).

Figure 251 is a comparative table which shows in a graphic way how Anopheles may ordinarily be distinguished from other common mosquitoes, such as Culex and Aëdes, in their different stages. The "floats" on the eggs of Anopheles are rarely absent; their size and markings sometimes serve as means of identification of species. Owing to the effects of surface tension the eggs of Anopheles tend to assume geometrical patterns on the surface of the water. The larvae, besides the absence of a breathing tube and their horizontal floating position at the surface of the water, have other identifying features such as the rosette-like palmate hairs on some of the segments, which serve to hold the larvae in the characteristic position by surface tension. The species of Anopheles larvae are sometimes very difficult to identify,

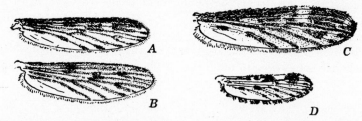

Fig. 250.   Wings of American Anopheles; A, A. crucians; B, A. quadrimaculatus; C, A. punctipennis; D, A. albimanus.   Drawn to scale.   (After Howard, Dyar, and Knab.)

and reliance must be placed on the form, number, and distribution of characteristic hairs. A key to the important American species is given on p. 682.

The pupae have short and more flaring breathing tubes than those of Aëdes or Culex, and the paddles at the end of the abdomen have an accessory hair in addition to the terminal one. The pupae of some of the American Anopheles can be identified by coloration (Burgess, 1946); those of A. quadrimaculatus are distinguished by a sharply defined black mark on the dorsal side of the first abdominal segment. The adult Anopheles are usually easily distinguishable by the resting position, with the proboscis, thorax, and abdomen all in a straight line and at an angle to the resting surface, in contrast to the parallel or drooping abdomen and humpbacked appearance of culicines, but some of them, e.g., A. culicifacies of India, resemble the culicines in resting position. A. quadrimaculatus is more culicine-like than are other North American Anopheles; it rests at only a slight angle to the surface, whereas punctipennis appears almost to stand on its head. Most Anopheles have the wings marked with dark or light spots or both,

Anopheles	*Culex, Aëdes,* etc.

EGGS

Eggs laid singly on surface of water; provided with a partial envelope, more or less inflated, acting as a "float."

Eggs laid in rafts or egg-boats or singly on or near water or where water may accumulate; never provided with a "float."

 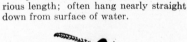

LARVAE

Larvae have no long breathing tube or siphon; rest just under surface of water and lie parallel with it.

Larvae have distinct breathing tube or siphon on eighth segment of abdomen; hang from surface film by this siphon, except in Mansonia, which obtains air from aquatic plants.

 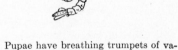

PUPAE

Pupae have short breathing trumpets; usually do not hang straight down from surface of water.

Pupae have breathing trumpets of various length; often hang nearly straight down from surface of water.

HEADS OF ADULTS

Palpi of both male and female long and jointed, equaling or exceeding the proboscis in both sexes.

Palpi of female always much shorter than proboscis, those of male usually long but sometimes short.

RESTING POSITION OF ADULT

Adult rests with body more or less at angle with surface, the proboscis held in straight line with body.

Adult usually rests with body parallel to surface, though sometimes at an angle. Proboscis not held in straight line with body, giving "humpbacked" appearance.

FIG. 251.

but even this is not constant, since a few culicines have spotted wings and a few Anopheles, e.g., *A. atropos* and *A. walkeri*, have unspotted ones. The long palpus of the female is a character which can always be relied upon.

Following is a key for the identification of the North American species north of Mexico, with comments on their distribution and importance:

1a. " White-footed " species with hind tarsi having last 3½ segments all, or nearly all, white; wings marked with both black and white spots. Several species in tropical America, several being very important malaria vectors. Only species reaching Texas and most important vector in West Indies and Central America ....*albimanus*.

1b. Dark-legged species without white stripes or areas on legs ....2.

2a. Wings not spotted, or spots indistinct
    (1) No white knee spots; inconspicuous rings on palpi; Gulf and Atlantic coasts, breeding in salt water; coloration very dark; not important .... *atropos*.
    (2) With narrow rings on palpi; eastern United States, breeding in fresh-water marshes; white knee spots; not important ....*walkeri*.
    (3) Small; dark palpi; no white knee spots; breeds in tree holes...*barberi*.

2b. Wings not uniformly colored ....3.

3a. Wings with two or four dark spots; white knee spots ....4.

3b. Wings with white or yellow spots along costal margin (Fig. 250C, D).....5.

4a. Apex of wing uniformly colored, dark; only important malaria carriers in United States; (Figs. 250B and 252) ....
    ....west of Rockies, *maculipennis freeborni*; in south, *quadrimaculatus*.

4b. Apex of wing with coppery spot; in northern states and Pacific slope....
    .... *maculipennis occidentalis*.

5a. Only one white spot on costal margin, at tip of wing (Fig. 250A); anal vein with 3 black spots ....*crucians*.

5b. A large yellow spot on outer third of costal margin involving three veins, another at tip, and another in basal third; fringe nearly all dark; extends farther north than most species (Fig. 250C) ....*punctipennis*.

5c. Four yellowish white spots along front of wing; fringe of wing alternating black and white; southwestern United States to Argentina; not important in the United States, but principal transmitter in mountains from Mexico to Argentina ....*pseudopunctipennis*.

Habits of Anopheles. Most Anopheles breed in natural waters such as ponds, swamps, edges of streams, rice fields, and grassy ditches. Our species all breed in standing water, but this is not true everywhere. In Europe and Asia some of the most important species breed in flowing streams, which necessitates entirely different methods for their control. Some species breed in brackish water, some in shaded water, some only in sunlight, and a few in artificial containers around houses. Some species show much more pronounced preferences than others. Our principal malaria vector in North America, *Anopheles quadrimaculatus,* is one of the least particular species. According to Hinman in 1940, optimum conditions for its breeding are afforded by clean, open water with dense aquatic vegetation and abundant flotage. Natural shade restricts the vegetation, thereby decreasing the protection and food of the larvae.

Shade-loving species of jungles and forests are *A. grabhamii* of tropical America, *A. funestus* of Africa, and *A. umbrosus* of southeast Asia; *A. albimanus* of tropical America, *A. gambiae* of Africa, and *A. barbirostris* of Asia breed only in sunlit waters. In Malaya the cutting down of jungle in the flat lands and exposure of sluggish water to sunlight changes a dominance of *umbrosus* to *barbirostris,* with a reduction in malaria; but when ravines in the hills are opened up and the sparkling streams cleared of vegetation and exposed to sunlight, the harmless jungle species disappear and the deadly *A. maculatus* takes their place. Thus in the two localities directly opposite conditions determine the presence or absence of malaria. *A. sundaicus,* an important malaria carrier in southeastern Asia, breeds in strongly brackish or even concentrated sea water, as in the holes of mud lobsters or in sea water pools inside the reefs of coral islands. *A. bellator,* an important vector in Trinidad, breeds in aerial plants in trees planted to shade cocoa groves.

The eggs of Anopheles are not as resistant to drying as those of Aëdes but will survive for as long as 3 weeks on drying mud, and even the larvae can live on moist mud for some time. The eggs hatch only in water and at temperatures above 60° C.; under favorable conditions they hatch in 1 to 2 days. The larvae are surface feeders; they seem to feed on any particles floating on or near the surface which are small enough to swallow. Anopheles larvae are not rapid in their development as compared with some mosquitoes; the time required under favorable conditions is from 2 to 3 weeks or more — from 1 to 3 days for the eggs, usually from 10 to 20 or more for the larvae, and from 2 to 7 for the pupae. The number of generations a year probably varies greatly with the species and conditions of food and temperature. It has been estimated that *A. quadrimaculatus* has from 8 to 10 annual generations in southeastern United States.

Adult Anopheles are for the most part twilight feeders, but there are many exceptions. Some species come forth with the first shade of late afternoon, others not until almost dark. A few species, e.g., *A. brasiliensis,* are diurnal; many forest species will bite willingly in the daytime if disturbed. The food preferences of adult females and their important bearing on malaria transmission have already been discussed. An important observation made by Roubaud is that the adults, at least of *A. maculipennis,* fly out into the open and invade other houses or sheds even if there is an abundant food supply where they have been resting after an earlier meal; as a result the Anopheles population of any spot is entirely changed in a few days; this flight in the open seems to be indispensable to the life of *A. maculipennis,* and it also has an important bearing on malaria transmission. Mosquitoes do not suck blood daily; usually blood meals are taken at intervals of several days.

Most Anopheles are rather sedentary in habit and seldom fly in numbers more than a fraction of a mile from their breeding places; *A. quadrimaculatus* is more of a traveler than most species, but even it rarely goes more than a mile from its breeding place, although occasionally in the fall before hibernation it may scatter in significant numbers up to 3 miles. *A. albimanus,* however, is reported to fly as far as 12 miles from Gatun Lake in Panama. Abundant Anopheles, nevertheless, usually indicate breeding places within a mile.

Many Anopheles hibernate either as adults or as larvae, and frequently in both ways, but usually not as eggs. Hibernating larvae bury themselves in mud or under debris at the bottom of water where they remain quiescent, coming to the surface only momentarily when disturbed. When the temperature rises they come to the surface to feed.

Malaria-carrying Species. Over a hundred species of Anopheles have been described, and a large percentage of them have been shown to be capable of transmitting malaria experimentally, but only about two dozen of them are important natural vectors of malaria. Often the habits of the species, as already shown, are of more importance than the ability to transmit the disease under experimental conditions. The difference in ability of some species of Anopheles to nurse one species or strain of malaria more readily than another still further complicates the task of evaluating the roles of different species, for a certain species of Anopheles may for this reason be an important transmitter in one place and not in another.

The methods used in determining the importance of particular species are various. The most valuable and reliable criterion is the relative number of individuals with infected salivary glands found in malarial houses. (For methods of dissecting mosquitoes for demonstration of oöcysts and sporozoites see Barber and Rice, 1936.) Supplementary information is obtained by observations on breeding and feeding habits (aided by precipitin tests), relative abundance and coincidence with outbreaks of the disease, and experimental transmission in the laboratory.

In North America *A. quadrimaculatus* (Fig. 252) and *A. freeborni* are the only important vectors of malaria, though others may occasionally transmit it or cause small local outbreaks. The principal vectors in other parts of the world are as follows: in Central America and the West Indies, the white-footed *albimanus;* in Trinidad, *bellator;* in tropical South America, others of the white-footed group, especially *darlingi, aquasalis,* and *albitarsus,* and in dry mountainous regions

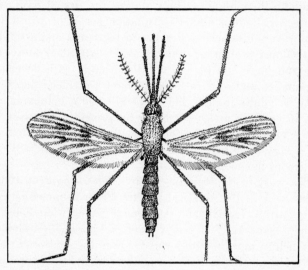

FIG. 252. The common North American malaria-transmitting mosquito, *Anopheles quadrimaculatus.*

from Mexico to Argentina, *pseudopunctipennis;* in Europe, certain races of *maculipennis,* and *superpictus;* in the Near East, *sacharovi, claviger,* and *superpictus;* in Africa, *gambiae, funestus, pharoënsis,* and *multicolor;* in India and southeast Asia, *minimus, culicifacies, philippinensis, sundaicus, varuna, aconitus, fluviatilis, maculatus, annularis,* and *stephensi;* in China and Japan, *hyrcanus, minimus,* and *pattoni;* in Borneo, *leucosphyrus;* in the South Pacific and Australian region, *farauti* and *punctulatus* (but only in islands as far east as the New Hebrides; the oceanic ones farther east have no Anopheles). These species account for the majority of malaria in the world, but many other species also contribute and may be locally important.

The effect of anti-anopheles campaigns on the prevalence of malaria is discussed in Chapter 9, pp. 209–212.

Mosquitoes and Yellow Fever

History and Nature of Yellow Fever. Once the scourge of the entire Western Hemisphere, yellow fever is now confined to the hinterland of South America and to central Africa. In Africa it was formerly thought to be confined to West Africa, but it also occurs in Sudan, and protection tests with serum show that it extends all the way to the Red Sea in Eritrea and south to northern Rhodesia. It is caused by a filtrable virus (see p. 231) which is present in the blood and available to mosquitoes only during the first 3 days of illness. After infection there is a short incubation period of 3 to 6 days, followed by severe headache and aches in the bones and a sudden fever with flushed and swollen face and dry skin. After 3 or 4 days the fever subsides and there is a period of calm, usually with development of severe jaundice and often a " black vomit " of blood and bile. The mortality in adults is high, but there are many inapparent cases in children in endemic areas, as shown by protective antibodies in the serum. A highly effective protective vaccine is available and has been used on a very large scale in rural South America and in West Africa and for troops in endemic areas.

The discovery of the transmission by *Aëdes aegypti* in 1900 by the illustrious work of the American Yellow Fever Commission composed of Reed, Carroll, Lazear, and Agramonte ended what Soper in 1937 called the " Dark Age " of yellow fever and began the " Golden Age," during which so much progress was made in the control of the disease that for a few months in 1927 it was thought to have been completely eradicated from the Western Hemisphere. Then came the " Age of Disillusionment," with the dramatic revelation that yellow fever exists in a jungle form, usually silent and unrecognized, over vast areas in South America from Colombia to Paraguay. Forest animals, particularly monkeys (marmosets and saimiri monkeys), in which the virus may circulate in the blood for 7 or 8 days, serve as natural vertebrate hosts. Marsupials may play a less important part (see Waddell and Taylor, IV, 1948). Mosquitoes of the genus Haemogogus (see following section) that breed in the treetops serve as vectors. They never leave the forest canopy even to invade small villages, so human cases occur only among people actually working in the jungle, especially in felling trees, and in the absence of *Aëdes aegypti* there is no spread from man to man.

A similar jungle form of the disease exists in parts of Africa, transmitted on plantations by *Aëdes simpsoni*, which breeds in axils of leaves, and in forests by *A. africana* and probably *A. vittatus*, which

breed in rock pools.   Other species of Aëdes in both Africa and South
America and a few species of Eretmopodites, Mansonia, Culex, and
Anopheles are capable of acting as vectors, though only a few are
efficient transmitters; among these are *Aëdes luteocephalus* and
A. stokesi in Africa, and *A. fluviatilis* and *A. leucocelaenus* in South
America.   The last is a potential vector of the jungle form of the
disease.

When persons with yellow fever enter a town or city where *Aëdes
aegypti* is prevalent, the disease changes from a sporadic to an epidemic
form.   This was the only kind of yellow fever known prior to about
1930.   It was once the greatest scourge of the Western Hemisphere,
not only in the tropical and semitropical areas where *Aëdes aegypti*
is at home, but also in such places as Boston and Philadelphia, where
great epidemics broke out late in the year after *A. aegypti*, imported
on sailing vessels in which they found abundant breeding places, had
become numerous.   The toll from yellow fever during the French
attempt to build the Panama Canal was appalling.

Before the transmission by *A. aegypti* was discovered and means of
control understood, epidemics raged in tropical cities until a high
percentage of people were either dead or immune, and in temperate
cities until frost stopped the mosquitoes.   The last outbreak in the
United States was in New Orleans in 1905, when for the first time an
epidemic was stopped by intelligent human effort.   No urban outbreak
of yellow fever has occurred in the Americas since 1933, although small
aegypti-transmitted outbreaks have followed jungle outbreaks several
times.   The jungle outbreaks tend to shift from place to place.

It commonly requires from 10 to 12 days for *Aëdes aegypti* to become
infective after becoming infected, although at high temperatures the
period may be shortened to as little as 4 days.   Transovarial transmission does not occur, but larvae exposed to liquid containing the
virus develop into infective adults.   In order to keep an epidemic
going it is necessary to have a fairly high incidence of *A. aegypti*.
Even where there are many nonimmunes an epidemic subsides when
the *aegypti* index, i.e., the number of premises on which it is breeding,
falls below 5 per cent.   It is doubtful whether an epidemic would start
if, by inspection and anti-*aegypti* work, the index were held to 2 or 3
per cent, as it can be without too great difficulty.

Since *A. aegypti* has a world-wide distribution in the tropics, there is
grave danger of the introduction of yellow fever into places where it
has not previously existed and where, because of the nonimmune condition of the people, it would become a terrible scourge.   With modern
airplane traffic the introduction of yellow fever in infected mosquitoes

into India, Malaya, or Australia from west Africa or Sudan or into North America from South America is an ever-present menace. In India reliance is placed on fumigation or spraying of boats and planes and strict quarantine of individuals coming from endemic areas; in our own country dependence is placed on fumigation, local *aegypti* control, surveillance of exposed persons, and availability of vaccine for whole populations if a case should appear. Control of *A. aegypti* in noninfected countries is important in order to lessen the danger of rapid spread if the disease *should* get in, but the South American countries, which have the jungle disease in their backyards, so to speak, cannot afford to stop short of extermination on a continental scale. Froes (1947) has outlined plans for this ambitious project. Most of Brazil and all of Bolivia has already exterminated this dangerous mosquito. It has also been virtually exterminated in Khartoum, so there is little danger now of yellow fever being carried to Egypt by Nile steamers.

Haemagogus spp. These vectors of jungle yellow fever in South America are closely related to Aëdes but have brilliantly metallic colors. They lay eggs as does Aëdes, and the larvae are very similar. In most of the species the males have short palpi like the females. Several species, especially *H. spegazzinii*, which has a wide distribution, and *H. capricornii* and *H. splendens*, which are locally distributed in Brazil, have been found naturally infected and are good transmitters experimentally. All of these breed in the bracts of aerial plants in treetops, and in the dry season they are seldom seen until a tree is cut down, whereupon they frequently buzz about in considerable numbers. *H. splendens* has its thorax and abdomen clothed in brilliant blue and green scales; *spegazzinii* and *capricornii* have the thorax brilliant green and copper and the abdomen purple and violet. Males of the last two species have never been found in nature, but those of *splendens* and others are often caught. There is no known method of control of these mosquitoes, and control of jungle yellow fever in man depends on wholesale vaccination of populations in endemic areas.

Biology of Aëdes aegypti. This mosquito is a member of the subgenus Stegomyia, which contains a group of originally tree-hole-breeding mosquitoes, several of which (e.g., *albopictus, scutellaris, pseudoscutellaris*, as well as *aegypti*) have become more or less domestic and have adopted man-made containers as breeding places. It was long known in medical literature as *Stegomyia fasciata*. It is a small black species, conspicuously marked with silvery-white on the legs and abdomen and with a white lyre-shaped design on the thorax

(Fig. 253). The female has very short palpi which are white at the tip. The wings are clear and somewhat iridescent.

Aëdes aegypti is a " pet " mosquito, as domestic as a rat or a roach. It is almost never found more than a few hundred feet from human habitations, and feeds readily on human blood. Long familiarity with man has made it an elusive pest. Its stealthy attack from behind

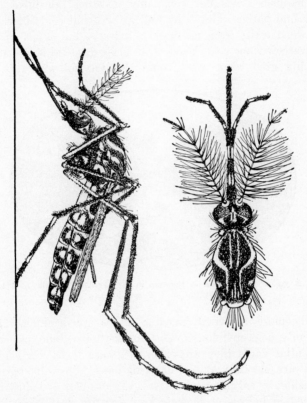

FIG. 253. *Aëdes aegypti*, ♀, and head of ♂. (After Soper.)

or under tables or desks; the suppression of its song; its habit of hiding behind pictures or under furniture; the wariness of its larvae — all these are lessons learned from long and close association with man. It is a diurnal mosquito, biting principally in the morning and late afternoon, with a siesta in the middle of the day, but it will bite at night when hungry.

Life Cycle and Breeding Places. *Aëdes aegypti* lays its eggs, after a blood meal, on the sides of a container, at or just above the water surface. A number of batches of eggs are laid, from 10 to 100 at a time, usually at intervals of 4 or 5 days, until a total of 300 to 750 has been laid over a period averaging about 6 weeks. The average length of life of the adults is about 60 to 80 days.

Aëdes aegypti has more completely forsaken its ancestral breeding places than any other mosquito, only rarely breeding in tree holes or broken bamboo stems but commonly utilizing rain-filled cocoanut shells around native villages, as well as artificial containers. It still prefers wood walls, such as those of barrels, but is also partial to earthenware or stone containers; clean glass or metal is less attractive but readily used when other containers are not available. Inside

FIG. 254. A yellow fever center in Panama in the pre-American days. (Drawn from photo from Thompson.)

houses the most important breeding places are drinking-water jars, water plants, neglected flower vases, unused toilets, and icebox drains; in residential yards they are cisterns, grease traps, tin cans, wide-mouthed jars, old tires, animal drinking pans, rain-water barrels, etc., and occasionally sagging roof gutters. In business or industrial areas they breed in barrels or buckets kept for fire protection, basement sumps, elevator pits, trash piles, etc., and in neglected spittoons. Neglected flower containers in cemeteries are a special menace. In places without a piped water supply, barrels or urns containing drinking water, tanks, and wells with wood, brick, or stone sides are important. Other places are the holy-water fonts in churches and the bilges of boats.

In the southern United States, *A. aegypti* survives the winter in the egg stage in dry containers, some even resisting freezing. Those in wet containers, as Hatchett in 1946 found in Houston, are in a precarious situation since they hatch during warm spells and are then killed later by cold spells. The larvae survive in fire barrels and other protected and more or less permanent receptacles or in large cisterns in which the water does not become too cold. These " mother foci " are also important in seeding secondary, less permanent, containers during the summer. Since this mosquito seldom flies more than a few hundred feet, although a few are often carried by cars, trains, or boats, its presence in numbers indicates a breeding place close at hand.

The eggs require several days for development of the embryo, and then they hatch within a few minutes after being submerged. Often when containers are filled with fresh drinking water, larvae appear almost at once. The eggs remain viable in the dry state for at least

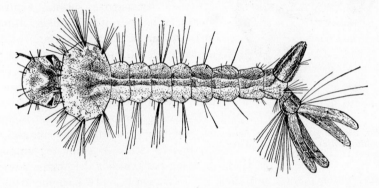

FIG. 255.   Larva of yellow fever mosquito, *Aëdes aegypti*.   × 10.
(After Howard, Dyar, and Knab.)

a year, but when wetted, all may not hatch; some may require several wettings. Hatching does not occur readily in perfectly fresh water, but it is favored by presence of bacteria. The larvae (Fig. 255), however, do not thrive in very filthy water such as *Culex quinquefasciatus* delights in, but will tolerate considerable amounts of acid, alkali, or salt.

When disturbed, even by a shadow, the larvae swim to the bottom, which they hug so closely that if a container is dumped, a large proportion of them may remain in a cupful of water that is left behind. Under favorable conditions the time from egg to egg is about 16 days — 2 to 3 for hatching, 5 to 6 for the larvae, 1½ to 2 for the pupae, and 6 to 7 before the adult lays eggs again.

Aëdes aegypti probably originated in Africa, but it has followed man to all parts of the world because of its tendency to " stow away " in boats, trains, airplanes, and automobiles. It is a permanent resident in all tropical and subtropical parts of the world and is annually carried to places far outside its permanent range. In the United States it lives through the winter in sufficient numbers to become abundant early in the season only on the Gulf Coast, but it survives in numbers sufficient to produce a good population *late* in the year in many interior cities. In the Oriental region, for some unknown reason, it does not thrive so well as three other domestic members of the Stegomyia group, *scutellaris* and *pseudoscutellaris* in the South Pacific islands, and *albopictus* in southeast Asia and Honolulu.

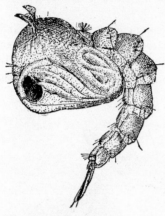

Control of Aëdes aegypti. Since this mosquito breeds almost exclusively in artificial containers, special control measures apply to it. Drainage, filling in, airplane dusting, and large-scale oiling, so useful for malarial and other ground-breeding mosquitoes, have no part in *A. aegypti* control. The principal useful methods are as follows: (1) turning "bottoms up," destroying, or removing miscellaneous containers exposed to rain; (2) emptying animal drinking pans, icebox drip pans, flower vases, water plants, spittoons, etc., frequently; (3) keeping drinking water in jars, barrels, etc., constantly covered with cloth except when dipping water; (4) sealing up, filling up, draining, or destroying unused cisterns and tanks where feasible; (5) mosquito-proofing used overhead cisterns and stocking attic or underground cisterns and wells with Gambusia; treating water in fire-protection buckets or barrels, stranded boats, etc., with larvicides; puncturing or straightening sagging roof gutters; and stocking concrete fish ponds or lily ponds with Gambusia.

Fig. 256. Pupa of yellow fever mosquito, *Aëdes aegypti*. × 10. (After Howard, Dyar, and Knab.)

For cisterns or other drinking containers where water can be drawn off from below and which for any reason cannot be mosquito-proofed, oil applied to the surface at weekly intervals is most satisfactory. For other water that cannot conveniently be disposed of, as stored rain water or water in fire barrels or buckets, stranded boats, horse troughs, cemetery urns, abandoned cisterns, flooded basements, or elevator pits, either DDT or phenothiazine is highly satisfactory. These can be applied mixed with a wetting agent (soap, detergents, flour) or wetted with 30 per cent alcohol for phenothiazine or with xylene for DDT. About 3 grams of phenothiazine or 1 gram of DDT in 50-gallon barrels prevents maturing of larvae for several months. Catch basins do not breed mosquitoes when treated with a light DDT spray and when the walls are given a residual spray.

Any *A. aegypti* campaign requires publicity in the form of pamphlets, newspaper articles, movie shorts, radio flashes, and work in schools, since public cooperation is essential to success. If extermination is the goal, it is necessary, after the breeding index is reduced to 1 per cent or less, to rely on adult catches to locate the last few hidden breeding places, which are sometimes extremely difficult to find.

Mosquitoes and Dengue

Dengue or " breakbone " fever is another virus disease (see p. 232) transmitted principally by mosquitoes of the Stegomyia group. The virus is believed to be related to that of yellow fever but differs strikingly in not attacking the liver and in producing immunity of relatively short duration, sometimes only for a season, though some instances of apparent failure of immunity is undoubtedly due to the existence of at least three different immunological strains. The disease commonly breaks out in explosive epidemics that spread with amazing rapidity and sometimes affect a high percentage of a population, especially after the disease has been absent for a number of years. Such an epidemic spread through Texas in 1922; there were estimated to have been 600,000 to 1,000,000 cases in a few months, and 70 per cent of the people in Galveston and Houston were attacked. The disease is widely distributed in all warm parts of the world — north as far as our Gulf states, the Mediterranean countries, and southern China.

The disease starts suddenly with a high fever, flushed face, and severe prostration. Often after a brief let-up there is a return of the fever and a transitory rash. Leucopenia is a marked symptom. The infection is not fatal, but there is a long convalescence. No effective vaccine is yet available for large-scale protection.

The relation of mosquitoes to dengue was first pointed out by Graham in Beirut in 1902. Ashburn and Craig in the Philippines in 1907 showed that laboratory-bred mosquitoes fed on dengue patients could transmit the disease for 3 days after the onset of the fever. Some of the earlier work incriminated the house mosquito, *Culex quinquefasciatus*, as the transmitter, but later work showed this to be an error; only *Aëdes aegypti* and other members of the Stegomyia group are known to be implicated, except a closely related form, *Armigeres obturbans*, in Formosa. In some countries there are dengue-like diseases the transmission of which is uncertain, and it is sometimes difficult to distinguish between true dengue and sandfly fever.

According to the work of Chandler and Rice, *A. aegypti* becomes infected after feeding on patients in the first to fifth days of the disease and can transmit the infection as early as 24 hours after an infective feed, but Siler *et al.* in the Philippines got different results; they found the patient to be infective for the mosquito for only 3 days, and for 6 to 18 hours prior to the onset, and they also failed to transmit the disease in less than 11 days after a mosquito had obtained an infective feed.   This incubation period was later shortened to 8 days by Schule. The only adequate explanation for these discrepant results lies in the possibility of transovarial transmission in mosquitoes and the use by Chandler and Rice of infected stock for breeding experimental mosquitoes.   The fact that papatasi fever is transovarially transmitted among sandflies makes it appear probable that this can also occur in the case of dengue and mosquitoes, in spite of some preliminary results to the contrary.   The rapid spread of dengue epidemics does not fit in well with a long incubation period in mosquitoes unless hereditary transmission is possible.   Once a mosquito becomes infective it appears to remain so for the rest of its life.

An interesting feature of the epidemiology of dengue is Usinger's (1944) observation in the Honolulu outbreak that the incidence of cases is correlated with density of human population rather than density of mosquitoes; where people are crowded a few mosquitoes suffice, but where people are scattered even dense hordes of stay-at-home mosquitoes fail to spread the disease efficiently.

Aëdes aegypti is the only important transmitter of dengue in most parts of the world, but in the Oriental region it is supplemented by two other Stegomyias closely related to each other, *albopictus* and *scutellaris* (=*variegatus*).   These have a silvery white stripe down the middle of the thorax; *scutellaris* also has two wavy white lines on the sides of the thorax whereas *albopictus* has irregular white patches instead. *A. albopictus* is widely distributed in southeast Asia and is one of the three mosquitoes that have been introduced into the Hawaiian Islands (the others are *A. aegypti* and *C. quinquefasciatus*).   In Oriental cities, however, *A. aegypti* predominates, whereas in Honolulu 75 per cent of the Stegomyias are *albopictus;* according to Usinger (1944) this was the primary vector in a dengue outbreak in Honolulu in 1943–1945. In the other Pacific islands *A. scutellaris* occurs, and both species are found in the Philippines and New Guinea, but in most of these islands *A. aegypti* is probably the most important dengue carrier.

A. albopictus and *scutellaris* have habits very much like those of *aegypti* except that, in addition to breeding in artificial containers, they also breed in axils of leaves and tree holes in jungles far from urban centers and are therefore more difficult to control and probably impossible to exterminate.

For control of *Aedes aegypti* and other container-breeding mosquitoes, see p. 692.

Mosquitoes and Filariasis

Manson's discovery in 1879 that mosquitoes serve as intermediate hosts for filariae marked the beginning of a new era in medical science; it was the first evidence of the development in the bodies of insects of organisms causing human disease. An account of the filarial worms, including the development in mosquitoes, will be found in Chapter 19, pp. 444–452. *Wuchereria bancrofti* and *W. malayi* are the only filarial infections of man known to be transmitted by mosquitoes, though some of the others undergo partial development, up to the " sausage " stage, in these insects. The species of the genus Dirofilaria which inhabit the heart and subcutaneous tissues of dogs are transmitted by mosquitoes, though not so readily as by fleas.

Transmitters of Wuchereria bancrofti. In contrast to the condition existing in malaria and yellow fever, *W. bancrofti* is not limited to one group of mosquitoes for intermediate hosts, though by no means all species of mosquitoes serve equally well as transmitters. Some fail entirely, some allow only partial development to occur, and some allow only a relatively small percentage of the ingested embryos to reach the infective stage; others, on the other hand, are too hospitable and are frequently killed by the heavy infections which develop; apparently the most critical time for the mosquitoes is during the migration of the matured larvae from breast muscles to proboscis.

Although certain species of all the main groups of mosquitoes serve as intermediate hosts, it is interesting to note that most of the successful " nurses " are the species which are particularly domestic in habit and feed mainly on human blood. The nonperiodic form of filariasis of the eastern South Pacific (see p. 450), which caused many cases among American troops in the Samoan and Fiji islands during World War II, is transmitted principally by the day-biting *Aëdes pseudoscutellaris*, a species very similar to *A. scutellaris*. This is a very efficient vector. The periodic form, found in all other parts of the world where *W. bancrofti* occurs, is most frequently transmitted in cities by *Culex quinquefasciatus* (=*fatigans*) or by the closely related *C. pipiens*. This is not because these mosquitoes are the most efficient vectors but because they are the most abundant mosquitoes. A number of species of Anopheles have been found to be better intermediate hosts than these species of Culex, and where abundant in small towns or suburbs they undoubtedly play an important role in transmission. This is true of *A. farauti* in New Guinea and the more western Pacific islands, *A. gambiae* and *funestus* in Africa, *A. darlingi* in South America, *A. hyrcanus* in China, and a number of species in India. In Japan *Aëdes togoi* has been reported as a transmitter.

Successful transmission of filariae, as of plague, depends on more than mere ability of the insects to allow development of the parasites; some of the cases of frequency of filarial infections in one locality and rarity in another not far distant, with suitable transmitting mosquitoes in both places, have not been satisfactorily explained. Undoubtedly conditions of temperature and humidity are involved. Sundar Rao, in Calcutta, found a distinct seasonal variation in the percentage of infected " wild " mosquitoes (*C. quinquefasciatus*) ranging from 3 per cent in July to 12.5 per cent in November and December. Humidity and temperature also influence the successful transfer of larvae to a host when a mosquito harboring them bites.

C. quinquefasciatus, better known in medical literature as *C. fatigans*, is the common brown house mosquito of all warm parts of the world. In America it becomes abundant in summer as far north as Washington and St. Louis. It is strictly nocturnal and will bite in complete darkness; therefore its activity supplements that of the yellow-fever mosquito, the house mosquito taking the day shift and the yellow-fever species the night shift. It is probably primarily a molester of birds, attacking man and other mammals as a second choice. It breeds in almost any standing water but prefers artificial containers and is partial to filthy water. It thrives in cesspools and open sewers. The larvae (Fig. 245*A*) have long breathing tubes and broad heads. Development from egg to adult can probably occur in 5 or 6 days under ideal conditions.

Transmitters of Wuchereria malayi. The form of filariasis caused by *Wuchereria malayi*, in contrast to *W. bancrofti* infections in most places, is strictly rural, because it is transmitted, exclusively or nearly so, by mosquitoes of the genus Mansonia. In India and Ceylon *M. annulifera* is the most important species, but in Malaya and the East Indian Islands several other species are involved (see p. 453).

Mosquitoes of the genus Mansonia differ from all others in their biology. The eggs of the tropical species are laid in clusters on the under surface of leaves of aquatic plants. The larvae have the breathing tube terminated by a spine (Fig. 249, *11*) with which they pierce the roots of the plants and draw air from them and so never come to the surface. The pupae use their breathing trumpets in a similar manner, and they, too, never rise to the surface until time of emergence.

Most of the species are found in the tropics. Some, including the important *malayi*-carrier in India, *M. annulifera,* are closely associated with the water lettuce, *Pistia stratiotes,* that grows extensively in tropical swamps. Iyengar in 1938 was able to control *malayi* infection in India by raking up and destroying this plant. In Malaya and Indo-China, however, the important *malayi*-carrying species, *M. longipalpis,* does not show this specificity but attaches itself to the roots of many plants, including swamp trees, and so is practically impossible to control.

Mosquitoes and Encephalitis

Encephalomyelitis caused by filtrable viruses has been observed in many parts of the world (see p. 232). In America horses suffer severely from the eastern and western equine strains but have only inapparent infections from the St. Louis strain, as indicated by development of virus-neutralizing antibodies. Many other mammals and also birds develop inapparent infections; after an outbreak in the Yakima Valley of Washington 50 per cent of the chickens, 25 per cent of domestic mammals and wild birds, and 18 per cent of wild mammals had virus-neutralizing antibodies in their serum for both western equine and St. Louis viruses. Human infections are not so numerous as might be expected, although there were over 1000 cases in the outbreak in St. Louis in 1933.

The disease comes on suddenly with malaise and intense headache; a continued fever reaches its peak on the third day and then gradually subsides, and there is marked drowsiness or comma. Nausea, vomiting, and convulsions are common. The fatality is 3 to 22 per cent in different outbreaks and is higher in adults. Human cases are often preceded by horse epizoötics; they usually occur in rural, irrigated areas, but occasional outbreaks occur elsewhere under conditions favoring abundant mosquitoes. The disease reaches a peak in midsummer and spreads in an erratic manner.

Numerous species of Culex and Aëdes have been shown to be capable of harboring and transmitting the viruses in the United States. *Culex tarsalis,* the only Culex in the United States with striped legs, is believed to be the most important vector in the western states. It is one of the few species not amenable to special " species eradication," since it breeds in all kinds of water, from lakes to water lying in hoof prints, and from crystal-clear water to sewage. Enormous numbers breed out from irrigation overflow water. *Aëdes vexans,* with somewhat similar habits, is an important vector in the northeast. The common *C. pipiens* is also a proved transmitter, both of the eastern equine virus in the United States and of the summer encephalitis of the Far East. In Japan and Okinawa *Culex tritaeniorhynchus* is suspected of being the vector of the Japanese B strain, which also occurs on Guam. *C. quinquefasciatus* and *C. annulirostris* can transmit this virus.

A sudden outbreak among horses and humans in Trinidad suggested introduction by invasion of salt-marsh mosquitoes from the Venezuelan coast, rather than through the medium of an infected bird.

Although mosquitoes appear to be important vectors, other means of transmission are possible. Two ticks, *Dermacentor andersoni* and *D. variabilis,* and certain bird mites (see pp. 512, 513) have been shown capable of transmitting American strains. The mites transmit the viruses transovarially and are important reservoirs of the infection. The Far East virus is said to be transovarially transmitted by mosquitoes, but the American strains seem not to be.

Mosquitoes and Dermatobia

In many parts of tropical America where the larva of a botfly, Dermatobia hominis (see p. 724), infests man and cattle, there has long

been a belief among the natives that the maggots, which develop under the skin, result from mosquito bites. Observations and experiments proved this to be true; mosquitoes normally serve as airplanes for the transportation of Dermatobia eggs to a suitable host. Occasionally when a Dermatobia is unable to find a mosquito and is under the immediate necessity of depositing eggs, she may oviposit on other captured arthropods or even on leaves.

The mosquitoes involved in nature seem to be, primarily

Fig. 257. *Psorophora* (*Janthinosoma*) *lutzii* with eggs of *Dermatobia hominis* attached to abdomen. (After Sambon.)

at least, species of Psorophora, subgenus Janthinosoma. In Central America *P. lutzii* alone has been incriminated, but in South America other species are concerned; *P. ferox* is the most frequent vector in

Colombia. *P. lutzii* (Fig. 257) is a dark, beautifully colored mosquito, with yellow markings on the thorax and with flashes of metallic violet and sky blue on its thorax and abdomen. It is said by Knab to be one of the most bloodthirsty of American mosquitoes and is found throughout tropical America. The larvae breed in rain puddles, the eggs being laid in dry depressions on the forest floor which will become basins of water after a tropical downpour. The eggs hatch almost with the first drop of rain and mature so rapidly that adult insects may emerge in 4 or 5 days. The larvae feed on vegetable matter and are themselves fed upon by their relatives of the subgenus Psorophora, which breed in the same rain pools.

Control and Extermination

Control of or protection against mosquitoes and mosquito-borne diseases may be undertaken in the following ways, in reverse order of permanent usefulness: (1) personal protection from adults, (2) destruction of adults, (3) destruction of larvae, and (4) elimination of breeding places.

Personal Protection. This method of dealing with mosquitoes has no permanent value whatever and does nothing to lessen the number of mosquitoes, but it is indispensable to the hunter or visitor in mosquito-infested places. Concerning the use of protective clothing, little need be said; the value of gloves, veils, high boots, leggings, etc., is obvious. During World War II several repellents which give protection for a number of hours were discovered and have proved a great boon where mosquitoes are a torment or where there is danger of acquiring a mosquito-borne disease. These repellents and their special uses are discussed on pp. 495–496.

Before World War II and the development of aerosol bombs and residual sprays, screening of houses to exclude mosquitoes or other insects or the use of bed nets was the first consideration in protection against mosquitoes and mosquito-borne diseases. Both are still of great importance in most situations, but there are places in this country where DDT residual spraying has proved cheaper and more effective for mosquitoes and flies, making screens actually unnecessary except to exclude light-attracted insects at night. To protect against all mosquitoes, nets should not be less than 18 meshes to the inch. Cloth net as used for bed nets is more effective than wire screen, but keeps out the breeze. When adequately screened houses or barracks are not available, the use of bed nets in places where mosquito-borne diseases are prevalent is essential, and care must be taken to see that they are tightly closed and not in contact with sleepers.

Destruction of Adults. The spraying of human habitations with insecticides at regular intervals has long been recognized as a valuable aid against malaria (see p. 210), but the development of the aerosol bomb (see p. 493) greatly increased its effectiveness. Spraying was of inestimable value during military operations in malaria-ridden areas. The most important development, however, has been residual spraying with DDT (see p. 210 and p. 493). Application with power sprayers of an emulsion of DDT at such a rate as to leave 200 mg. of DDT per square foot is effective for periods up to 3 to 4 months in destroying practically all mosquitoes and almost all other insects resting on the sprayed surfaces. Although not truly repellent, the DDT causes mosquitoes to become restless soon after coming in contact with it, so that they lose interest in feeding and leave the house; most of them die. The effect is slow but sure. This method of protection against mosquitoes has been applied with sensational success in many parts of the world. It is most effective, of course, for species that tend to roost inside houses. In California marked reduction in numbers of Anopheles has been obtained by spraying hibernating places during the winter.

Outdoor destruction of adult mosquitoes is possible with an aerosol generator vaporizing a mixture of equal parts of water and 10 per cent DDT in oil; 15 gallons per 1000 ft. of front kills adults up to a mile downwind under favorable conditions and up to 1000 ft. in forests, and will kill larvae for about 2000 and 1000 ft., respectively.

Destruction of Larvae. The classical methods of destroying mosquito larvae in their breeding places have been (1) oiling, (2) application of emulsified larvicides, (3) Paris green dusting (for Anopheles only), (4) clearing of brush and floating vegetation to permit fish, particularly Gambusia, to reach the larvae and devour them, and (5) fluctuation of water level. The choice of method or methods depends, of course, on local conditions. The first three methods have been discussed on p. 494.

The larvicide used most extensively now is DDT solution or emulsion. In laboratory tests 1 part of DDT to 30 million parts of water is enough to kill mosquito larvae, though it takes 50 hours; 1 ppm. kills them all in an hour. If evenly distributed, 1 lb. of DDT would be enough to kill 95 to 100 per cent of Anopheles larvae on 1000 acres. The usually recommended dosage for practical work is 0.1 or 0.2 lb. of DDT per acre in the form of a 5 per cent solution in oil or a 5 per cent suspension. This requires 1 to 2 qt. per acre as compared with 15 to 35 qt. of diesel oil. From boats, as little as 0.03 lb. per acre in a 2.5 per cent solution in kerosene gives a 90 per cent kill. From planes the application can be made in 200-foot swaths; 1 ton of DDT will go 18 miles. Spraying of 0.4 to 0.8 lb. per acre in 4 to 8 qt. of liquid, even over heavy jungle, gives 99 per cent reduction of both adults and larvae within 24 hours. In one experiment, 10,000 Anopheles were caught in a horse trap before spraying, and released; 24 hours after spraying one adult was caught, and no larvae were dipped where previously there had been 10 or 12 per dipper. With larger dosages residual effects for two or three weeks can be obtained.

At dosages of 0.1 lb. per acre there is no danger to fish, but above 0.2 lb. many fish are killed. No harmful effect on birds or mammals has been observed from recommended dosages.

In treating catch basins, cesspools, sewer inlets, etc., a residual effect good for several months can be obtained by spraying the side walls. For a sewage farm, application of 8 oz. of a 25 per cent emulsion every day or two to the water in the main pipeline did the work of spraying 75 to 100 gallons of diesel oil. By treating a main irrigation ditch with a few gallons of emulsion applied slowly over a period of an hour or so, larvae were killed for distances of many miles; in one case no larvae were found in 100 miles of irrigation canals where previously 3 to 17 *A. freeborni* larvae per dip were obtained. Such an operation would have required 4000 gallons of diesel oil, several men, and a large spray rig for a week.

Natural Enemies. Certain kinds of fish are of very great value in control of mosquito larvae in natural waters. The viviparous *Gambusia affinis* (Fig. 258), widely distributed in southeastern United States and extensively introduced elsewhere, is one of the most valuable species because of its hardiness, ability to live in fresh, brackish, or foul water, and rapid multiplication. The edges of bayous, streams, ponds, etc., should be cleaned, and water weeds, floatage, and overhanging brush removed to allow the fish to operate freely in pursuit of the larvae; frequently no other control is necessary. Modern weedkillers such as 2,4-D are often helpful. Goldfish may keep lily ponds free if the mosquitoes do not breed more rapidly than the fish can eat them. In salt marshes, various species of killifish (Fundulus) are potent factors in destroying mosquito larvae. Great reduction in mosquito output can be obtained by draining marshes in such a way that the fish can get access to most parts of them. If swamps are converted into pools in their deepest parts, fish can sometimes control the mosquito output. Gambusia can be used to advantage in cisterns and exposed wells. Many southern cities have hatcheries for these fish to supply them to citizens who have use for them. Other natural enemies can sometimes be exploited in a similar manner.

In reservoirs it has been found very helpful in controlling mosquito breeding to fluctuate the water level at suitable intervals. When the level is lowered great numbers of larvae are stranded and die; when it is raised, fish can get easy access to larvae that were developing near the lower shore line.

The western newt or water dog, *Triturus torosus*, was shown by the writer to be a valuable natural enemy on the Pacific Coast, and it can

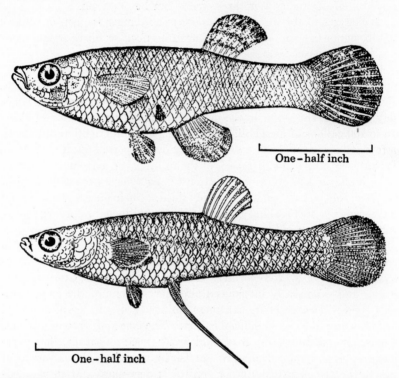

One-half inch

One-half inch

FIG. 258. *Gambusia affinis*, a voracious, mosquito-eating top minnow, useful for stocking ponds, cisterns, wells, etc. (After Jordan and Evermann.)

be utilized in such receptacles as barrels and troughs. Matheson has made similar observations on the eastern newt. Many other water inhabitants attack mosquito larvae or eggs, including predaceous beetles, bugs, mites, snails, and even ducks, so it is not desirable, when it can be avoided, to kill such life while attempting to kill mosquito larvae.

A number of aquatic plants are inimical to mosquito larvae for one reason or another, Chara apparently by producing a high oxygen content of the water, the bladderwort, Utricularia, by capturing the larvae in its traplike bladders, and surface-covering plants such as

Lemna (duckweed) by preventing the larvae from getting access to air.

Many birds, especially nighthawks, swifts, and swallows, feed actively on adult mosquitoes. Bats have been exploited as mosquito destroyers, and municipal bat roosts have actually been erected in San Antonio and recommended for other places, but scientific investigation has not substantiated the extravagant claims made for the efficiency of bats as mosquito destroyers. In the tropics wall lizards or geckos and jumping spiders destroy numbers of mosquitoes in dwellings.

Fig. 259. One of the first places to clean up in a mosquito campaign. A favorite breeding place for such annoying or dangerous species as the yellow fever mosquito; *Aëdes aegypti;* the house mosquitoes, *Culex pipiens* and *C. quinquefasciatus; Anopheles quadrimaculatus;* and others.

Elimination of Breeding Places. The only permanent method of control of mosquitoes is to eliminate the breeding places entirely wherever possible. The application of this method to container-breeding mosquitoes was discussed on p. 692.

Drainage is often practicable as a means of eliminating breeding places. Not only must small pools of standing water be eliminated but also the drains themselves must be made unsuitable for breeding. Sometimes other methods of control, such as filling in of depressions or protection of swamps by means of levees, dikes, or tide gates are more practicable. Drainage ditches with narrow bottoms, the sides of which are kept clean and straight, preferably by cement or board walls, are the best means of draining borrow pits, swampy depressions in streams, or outcrops of seepage water. Seepage water outcrops are the most difficult and often have to be drained by ditches which more or less follow the contours, ultimately connecting with main ditches leading away. Lined ditches cost more to build but are more permanent, more easily kept clean, and cheaper in the long run.

Subsoil drainage by means of tile or pipe is often necessary; in the Malayan hills Watson got wonderful results by thus draining ravines where *A. maculatus* breeds, and excellent results have been obtained from this method in Panama also. In some places effective drainage has been obtained by packing drains or tributaries of ravines with tree trunks and branches and a top covering of grass. Where water is held at the surface by an impervious stratum overlying a pervious one vertical drainage may be successful, by drilling holes through which the water can flow down to the deeper pervious strata. Salt marshes may be drained by appropriately placed drains averaging 200 to 300 ft. to the acre, the method successfully used by Headlee in New Jersey, with filling in of parts which cannot be so drained; the falling of the tide carries the water out of the ditches. When the tide is insufficient to do this, engineering projects of diking with tide gates or pumps must be resorted to. In some places dams and automatic siphons, to flush streams in the dry season when pools form in their beds, have been found useful.

Periodic draining of ponds and rice fields results in a great reduction in number of Anopheles larvae. In south India cycles of 5 wet days followed by 2 to 4 dry days were found to be highly effective in controlling *A. culicifacies* prior to the rainy season, when it no longer breeds actively in the rice fields. Enough dry days are required to dry the surface but not to crack the soil. In California 10-day intervals between drying have been employed, and in Portugal 16 days. For some of the most dangerous Anopheles, e.g., *A. gambiae* and *A. albimanus*, mere shading of streams or ponds to exclude sunlight is all that is necessary. In the case of *A. ludlowi*, on the other hand, *removal* of shade is the most effective control measure. In Trinidad, *A. bellator*, which breeds in epiphytic plants growing on immortelle trees, has been controlled by spraying the trees with 0.5 per cent copper sulfate to kill the plants; no regeneration of the plants has occurred for 10 years.

REFERENCES

AITKEN, T. H. G., Studies on the Anopheline Complex of Western North America, *Univ. Calif. Pub. Entomol.*, **7**, No. 11, 273, 1945.

AM. ASSOC. ADVANCEMENT SCI., A Symposium on Human Malaria, with Special Reference to North America and the Caribbean Region, Pub. 15, Section III, Anopheline Vectors, pp. 63–130, 1941.

BARBER, M. A., and RICE, J. B., Methods of Dissecting and Making Permanent Preparations of the Salivary Glands and Stomachs of Anopheles, *Am. J. Hyg.*, **24**, 32 (1936).

Boyd, M. F., *et al.*, Studies on the Bionomics of North American Anopheles, I–V, *Am. J. Hyg.*, **7**, 264; **9**, 346, 682; **12**, 449; *J. Preventive Med.*, **2**, 219 (1927–1929).

Brescia, F., Salt Marsh and Anopheline Mosquito Control by Ground Dispersal of DDT Aerosols, *J. Econ. Entomol.*, **39**, 698–715 (1946).

Burgess, R. W., Pigmentation as a Specific Character in Certain Anopheline Pupae, *J. Natl. Mal. Soc.*, **5**, 189–191 (1946).

California Mosquito Control Association, *Proc. and Papers 14th Ann. Conf.*, various authors (1946).

Chandler, A. C., Factors Influencing the Uneven Distribution of *Aëdes aegypti* in Texas Cities, *Am. J. Trop. Med.*, **25**, 145–149 (1945).

Cutkomp, L. K., Residual Sprays to Control *Anopheles quadrimaculatus*, *J. Econ. Entomol.*, **40**, 329–333 (1947).

Ferguson, F. F., Upholt, W. M., and Simmons, S. W.   A Summary of the Experimental Use of DDT as a Mosquito Larvicide, *J. Natl. Mal. Soc.*, **8**, 32–49 (1949).

Fróes, H. P., Plan for the Continental Campaign for the Eradication of the Aëdes aegypti (English summary of Spanish paper), *Bol. oficina sanit. panamer.*, **26**, 848–851 (1947).

Hackett, L. W., The Present Status of Our Knowledge of the Subspecies of *A. maculipennis, Trans. Roy. Soc. Trop. Med. Hyg.*, **28**, 109 (1934).

Hackett, L. W., Russell, P. F., Scharff, J. W., and Senior-White, R., The Present Use of Naturalistic Measures in the Control of Malaria, *League Nations Bull. Health Organisation*, **7**, 1016 (1938).

Hammon, W. McD., Encephalitis. Eastern and Western Equine and St. Louis Types as Observed in 1941 in Washington, Arizona, New Mexico, and Texas, *J. Am. Med. Assoc.*, **121**, 560 (1943).

Herms, W. B., and Gray, H. F., *Mosquito Control*, 2nd ed., Commonwealth Fund, New York, 1944.

Hinman, E. H., Biological Effects of Fluctuation of Water Level on Anopheline breeding, *Am. J. Trop. Med.*, **18**, 483 (1938).

Hinman, E. H., and Cutkomp, L. K., Block Residual Spraying of Premises with DDT for the Control of Malaria, *Am. J. Trop. Med.*, **27**, 449–461 (1947).

Howard, L. O., Dyar, H. G., and Knab, F., The Mosquitoes of North and Central America and the West Indies, *Carnegie Inst. Wash. Pub.*, **159**, Vols. I–V, 1912–1917.

Hunter, G. W., Welles, T. H., and Jahnes, W. G., Jr., An Outline for Teaching Mosquito Stomach and Salivary Gland Dissection, *Am. J. Trop. Med.*, **26**, 221–228 (1948).

King, W. B., Bradley, G. H., and McNeel, T. E., The Mosquitoes of the Southeastern States, *U. S. Dept. Agr. Misc. Pub.*, **386**, 1939.

Komp, W. H. W., A Technique for Staining, Dissecting, and Mounting the Male Terminalia of Mosquitoes, *Publ. Health Repts.*, **57**, 1327–1333 (1942).

Kumm, H. W., Osorno-Mesa, E., and Boshell-Manrique, J., Studies on Mosquitoes of the Genus Haemagogus in Colombia, *Am. J. Hyg.*, **43**, 13–28 (1946).

Matheson, R., *The Mosquitoes of North America*, Springfield, Ill., 1929.

Metcalf, R. L., Hess, A. D., Smith, G. E., Jeffrey, G. M., and Ludwig, G. L., Observations on the Use of DDT for the Control of *Anopheles quadrimaculatus, Publ. Health Repts.*, **60**, 753–774 (1945).

Penn, G. H., The Larval Development and Ecology of *Aëdes (Stegomyia) scutellaris* (Walker, 1859) in New Guinea, *J. Parasitol.*, **33**, 43–50 (1947).

Pupae of the Nearctic Anopheline Mosquitoes North of Mexico, *J. Natl. Mal. Soc.*, **8**, 50–69 (1949).

Ross, E. S., and Roberts, H. R., Mosquito Atlas, Parts I and II, American Entomological Society, Philadelphia, 1943.

Russell, P. F., Rozeboom, L. E., and Stone, A., Keys to the Anopheline Mosquitoes of the World, American Entomological Society, Philadelphia, 1943.

Shannon, R. C., and Putnam, P., The Biology of Stegomyia under Laboratory Conditions, *Proc. Entomol. Soc. Wash.*, **36**, 185, 217 (1934).

Soper, F. L., and Wilson, D. B., *Anopheles gambiae* in Brazil, 1930–1940, Rockefeller Foundation, 1943.

Species Eradication. A Practical Goal of Species Reduction in the Control of Mosquito-Borne Disease, *J. Natl. Mal. Soc.*, **1**, 5–24 (1942).

Taylor, R. M., and Fonseca da Cunha, J., An Epidemiological Study of Jungle Yellow Fever in an Endemic Area in Brazil, Pt. I, Epidemiology of Human Infections; and Laemmert, H. W., Ferreira, L. de C., and Taylor, R. M., Pt. II, Investigation of Vertebrate Hosts and Arthropod Vectors, *Am. J. Trop. Med.*, **26**, Suppl., 1–69 (1946).

Taylor, R. M., and Theiler, M., *The Epidemiology of Yellow Fever, Proc. 4th Intern. Congr. Trop. Med. and Malaria*, **1**, Sect. IV, 506–519, 1948.

Usinger, R. L., Entomological Phases of the Recent Dengue Epidemic in Honolulu, *Publ. Health Repts.*, **59**, 423–430 (1944).

Waddell, M. B., and Taylor, R. M., Studies on the Cyclic Passage of Yellow Fever Virus in South American Mammals and Mosquitoes, I, *Am. J. Trop. Med.*, **25**, 225–230 (1945); II, *ibid*, **26**, 455–463 (1946); III, *ibid*, **27**, 471–476 (1947); IV, *ibid*, **28**, 87–100 (1948).

See also References under various transmitted diseases.

CHAPTER 28

Diptera

III. FLY MAGGOTS AND MYIASIS

Disgusting as it may seem, man and animals are attacked not only by the numerous adult flies discussed in the last two chapters but also by the maggots or larval stages of many species of flies. Such an infestation by fly maggots is called myiasis. Nearly all cases are caused by larvae of flies of the suborder Cyclorrhapha (see p. 639). Exceptions are a few reported cases of infestation of the skin by a scale insect; of sinuses by the larvae of carpet beetles; and of the rectum by adult dung beetles.

The flies most frequently concerned in myiasis belong to two large groups, the Muscoidea (see p. 640) and the botflies. The latter are committed to parasitic life in the larval stage, and live for a very short time, probably not feeding at all, in the adult stage. Their mouthparts are reduced to mere vestiges. Many of the Muscoidea, on the other hand, are a nuisance in the adult stage as blood suckers or germ carriers, but some, such as the screwworms and the African tumbu fly, have to be reckoned with as important parasites in the larval stage, and a few, such as the housefly, may cause trouble in *both* stages. Many Muscoidea belonging to the families Calliphoridae and Sarcophagidae, commonly called blowflies or fleshflies, have maggots that feed on dead flesh, and it is not surprising that some of these should have adapted themselves to entering wounds and feeding on living flesh, e.g., the screwworms, or to developing in the foul-smelling soiled wool of sheep and attacking the skin underneath, e.g., the wool maggots.

Identification. Identification of full-grown larvae causing myiasis is usually not difficult so far as the genera are concerned, but accurate determination of species often requires breeding them out. The most important characteristics used for identification are the respiratory openings at the anterior and posterior ends of the abdomen (Fig. 261). The posterior openings consist of two stigmal plates; these are hardened, dark-colored, eyelike spots, in most species surrounded by a chitinized ring and a buttonlike mark, though in some of the Oestridae the whole plate is chitinized. On the plates the spiracular openings are

707

usually in the form of three slits, which may be straight, bent, or looped. The position and shape of the plates, the development of the ring and button, and the form of the slits are of great value in identification.

First-stage maggots are recognizable as such by the absence of anterior spiracles and posterior spiracular plates, but the genera and species are difficult to identify. Second-stage maggots are also difficult to identify; in the muscoid group they are recognizable as such by the presence of two instead of three spiracular slits.

Following are keys to the principal myiasis-producing adult flies and their larvae, including a few forms most likely to be confused with them, but not including adults of those only occasionally found in human feces.

Adult Myiasis-producing Flies

I. **MUSCOIDEA** (Muscidae, Calliphoridae, and Sarcophagidae). Eyes large (Fig. 262), touching or nearly so in ♂; proboscis well developed.

1*a*. Color metallic blue or green; **Calliphoridae** ....2.

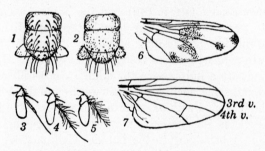

FIG. 260. Details of structure of myiasis-producing flies to illustrate key. *1*, Thorax of a Lucilia, dorsal view, showing well-developed bristles in median two rows on mesonotum, and hairless alulae. *2*, Thorax of *Callitroga americana*, dorsal view, showing absence of bristles in median two rows except at hind end of mesonotum, and hairy alulae. *3*, Antenna of Wohlfartia, with naked arista. *4*, Antenna of Sarcophaga, with arista feathered on basal half. *5*, Antenna of *Callitroga*, with arista feathered to tip. *6*, Wing of *Gastrophilus intestinalis*, showing straight fourth vein not reaching margin, and spotting of wing. *7*, Wing of Fannia, showing straight fourth vein. Compare fourth vein in Figs. 261 and 262.

1*b*. Color gray or yellowish with dark markings; **Sarcophagidae** ....4.

1*c*. Color yellowish brown; **African Calliphoridae** ....5.

2*a*. Bristles on mesonotum mostly wanting (Fig. 260, *2*); blue or greenish blue; face golden or orange-red; palpi short; antennae feathered to tip (Fig. 260, *5*) ....*Callitroga* and in old world, *Chrysomyia.*

2*b*. Bristles well developed on mesonotum (Fig. 260, *1*) ....3.

3*a*. Small; green or coppery; face silver; alulae bare (Fig. 260, *1*) *Phoenicia.*

3*b*. Large; blue; face red or golden; alulae hairy ....*Calliphora.*

3*c*. Larger; bluish black; face black ....*Phormia.*

4*a*. Abdomen yellowish basally, dark at apex, with longitudinal dark stripe;

proboscis fleshy ....*Musca.*
(1) Similar but more slender; fourth wing vein straight, not curving
    up towards third (Fig. 260, 7) ....*Fannia.*
4b. Abdomen checkered gray and black; arista feathered except at tip
    (Fig. 260, 4) ....*Sarcophaga.*
4c. Abdomen gray spotted with black; arista bare (Fig. 260, 3)..*Wohlfartia.*
5a. Abdominal segments all about equal (Fig. 265) ....*Cordylobia.*
5b. Second abdominal segment of ♂ elongated (Fig. 262); third abdominal
    segment of ♀ indented ....*Aucheromyia.*
II. **BOTFLY GROUP (Gastrophilidae, Cuterebridae, and Oestridae).** Eyes
small, widely separated (Figs. 270, 272); proboscis greatly reduced or
absent.
  1a. Body not markedly hairy; proboscis small, in pit; arista feathered on
    one side ....Cuterebridae.
    (1) Body blue, wings brown; tropical American skin maggot of cattle
      and man (Fig. 270) ....*Dermatobia.*
    (2) Body moderately hairy, black and white; anal vein poorly devel-
      oped; skin maggots of rodents and cats ....*Cuterebra.*
  1b. Body hairy, beelike ....2.
  2a. Abdomen elongated; fourth vein of wing straight, not extending to
    margin of wing (Fig. 260, 6) (horse bots) ....Gastrophilidae.
    (1) Abdomen brown, tipped with red (Fig. 273, 4) ....
    .... *Gastrophilus haemorrhoidalis.*
    (2) Abdomen light at each end with black band in middle; wings not
      spotted ....*Gastrophilus nasalis.*
    (3) Abdomen brown, dirty white at base; wings spotted (Fig. 260, 6)
    .... *Gastrophilus intestinalis.*
  2b. Abdomen short, rounded; fourth vein of wing curved forward at tip,
    sometimes closing first posterior cell (Fig. 272); mouthparts vestigial;
    arista bare; **Oestridae** ....3.
  3a. Middle part of face narrow; color dirty or grayish ....*Oestrus.*
  3b. Middle part of face broad; color mainly blackish ....*Hypoderma.*
    (1) Apex of abdomen orange; thorax not distinctly striped ....*H. bovis.*
    (2) Apex of abdomen lemon-yellow; light lines on thorax ....*H. lineata.*

Full-grown Larvae of Myiasis-producing Flies

I. Larvae cylindrical, tapering anteriorly (Figs. 231, 262); fairly smooth, without conspicuous colored spines; skin not leathery; stigmal plates separated,
well chitinized, with 3 spiracular slits **(MUSCOIDEA).**
  1a. Chitinous ring completely encircles plate; button well developed......2.
  1b. Chitinous ring incomplete; button region poorly chitinized ....5.
  2a. Two mouth hooks; slits straight, or oval and only slightly bent ......3.
  2b. One mouth hook; slits S-shaped or in loops ....4.
  3a. Button enclosed in ring; slits straight, elongate, directed inward and
    downward (often nearly horizontal in *Calliphora*) (Fig. 261) ......
    ....*Calliphora, Lucilia,* and *Phoenicia.*
  3b. Button inside ring; slits oval, may be slightly bent (Fig. 261)..*Muscina.*
  4a. Slits have several loops; stigmal plates D-shaped, close together (Fig.
    261) ....*Musca.*

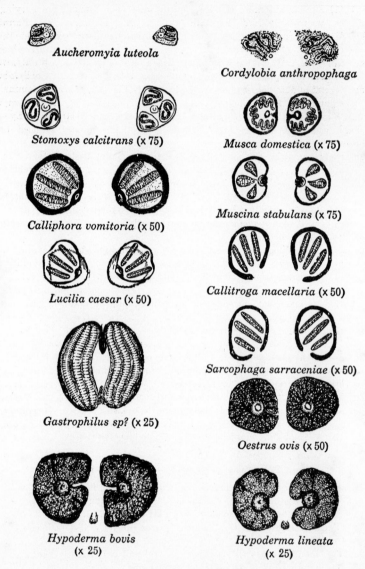

Aucheromyia luteola

Cordylobia anthropophaga

Stomoxys calcitrans (x 75)

Musca domestica (x 75)

Calliphora vomitoria (x 50)

Muscina stabulans (x 75)

Lucilia caesar (x 50)

Callitroga macellaria (x 50)

Gastrophilus sp? (x 25)

Sarcophaga sarraceniae (x 50)

Oestrus ovis (x 50)

Hypoderma bovis
(x 25)

Hypoderma lineata
(x 25)

Fɪɢ. 261. Stigmal plates and spiracular openings of various maggots. Note distance apart of opposite stigmal plates, form and position of spiracles, presence or absence of button, etc.

4*b*. Slits S-shaped and well separated; stigmal plates separated by nearly twice their diameter (Fig. 261) ....***Stomoxys.***

5*a*. Stigmata in pits surrounded by fleshy tubercles (Fig. 267); slits vertical, the first one often directed downward and outward......**Sarcophagidae.**

5*b*. Stigmata not in pits ....6.

6*a*. Large break in ring; no definite button (Fig. 261); posterior margin of eleventh segment without dorsal spines ....***Callitroga.***

    (1) Main tracheae large, pigmented (Fig. 264) ....*C. americana.*

    (2) Main tracheae small, not pigmented (Fig. 264) ....*C. macellaria.*

6*b*. Ring often nearly complete, but no definite button ....***Chrysomyia.***

6*c*. A weakly chitinized button present....***Phormia;*** in birdnests..***Apaulina.***

II. Larvae leathery, usually more or less flattened, not tapering from posterior to anterior end; often with conspicuous, colored spines (bots).

1*a*. Body with rings of large, dark spines (Fig. 273, 5); stigmal plates in contact, each with 3 bent slits (Fig. 261) (horse bots) ....***Gastrophilus.***

1*b*. Body entirely covered with black spines; stigmal plates with 3 convoluted spiracles spread laterally, converging medially to lower inner angle; in skin of rodents and cats ....***Cuterebra.***

1*c*. Body not as above ....2.

2*a*. Stigmal plates with 3 slits in each ....3.

2*b*. Stigmal plates solid, with numerous small openings ....5.

3*a*. Body with last segment retractile; anterior end large; cuticle sparsely studded with dark spines; stigmal plates close together; slits slightly bent (tropical American skin maggot) (Fig. 271) ....***Dermatobia.***

3*b*. Stigmal plates well separated ....4.

4*a*. Plates very poorly developed, less than their own width apart, the slits crooked (Fig. 261); body studded with small yellow spines (African skin maggot) ....***Cordylobia.***

4*b*. Plates small, very far apart, the slits horizontal (Fig. 261); rings of small spines on body (African bloodsucking maggot) ....***Aucheromyia.***

5*a*. Button well inside plate (Fig. 261); body with rows of strong spines on ventral side; in nostrils and other parts of head of sheep ....***Oestrus.***

5*b*. Button on inner margin of plate; in nostrils of horses ......***Rhinoestrus.***

5*c*. Button in median indentation of plate (Fig. 261); no conspicuous spines; in skin of cattle (Fig. 272) ....***Hypoderma.***

    (1) Plates kidney-shaped (Fig. 261); no spines on last segment....
.... *H. lineata.*

    (2) Plates deeply indented; no spines on last 2 segments ......*H. bovis.*

III. Larvae of odd types occasionally found in feces.

1. Large, flat, dark-colored, 11-segmented, with distinct head (a member of the soldier-fly family, Stratiomyidae) (Fig. 268*D*)...*Hermetia illucens.*

2. Cylindrical, with long tail-like process (rat-tailed maggot, member of family Syrphidae) (Fig. 268*C*)...............................***Eristalis.***

3. Small larvae with spiracles on tubercles; acalyptrate flies of families Piophilidae, Drosophilidae, etc. (cheese skippers, fruit flies, etc.) (Fig. 268*B*).

4. Flattened, with fleshy processes (Fig. 268*E*) ....***Fannia.***

Types of Myiasis. Maggots attack their hosts in a number of different ways. The Muscoidea group includes maggots that (1) suck blood; (2) invade wounds and natural cavities (nose, ear, etc.); (3) attack skin under soiled wool, causing "strike" in sheep; (4) live in boils under the skin; and (5) live in or pass through the intestine or urinary tract. The botfly group includes species that (1) live in boil-like lesions in the skin; (2) cause warbles in the skin of cattle; (3) attack the nasal passages, sinuses, or other parts of the head of domestic animals or deer; and (4) live in the stomach or rectum of horses. Each of these will be briefly considered below.

Muscoid Maggots

1. Bloodsucking Maggots

A number of species of flies allied to the blowflies deposit their offspring in the nests of birds, where the maggots attach themselves to the nestlings and suck blood. In northern United States and Canada, species of Apaulina, and in the Old World, Protocalliphora, have this habit. Hole-nesting passerine birds and hawks suffer most.

The only larva that sucks blood by puncturing the skin of man is the Congo floor maggot, *Aucheromyia luteola*, found throughout tropical Africa south of the Sahara Desert. Its range closely coincides with that of the Negro and Bantu races of men; it does not occur in countries inhabited by Arabs and Berbers.

The adult fly (Fig. 262*A*) is related to the blowflies but is a dirty yellowish brown with the tip of the abdomen rusty black. The adults resemble those of Cordylobia in general appearance (see key, p. 709, and Fig. 265). They are seldom found far from human dwellings. The female lays her 30 to 80 eggs in dust or debris in shady places, especially on the floors of native huts, where they hatch within 2 days. Within 4 or 5 hours the larvae are ready to suck blood but can live nearly a month without food, remaining buried an inch or so in the dust of floors. The whole life cycle, from egg to egg, takes about 1½ months under favorable conditions.

The leathery-skinned maggots (Fig. 262*B*) when unfed are dirty white and somewhat flattened, but after filling up on blood they are dark brown and plump. They have powerful mouth hooks for piercing skin and sucking blood. The maggots, sometimes 100 or more in a hut, lie buried in dust under sleeping mats in the daytime and come forth at night to suck blood from the sleepers; the bites are not very irritating.

The Congo floor maggot is not known to attack any animals but man in nature, though a closely allied maggot, Choeromyia, lives in the burrows of the wart hog and other hairless mammals. Its bite is more painful to man than that of the normal human parasite.   The attacks of the floor maggot can easily be avoided by sleeping on mats or beds raised just a few inches from the ground.

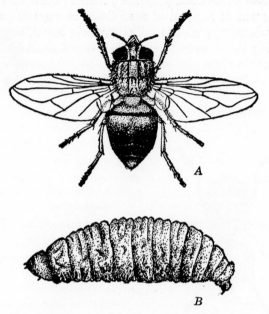

A

B

FIG. 262.   Congo floor maggot and adult fly, *Aucheromyia luteola.*
A, × 3; *B,* × 4.   (After Manson.)

2. Myiasis of Wounds and Natural Cavities (Screwworms)

Secondary Invaders.   A large number of flies belonging to the muscoid group, which normally deposit their larvae in decaying flesh of dead animals, occasionally, probably more or less by accident, deposit their eggs or larvae in neglected wounds or sores when offensive discharges are exuding from them.   Included in this group are many blue, green, or coppery-colored species of Calliphoridae belonging to the genera Calliphora, Phoenicia, Phormia, Callitroga, Chrysomyia, and others, and gray and black Sarcophagidae of the genera Sarcophaga and Wohlfarti (see key on p. 728).   There are, however, a small number of species which are *commonly* found as secondary invaders of wounds.   These include *Callitroga macellaria, Phormia regina,* several species of Phoenicia and Lucilia, and one or two species of Sarcophaga in this country, and *Chrysomyia megacephala* in the Orient.   A number of species deposit their eggs in befouled wool of sheep and later invade the body (see p. 718).

The secondary invaders are not primarily attracted by living tissue but only by decomposed tissue or other decaying matter such as would be found in a dead animal. For this reason, and because their excretions have bactericidal properties, some of them were extensively used as a means of removal of dead tissue in cases of osteomyelitis, before the advent of penicillin. The maggots would, however, attack healthy living tissue when dead tissue was not available, as Stewart demonstrated in 1934 in the case of the supposedly exclusively saprophagous *Phoenicia sericata,* which has been widely used as a "surgical maggot."

Primary Invaders (Screwworms). Of far greater significance are three species which deposit their eggs on fresh wounds of living animals and feed primarily upon the living tissues. They do not deposit their eggs on the unbroken skin but require only an insignificant wound or scratch, very often a tick bite. Apparently the odor of fresh blood is attractive to them. They are also attracted by the odors emanating from diseased natural cavities of the body and may oviposit in the external ear, mouth, nose, eye, or vagina, whence they penetrate to the middle ear, sinuses, or other parts of the body. Severe infestations in man may lead to a loathsome and horrible death.

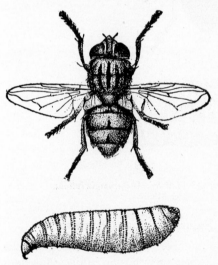

FIG. 263. Screwworm fly, *Callitroga americana,* adult and maggot. × 3. (Adult after Castellani and Chalmers, larva after Blanchard.)

As already noted only three species of flies are known *normally* to attack living animals in this manner and to feed on living flesh. These are the American screwworm fly, *Callitroga americana;* the Old World screwworm, *Chrysomyia bezziana,* of southern Asia and South Africa; and *Wohlfartia magnifica* of eastern Europe.

Callitroga americana. It was not until 1933 that this highly injurious fly, long known as *Cochliomyia americana,* was differentiated from a very close relative, *C. macellaria,* by Cushing and Patton. The adult flies are so much alike that they cannot be distinguished except by details of the genitalia, but the maggots show easily recognizable differences (see key, p. 711, and Fig. 264). *C. macellaria* commonly breeds in carcasses and only secondarily invades foul-smelling wounds (often those left by the other species), but *C. americana* is a true parasite. It only rarely lays its eggs in dead meat, although in the laboratory it will do so if the meat is at body temperature. Like other maggots that feed on living tissue, those of *C. americana* have the floor of the pharynx smooth, whereas in all carrion-feeding larvae the pharynx has longitudinal ridges, though nobody knows why.

Much of the recorded biology of screwworms up to 1933 really applies to *C. macellaria*, for *americana* is rarely caught in carcass traps but *macellaria* commonly is. The parasitic species occurs from the Gulf Coast states to Argentina and at least occasionally gets north to Kansas. It normally survives the winter south of 30 deg. N. lat., but in cold winters only in small areas in Arizona, southern Texas, and Florida.

It does not survive when the mean daily temperature falls below 49° F. for 3 months or 53° F. for 5 months; adults are killed below 20°, and pupae at 15° F. It has no true hibernation. It survives in wounds or in soil in warm winter weather and is shipped north with infested cattle in the spring. Since its pupae are adversely affected by moisture in the soil, it rarely establishes itself where the rainfall exceeds 4 or 5 inches a month.

The adult screwworm flies (Fig. 263) are large, handsome, greenish blue flies with orange-red faces and eyes (see key, p. 708). The eggs number from 150 to over 300 but are not all laid in one wound. The incubation period is longer than that of *C. macellaria* and is seldom less than 12 hours. The larvae (Fig. 263) are whitish with bands of minute spines; they can be distinguished from the larvae of *C. macellaria* by the much larger spiracles and large, heavily chitinized main tracheal tubes (Fig. 264). Eating away at flesh and even bone, they grow to a length of 12 to 15 mm. when mature; they then spontaneously leave the animals, bury themselves in loose earth, and pupate. When infested animals die, the larvae leave within 48 hours and pupate under or within a foot of the carcass in the upper half-inch of soil. In experimental guinea pigs the maggots regularly mature and leave a wound on the fifth or sixth day. The pupal period is 7 to 9 days in summer but may be prolonged to 10 or 12 weeks in winter. *C. macellaria* may complete its whole life cycle in 9 or 10 days, but *C. americana* is slower, requiring from 18 to 22 days in summer weather.

Although screwworms affect cattle, sheep, and goats most frequently, in 1935 there were over 100 human cases in the southern United States. In man the commonest site of infestation is the nose, whence the sinuses and nasopharynx are invaded, but the mouth, eyes, ears, vagina, and wounds are also attacked. Halitosis seems to be an attraction to screwworm flies as

well as a repellent to romance, though the magazine advertisements have neglected to mention it. Sometimes Dermatobia lesions, boils, etc., are invaded, though more frequently by saprophagous species.

The damage done may be very extensive and is not

FIG. 264.   Posterior ends of *Callitroga macellaria* (left) and *C. americana* (right), ventral view.   Note large, heavily chitinized, dark trachea of *C. americana* and small, slightly chitinized, uncolored trachea of *C. macellaria*.

infrequently fatal. Reports of 179 cases compiled by Aubertin and Buxton show that 15, or 8 per cent, died.

There is usually an abundant discharge of pus, blood, and scraps of tissue, accompanied by intense pain. Often nervous conditions develop, such as delirium, convulsions, visual disturbances, and loss of speech.

Small numbers of larvae are fatal to laboratory animals; guinea pigs usually succumb to nine or more. It is evident, therefore, that they are highly toxic and that their damage is not limited to the tissue destruction they cause, though sometimes, when the infestation is in the head, this is bad enough. According to experiments by Borgstrom (1938) in the Rice Institute laboratory, the maggots are invariably accompanied by proteolytic bacteria which aid them in attacking the tissues; there seems to be a symbiotic relation between them, the larvae killing the tissues with their toxins and making them available for the proteolytic enzymes of the bacteria, and the bacteria then decomposing the tissues to make them available for the larvae. After a day or two the wounds usually have pure cultures of these proteolytic bacteria (Proteus). In Florida, however, Emmel (1945) found screwworm flies to be vectors of " joint ill," a streptococcus condition of calves; the germs invade the body from navels infested by the maggots.

Immunity to the toxic effects of the infestation is developed, but, since the larvae do not feed directly on living tissue as does Cordylobia, there is no interference with growth of the larvae.

The damage done by screwworms to domestic animals amounts to millions of dollars in the United States. Wounds made by shears, barbed wire, thorns, ticks, parturition, etc., are commonly invaded, and myiasis of the cloaca of chickens is not infrequent. In our southern coastal areas from August to October about 12 per cent of cattle have infestations; during this season 85 per cent of all screwworm infestations begin in the bites of the Gulf Coast ear tick, *Amblyomma maculatum* (see p. 534). Next in importance are wounds made in shearing. Wounds made by castration, earmarking, and branding are also important. The flies frequently oviposit in the sores made by bots, especially Dermatobia in cattle and Cuterebra in rabbits (see pp. 724 and 726).

The Old World Screwworm, Chrysomyia bezziana. This fly is widely distributed in Asia and Africa and has habits similar to those of *Callitroga americana*, whereas its close relative, *Chrysomyia megacephala*, is the counterpart of our *Callitroga macellaria*. *C. bezziana* is a common cause of human myiasis in India, but in Africa and in the Philippines it confines its attentions largely to animals. The maggots are very destructive and cause horrible, stinking sores.

Wohlfartia magnifica. This fly, a member of the family Sarcophagidae (fleshflies) (see key, p. 708), is found in southeastern Europe, Asiatic Russia, and Asia Minor and has habits similar to those of the screwworms. It is said to be a great pest in war, breeding in the wounds of soldiers. The eggs of this fly, as of other sarcophagids, hatch before being deposited. The young larvae are placed directly in the wounds or cavities which the fly chooses for them. According to Portchinsky 150 or more larvae are deposited at a time; one instance is recorded of 70 maggots being extracted from a human eye after about this many had already escaped or been thrown away. The larvae of Wohlfartia are larger than those of the calliphorine flies and so are capable of even greater damage.

Treatment and Control of Screwworms. When discovered, the larvae should be removed as speedily as possible, especially if in the head. Usually they may be expelled by applying antiseptic douches, the larvae being removed with appropriate instruments. Stewart and Boyd in 1934 found a single application of 5 per cent chloroform in a light vegetable oil to be very effective when applied for 30 minutes by douching the affected parts and, in wounds, then applying a saturated dressing. For animals Dove in 1935 recommended treatment with benzol followed by pine-tar oil as a repellent and aid to healing, but the most favored treatment is application of " smear 62 "; 3½ parts by weight of diphenylamine is dissolved in 3½ parts of benzene; 1 part of turkey-red oil is added and shaken up; and then 2 parts of lampblack is gradually stirred in to give a molasses consistency. It is applied to wounds with a paint brush; care should be taken near the eyes. Even salt water is often effective in removing the maggots and should be used if no better wash is at hand. Maggots in the ear, if outside the ear drum, should be removed by means of water or milk saturated with chloroform of carbon tetrachloride, but if the maggots have already pierced the ear drum, surgery will probably be necessary. Often when infections are two or three days old surgery must be resorted to and the larvae removed by means of curved forceps. Frequent antiseptic washes prevent the injuries made by the maggots from becoming infected with bacteria.

Control consists in preventing wounds or treating them prophylactically before infestation and in promptly treating infestations before the larvae drop out and pupate. Elimination of the tick, *Amblyomma maculatum* (see p. 550), by modern methods is an important factor. Shearing or surgical operations should be done early in the fall in order to leave a wound-free period after October 1, thus decreasing the chances of a carryover through the winter. As noted above, the fly usually survives the winter only in southern Texas and Florida; control in these places during early winter would prevent spring importation into northern states. In Texas, however, extermination would necessitate killing the thousands of wild pigs that roam the brush unattended and are heavily infested, and would require some cooperative agreement with Mexico. The extent of dispersal of the fly into northern states varies in different years. In 1943, a drouth year, Texas exported great numbers of screwworms in an early northward movement of cattle, and even such remote places as Montana and Minnesota had a bad screwworm year. Such a situation could easily be avoided by enforcing examination and treatment of animals either before or after shipment.

3. Wool Maggots Causing " Strike "

Sheep suffer from attacks by maggots which develop from eggs laid by carrion-feeding flies in damp wool soiled by feces or urine. Bacterial action produces ammonia, causes dermatitis, and attracts the flies. Such an infestation is called a " strike." The maggots eat into the flesh and often cause the death of sheep. Wool maggots are said to cause as much loss of sheep in parts of Australia as all other factors combined. Breeding in wool is a recently developed habit on the part of the flies — a result of changing conditions making for more blowflies, more vulnerable types of sheep, and perhaps less natural food for the flies. *Phoenicia cuprina* causes 96 per cent of the wool maggot trouble in Australia. In Europe the very closely related *P. sericata* is the species concerned. In Texas and California, the American states where "strike" is most frequent, the blue-black *Phormia regina* is the most important fleece worm; this is also the chief villain in South Africa.

Better control than that obtained from dipping is gained from jetting 0.5 per cent benzene hexachloride or DDT on the breeches of ewes and the heads of rams. Wool sprayed or jetted remains toxic to maggots for 5 or 6 weeks.

4. Muscoid Skin Maggots

Two genera of muscoid flies, Cordylobia and Wohlfartia, pierce the skin of animals and develop in boil-like lesions in the skin after the manner of certain bots (Dermatobia, Cuterebra, and Hypoderma) which are discussed on pp. 724, 726, and 727.

African Skin Maggots (Cordylobia anthropophaga). This yellowish brown fly (Fig. 265), known as the "ver du cayor" or tumbu fly, is found throughout tropical Africa. Although rodents are probably the primary hosts, a large number of tender-skinned wild and domesticated animals especially dogs, are attacked, and man is a frequent victim.

According to Blacklock and Thompson (1923) the eggs are laid by preference in dry sand and occasionally in cloth if either has been contaminated by excreta or has body odors, so clothing left exposed to flies may be dangerous. The eggs

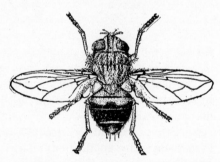

Fig. 265. Adult ♀ of African skin maggot, *Cordylobia anthropophaga.* × 3. (After Castellani and Chalmers.)

hatch in about 4 days. Upon stimulation by heat or touch the young larva becomes alert and active, attaches itself to skin, crawls to the nearest wrinkle or crevice, tears a hole with its mouth hooks, and within a minute or two has buried itself under the surface if the skin is not too tough. First attacks are painless, but there are marked reactions to subsequent attacks. The three larval stages (Fig. 266) are passed through in 8 days or more; the mature larvae then leave the tumor and pupate in the ground, the adult flies emerging after 8 or 10 days under favorable conditions.

Blacklock and Gordon made some interesting observations on immunity to this infestation, showing that larvae are unable to develop in previously infested skin. This the writer has interpreted as a specific reaction of the skin tissue which makes it unavailable as food for the larvae. The immunity is local and temporary in nature, gradually spreading in the skin, and is retained even when immune skin is grafted into another animal.

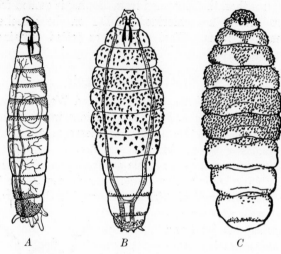

A	B	C

FIG. 266.   A, B, and C, first-, second-, and third-stage larvae of *Cordylobia anthropophaga;* A, × 60; B, × 15; C, × 4.   (After Blacklock and Thompson.)

The boil-like lesions are often considerably excavated, apparently by a histolytic action of the larvae, and heavy infestations in animals may even cause death.

Large maggots can be removed with forceps, but smaller ones are best removed by applications of liquid paraffin.   The larvae back out into the paraffin searching for air and by addition of more drops can usually be induced to emerge far enough to be captured or squeezed out.

FIG. 267.   Posterior end of third-stage larva of *Wohlfartia vigil.*   (After Walker.)

Wohlfartia vigil and W. opaca.   Most of the species of Wohlfartia, like those of Sarcophaga (both members of the Sarcophagidae — see keys, pp. 708 and 711) are not primary myiasis producers, but, as we have already seen, *W. magnifica* is an Old World screwworm, and two American species, *W. vigil* and *W. opaca*, are invaders of healthy skin.

Walker in 1920 called attention to a number of cases of infestation of the otherwise healthy skin of young children by the maggots of *Wohlfartia vigil* in Toronto, Canada.   Later, Ford (1936) reported additional human cases and 180 cases in small animals.   In very small animals 5 to 20 larvae are said to cause death within 10 days. Young mink are frequently killed by them on farms in the upper Mississippi valley. Ford observed that the female flies habitually deposit their larvae on the skin of animals, especially young and tender ones, when available; the larvae are unable to penetrate adult human skin.

Tender-skinned babies sleeping outdoors unscreened are liable to nasty infestations. Larval development is rapid, sometimes requiring only 5 days in hot weather but usually occupying 6 to 9 days. The majority of human cases have been reported from the Toronto region, but scattered cases have been noted in various localities in the west where *W. vigil* is replaced by *W. opaca*. This species, called the fox maggot, is a common and important parasite of foxes and mink in the west and causes losses running to thousands of dollars on farms where these animals are raised. Rarely cases occur in dogs.

5. Myiasis of the Intestine and Urinary Tract

Intestinal Myiasis. Many species of fly maggots may accidentally be taken into the intestine of man. To quote from Banks, " When we consider that these dipterous larvae occur in decaying fruits and vegetables and in fresh and cooked meats; that the blowfly, for example, will deposit on meats in a pantry; that other maggots occur in cheese, oleomargarine, etc., and that pies and puddings in restaurants are accessible and suitable to them, it can readily be seen that a great number of maggots must be swallowed by persons each year, and mostly without any serious consequences." The reason for the lack of serious consequences is the fact that most maggots are killed in the stomach and thus fail to establish themselves. This is rather surprising since the maggots are unusually resistant to many chemicals that would quickly destroy other animals. Causey in 1938 fed larvae of a number of species to dogs and cats and found the larvae to be killed or immobilized in the stomach within 3 hours; none of them passed through the alimentary canal alive. In another experiment fifty human volunteers were fed living maggots of *Musca domestica*, Calliphora, and Sarcophaga under conditions planned to avoid destruction in the stomach. Fifty per cent had gastro-intestinal disturbances — nausea, vomiting, cramps, and diarrhea — but the symptoms disappeared in 48 hours after elimination of the larvae, only a few of which were recovered alive after being vomited or passed in the feces.

Possibly intestinal myiasis is associated with low hydrochloric acid in the stomach or with particular conditions favoring rapid passage into the intestine. It is also possible that sometimes the flies get access to the intestine via the anus rather than the mouth, for some of the flies involved, particularly Sarcophaga and two species of Fannia (see p. 711), normally deposit their eggs in feces and decaying organic matter, and their eggs or larvae would rarely be found in edible food.

Excluding the species of Gastrophilus, which are true parasites of the alimentary canal (see p. 730), all the fly larvae recorded as causing intestinal myiasis are accidental parasites and probably in most cases pseudoparasites, actually no more parasitic than a swallowed goldfish. Some workers doubt that any of the numerous species found in human feces stop to nourish themselves, much less multiply, en route, but the evidence is against this extreme view, for there are well-authenticated cases of digestive disturbances occasioned by them. Even if they do not attack the mucous membranes they may cause nausea and abdominal discomfort by their movements.

Occasional remarkable cases are recorded of long-standing infections, even when opportunities for reinfection do not appear to exist. There are reports of living larvae of fleshflies or their allies persisting and causing symptoms for periods of weeks or even months. Herms and Gilbert (1933) described a case in which the history suggested intestinal myiasis extending over many years. For 4 months larvae of Calliphora, Phoenicia, and Sarcophaga were found at intervals, accompanied by attacks of severe abdominal distress and intestinal hemorrhages. During this time the manner of life of the patient made the probability of repeated infection seem very remote. Lyon and Mizelle in 1945 reported a case in which *Phoenicia sericata* and an unidentified Sarcophaga were obtained from a woman who complained of having passed worms for a period of a month. Similar long-standing cases have been reported involving *Musca crassirostris* and the maggots of a small acalyptrate fly of the genus Aphiochaeta (see p. 617).

Herms suggested the possibility of reproduction in the digestive tract by a process of pedogenesis, i.e., premature reproduction by larvae without transformation into adult flies. Such a method of reproduction is thought actually to have been observed by Parker in 1922 in a species of Calliphora. In some cases, however, it is a problem for a psychiatrist rather than an entomologist. The writer was once informed by a woman that she had been passing worms in her stool for over a year and suffering gastro-intestinal disturbances from them, and she brought a stool swarming with larvae of Aphiochaeta to prove it. She had been fascinated by seeing the larvae develop in stools saved in covered receptacles. When, however, a flytight jar was supplied for additional specimens, no more larvae were found.

The commonest fly maggots found in human feces are small species that breed in dead vegetable or animal matter. They include several genera of small acalyptrate flies, among them *Piophila casei*, the cheese skipper (Fig. 268*A* and *B*); Drosophila, the fruit fly, famous in genetics;

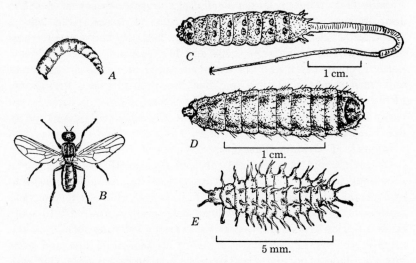

FIG. 268. Maggots occasionally found in human feces. *A* and *B*, cheese skipper and adult, *Piophila casei*, × 3 (after Graham-Smith, from Riley and Johannsen); *C*, rat-tailed maggot, *Eristalis tenax* (adapted from Patton and Evans); *D*, *Hermetia illucens* (adapted from Meleney and Harwood); *E*, larva of lesser housefly, *Fannia canicularis*. (Adapted from Hewitt.)

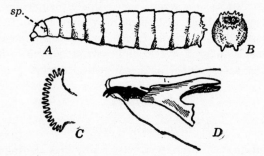

FIG. 269. Larva of fleshfly, Sarcophaga; *A*, side view of larva; *B*, posterior view showing posterior spiracles in depression; *C*, anterior spiracle, marked *sp.* in Fig. *A*; *D*, skeleton of pharynx, with mouth hooks. (After Riley and Johannsen.)

Aphiochaeta; Sepsis; etc. The larvae of most of these have the posterior spiracles on tubercles but otherwise resemble miniature housefly larvae. Some, like the cheese skipper, can flick themselves about; the presence of this species is sometimes considered a mark of particularly good cheese.

Although undoubtedly harmless in most cases, these fly maggots sometimes damage the intestinal mucosa and cause loss of appetite, vomiting, colicky pains, headache, vertigo, etc. Other maggots occasionally found and connected with digestive disorder are two species of Fannia (Fig. 268E); *Musca domestica;* several species of fleshflies (Sarcophaga) (Fig. 269); rat-tailed maggots (Eristalis) (Fig. 268C); and a soldier fly, *Hermetia illucens* (Fig. 268D). The characteristics of these will be found on pp. 709 and 711.

Fly maggots can usually be expelled readily by means of the purges and various anthelmintics used for intestinal worms. Prevention, of course, consists principally in being careful of what is eaten, especially in regard to such foods as raw vegetables, cheese, and partly decayed fruits and meats.

Myiasis of Urinary Passages. Myiasis of the urinary passages, both urethra and bladder, is a rare but occasional occurrence. The flies implicated are usually the lesser housefly, *Fannia canicularis,* and the closely allied latrine fly, *F. scalaris.* The writer in 1941 reported a case in which Phoenicia larvae were recovered. In most cases infection occurs from eggs laid near the external opening of the urethra, the larvae working their way up into this tube and even into the bladder; apparently they need very little oxygen. One case of infection of a boy's bladder by the larvae of a Psychoda was recorded by Patton; he thinks that the larvae burrowed through from the rectum to the bladder. Hoeppli and Watt found that larvae of *Chrysomyia megacephala* when placed in the urinary bladder taken from a freshly killed pig and filled with human urine, if fed daily, would live for 9 days, whereas *Phoenicia sericata* lived only 3 days. Contamination is favored by sleeping without covers in hot weather, giving flies free access to the anal and genital region.

Botflies

1. Skin Bots, Cuterebridae

The flies of this family are robust hairy flies distinguished from other bots (Oestridae and Hypodermatidae) by having a deep groove under the head containing a reduced proboscis.

Dermatobia hominis. This big, blue, brown-winged fly (Fig. 270) is found from Mexico to northern Argentina. Its larvae develop not only in man but also in many other animals, including cattle, dogs, hogs, goats, turkeys, and, more rarely, horses and mules. In certain parts of South America the hides of cattle become so riddled with the perforations made by the larvae that they become quite worthless. The infestation in man is contracted chiefly in low forest regions and very seldom in houses. Dunn in 1934 stated in Panama that cattle become infested literally with thousands of larvae and are frequently killed by them. Human infestation is also very common.

The adult fly is about the size of a large blowfly, with the legs and face yellowish, the thorax bluish black with a grayish bloom, the abdomen a beautiful metallic violet blue, and the wings brown.

The method by which these flies give their offspring a start in life is unique. When ready to oviposit, the female captures an insect, usually a large mosquito of the genus Psorophora but occasionally various other Diptera or even ticks, and glues her eggs by means of an adhesive, quick-drying cement to the underside of the abdomen of her

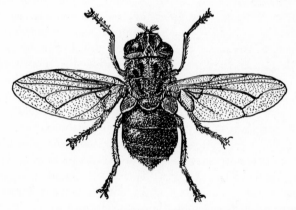

Fig. 270. Adult of South American skin maggot, *Dermatobia hominis*, × 2½. (Adapted from Castellani and Chalmers.)

captive (see p. 698 and Fig. 257). A total of 200 eggs may be laid by one female fly, from 8 or 10 to several dozen on individual mosquitoes. The eggs require several days' incubation before they are ready to hatch.

When mosquitoes burdened with ripe eggs alight upon the skin of warm-blooded animals the maggots emerge, penetrate the skin of the host, and begin their development. If the young larva does not have time to emerge while its mosquito transporter is biting it is said to draw back into the egg shell and await another opportunity. Clothing does not afford protection, since the larvae readily penetrate it.

The time required for the larvae to reach maturity in the host's skin varies from 5 to 10 weeks. They ultimately reach a length of 18 to 24 mm. (Fig. 271). The anterior end of the larva is broad and is provided with double rows of thorn-shaped spines; the posterior portion is slender, smooth, and retractile. As the larva develops, a boil-like cyst forms about it, opening to the surface of the skin by a little pore which is plugged by the posterior end of the maggot and is used for obtaining air.   At intervals these warblelike boils cause excruciating pain.

When mature, the larvae voluntarily leave their host and fall to the ground to pupate.   They transform into the adult form in the course of several weeks.   After the worms have evacuated their cysts or have been removed, the wounds sometimes develop serious or even fatal infections.   Dunn reported a fatal case in which the larvae entered the brain of a child through a fontanelle.   Many calves are killed by secondary infestation by screwworms (see pp. 714).

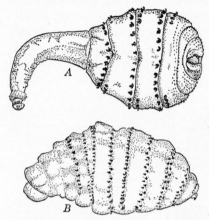

FIG. 271.   First-stage (*A*) and third-stage (*B*) larvae of *Dermatobia hominis*. (*A* adapted from Blanchard, from Neveu-Lemaire.)

The method usually employed to remove the maggots is to apply tobacco juice or tobacco ashes to the infested spots, thus killing the worms and making their extraction easy.   Another method used by natives in some parts of South America is to tie a piece of fat tightly over the entrance to the boil. The larva, deprived of air, works its way out into the fat, being thus induced to extract itself.   A much more satisfactory method is to enlarge the entrance to the cyst with a sharp clean knife and remove the worm with a forceps.   Antiseptic treatment of the wound obviates danger of subsequent infection.   The wound heals quickly but leaves a scar.

In Central America great reduction in Dermatobia infestation has been obtained by spraying cattle with a solution containing 18 grams of DDT, 14 cc. of kerosene, extract of 40 grams chopped derris leaves, 6 grams of soap, and 400 cc. of water per animal; this eliminates ticks as well.

Cuterebra spp.   This genus contains a number of species of large beelike flies the larvae of which develop individually in the skin of rodents and rabbits, fairly frequently in cats, and rarely in dogs.   The full-grown larvae are large robust maggots, sometimes over an inch long; they are easily recognized by their complete covering of black spines which gives them a jet-black color.   The younger instars have only rings of spines. Usually an animal harbors only one or a few maggots, but occasionally there are more.

According to Dalmat (1942) the flies lay very large numbers of eggs, depositing them in the burrows or habitats of the host, where they hatch intermittently. The larvae attach themselves to a host when the opportunity comes. They live in the host about a month and have a long pupal period in the soil; probably there is usually only one brood a year.

The maggots seem to be definitely injurious to their hosts. Cuterebra lesions in cats and dogs are remarkably dirty and persistent. Most screwworm infections in rabbits develop in Cuterebra sores. Infested squirrels are considered inedible by hunters and are thrown away.

Bots Causing Warbles in Cattle (Hypoderma spp.)

Hypoderma. The warble or heel flies (see key, p. 000, and Fig. 272) are hairy black and yellow flies which lay their eggs on the hairs

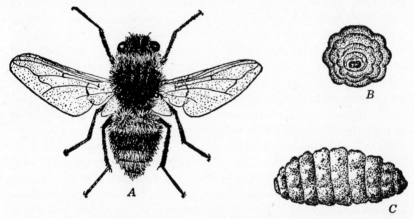

Fig. 272. *Hypoderma bovis; A*, adult (adapted from Patton and Evans); *B*, third-stage larva, posterior view; *C*; same, lateral view, × 1½.

of the lower part of the legs or flanks of cattle, causing them great annoyance. The annoyance is purely instinctive, for the flies do not bite or sting, yet the animals act terror-stricken. The eggs hatch in a few days; the spiny larvae, 1 mm. long, burrow into the skin, and then for several months they ramble about among the viscera in the abdomen and thorax; they are especially numerous between the muscular and mucous coats of the esophagus and occasionally enter the spinal canal. During this stage they are glassy smooth.

Toward the end of the winter they begin to appear in the skin of the back, where they form little cystlike lumps or warbles. The larvae

(Fig. 272) develop in the warbles for about 1 to 3 months, moult twice, and become opaque, spiny maggots which make a little breathing hole in the skin, into which they thrust the posterior end with its spiracles. They usually emerge in spring or early summer, fall to the ground, and pupate. The pupal stage lasts 2 to 7 weeks. The pupae are very resistant to cold but are killed by excessive moisture.

There are two species in cattle, *Hypoderma bovis* and *H. lineata* (see keys and Fig. 261), but they are much alike in their biology except that *H. bovis* appears about a month later than *H. lineata* in all its stages. In the United States this species is limited to the northern and central states. *H. crossii* of Indian goats is said to undergo its entire development in the subcutaneous skin of the back.

Hypoderma larvae are occasional accidental parasites of man, but being in an abnormal host they do not behave in a normal manner but wander aimlessly about in the skin, causing " migrating lumps." *H. diana* of deer in Europe is a more frequent accidental parasite of man than are the cattle species. Hypoderma has been reported to cause myiasis of the human eye in Norway and Russia.

Warbles cause losses amounting to millions of dollars by irritation to cattle caused by the larvae, annoyance caused by the flies, and damage to hides.

Formerly it was necessary to squeeze out the " ripe " grubs by hand, yet in 1896 an optimistic entomologist said warbles in cattle could be practically exterminated in a year — a goal which was actually reached in Clare Island, Ireland, but not elsewhere. Now, however, the possibility of extermination looks bright, for the grubs can be killed by application of an ointment (lanolin 78 parts, water 9, benzene hexachloride 9, and rotenone extract 1) or by brushing with 5 per cent rotenone extract in linseed oil. It is probable that compulsory cattle-grub eradication will come soon, and then Hypoderma, like Boöphilus, will be only a memory in this country.

Head Bots (Oestridae)

The family Oestridae contains robust flies with a hairy " pile " of black, yellow, or gray which while on the wing deposit their newly hatched larvae (or eggs in some species) in or on the nostrils of sheep, goats, deer, and camels, or, rarely, in man. The larvae are large grubs an inch or more in length. The important species are *Oestrus ovis*, a world-wide parasite of sheep and goats, *Rhinoestrus purpureus* of horses in the Old World, *Cephalopina titillator* of camels in North Africa and Asia, and *Cephenemyia* spp. of members of the deer family in North America and Europe.

Oestrus ovis. The larvae of this grayish brown fly, which was imported from Europe, are a pest in the United States particularly in the southwest, where over 95 per cent of sheep and goats are infested. The flies deposit their larvae in the nostrils. The young larvae live in the nares, but later invade the frontal sinuses and sometimes other parts of the head. Occasionally they find their way into the tear duct and reach the eye, sometimes destroying it. They develop slowly through the winter and mature and drop out in the following spring or summer. In Canada the average pupal period is about one month. In warm countries there may be two broods, adults appearing in May and June and again in October and November. The full-grown larvae are over an inch long.

The irritation caused by the grubs makes the animals restless and they stop feeding. They develop a nasal discharge and sneeze frequently. The parasites can be reached most easily while in the nares during the winter. Treatment consists in spraying into the nostrils with a 3 per cent saponified cresol or a mixture of carbon bisulfide, alcohol, and water — 50 cc. of a 1 : 10 : 40 mixture for sheep, 25 cc. of a 1 : 20 : 80 mixture for lambs. Sometimes a violent sneeze brought on by the use of pepper will expel them.

This fly sometimes deposits its eggs on the eyes, nostrils, and lips of shepherds whose breath smells of fresh sheep or goat cheese or curds, particularly in Algeria, Asia Minor, and parts of South America. The grubs may cause serious damage to the eyes.

Other Oestridae. The larvae of the purplish-hued *Rhinoestrus purpureus* are frequent parasites of the head of horses in Europe, Siberia, and north Africa, having habits quite similar to those of *Oestrus ovis*. The larvae invade the nostrils and eyes and sometimes other parts of the head and throat. Like the sheep bot, the fly sometimes darts at humans and deposits its larvae in the eyes, where they may cause serious damage if not promptly removed.

Cephalopina titillator causes great discomfort to camels; it lives in the nostrils and nasopharynx for 10 or 11 months. The deer head-bots, *Cephenemyia* spp., are well known to hunters; nearly all deer are infested by them, but they seem usually to do little damage, though sneezing fits are sometimes observed and occasional cases of " craziness," possibly due to rare penetration of the parasites into the brain. The adults of Cephenemyia are among the swiftest flying insects known; they are said to get up a speed of 800 miles an hour. Females are rarely seen. The males of our western *C. jellisoni* rest on sunwarmed rocks on inaccessible mountaintops. Bagging one is more of a feat for a hunter than getting a mountain goat or a condor; when found in their remote retreats they have to be shot with .22-caliber dust shells!

Horse Bots (Gastrophilus spp.)

The genus Gastrophilus, constituting a separate family Gastrophilidae (see key, p. 709), contains flies the larvae of which develop in the stomach or rectum of horses. The adults are hairy beelike flies, clothed in dark brown or black with yellow markings, and in one

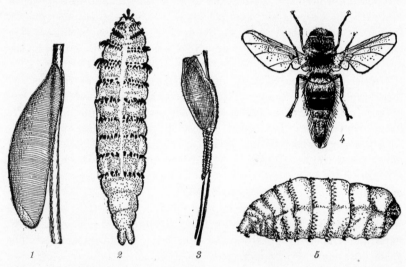

FIG. 273.   Gastrophilus; *1, 2,* and *5,* egg, first-stage larva, and third-stage larva, respectively, of *G. intestinalis; 3* and *4,* egg and adult of *G. haemorrhoidalis.*   (*1* adapted from Collinge, *2–4* from Hadwen and Cameron.)

species has an orange-red tip to the abdomen (Fig. 273, *4*). The wings of the commonest species, *G. intestinalis,* have smoky markings (Fig. 260, *6*). The abdomen in the females is elongated.

Each of the species has somewhat different habits, but all cause an amazing amount of annoyance while laying eggs, the horses becoming excited and often frantic; on warm days a horse may be so worried fighting botflies (gadflies) that he cannot graze at all. The adults usually live for only about 3 to 10 days, but during that time a female lays several hundred eggs which she attaches to hairs on parts of the horse which vary with the insect species. The first-stage larvae (Fig. 273, *2*) have rings of black spines; third-stage larvae (Fig. 273, *5*) are heavy-bodies and rather squarish posteriorly; all but *inermis* have heavy spines on some of the segments — one row in *nasalis,* two in the others. In *G. intestinalis* the spines of the first row are larger than those of the second (Fig. 273, *5*), and vice versa in *haemorrhoidalis.*

The common horse bot, *G. intestinalis* (*equi*), lays its eggs on the hairs of the forelegs of the horse, where they incubate for 1 to 2 weeks. When ripe, the warmth and moisture of the animal's tongue when licking cause them to hatch and adhere to the tongue. In the mouth they excavate tunnels under the mucous membranes, principally of the tongue, and after 3 or 4 weeks migrate to the stomach, where they live, often in large colonies, until mature and ready to pupate. They then release their hold and are passed in the droppings.

G. haemorrhoidalis (nose fly) (Fig. 273, *4*) strikes at the lips and nose to lay its eggs. The young larvae burrow about in the lips and tongue, later developing in the stomach and duodenum. This species leaves these parts in early spring and finishes its development in the rectum. *G. nasalis* (chin fly) lays its eggs on the chin and throat, where they hatch unaided. The larvae burrow into the mouth and invade spaces around and between the teeth, below the gums, causing pus pockets. They may live in this locality for a month and undergo their first moult before they continue on their way to their final site of development in the lower stomach and duodenum. *G. inermis* lays its eggs on the cheeks, where it causes a dermatitis; the larvae burrow through the tissues to the mouth and then go to the rectum. *G. pecorum* lays its eggs on the hoofs or even on the food. After being licked the larvae hatch and burrow in the cheeks, then live for a time in the pharynx, and continue development in the stomach, but, like *G. haemorrhoidalis*, reattach to the rectum before finally leaving the body.

A few of these bots do very little damage, and some farmers think that a horse just naturally ought to have a few, but when numerous the bots cause gastro-intestinal disturbances. The worms in the stomach are persuaded to let go by giving carbon bisulfide in gelatin capsules at the rate of 1.5 drams per 250 lb. of horse.

Gastrophilus occasionally penetrates into man, but instead of behaving in an orthodox manner, the larva wanders about under the skin and is called a " larva migrans." *G. intestinalis* is the species most frequently concerned.

REFERENCES

AUBERTIN, D., and BUXTON, P. A., Cochliomyia and Myiasis in Tropical America, *Ann. Trop. Med. Parasitol.*, **28**, 245 (1934).

BANKS, N., The Structure of Certain Dipterous Larvae....*U. S. Bur. Entomol. Tech. Bull.* **22**, 1912.

BELSCHNER, H. G., A Review of the Sheep Blowfly Problem in New South Wales, *N. S. Wales Dept. Agr.*, 1937.

BISHOPP, F. C., The Horse Bots and Their Control, *U. S. Dept. Agr. Farmers' Bull.* **1503** (1941).

Bishopp, C., Laake, E. W., Brundrett, H. M., and Wells, R. W., The Cattle Grubs or Ox Warbles, their Biologies and Suggestions for Control, *U. S. Dept. Agr. Bull.* **1369**, 1927.

Blacklock, D. B., and Gordon, R. M., The Experimental Production of Immunity against Metazoan Parasites and an Investigation of its Nature, *Ann. Trop. Med. Parasitol.*, **21**, 181 (1927); **24**, 5 (1930).

Blacklock, D. B., and Thompson, M. G., A Study of the Tumbu Fly, *Cordylobia anthropophaga*, in Sierra Leone, *Ann. Trop. Med. Parasitol.*, **17**, 443 (1923).

Borgstrom, F., Experimental *Cochliomyia americana* Infestations, *Am. J. Trop. Med.*, **18**, 395 (1938).

Cushing, E. C., and Patton, W. S., *Cochliomyia americana* sp. n., or the Screwworm Fly of the New World, *Ann. Trop. Med. Parasitol.*, **27**, 539 (1933).

Dalmat, H. T., A Contribution to the Knowledge of the Rodent Warble Flies, *J. Parasitol.*, **29**, 311–318 (1943).

Dove, W. E., Myiasis of Man, *J. Econ. Entomol.*, **30**, 29 (1937).

Emmel, M. W., The Primary Screwworm Fly, *Cochliomyia americana* C. and P., as a Vector of Joint Ill in Calves, *J. Am. Vet. Med. Assoc.*, **106**, 223 (1945).

Ford, N., Further Observations on the Behavior of *Wohlfartia vigil*, with Notes on the Collecting and Rearing of the Flies, *J. Parasitol.*, **22**, 309 (1936).

Gassner, F. X., and James, M. T., The Biology and Control of the Fox Maggot, *Wohlfartia opaca* (Coq.), *J. Parasitol.*, **34**, 44–50 (1948).

Hadwen, S., and Cameron, A. E., A Contribution to the Knowledge of the Botflies, *Gastrophilus intestinalis* DeG., *G. haemorrhoidalis* L., and *G. nasalis* L., *Bull. Entomol. Research*, **9**, 91–106 (1918).

Hall, D. G., *The Blowflies of North America*, Baltimore, 1948.

Herms, W. B., and Gilbert, Q. O., An Obstinate Case of Intestinal Myiasis, *Ann. Internal Med.*, **6**, 941 (1933).

Kenney, M., Experimental Intestinal Myiasis in Man, *Proc. Soc. Exptl. Biol. Med.*, **60**, 235–237 (1945).

Knipling, E. F., and Rainwater, H. T., Species and Incidence of Diptera Concerned in Wound Myiasis, *J. Parasitol.*, **23**, 451 (1937).

Laake, E. W., Cushing, E. C., and Parish, H. E., Biology of the Primary Screwworm Fly, *Cochliomyia americana*, and a Comparison of Its Stages with Those of *C. macellaria*, *U. S. Dept. Agr., Tech. Bull.* **500** (1936).

Parman, D. C., Effect of Weather on *Cochliomyia americana* and a Review of Methods and Economic Applications of the Study, *J. Econ. Entomol.*, **38**, 66–76 (1945).

Patton, W. S., and Evans, A. M., *Insects, Ticks, Mites, and Venomous Animals of Medical and Veterinary Importance*, I. Medical, London, 1929.

Pfadt, R. E., Effects of Temperature and Humidity on Larval and Pupal Stages of the Common Cattle Grub, *J. Econ. Entomol.*, **40**, 293–300 (1947).

Sambon, L. W., Tropical and Subtropical Diseases (Dermatobia), *J. Trop. Med. Hyg.*, **25**, 170 (1922).

Wells, K. W., and Knipling, E. F., A Report of Some Recent Studies on Species of Gastrophilus Occurring in Horses in the United States, *Iowa State Coll. J. Sci.*, **12**, 181 (1938).

Sources of Information

The following periodicals are those in which a very considerable part of the literature on parasitology can be found, either in original or abstract form, and which are therefore desirable in libraries where parasitological study or research is being carried on. The starred periodicals are important for their abstracts or references. Important general books on parasitology are listed at the end of Chapter 1.

UNITED STATES AND CANADA

American Journal of Hygiene, Baltimore, 1921–
American Journal of Public Health, New York, 1911–
American Journal of Tropical Medicine, Baltimore, 1921–
American Journal of Veterinary Research, Chicago, 1940–
American Midland Naturalist, Notre Dame, Indiana, 1909–
Biological Abstracts, Philadelphia, 1926–
Canadian Journal of Research (Sect. C-D, from Vol. 13), Ottawa, 1929–
Index Medicus, Washington, 1879–
Journal of the American Medical Association, Chicago, 1883–
Journal of the American Veterinary Medicine Association, New York, 1877–
Journal of the National Malaria Society, Tallahassee, 1942–
Journal of Parasitology, Lancaster, Pa., 1914–
North American Veterinarian, Evanston, Ill., 1920–
Proceedings of the Helminthological Society of Washington, Washington, 1934–
Proceedings of the Society for Experimental Biology and Medicine, New York, 1903–
Public Health Reports, Washington, 1878–
Rockefeller Foundation, International Health Division, *Annual Reports*, New York, 1913–
Rockefeller Institute for Medical Research, *Monographs*, New York, 1910–
Transactions of the American Microscopical Society, Menasha, Wis., 1892–
U. S. Bureau of Animal Industry, *Bulletins*, Washington.
U. S. Bureau of Entomology, *Bulletins*, Washington.
U. S. Hygienic Laboratory, *Bulletins* (continued as *National Institute of Health Bulletins*), Washington, 1900–
U. S. Naval Medical Bulletin, Washington, 1907–

FOREIGN

Acta Medica Scandinavica, Stockholm, 1919–
Anales del Instituto de Biologia, Mexico City, 1930–
Annales de la société belge de médecine tropicale, Antwerp, 1920–
Annales de parasitologie humaine et comparée, Paris, 1922–
Annals of Tropical Medicine and Parasitology, Liverpool, 1907–
Archiv für Schiffs- und Tropen-Hygiene, Leipzig, 1897–
Archives de parasitologie, Paris, 1898–1919.

Boletin de la oficina sanitaria panamericana, Washington, 1922–

Brasil-Medico, Rio de Janeiro, 1887–

British Medical Journal, London, 1857–

Bulletin de la société de pathologie exotique, Paris, 1908–

Bulletin of Entomological Research, London, 1910–

*Centralblatt für Bakteriologie und Parasitologie, 1 Abteilung, Original und Referat, Jena, Germany, 1887–

    (Referat contains references and reviews of many articles dealing with infectious diseases.)

China Medical Journal, Shanghai, 1887–1931, continued as *Chinese Medical Journal,* 1932–40.

Comptes rendus de la société de biologie, Paris, 1849–

Geneeskundig Tijdschrift voor Nederlandsch-Indie, Batavia, 1852–1941.

*Helminthological Abstracts, St. Albans, England, 1932–

Indian Journal of Medical Research, Calcutta, 1913–

Indian Medical Research Memoirs, Calcutta, 1924–

Journal of Helminthology, London, 1923–

Journal of the London School of Tropical Medicine, London, 1911–1913.

Journal of Tropical Medicine and Hygiene, London, 1898–

Lancet, London, 1823–

Medical Journal of Australia, Sydney, 1914–

Memoirs, Liverpool School of Tropical Medicine, 1901–1906, 1924–

Memoirs do instituto Oswaldo Cruz, Rio de Janeiro, 1909–

Parasitology, Cambridge, 1908–

Philippine Journal of Science, Manila, 1906–

Publicaciones, Instituto de parasitologia y enfermedades parasitarias, Universidad nacional, Buenos Aires, 1938–

Publicaciones, Mision de estudos de patologia regional Argentina, Jujuy, 1930–

Puerto Rico Journal of Public Health and Tropical Medicine, San Juan, 1925–

*Review of Applied Entomology, Series B (Medical and Veterinary), London, 1913–

    (Contains reviews of work on medical and veterinary entomology.)

Revista de medicina tropical y parasitologia, clinica y laboratorio, Havana, 1935–

Revista Kuba de medicina tropical y parasitologia, Havana, 1945–

Revista serviço especial de saúde pública, Rio de Janeiro, 1947–

Revue pratique des maladies des pays chauds, Paris, 1922–

Rivista de parassitologia, Rome, 1937–

Transactions of the Royal Society of Tropical Medicine and Hygiene, London, 1907–

*Tropical Diseases Bulletin, London, 1913–

    (Contains reviews of all important work on tropical diseases, including nearly all work on human protozoan parasites and helminthology.)

*Tropical Veterinary Bulletin, London, 1912–1930, succeeded by *Veterinary Bulletin,* Weymouth, 1931–

Zeitschrift für Parasitenkunde, Berlin, 1928–

    (Vols. 1 to 6 as *Zeitschrift für Wissenschaftliche Biologie,* Abt. F.)

INDEX